HANDBOOK OF
FACILITIES PLANNING

VOLUME I
LABORATORY FACILITIES

Early chemistry: Alchemy symbols for basic elements and chemicals. (Plaque in lobby of Chemistry Building, Oregon State University)

HANDBOOK OF FACILITIES PLANNING

VOLUME I
LABORATORY FACILITIES

Edited by

Theodorus Ruys, AIA

VNR VAN NOSTRAND REINHOLD
_____ **New York**

Although great care has been taken in the compilation and publication of this volume, no warranties, express or implied, are given in connection herewith and no responsibility can be taken for any claims arising herewith.

Comments, criticisms, and suggestions regarding the subject matter are invited. Any errors or omissions in the data should be brought to the attention of the Editor.

Copyright © 1990 by Theodorus Ruys
Library of Congress Catalog Card Number 89-25049
ISBN 0-442-31852-9

Printed in the United States of America

Van Nostrand Reinhold
115 Fifth Avenue
New York, New York 10003

Van Nostrand Reinhold International Company Limited
11 New Fetter Lane
London EC4P 4EE, England

Van Nostrand Reinhold
480 La Trobe Street
Melbourne, Victoria 3000, Australia

Nelson Canada
1120 Birchmount Road
Scarborough, Ontario M1K 5G4, Canada

16 15 14 13 12 11 10 9 8 7 6 5 4 3 2 1

Library of Congress Cataloging-in-Publication Data

Handbook of facilities planning / Theodorus Ruys, editor.
     p.   cm.
     Includes bibliographical references.
     Contents: Vol. 1 Laboratory facilities.
     ISBN 0-442-31852-9 (v. 1)
     1. Physical laboratories—Planning—Handbooks, manuals, etc.
     I. Ruys, Theodorus.
Q180.57.H36 1990   89-25049
507'.24—dc20   CIP

Long range planning does not deal with future decisions, but with the future of present decision.

Peter Drucker

Read not to contradict and confute; nor to believe and take for granted; not to find talk and discourage; but to weigh and consider.

Francis Bacon

Editor

Theodorus Ruys, AIA—Architect and Consultant. Degrees: Bachelor of Architecture, University of Illinois; Masters in Architecture, University of Washington. Memberships: the National Fire Protection Association Standard No. 45 Committee, the American Association of Laboratory Animal Science, American Institute of Architects.

Board of Advisors

Bryan H. Atkinson, PE—Atkinson Koven Feinberg, New York. Principal; Chartered Engineer, registered in the United Kingdom and 14 states in the United States. Memberships: ASHRAE Technical Committee TC 9.1; Currently working on updating the ASHRAE *Systems Design Guide,* Chapter 2, All Air Systems.

Murray A. Cappers, Jr.—Allied-Signal, Inc. (formerly Allied Chemical), Morristown, New Jersey. Director, Loss Prevention; Degrees: Bachelor of Science in Chemical Engineering from Worcester Polytech Institute. Memberships: Professional member of the Society of Fire Protection Engineers and a charter member and past president of the New Jersey Charter SFPE; member of the American Institute of Chemical Engineers, Safety and Loss Prevention section; professional member of the America Society of Safety Engineers; steering committee for the Safety and Health Group of ORC, Washington, DC; the National Fire Protection Association; Vice Chairman of NFPA No. 45, Fire Protection for Laboratories Using Chemicals, currently serving a 3-year term on the Board of Directors of NFPA.

John M. Fresina, CSP—Director, Safety Office, Massachusetts Institute of Technology. Mr. Fresina served on the National Research Council, the National Fire Protection Association, and the Campus Safety Association in that capacity.

Paul A. Jarvis, PE—Formerly Director, Division of Engineering Services for the National Institute of Health; Chief Engineer for the Science and Education Administration for the U.S. Department of Agriculture; Chief of Facilities Engineering for the U.S. Environmental Protection Agency; and consultant to the UNDP and the World Health Organization for laboratory design.

Ulrich M. Lindner—Earl Walls Associates, San Diego, California. Principal; Education: Diplom-Ingenieur in Architecture, Akademie fur Angewandte Technik, Augsberg, Germany. Mr. Lindner is an architect and laboratory consultant and has been involved on laboratory projects in many parts of the world. In 1963 Mr. Lindner joined Earl Walls Associates and was involved in developing the firm into the universally recognized laboratory planning firm that it is today. Mr. Lindner lectures in laboratory design for the University of Wisconsin, Extension.

Norman L. Nelson, PE—CH2M Hill. Senior Mechanical Engineer and Project Manager. He is a member of ASHRAE and is registered as a professional engineer in five states.

Norman V. Steere, PE—Laboratory Safety and Design Consultant, Norman V. Steere Associates; Membership: Chairman, NFPA No. 49: Properties of Hazardous Chemicals and NFPA No. 45: Standard on Fire Protection for Laboratories Using Chemicals.

Contents

List of Figures

List of Tables

Foreword

Theodorus Ruys, Architect, editor, author, workshop leader, laboratory planner and designer has created a reference work on laboratory planning which has been very much needed by the research/development and academic communities. He has assembled a powerful task force of nationally known laboratory planners/writers to create this work. It appears on the scene at a moment in time when it is very much needed. It will, without question, prove to be a valuable reference work, not only for many of us who are involved in laboratory design, but it will be a valuable resource for all who plan and design laboratories, for those who need new laboratories, and for those who need to communicate with laboratory users and professional laboratory planners.

Today's laboratory has grown so complex that not even those who are constantly involved in their use and planning can hope to keep abreast with all the building and fire codes, health and safety codes, hazardous materials and environmental codes, let alone with the new technology that comes into being and is used in the laboratory each year. Construction materials and finishes are increasing in sophistication and complexity, so that only a multidisciplinary approach which includes the owner, the lab user, the laboratory planner, and the architectural team can hope to produce a functional, cost effective and aesthetic laboratory facility. This Handbook represents that multidisciplinary approach.

This Handbook is just that—a hands-on guide to a wide range of topics including differences and similarities between bioscience and physical science laboratories; laboratory planning—determining the program requirements, gathering and documenting the information, comparing the information gathered with space guidelines and laboratory design principles to give us the program informa-tion necessary to plan both space and relationships for people and equipment and services; the need for design to enhance communication as well as provide adequate security for laboratory equipment; and the definition of building systems including structural, mechanical, heating, ventilating and air conditioning, electrical, materials handling, waste handling and disposal systems and many other topics. These are covered in simplicity and detail. Also included are sections on energy conservation; ramifications of codes, regulations and standards; and cost issues to complete this text of "How To" plan laboratories.

In assembling this team of experienced professionals to contribute the various sections of this Handbook, the Editor has done an excellent job of finding the people who are both knowledgeable, and who can express themselves, in a way that will be useful to current and future generations of laboratory planners and users.

After assimilating this information, one should be ready to talk knowledgeably with the experts about how to design your next laboratory. It should be clear that planning laboratories is a specialty and it may benefit those who need laboratories to utilize a professional laboratory designer on their design team. The state-of-the-art and down-to-earth knowledge of how laboratories work expressed in this Handbook will yield a more functional product and almost always lead to significant cost savings in construction and in minimizing future changes to upgrade the laboratory to make it work. Whatever the readers role in the design team, this work will prove to be an invaluable working document for your next laboratory design whether it is a new building or a renovation.

Theodorus Ruys has spent most of his professional career designing laboratories. He is to be commended for this work.

Thomas E. McLellan
Principal McLellan & Copenhagen

Preface

It is estimated that there are approximately 74,000 laboratories in the United States, classified as industrial, clinical and academic. Approximately 1 million employees work in these laboratories. How well these buildings perform in supporting these laboratory operations or in providing a safe environment depends to a large degree on the understanding and knowledge of those responsible for planning and designing these facilities.

This handbook is an attempt to document in one volume the combined knowledge of many individuals who have made it their career to plan laboratory facilities. The reader is exposed to as many ideas and viewpoints as exist among these individuals and is expected to apply these to his or her own facility. There are no fixed solutions.

The need for this type of handbook has been felt for a long time because so little has been written on planning laboratories as a facilities type. By comparison, many books are available about office buildings and health care facilities. Laboratory facilities have some peculiar problems that must be dealt with:

- They must be very flexible and adaptable because the nature of the work in many laboratories is unpredictable.
- They are potentially hazardous workplaces and can cause unsafe conditions in the environment.
- They are high energy users.

- They are very expensive to build and operate.
- They are occupied by a high percentage of rare, creative individuals.
- They house very delicate instruments.

This handbook covers these issues in some detail and explains how they must be dealt with.

A large part of the successful planning of a facility depends on how the design team understands the needs of the users, which is a matter of communication. A chapter has therefore been included on the process of facilities planning. The concepts of reliability and validity, so common in the vocabulary of researchers, have been introduced and applied to the planning process.

This type of book could not have been completed without the help and suggestions of many individuals. This has been greatly appreciated. Thank you.

This handbook has been designed to present a complete and orderly discussion of pertinent information in this field. However, there have been some arbitrary choices and, undoubtedly, some omissions. Nevertheless, the editor is confident that the reader will find this a useful book.

The editor anticipates that there will be periodic revisions of this handbook. Therefore, any comments and suggestions will be appreciated.

Acknowledgments

The following copyright holders have generously given permission to quote or reproduce illustrations from copyrighted works:

American Institute of Architects
American Institute of Chemical Engineers
American National Standards Institute
American Society of Heating Refrigerating and Air Conditioning Engineers
American Sterilizer Co.
Bally Engineered Structures, Inc.
Chi Systems, Inc.
Edwardo Calderon
ENRECO
Flad and Associates
Garikes Wilson Atkinson, Inc.
Getinge International, Inc.
Guardian Equipment and Markson Science, Inc.
HDR, Inc.
Herman Miller, Inc.
Karl Bischoff
Kewaunee Scientific Corp.
Koch Engineering Co., Inc.
Lab Safety Supply Co.
Lipshaw Corp.
MPS
Nash Engineering Co.
National Council on Radiation Protection
National Fire Protection Association
N. Miyamoto
Ohio State University
Paul Warchol
Schlage Electronics
Scientific Apparatus Makers Association
Speakman Co.
The NBBJ Group
T.J. Allen
T&S Brass and Bronze Works, Inc.
United Air Specialists, Inc.

Contributors

Bryan H. Atkinson, PE—Atkinson Koven Feinberg, New York. Partner; Chartered Engineer, registered in the United Kingdom and 14 states in the United States. Memberships: ASHRAE Technical Committee TC 9.1; Currently working on updating ASHRAE *Systems Design Guide,* Chapter 2, All Air Systems.

Ralph M. Baltzo—President of Ralph Baltzo & Associates. Master's Degree in Radiological Science, University of Washington; Certified Health Physicist; Member, Health Physics Society; formerly Assistant Professor of Public Health and Community Medicine and Director of Radiation Safety Division, University of Washington.

W. Emmett Barkley, PhD—Director of Laboratory Safety, Howard Hughes Medical Institute; formerly Director, Division of Engineering Services (DES), NIH; Degrees: Bachelor of Civil Engineering, University of Virginia; Master's in Environmental Health, University of Minnesota; Ph.D. in Environmental Health, University of Minnesota. Recipient of many awards, the most recent of which is the Public Health Service Distinguished Service medal in 1989, the highest award given to the PHS Commissioned Corps. Lecturer, author and consultant on biohazard control and containment issues. Memberships: American Biological Safety Association, Commissioned Officers Association, American Association for the Advancement of Science.

Steve Bettge—Director of Life Safety and Hardware. Building code analyst and hardware consultant; Managing Associate, The NBBJ Group. Certified architectural hardware consultant. Degrees: Bachelor of Science in Industrial Education, Purdue University. Memberships: International Conference of Building Officials, National Fire Protection Association, Washington Association of Building Officials, Society of Fire Protection Engineers, Door and Hardware Institute.

Dennis Eagleson—The Baker Company, Inc., Sanford, Maine. President and CEO. A manufacturer of biological safety cabinets and clean air equipment used in the life sciences. Mr. Eagleson is a charter member of the American Biological Safety Association, a member of the American Society of Testing and Materials, a senior member of the Institute of Environmental Services, and an Industry Advisory Council member of the National Sanitation Foundation.

Jack Kasica, PE—Vice President, Syska & Hennessy, New York. Degrees: Associate in Applied Science, State University of New York; BECE, City College of New York. Licensed in New York and New Jersey. Memberships: American Society of Sanitary Engineers, Society of American Value Engineers, International Society of Pharmaceutical Engineers.

Wilmar A. Kohne, P.E.—Senior Mechanical Engineer. Industrial Design Corporation. Degrees: Bachelor of Science in Mechanical Engineering, Washington State University; Bachelor of Arts in Business Administration, Washington State University. Membership: ASHRAE, Professional Engineers of Oregon.

Anne DeVoe Lawler—Attorney, Ferguson and Burdell, Seattle. Partner. Her practice focuses on the areas of commercial real estate law, land use, and hazardous waste law. Ms. Lawler is a member of the Real Property, Probate and Trust and the Land Use and Environmental Law Section of the Washington State Bar Association. She graduated magna cum laude from Duke University in 1975, and received her law degree from the University of Washington in 1980, where she was a Managing Editor of the *Washington Law Review.* After law school,

Ms. Lawler was a clerk for Judge Eugene A. Wright of the U.S. Court of Appeals, Ninth Circuit.

Bradley D. Leathley—Director of Advanced Technology and Research Facility Design. Managing Associate, The NBBJ Group. Masters Degree in Architecture, University of Washington. Member of the Society of Research Administrators.

Ulrich M. Lindner—Earl Walls Associates, San Diego, California. Principal; Education: Diplom-Ingenieur in Architecture, Akademie fur Angewandte Technik, Augsberg, Germany. Mr. Lindner is an architect and laboratory consultant and has been involved in laboratory projects in many parts of the world. In 1963 Mr. Lindner joined Earl Walls Associates and was involved in developing the firm into the universally recognized laboratory planning firm that it is today. Mr. Lindner lectures in laboratory design for the University of Wisconsin, Extension.

Ernest G. Lunsford, Jr.—Section Chief, Design and Construction Branch, Division of Engineering Services, National Institute of Health. Degrees: Bachelor of Science in Mechanical Engineering, Duke University, Membership: American Biological Safety Association.

Alfred Lyons—Group Vice President, Syska & Hennessy, New York. Education: Bachelor in Engineering, Cornell University; Masters in Business Administration, New York University.

D. Keith Lyons—Atkinson Koven Feinberg, New Jersey. Education: Bachelor of Architecture, Drexel University. Memberships: Association of Energy Engineers, International Society of Pharmaceutical Engineers, American Society of Heating, Refrigeration and Air Conditioning Engineers.

Robert E. Marshall—Associate, Syska & Hennessy, New York. Senior electrical engineer. Degree: Bachelor of Science in Electrical Engineering, Newark College of Engineering (now New Jersey Institute of Technology).

Sandra Matson—Managing Partner Matson/Carlson/Whitacre. Certified professional cost estimator. Degree: Associate degree in Structural Engineering Technology, Seattle Community College. Memberships: Certified Member, American Society of Professional Estimators, and Society of American Value Engineers; Associate Member, American Institute of Architects.

Norman L. Nelson, PE—CH2M Hill. Senior mechanical engineer and project manager. Registered as a professional engineer in five states. Membership: ASHRAE.

Daniel K. Paulien—President, Paulien & Associates/Planning and Development Service, founded in 1979. Paulien previously served as director of planning for the Auraria Higher Education Center, a three-institution urban renewal campus in Denver. He also served as Coordinator of Facilities Planning and Research for the Colorado Commission on Higher Education.

Dale Pekrul—Senior Consulatant, Paoletti/Lewitz/Associates San Francisco, specializing in the areas of architectural and engineering acoustics, measurement and anaylsis of mechanical and industrial systems with respect to the control of noise and vibration. Degree: Bachelor's degree in mechanical engineering, Purdue University.

Theodorus Ruys, AIA—Architect and consultant. Degrees: Bachelor of Architecture, University of Illinois; Masters in Architecture, University of Washington. Memberships: NFPA Standard No. 45 Committee, American Association of Laboratory Animal Science, American Institute of Architects.

Norman V. Steere, PE—Laboratory Safety and Design Consultant, Norman V. Steere Associates; Memberships: Chairman, NFPA

Standard No. 49: Properties of Hazardous Chemicals and NFPA No. 45: Committee Standard on Fire Protection for Laboratories Using Chemicals.

Bea D. Sennewald, AIA—Vice President, Henningson, Durham and Richardson, Inc., Alexandria, VA. She heads the firm's design program for the architecture and engineering of research buildings. Degrees: Bachelor of Arts, Antioch University; Master of Architecture, University of Oregon.

Nolan Watson—Director of Academic Services for the Health Sciences, University of Washington. His responsibilites include facilities planning and management of the 2.3 million square foot health-related research and teaching complex. In addition, he has a private consulting firm and provides programming and laboratory planning services. Prior to accepting his present position, Mr. Watson was a laboratory scientist in physiology.

Michael A. Wodka—Principal; Context design research and development. Formerly a senior research associate and designer at Herman Miller Research corporation and Herman Miller, Inc., and a senior associate at the Facility Management Institute. A major part of his 22-year design and research career has been spent studying laboratory operations, use and planning, as well as designing laboratory bench systems. Mr. Wodka received his design degree from Carnegie-Mellon University. Memberships: Society of Manufacturing Engineers, Industrial Design Society of America, American Society of Testing and Materials.

Robert Zalosh, Ph.D—Factory Mutual Research Corporation. Assistant Vice President and Manager of Applied Research Department. His research has included work on gas explosion venting, vapor cloud explosions, and various special industrial fire protection projects. He has also been an Adjunct Associate Professor in the Worcester Polytechnic Institute Center for Fire Safety Studies. Memberships: National Research Council Committee on Risk Appraisal in the Development of Facilities Design Criteria, American Society of Mechanical Engineers Risk Analysis Task Force.

Abbreviations

AAALAC—American Association for Accreditation of Laboratory Animal Care

AALAS—American Association for Laboratory Animal Science.

AAMI—Association for the Advancement of Medical Instrumentation

acfm—actual cubic feet per hour

ACGH—American Conference of Governmental Industrial Hygienists, Inc.

ACIL—American Council of Independent Laboratories, Inc.

ACS—American Chemical Society

AHJ—authority having jurisdiction

AIA—American Institute of Architects

AIA—American Insurance Association

AIHA—American Industrial Hygiene Association

AMAA—Adhesives Manufacturers Association

amp—ampere

ANSI—American National Standards Institute, Inc.

ASA—Acoustical Society of America

ASC—Adhesive and Sealant Council

ASHRAE—American Society of Heating, Refrigeration and Air Conditioning Engineers

ASME—American Society of Mechanical Engineers

Asp—aspirator

ASSE—American Society of Safety Engineers

ASTM—American Society for Testing and Materials

atm—standard atmosphere (unit of pressure)

Atm exh—Atmospheric exhaust

Avg—average

bldg—building

BOCA—Building Officials and Code Administrators International

BOECKH—Building Cost Modifier American Appraisal Associates

BSI—British Standards Institute

Btu—British thermal unit

Btuh—Btu/hr

°C—degrees Celsius

CABO—Council of American Building Officials

CAP—Canadian Association of Pathologists

CAP—College of American Pathologists

CAV—constant air volume

CCAC—Canadian Council on Animal Care

CCPS Guidelines—Center for Chemical Process Safety Guidelines

CCTV—closed circuit TV

CD—construction documents

CDC—Center for Disease Control

Cent—centrifuge

cfh—cubic feet per hour

cfm—cubic feet per minute

CMU—concrete masonry unit

COP—coefficient of performance

corr—corridor

CPM—critical path method

cpm—cubic feet per minute

CPSC—U.S. Consumer Products Safety Commission

CRT—cathode ray tube

CSA—Canadian Standards Association

CSI—Construction Specifications Institute

cu ft—cubic foot

CW—cold water

dB—decibel

DD—design development

Deion—deionized

DGSF—departmental gross square feet

DOP—di-octyl-phthalate

DPB—discounted payback

DR—drain

EFF—efficiency

EIA—environmental impact assessment

elec—electricity

ELF—equivalent linear feet of space

EM—electron microscope

ENR—*Engineering News Record*

EPA—Environmental Protection Agency

Equipm—equipment

ETL—ETL Testing Laboratories, Inc. (equipment labeling)

Exh—exhaust

°F—degrees Fahrenheit

FCC—U.S. Government Printing Office

FIC—furnished and installed by contractor

FIO—furnished and installed by owner

FMEA—Failure Modes and Effects Analysis

FMS—Factory Mutual System

FOIC—furnished by owner, installed by contractor

fpm—feet per minute

FRP—fiberglass-reinforced polyester resin

FS—federal specifications

GLP—good laboratory practice

gpd—gallons per day

gpm—gallons per minute

GSA—General Services Administration

GSF—gross square feet

GWB—gypsum wall board

HDD—heating degree day

HEPA—high-efficiency particulate air filter

HP—horsepower

hr—hour

HVAC—heating, ventilation, air conditioning, cooling

HW—hot water

IAPMO—International Association of Plumbing and Mechanical Officials

IBBM—iron body bronze mounter

ICBO—Uniform Building Code, International Conference of Building Officials

in.—inch

JB—junction box

K—thousand

KW—kilowatt

KWH—kilowatt-hour

Lab—laboratory

lb—pound

lbs—pounds

LCC—life cycle costs

LF—linear feet

LOC—Library of Congress

LP—liquified petroleum

mech space—mechanical space

mech—mechanical equipment

min—minute

misc equip—miscellaneous equipment

MMBtu—million Btu

MRI—magnetic resonance imaging

N/A—not applicable

NAS—National Academy of Sciences

NASF—net assignable square feet

NBC—National Building Code

NBS—National Bureau of Standards

NC—noise control

NCCLS—National Commission for Clinical Laboratory Standards

NCRPM—National Council on Radiation Protection

NCSBC—National Conference of States on Building Codes and Standards

NFIRS—National Fire Incident Reporting System (NFPA)

NFPA—National Fire Protection Association

NFSA—National Fire Sprinklers Association

NIOSH—National Institute for Occupational Safety and Health

NMR—nuclear magnetic resonance

NPCA—National Paint and Coatings Association

NSF—National Sanitation Foundation

NSF—National Science Foundation

NTIS—National Technical Information Service

ORC—organic rankine cycle

OSHA—Occupational Safety and Health Administration or Act.

OTA—Office of Technology Assessment

pcf—pounds per cubic feet

PE—polyethylene

PE—professional engineer

PHA—preliminary hazard analysis

Plam—plastic laminate

POR—program of requirements

PP—polypropylene

ppm—parts per million

PS—product standards

psi—pounds per square inch

PVC—polyvinylchloride

PVDF—polyvinylidifluoride

Ref—refrigerator

RF—radio frequency

RFC—Resilient Floor Covering Institute

RH—relative humidity

RO—reverse osmosis

RPM—revolutions per minute

S St—stainless steel

SAMA—Society of Apparatus Makers Association

SBC—Southern Building Code Congress International

scfm—standard cubic feet per hour

SD—schematic design

SEI—Safety Equipment Institute

SF—square feet

SFPE—Society of Fire Protection Engineers

SIR—savings to investment ratio

SPB—simple payback

SPE—Society of Plastics Engineers

sq ft—square foot

sq in.—square inch

SRA—Society of Research Administrators

ST—steam

Staffing FTE—staffing full-time equivalent

TDS—total dissolved solids (water purity)

temp—temperature

TLV (ppm)—threshold limit value

torr—1.0 μm = 0.00 torr

UBC—Uniform Building Code

UF—ultrafiltration

UL—Underwriters Laboratory

UPS—uninterrupted power supply

USDA—U.S. Department of Agriculture

USDHEW—U.S. Department of Health, Education and Welfare

USDHHS—U.S. Department of Health and Human Services

USP—United States Pharmacopeia

USTBCB—U.S. Architectural Transportation Barriers Compliance Board

UV—ultraviolet

V—volts

VAV—variable air volume

1
General

1.1 CHARACTERISTICS OF LABORATORIES *M. Wodka*

1.1.1 The Search for Classification

Laboratories today are designed for the support of over 1.0 million active scientists and engineers. However, even if this number is expanded to include technicians, students and administrative support personnel, these unique facilities are created for and used by only a very small portion of the total population. Yet, laboratory facilities are among the most specialized and expensive kinds of architectural space. How these facilities are used and what facility requirements are most important to support these purposes are not well understood.

There are many reasons for this lack of understanding. The growth and changes which science has experienced in this century alone contradict the stereotyped image of the lone scientist in a white coat pouring vaporous chemicals from one test tube into another in a garret laboratory. The changing

expectations and values that our society places on the information produced in laboratories influence what happens in laboratories. Furthermore, scientific people, by their very nature and training, may unwittingly obscure attempts to understand laboratories and how they work by cloaking information in scientific jargon and tradition.

How then, at the beginning of the laboratory planning process, can we analyze and identify basic patterns in laboratory utilization and develop a way of classifying laboratories based on salient similarities and differences? Are there, in this apparently well-established but less than well-understood facility, factors which could be more apparent in classifying laboratory types than the traditional nomenclature of scientific subject matter such as "chemistry" or "research and development" (R&D)? If laboratory facilities could be more clearly redefined at the beginning of a project, then managers, scientists, planners and suppliers might be guided to a better understanding of why certain types of facilities and equipment seem so appropriate in one laboratory and less so in another.

Problems Encountered by Others

Most attempts to create a classification are quickly confounded by the complexity of laboratories. In addition, the very word "laboratory" embodies the duality of space and building, which are often difficult to separate. Overall, most approaches to classification start at the building level and become more detailed at the space level.

However, to be useful, classifications must help shape our concepts and form a base for our programming data. Comparison is required to achieve this: comparison of new data with past information and comparison of norms or standards with program requirements. In most cases, unless you are an experienced laboratory designer, the comparative data base is missing. Even for experienced individuals, there is a natural tendency to repeat what works rather than to test new ideas rigorously against a more overtly stated model. Finally, it is difficult for laboratory users to imagine facilities they have not experienced. Many of the descriptive responses from laboratory users are based on what people are used to or have been trained to do. In other words, what they have is all right and is what they want again, even though many inappropriate relationships between work processes and facilities can be observed.

Issues That Form Basic Differences

To help in this search for a preliminary classification, we need to expand our scope of examination. Kuhn (1979), in his book *The Essential Tension,* described his own problems with understanding and classifying scientific practices:

> I would now insist that scientific communities must be discovered by examining patterns of education and communication before asking which particular research problems engage each group.
> I have tried to insist . . . that though science is practiced by individuals, scientific knowl-

edge is intrinsically a group product and that neither its peculiar efficiency nor the manner in which it develops will be understood without reference to the special nature of the groups that produce it. (p. 53)

Consideration of issues beyond the specific field of research is necessary to frame a useful classification scheme. A review of the essential differences in scientific practice; a deeper understanding of the scientific community and how it has changed; and a review of the personality types that tend to populate the scientific community are meaningful parts of classification.

1.1.2 The Essential Differences Across Science as It Affects Facilities

The distinction between basic science and applied science may seem too trivial to draw attention to since, as the names imply, applied science aims at practical, societally useful ends and basic science does not. However, it becomes important to understand the distinction when we are talking about laboratories if we add invention (or technology) to the mix. All of these variations of science are practiced in places called laboratories. However, the objectives, methods and responsibilities of each appear to be different enough to be included in a discussion of the ways in which the laboratory environment can be classified. These differences begin to hint at which facility issues are most relevant in each scientific division and what the reasons for the differences are.

Difference in Practice

Basic science can be viewed, as Kuhn described it, as a process based on preestablished rules and done by people who are traditionalists. It is science practiced as theoretical puzzle solving. This differs greatly from applied science, which is the kind of science more widely practiced today. In contrast to basic science, which is relatively free to choose its own problems, work to its own means and ends, and concern itself with scientific understanding, whether useful to society or not, applied science is more strongly directed by social, military, or economic choices of problems to be solved. The output of applied science is not more pieces of the puzzle but specific, useful concepts applicable to solving stated problems. This means more organized management and judgment of the worth of the laboratory's output based on a different set of values, and goals in comparison to basic science.

Only 13% of the scientific activity in this country is considered basic science, according to the National Science Foundation. However, the laboratory facility model that has developed from the way basic science is practiced appears to be the model for all scientific divisions, regardless of the differing objectives and practices of science. If the intent and output of the various scientific endeavors can differ so greatly, the facilities in which the work is done must be influenced by these differences.

Who Works in the Laboratory

Information from the National Science Foundation estimates our practicing scientific and R&D engineering community to be approximately 1.5 million people. About 800,000 are listed as scientists and the remainder as engineers. As a single working group, they are a rather small and very specialized community within our work force. Price (1986), in his book *Little Science Big Science,* explains that science is a specialized group and tends to break into ever more specialized subgroups. Individuals in each scientific subgroup follow each other's professional development very closely through published works, and often visit and take up residence at each other's labs. This suggests an "invisible college," as Price calls this activity. An infrastructure of tightly knit, sometimes very small communities exists and exerts strong professional pressure on its members to do things in certain ways. It is hard for scientists to ignore these standards, which include what a good lab is, and still be viewed by peers as practicing appropriately.

Impact of Personality on Views of the Laboratory

Scientists exhibit personality traits that also contribute to the problems of understanding laboratory facilities. A widely used psychological type indicator suggests that people entering science share a tendency to value logical deduction, believe in orderliness and harbor a healthy degree of skepticism.

However, this same personality indicator suggests the people drawn to careers in basic science tend to accept the scientific group conventions that promote particularly structured, organized work and workplaces that suit the groups' views. They also tend to believe that getting on with the experiment at hand is most important. Therefore, if a particular lab plan is in place, they may view redesigning it as a waste of time, even though they must do some jury rigging of their apparatus in order to use it. Progress for these people, in particular, seems to be equated with changes to the experimental setup rather than with changes to the workplace. Unless the laboratory facility forces work to halt because no more experimental accommodations can be made, the workplace is left as is.

On the other hand, the personality indicator suggests that people in applied R&D value innovation and uniqueness over adherence to group conventions, in contrast to their kin in basic science. These "inventors" tend to see the whole environment as part of their experiments and often alter both apparatus and workplace in their attempts to be creative. These innovators value uniqueness, in comparison to their basic scientific counterparts, who are the model of the classic scientist described earlier.

The Impact of Organizations

Most basic science is conducted in our universities. This work is controlled by the individual scientist receiving the grant. The organizational setting is what Mintzburg (1979), a noted organizational theorist, calls a "professional bureaucracy": an organization where the majority of the decision-making power is in the hands of the professionals. In these organizations, decisions on what gets done, where and why are dominated by the scientist. The organization essentially is a host. Therefore, facility decisions are guided by the objectives of the scientific enclave rather than the administrative forces.

In the corporate world, where the professionals are not in such specific control, facility issues are sometimes driven to diverging ends by administrative forces on the one hand and scientific or development forces on the other. Here, accommodation of flexibility versus first cost, for example, are issues seen from different vantage points.

1.1.3 A Laboratory Classification Scheme

The approach to classification proposed here is based on the interaction of two major forces: the scientific objective and the procedural objective. Research on laboratory facility design over the past 8 to 10 years suggests that, as a basis for classification, these forces contain an excellent mix of goals that agree well in most lab planning situations.

A Distinction Between Objectives

The first classifying force is the functional difference in laboratories based on differences in scientific objectives rather than on the usual distinction in the field of practice. These differences can be described by four terms: "basic science," "applied science," "invention" and "analysis." Each of these represents a different goal for the production of laboratory output and therefore forms a different element in classification. See Table 1.1-1.

These four scientific divisions allow us to define differences in the centers of control and decision making for laboratory output. Also, it is possible to identify the most important beneficiaries of this lab output by using these four divisions, as well as key physical characteristics that may be found in programming.

The basic science lab. This lab's activities are dedicated to advancing understanding and pure scientific knowledge. Its output is judged by scientific peers, and the value of the work done is seen in very academic terms. To allow this to occur, with the high quality and thoroughness demanded by good scientific practice, there is much individual control of projects following personally chosen objectives. Lab work is usually bench scale, and the facility is often broken into ownership of individual labs by the scientist in charge.

Table 1.1-1. Classification Based on Scientific Objectives

General Lab Descriptions by Scientific Objective	Basic	Applied	Invention	Analysis
Management Control	One person very influential	One person with corporate influence	Corporate with personal influence	Corporate with personal influence
Project Determinist	Scientific curiosity	Problem stater	Market needs	Customer
Output	Understanding and knowledge	Concepts and solutions to specific problems	Products	Data
Accountability	Scientific peers	Problem stater (military, society, corporate, etc.)	Problem stater (marketplace and profit)	Data customer
Value of Results	Universal truth	It works under these conditions	How to make it	Accuracy, consistency, turnaround

The applied science lab. This lab uses the techniques and methods of science to produce practical, societally useful results. These results may be in the form of a concept or a verification of a hypothesis in order to solve a stated problem. In this case, the work is judged by those who stated the problem, and these persons are often not scientists. This is an important distinction because the concept of a client enters the picture at this level of science. In basic science, the client can be viewed as science itself. In applied science, there is a definite judgment made by outsiders. Quality is based on the success of the solution proposed. This naturally leads to less control over one's work, since fitting the solution and the problem together demands a different approach to lab practice compared to pure discovery for its own sake. Work here ranges from a high degree of bench-scale activity to larger functions that may include pilot production spaces.

The invention lab. Even more responsive to external pressures is the lab where actual products are invented. These places are part of classic corporate R&D operations. The problem here is often defined in terms of taking an applied science finding or principle and making it practical for the marketplace. In these situations the issues relate to how to make "it," and success is clearly defined by sales and profits. These labs usually have real products or subcomponents requiring space that supports everything from bench-scale activity to hangers for huge objects or pilot production.

The analysis lab. The analytical lab supports the other labs by providing service. The focus here is producing data, as opposed to providing basic understanding, useful concepts or hardware. Analytical lab personnel usually make no judgments as to the value of the data they produce. Therefore, like basic science labs, these labs are concerned with accuracy, truth and specific knowledge. However, they are also responsible to outside customers who judge their output and set their problems, which makes their accountability more like that of applied or invention labs. While the work is most likely to be bench scale in size, repetitive operation and high efficiency are the key goals.

Process Complexity

The second set of classifying variables produced is laboratory process complexity. These can be described in two terms: project mix in the lab and process mix in the lab. See Table 1.1-2.

Table 1.1-2. Classification Based on Process Complexity

General Lab Descriptions by Process Complexity Issues	Single-Project Labs		Multiple-Project Labs	
	Single Procedure	Multiple Procedures	Single Procedure	Multiple Procedure
User control Over Project Changes	User controlled	User controlled	More control by organization	Highly driven by organization's needs
Facility Control by Users	Usually controlled by user	Usually controlled by user	More control by organization	Driven by organization's needs
Rate of Project Changes	Mixed; > 9 months typical	Mixed	Fast change; projects < 6 months	Fastest; projects < 6 months
Predictability of Change Points	Predictable	Predictable, with some surprises	Hard to predict because of organizational change	Difficult to predict
Complexity of Facility Issues	Less complex	Somewhat complex	Somewhat complex	Very complex

Project mix. Based on a variety of research, it appears that lab projects are organized in two ways. The laboratory unit may be in charge of a single project or report to a single consumer of its service. On the other hand, the laboratory unit may handle a variety of projects or be responsible to a number of potential consumers. This single-project or multiple-project designation provides insight into how complex the overall project management problem is in a given lab. In addition, many facility issues are related to the mix of projects and their rates of change. The need for various kinds of flexibility and space variation are two examples.

Procedure or protocol mix. A second variable related to process complexity is the mix of specific procedures or protocols used in the lab. Again, two divisions appear. One is the lab that executes its projects or reports to consumers by utilizing one experimental or analytical procedure. While this may involve a number of steps, the procedure is de-fined as one activity leading from a start to a finish. The other is the multiple-procedure lab. Here there are a number of activities, each with its own internal procedures that are done independently of one another. These activities may be going on simultaneously, or the lab may institute any one of them at any one time. This variable can affect individual room requirements for furniture flexibility and utility service variations.

Application of the Classification Matrix

By placing these eight elements in a matrix, a classification structure can be filled out to aid in planning. See Figure 1.1-1. The classification matrix provides for 16 potential classifications of laboratories. While all 16 may not actually exist, the matrix is an excellent indicator for predicting the complexity of facility issues across categories.

The categories can be applied to both laboratory buildings and laboratory spaces. Again, especially where buildings are con-

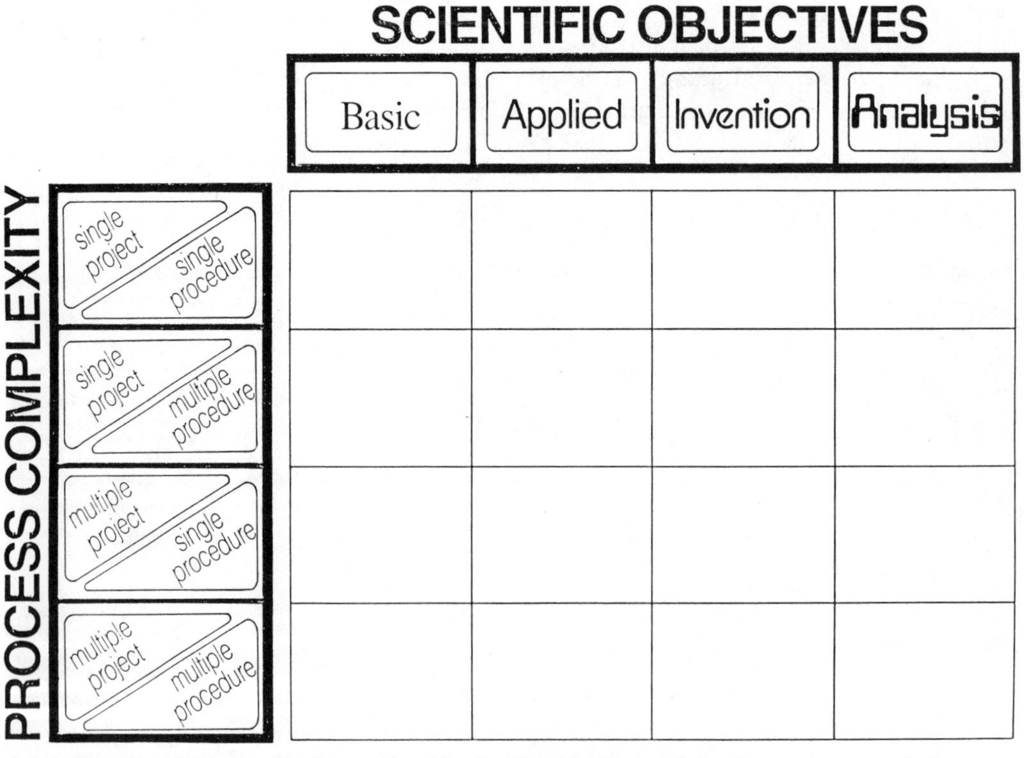

Fig. 1.1-1. Basic classification matrix with scientific objectives applied against process complexity.

cerned, all categories may not be achievable. However, through this classification scheme, it is possible to envision the category and determine its potential functionality, criteria, and complexity.

Some data from surveys conducted by Wodka (1981) and Levy and Wodka (1986) have been applied to the matrix to develop descriptions for different characteristics of laboratories. Some of these are general characteristics, while others are more specific. This arrangement allows the 16 categories to be clustered into related sets, depending on the characteristic chosen. This is a handy tool for the planner to use in developing more specifics. See Figure 1.1-2.

Classification Clusters

The classification matrix also allows new clusters to emerge. The clusters shown are based on the surveys mentioned before. They group operational and physical similarities from the survey data by Wodka (1981)

that describe what well-planned labs have in common. These data are for laboratory rooms, not whole buildings. Therefore, terms such as "open space" refer to aisles and floor space not occupied by equipment or benches typically installed in the room.

Cluster 1: The independent discovery laboratory. These laboratories operate with a minimum amount of project cross-fertilization. Individual projects usually remain independent to maintain scientific purity and personal control. See Figure 1.1-3.

This type of laboratory usually is designed with flexibility primarily in terms of versatility, that is, a general functional arrangement that can stay in place while the work process is modified. Large-scale convertibility is a secondary function occurring at rather widely separated intervals, sometimes as far apart as 10 years.

These laboratories often need only limited plumbed utilities, which suggests that conventional redundant distribution may not be

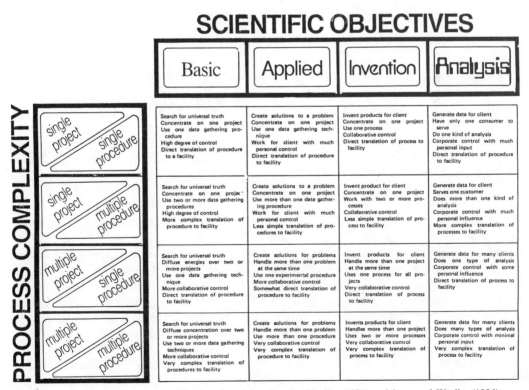

Fig.1.1-2. Classification matrix filled in with survey data by Wodka (1981) and Levy and Wodka (1986).

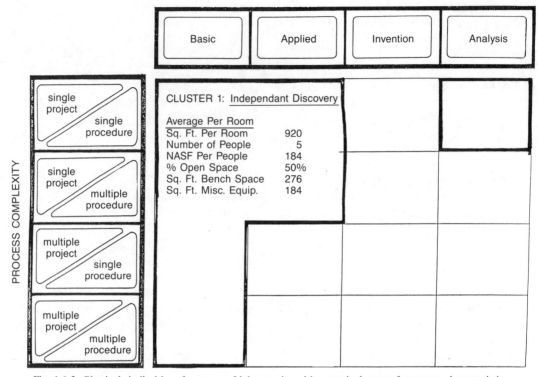

Fig. 1.1-3. Physical similarities of a group of laboratories with a particular set of common characteristics.

the most appropriate technique. This laboratory cluster has a moderate need for widely distributed electrical service. Change, when it occurs, is usually precipitated by a change in method rather than by a change in timing or in a field of study. This suggests more local revision of the space and key components rather than wholesale remodeling. These laboratories work well with about one-half of their gross square footage of floor space in the given room left open after all equipment is located. Of the remaining 50%, 30% of this floor space is typically devoted to the benches. The independent discovery laboratories in the study by Wodka (1981) had about 184 net assignable square feet (NASF) per person of open floor space, which often is about 20% of the available square footage in a given room.

These laboratories are presently acquiring large pieces of computerized equipment, which is causing an increase in bench changes. The most significant renovation activity is the need for additional ventilation and the trade of bench top for hood space or floor space for electronic equipment and computers. This is due to the increasing need in this type of lab to investigate nature by making ever smaller measurements, which require more sophisticated equipment and environmental contamination control.

Cluster 2: The interactive commercial laboratory. These laboratories rely on information exchange among employees and project cross-fertilization, and often have parallel programs with scientists working on segments of the same problem. The interaction between these programs is essential in solving large, complex problems. See Figure 1.1-4.

These laboratories require much more convertibility—the ability to change the environment at both large and small scales to fit

SCIENTIFIC OBJECTIVES

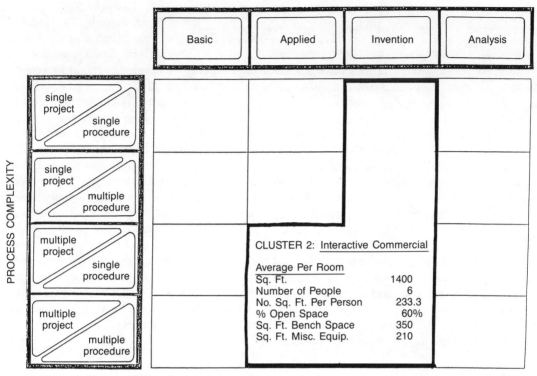

Fig. 1.1-4. Physical similarities of another group of laboratories with a second set of common characteristics.

new programs—than other labs do. They use a rather limited number of utility services that are typically plumbed into the lab. Like the independent discovery laboratories, they may be prime candidates for new approaches to utility service distribution that would reduce the total number of linear feet of pipe and limit the connections between utility mains and bench. However, these laboratories often use electrical service extensively. Change here is precipitated by changes in program and timing, which feed the need for convertibility. This type of laboratory works well with about 60% of the gross floor area in a given laboratory left open and about 25% of the floor area devoted to benches. The remaining space is usually occupied by free-standing equipment carts, experimental apparatus or computers.

Because laboratories in this cluster tend to have either multiple processes or programs, the so-called open-plan lab has become more popular. A greater amount of shared space is useful in these situations; this amounts to about 233 NASF of floor area per person based on the total gross square footage of a given laboratory room. This square footage can vary by about 10%, depending on specific planning conditions. Like the independent discovery laboratories, these laboratories also are now using more computerized equipment, since the corporate world is very interested in getting the research done as rapidly and economically as possible. Investment in this equipment is seen as a step toward productivity in the research field. Therefore, bench rearrangement is on the increase.

Comparing overall room size, the Cluster 2 laboratory is somewhat larger, although it may overlap Cluster 1. Project work areas ranging from 750 to 1,000 sq ft seem most appropriate. Based on the study data by Wodka (1981), this results in a typical room size of 1,400 sq ft. This figure is the total for the project space, including open space for aisles and miscellaneous equipment.

Cluster 3: The quantitative service laboratory. While these laboratories have a great deal of interaction, the interaction differs in that it occurs on a client–consultant basis rather than on a cross-fertilization basis. This is due to the nature of the skills used in these labs and the service they perform in support of scientific pursuit. These laboratories focus on versatility as the primary aspect of flexibility, since the activities they support usually occur over long periods of time. See Figure 1.1-5. The quantitative service laboratories, like the interactive commercial laboratories, also use many electrical services. Change in this cluster is precipitated by changes in methods and in timing. On occasion some conversion of components is appropriate, but this is usually in localized areas and does not often include complete

revamping of a laboratory space, as often occurs in the Cluster 2 laboratories.

These laboratories require a greater amount of open space than Cluster 1 and Cluster 2 laboratories. Good planning in these laboratories generally results in a room with 70% of the floor area used for aisles and 25% for benches. The remaining 5% is swing space for planning variations. The proportion of lab space devoted to benches is not particularly high, because these labs are often filled with self-contained equipment which occupies floor space. However, room sizes are usually large in this cluster and 25% represents quite a bit of bench space, which is a vital part of gaining versatility in light of the equipment used. A minimum of open floor area per person appears to be approximately 337 NASF; this can range as much as 15% higher, because many of these labs require a lot of open space to move samples in and out.

These laboratories also are experiencing

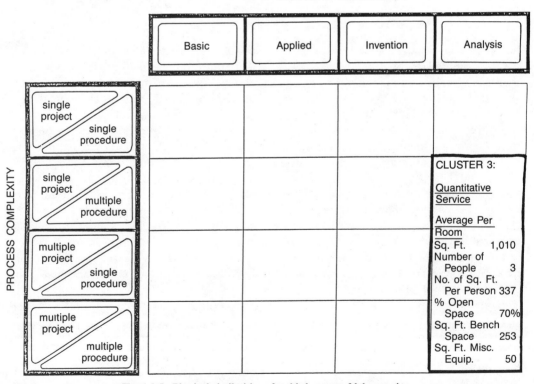

Fig. 1.1-5. Physical similarities of a third group of laboratories.

an even higher increase in the use of computerized and automated equipment, a trend which will continue to grow rapidly as more and more analytical procedures are automated. Cluster 3 laboratories are the second largest of the three groups in overall work area size. In this group, the average well-planned room had 1,010 gross sq ft (Wodka, 1981).

REFERENCES

Kuhn, Thomas S., 1979. *The Essential Tension*. Chicago: University of Chicago Press.

Levy, David, and Wodka, Michael, 1986. *The Industrial Laboratory: User Needs, Choices and Options*. Ann Arbor, MI: Herman Miller Research Corporation.

Mintzburg, Henry, 1979. *The Structuring of Organizations*. Englewood Cliffs, NJ: Prentice-Hall.

Price, D.J., 1986. *Little Science Big Science*. New York: Columbia University Press.

Wodka, Michael, 1981. *Laboratory Management and Environment Analysis*. Ann Arbor, MI: Herman Miller Research Corporation.

1.2 DIFFERENCES AND SIMILARITIES IN CHEMICAL, BIOSCIENCES AND PHYSICAL SCIENCES LABORATORIES   *U.M. Lindner*

1.2.1 Introduction

No two laboratories are ever alike. They always reflect the occupants' work habits, personality and special interests.

Certain types of work do, however, require certain kinds of furnishings, tools and equipment. For this reason you will find that a well-designed organic chemistry lab (or pharmacology lab or laser lab) will generally be usable for anyone who does organic chemistry (or pharmacology or works with lasers).

On the following pages, it will be evident that certain features of laboratories recur despite the fact that the tasks require different use of the space.

A general rule to remember is: simplicity and clarity of plan. See Figures 1.2-1 and 1.2-2.

Quite often, entire floors or even entire buildings can be designed with generic laboratory space. Future occupants then adapt the generic lab to suit their work habits and special interests without remodeling simply by placing equipment and work zones to suit their individual needs.

1.2.2 Chemistry Laboratories

Chemistry laboratories tend to break down into the following generic spaces: organic chemistry, inorganic chemistry, physical chemistry and analytical chemistry.

Organic Chemistry

Organic chemistry is defined as all chemistry dealing with the compounds of carbon. By that definition, the majority of chemicals handled by organic chemists are either toxic, odoriferous, carcinogens, dangerous reactors, or all of these. Therefore, most organic chemistry work is accomplished in fume hoods. The need for hooded (or exhausted) work space characterizes the organic chemistry lab. See Figure 1.2-3.

In addition to the above generic lab space, desk space for researchers, technicians, post-doctoral personnel and students must be provided. This can be done in a variety of ways. A rule of thumb, however, is that a chemist's desk should be located away from the lab bench/hood areas but close enough so that the chemist can see and "smell" his or her work. This means that Figure 1.2-3 could be supplemented. See Figure 1.2-4.

Care should be taken that any glass used in the safety partition is laminated safety glass or, better still, polycarbonate.

Services (piped services) are typically as follows:

- Hot water
- Cold water
- Deionized water (or other type of clean water)
- Vacuum
- Compressed air (not higher than 35 psi on the bench)
- Gas (carefully and judiciously placed; flammable solvents and open flame do not mix)

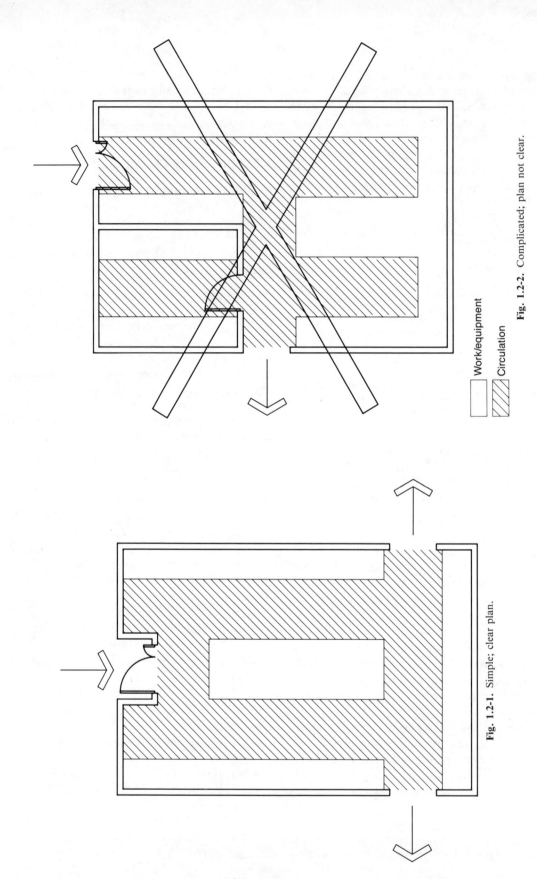

Work/equipment

Circulation

Fig. 1.2-2. Complicated; plan not clear.

Fig. 1.2-1. Simple; clear plan.

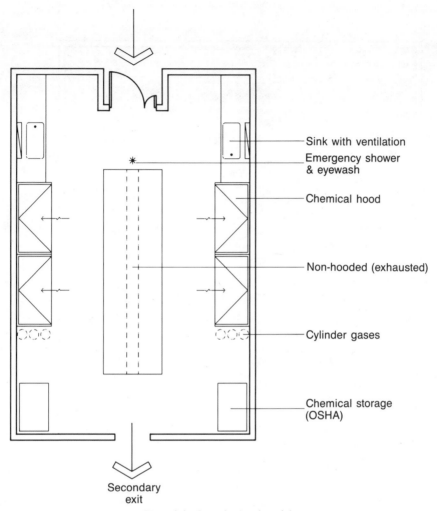

Fig. 1.2-3. Organic chemistry lab.

- Steam (low pressure, for heating)
- Electric power

Besides the fume hoods, there should be cleanup sinks—ideally with a means of ventilation, as glassware is often rinsed with solvents. A method to produce cylinder gases should also be provided, either within the lab or, more safely, from the outside. Storage for chemicals (solvents and acids) must also be provided in accordance with applicable codes.

Materials used in organic chemistry labs are usually corrosion resistant. Tops and sinks should be acid and solvent proof, as should the liner and top in all hoods. Floors and wall coatings, as well as duct materials for fume hoods, should be the most corrosion-resistant variety available.

Inorganic Chemistry

Inorganic chemistry is defined as all chemistry dealing with compounds other than those of carbon. Again, by that definition, inorganic chemists handle compounds *generally* less demanding of hood space than those of organic chemists. Therefore, inorganic chemistry labs generally require less hood space, and a generic inorganic lab might develop. See Figure 1.2-5.

Again, the laboratory sketch (Figure

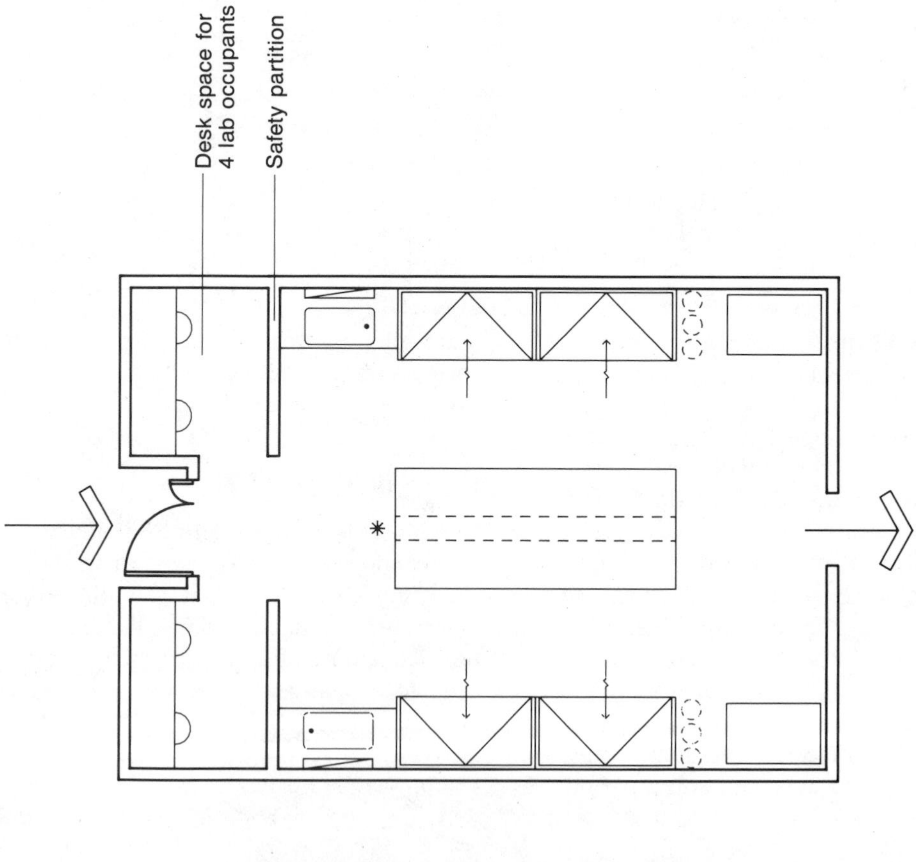

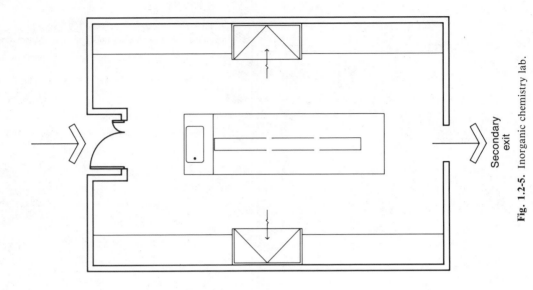

Desk space for
4 lab occupants

Safety partition

Secondary
exit

Fig. 1.2-5. Inorganic chemistry lab.

Fig. 1.2-4. Organic chemistry lab (alternate).

1.2-5) must be supplemented by desk space for technicians, postdoctoral employees, students and researchers. Figure 1.2-6 suggests one of many ways to accommodate in-lab desks.

Note that an alternative way to locate the chemical hoods is also suggested. The face of the hood is out of the normal traffic pattern, yet provides easy access for lab occupants.

Services (piped services) are typically as follows:

- Hot water
- Cold water
- Deionized water (or other type of clean water)
- Vacuum
- Compressed air (not higher than 35 psi on the bench)
- Gas
- Electric power

Cleanup sinks with eyewash devices, cylinder gases (preferably located outside of the lab) and chemical storage cabinets for solvents and acids should also be provided.

The materials used in inorganic chemistry labs can generally be the same as those used in organic chemistry labs.

Physical Chemistry

Physical chemistry deals with the scientific analysis of the properties and behavior of chemical systems primarily by physical theory and technique. Therefore, a physical chemistry lab is characterized by the large amount of electrical power required and by the fact that floor space for equipment, gen-

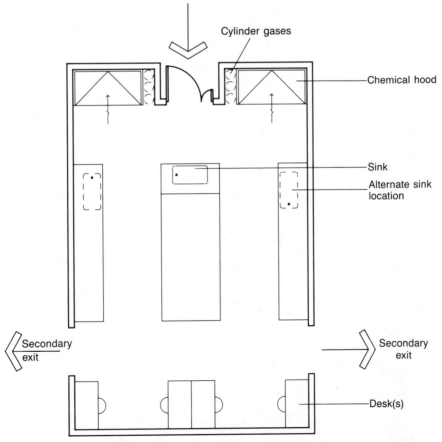

Fig. 1.2-6. Inorganic chemistry lab (alternate).

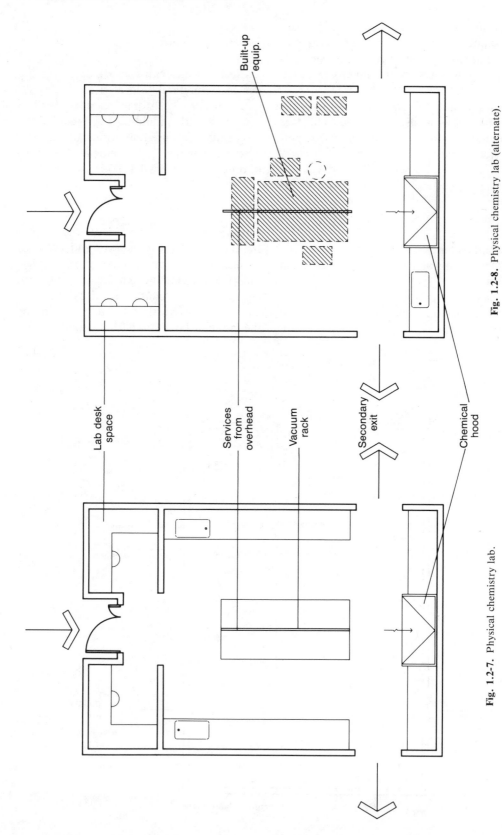

Built-up equip.

Lab desk space

Services from overhead

Vacuum rack

Secondary exit

Chemical hood

Fig. 1.2-8. Physical chemistry lab (alternate).

Fig. 1.2-7. Physical chemistry lab.

erally accessible from four sides, is required. Such floor space is occupied by incredibly complex machinery, mostly one of a kind, or by what are commonly known as "vacuum racks," all fully serviceable with power and piped systems. Such systems are best provided from overhead. Figures 1.2-7 and 1.2-8 suggest possible designs for a physical chemistry lab.

Services (piped services) are typically as follows:

- Hot water
- Cold water
- Deionized water
- Vacuum
- Compressed air
- Gas
- Electric power

In addition, the services might include a means to distribute a cooling water system, liquid nitrogen, high-pressure air and electrical services of larger capacity, with voltages ranging from 110 to 220 and possibly 480 V, depending on the individual's or the group's research direction.

Materials will generally follow the recommendations for organic chemistry.

Analytical Chemistry

Analytical chemistry studies, quantitatively and/or qualitatively, the chemical composition and structure of substances. Sophisticated balances, gas and paper chromatography, mass and optical spectrometry are but a few of the instruments and techniques used in a modern analytical laboratory.

The laboratory itself incorporates and combines features of other types of chemistry, such as inorganic chemistry. The layout could vary from that of the wet chemistry lab shown in Figure 1.2-6 to a space housing highly sophisticated apparatus similar to that shown in Figure 1.2-8. The general characteristics of a lab housing highly calibrated electronic apparatus are close and accurate temperature control, reasonable vibration control and availability of clean electrical power.

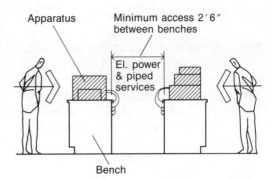

Fig. 1.2-9. Rear access to analytical instrumentation on fixed benches.

Because of all the sophisticated electronic instrumentation present, the lab should be designed to provide easy access for maintenance and/or calibration. As shown in Figure 1.2-8, access to floor-mounted equipment is required, preferably on all four sides, but certainly from the front and back.

Various methods of providing back access to many types of bench-mounted apparatus have been employed; two of the more successful designs are shown in Figures 1.2-9 and 1.2-10.

Figure 1.2-9 shows a split laboratory bench with sufficient access for a person to enter and set up or maintain the instrumentation. The services to these benches certainly include electrical power and a number of piped gases, and could include cooling water and drainage points such as funnel drains or cupsinks.

Figure 1.2-10 shows the apparatus mounted on sturdy but movable racks which can be pulled away from the wall to gain access to the rear of the equipment.

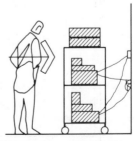

Fig. 1.2-10. Rear access to analytical instrumentation on movable benches or racks.

1.2.3 Biosciences Laboratories

These laboratories, sometimes also called "life sciences laboratories," serve as work spaces for a host of special research interests reflecting the investigators' research direction. They are distinguished by the support space that is required for each laboratory or group of laboratories.

In most cases, such support space houses shared equipment, such as centrifuges, freezers, or gas chromatographs; spaces that need to be separated and enclosed for environmental reasons, such as cold rooms, warm rooms or containment laboratories; or spaces that house specialized functions, such as flow cytometry, tissue culture or autoclaving.

The other distinguishing feature of bio-sciences laboratories is their need for and proximity to living research objects such as greenhouses, vivariums, or animal quarters and hospitals or clinics for the human subject.

There are several generic laboratory designs that could be used for a large number of bioscience-oriented research studies. See Figures 1.2-11 and Figure 1.2-12.

With minor adaptations and well-designed support space, research such as virology, immunology, serology, physiology, cell biology, pharmacology, clinical research or agricultural research could be accomplished in such generic laboratories. Simplicity and clarity of plan are necessary for every approach and any design.

Desk space for technicians, postdoctoral fellows and students is also very important.

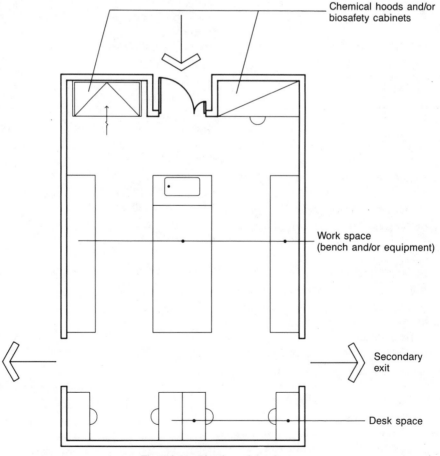

Fig. 1.2-11. Bioscience laboratory.

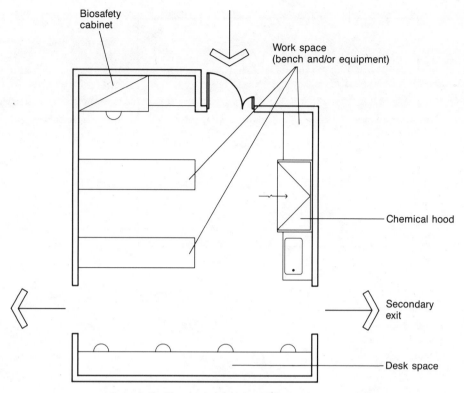

Fig. 1.2-12. Bioscience laboratory (alternate).

In contrast to chemistry labs, desk space for most bioscience research does not necessarily have to be inside the laboratory. As long as spaces such as offices, alcoves and cubicles can be placed reasonably close to the laboratory, they can be located elsewhere. See Figures 1.2-13 and 1.2-14.

As indicated earlier, well-designed, strategically located support space is key to the well-functioning bioscience laboratory. The support space should be designed using the same principles used in creating the laboratory, i.e., the same modules, ergometric dimensions and principles. Indeed, support spaces *are* laboratories, but of a specialized kind.

What will vary from the generic lab are factors such as electrical services, piped services, environmental conditions, finishes and furnishings.

The best resource for the design of such specialized spaces is the scientist. It is the designer's task to fit these special spaces within the building and within the design parameters of the mechanical and electrical systems.

In our experience, an area equivalent to one-third of the net laboratory space is a minimum requirement for support of bioscience research.

Services (piped services) are typically as follows:

- Hot water
- Cold water
- Deionized water (or other type of clean water)
- Vacuum
- Compressed air
- Gas
- Electric power

Steam (usually medium pressure) is used for sterilization and glassware washing.

Fume hoods, as well as biosafety cabinets and laminar flow hoods, are used in all areas of bioscience research. Storage for chemicals

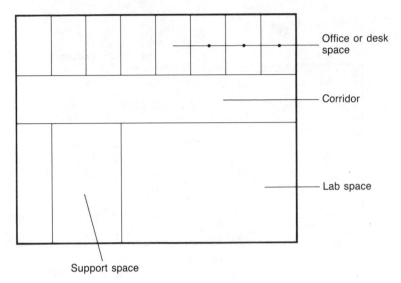

Fig. 1.2-13. Desk space for bioresearch.

(solvents and acids) must be provided in accordance with applicable codes.

Materials used in biosciences research labs should be corrosion resistant. However, while the same corrosion-resistant materials that are good for chemistry labs should also be good for bioscience research, there is a difference.

To facilitate cleaning and combat the growth of bacteria, as well as to provide sur-

faces for radioisotope work (which is done to some extent in almost any bioscience lab), nonabsorbing materials, such as stainless steel sinks and benchtops, and acid-resistant plastic laminates are recommended.

1.2.4 Physical Sciences Laboratories

Physical sciences laboratories are distinguished from other types of laboratories in a number of ways.

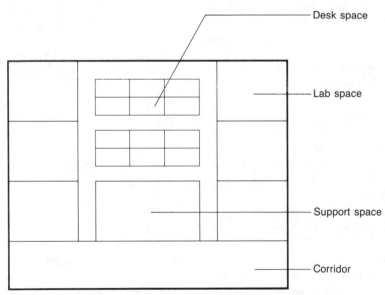

Fig. 1.2-14. Desk space for bioresearch (alternate).

First, there is only a small amount of built-in furniture.

Second, there is an abundance and a variety of electrical power. This, of course, is due to the fact that in most physical sciences research labs the floor space is occupied by an array of mind-boggling apparatus and instrumentation, both home-built and store bought. Almost all of this equipment requires power of varying voltage and amperage.

Some standard outfitting should be provided for most physical sciences labs, i.e., some work benches, a sink and desk space. Such areas might very well start out looking as indicated in Figure 1.2.-15.

Power and piped services are usually provided from an overhead suspended service carrier.

The scientists will then build the experiment within the empty floor space, connect to the overhead services and provide additional work surfaces with movable tables that can easily be rearranged.

In designing such a lab, it is important to remember that adequate and safe circulation space is required, as is access to the apparatus for setup, maintenance and everyday adjustments. See Figure 1.2.3-16.

It is hard to establish a guide for either the casework requirement or the electrical, plumbing and heating, ventilation, air-conditioning, cooling (HVAC) services. One could, however, suggest the following:

Casework

From 6 to 12 linear feet of built-in casework is required, usually in the form of benches. Additional furnishings will usually be provided by movable furniture, such as tables, storage cabinets (usually locker-type cabinets with locking devices for storage of parts and components), chemical/solvent storage cabinets, an occasional fume hood or laminar flow cabinet, optical tables or laser tables, movable desks, and so on.

Electrical Services

Assume the worst! Be certain to know how this power will be used. For instance, there is always a need for a 120/208 V electrical raceway. Assume a minimum of 10–20 amp circuits for a 600 SF laboratory. How do you supply other power? Is power supplied to the panel only, or to a shutoff switch on the wall inside the lab? How much power is required? How do you feed from the building transformer—by conduit or by bus? Do you provide laboratory power emergency shutoffs at the exit door(s)?

When designing a laser lab, the designer must provide for automatic power shutoffs at the entry points to the lab, keeping in

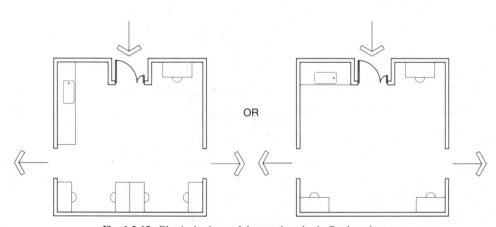

Fig. 1.2-15. Physical sciences laboratories—basic fixed equipment.

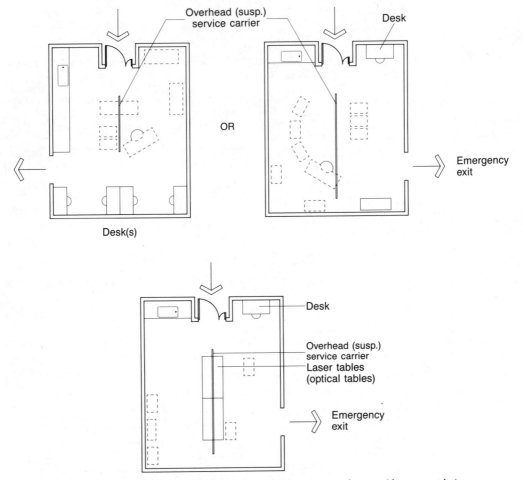

Fig. 1.2-16. Physical sciences laboratories—adequate space and access (three examples).

mind that the first prerequisite is designing for safety and, secondly, for efficiency.

Plumbing Services

Most physical sciences laboratories require either access to a central cooling water loop system furnished with the building or a cooling water system dedicated to a certain instrument. It is important to know how the building's cooling water works, i.e., how it can be accessed and recirculated. Scientists have frequently moved into a new facility where they were promised a cooling water system, only to find out that the system as designed would not work for their purposes—an obvious waste of money.

Often the researcher will prefer the safety of the familiar individual chiller, heat exchanger, or pumps, which are not shared with anyone else. This, of course, provides no backup system and creates problems of noise, heat generation, floor drains, tap water, and so on for the designer.

HVAC Services

The mechanical system in physical sciences labs is usually different from those of a typical chemistry or biosciences laboratory; this is particularly true of the air conditioning. Most of the lab equipment produces heat and therefore needs additional cooling, which is provided either by cooling water or by both cooling water and additional air flow.

Temperature control is always a very important aspect of physical sciences laboratories. Most equipment works best at cooler temperatures (69° to 72°F), but more critical is the fact that temperature fluctuations of more than ± 2°F over any 24-hour period can distort tests and experiments.

Humidity control is also important and will usually be required in the neighborhood of 35 to 50%, ± 5%.

The researcher is the best source of design information for such laboratories and their systems. However, if a state-of-the-art facility is required, user information can be misleading unless the designer fully understands how all the systems work, how the architecture of the building can or cannot accommodate the user, and how codes and safety issues affect the user's requirements.

1.3 COMMON ERRORS IN LABORATORY FACILITIES PLANNING   *T. Ruys*

1.3.1 Introduction

Laboratory facilities are complex, and their planning requires knowledge of the building type and the client's needs. This section deals with the most common errors:

- Errors in communications
- Errors in perception
- Errors in information transfer
- Errors in judgment

Each will be covered in detail, and examples will be given in the following sections.

1.3.2 Errors in Communications

Probably the most common error in communications occurs because laboratory users and planners speak different languages. The former speaks of functional requirements, the latter about the physical environment. When the user asks for a radioisotope laboratory, the planner should know that this type of lab requires secured access, a radioisotope hood and negative air pressure.

More questions are also in order about the level and type of radioactivity, which may require special materials for bench tops and special filtration of the exhaust air. It is also not uncommon that the right information is transferred, but for the wrong reasons. For instance, the right requirements are given for a radioisotope laboratory, but such a laboratory may no longer be required because that program will be terminated before the new laboratory is built or because that part of the work can be contracted to an outside organization and thus no longer requires a laboratory.

It is important for laboratory planners to understand the notions of "reliability" and "validity." These terms are often used in research and can be applied to planning as well. There are four types of reliability in research. For our purposes, reliability means securing consistent results by different means. For instance, if an individual asks for a laboratory of 500 net SF, the results should be based on an interview (the user told us, and the need was justified), on observation (we saw the lab) and on measurement (the benches, equipment aisles, etc., were measured). The observed phenomena have to be validated before we may use the data collected. We may check the reliability by verifying (1) data by the same observer at different times; (2) data by different observers at the same time; (3) data acquired by different techniques; and (4) comparable findings on related projects. In addition, we may reduce observational errors, as noted elsewhere in this chapter.

Reliability is a necessary condition for validity; in other words, there can be no validity without reliability. However, one can have high reliability without validity: a great laboratory for the wrong reasons. But who is going to be the judge? Or what are the set of rules by which the results are judged?

Validity is the degree to which any plan or layout succeeds in doing what it is intended to do. The objective and the criteria for measuring success or failure have to be present to establish validity. There are many types of validity. For our purposes, validity is measured both upon completion of the laboratory (consensual validity) and in the future (predictive validity). Consensual validity is, of course, measured by the laboratory users when they first enter their new laboratory and agree either that it meets their criteria or does not. Predictive validity is measured when changes are required in the future and it is determined whether these can be accommodated or not (see flexibility). To complicate matters, a criterion may have one measure of reliability but many measures of validity. Validity is therefore a much broader issue than reliability. It refers to the measuring device itself, the goals and objectives, the database and the interpretation of the data. This means that the failure to validate each step in the planning process may affect the overall validity:

- Biased objectives (sample of one by the CEO)
- Wrong assumptions
- Inappropriate or irrelevant data
- Planner or designer biases
- Due to wrong inferences made/planner's lack of understanding
- Omitted criteria

The best way to ensure the validity of results is to collect reliable data in the program of requirements (POR) discussed in Section 2.3, "The Process of Documentation of Needs," and to measure or collect these data by several different means, as discussed in Section 2.5, "Techniques and Tools to Gather Data." One of the worst errors in communications is to proceed with the design before adequate planning data have been collected, i.e., to design by trial and error.

It may happen that in collecting data, planners have talked to the wrong people—for instance, to management instead of to the hands-on individuals. Individuals low on the corporate ladder often are intimidated in the presence of their boss and will not volunteer information or express new ideas. That is the typical setting for a sample of one, i.e., the biased objective of the CEO. See Figure 1.3-1.

1.3.3 Errors in Perception

Probably the most serious error in perception is in our understanding of the client we are trying to serve. The client is the owner of

Fig. 1.3-1. Inadequate space for carts and access to washers, dryers, and autoclaves (Edwards Calderon).

the facility we plan. This may be an individual or a group of individuals. Sometimes we never meet the owner(s). The owner often is represented by one individual, and we rely on this individual to tell us what is needed without verifying this information. That individual may not be available when the building is built in order to defend the ideas or data that led to the design. The opposite is often also an error: We perceive the users as the client because we deal with them often and intimately in the planning process. We have to guard against this error because it is the broad, long-range goal of the owner that we are planning for, not the immediate, short-term goal of the user. Sometimes our client is a third party such as a developer or an architectural firm. We have to assist these third parties to serve their clients as if they are our own.

The error of perception can be that of the building owner or the laboratory planner or architect. The building owner may misunderstand the role of the planner or the architect and may assume greater knowledge on their part, thus providing inadequate information. The architect may assign more importance to certain criteria and minimize others. For instance, the exterior design and the building's image may be emphasized at the expense of interior functional planning. This biased approach is fairly common because the project's priorities often have not been established.

Some errors are the result of "professional blinders": the inability to think or conceive of other ways of doing the same thing. Very often there is one attitude associated with these blinders: "It was good enough for me then or for that purpose, so it is good enough for me now." The other side of the coin, of course, is for the planner to envision a Taj Mahal where a simple, straightforward laboratory facility has been requested.

Another error of perception is caused by lack of trust. It often takes years before a construction project is funded, and at that point, everyone is in a hurry to get it built. The individuals for whom the laboratories are intended often perceive the process as bypassing their interest and input, and either lose interest or stall the decision-making process. If input is desirable, it is crucial to explain the process of incremental data gathering and checkpoints to them in order to ensure their cooperation.

Many errors are the result of field observations. "Seeing is believing" is an engraved concept in people. Psychologists have pointed out, however, that we do not always perceive correctly. Some of the more common errors in observation are (1) being attracted more to conspicuous, dramatic and interesting factors; (2) judging outward appearances in light of the observer's own professional and cultural standards (Young, 1966); (3) due to inferences required between what is observed and the recorded; (4) due to the number of aspects observed which operate simultaneously; (5) due to the size of the unit of observation; and (6) due to the effect of the observation on the entity observed.

The reliability of the observed data will increase validity but will not ensure it. We still need to answer the following questions: Does the observed measure what it purports to measure? Is there internal validity? The universe from which the sample is drawn has to be known. Any assumptions made have to be understood and the effect on the data recorded.

Other errors of perception occur during interviews: due to the interviewers, due to the respondents and due to the interactional process between interviewer and respondent. Interviewer-related errors (1) occur when the interviewer reacts to the respondent's appearance, status or group membership; (2) are due to attitude structure expectations where the interviewer assumes that the respondent has a logical, consistent and integrated structure of information and attitudes; (3) occur when the interviewer's biases interfere in the direction of his or her own attitudes and preferences; (4) are due to interviewing differences in probing and coding by several interviewers on the same project.

Respondent-related errors are due to the

interview itself and to the appearance, status or group membership of the interviewer. This error may be significant if there is too great a disparity between interviewers and respondents and if the interviewer is perceived to be a part of the boss's staff. Errors due to interactional processes are covered above. Another possible error is the interviewer's reluctance to ask embarrassing questions.

To minimize interview errors, the role relationships in interviewing must be considered, the respondent's cooperation must be sought and the interviewing techniques themselves must be reviewed. Role relationships are important: The interviewer must have the confidence of the respondent; the use of jargon familiar to the respondent may assist in creating rapport; the interviewer must be outside the power hierarchy of the respondent so that he or she is not perceived as having influence over promotion or salary; overrapport with one group or respondent is to be avoided because it will affect the answers of other respondents; in conducting in-depth interviews, the interviewer has to be familiar with the respondent's circumstances.

1.3.4 Errors in Information Transfer

The success of a building project depends on how well the design team understands the design criteria. The criteria are interpreted and recorded by the laboratory planner, who may or may not be a part of the design team. It is vital that the planner understand that he or she is not designing when collecting data; if this individual is an employee of the building owner, he or she must be divorced from project politics in order to collect unbiased data and criteria. Close involvement with the users and knowledge of their problems and needs may influence even the most unbiased planner to take sides on an issue. It is a major error when the planner becomes a part of the problem rather than the solution. It has to be very clear that the planner is neutral on the issues.

Another error in information transfer occurs when information is accepted untested.

This transfer becomes a wish list rather than a needs list, opinions rather than facts. A needs list is tested against available space standards and budget dollars. Some space users ask for twice as much space in the hope that they will get just what they need. Others are very timid and ask for slightly more space than the closet they have been working in for years. It is up to the laboratory planner to guard against both excesses by testing these requests against comparable standards, by observation and by measuring the linear feet of benches and equipment needed.

Another common problem is too much or premature information. Sometimes a laboratory facility is designed to fit the current situation, without regard to future changes. At other times, a laboratory is planned in great detail without knowing whether the budget can afford it. It is important that the planner record all the information required for the schematic design in the concept program of requirements—no more, no less—as well as all the information required for the design development phase in the detailed program.

Other errors of information transfer happen because the tools we use for data gathering, questionnaires and checklists are the cause of errors. Questionnaires are often mailed or used during interviews. They can be open-ended (unstructured) or closed (structured). The difficulty with mailed questionnaires is that they are difficult for many people to fill out; the lack of control results in incomplete answers, which makes the data much less reliable. The disadvantages of interview questionnaires are the expense, the possible biases between interviewer and respondents mentioned earlier and the pressure for an immediate answer. Structured questionnaires or checklists may not include data important to the respondent.

A number of errors result from the questions themselves: (1) Questions are unclear; words with double meanings; long sentences or sentences with two possible answers; words that are difficult or unfamiliar to the respondent. (2) The questions are not specific enough. The time, place and context which the respondent has to assume to answer are not clear; all alternatives or none which that respondent should bear in mind are not included. (3) Questions on unfamiliar topics are not prefaced with an explanatory note or illustration. The questions are not phrased in terms of the respondent's own experience. (4) Questions may create ego defenses. Allow for a denial on the part of the respondent. Avoid the problem by using euphemisms ("custodian" in lieu of "janitor"). Place positive statements first ("What do you like best, what least?"). Introduce face-saving phrases and words (do you happen to know . . . ?).

1.3.5 Errors in Judgment

These types of errors are potentially the most embarrassing because they are the result of lack of knowledge rather than lack of skills. Planners may be forgiven for a misunderstanding or the wrong perception and may not be held accountable for an error in information transfer, but they have been retained to provide professional judgment. Probably the most common error of this type is to plan or design more facilities than the budget will allow. This causes two problems: (1) It raises the expectations of the individuals concerned and reduces their confidence after the project is cut back. It is psychologically more desirable to be conservative at first and add scope than to be over the budget and cut back. (2) It wastes time and effort and costs money to replan or redesign to a reduced scope.

The following errors of judgment fall into the categories of outright blunders: omissions, downgrading to reduce costs and decisions that cause hazardous conditions. The following checklist will help readers to evaluate their own facility or planning effort. This checklist is the result of a survey mailed to laboratory planners, architects, laboratory users and plant engineers. The errors mentioned have been tallied and are shown in parentheses. These are actual cases. The recommended design conditions are covered elsewhere in this handbook.

1. Blunders

- Long span structure in steel in a facility with vibration-sensitive equipment (1).
- Precast concrete structures without stiffening in a facility with vibration-sensitive equipment (2).
- A structural system which doesn't allow future penetration for new drains or fume hood exhausts (2).
- A structural system with a life load allowance which will not accommodate the function (5).
- Piping and conduit buried in concrete slab (3).
- Small floor areas that cannot accommodate enough laboratories for one program or discipline (4).
- Laboratory modules not deep enough (5).
- Door width and/or height which will not accommodate items to be housed in the facility (many).
- Drains too small to accommodate the waste water generated in cup sinks, perchloric acid fume hood washdown system and glassware washers (3).
- No allowance to expand the facility vertically or horizontally.
- Sliding wall cabinet doors that fall out of the track because the cabinet bottom sags.
- Wall cabinets that fall off the wall because of inadequate fastenings.
- Fixed cabinets that cannot be rearranged or removed.
- The use of asbestos, particularly in piping insulation and structural fireproofing. This is a blunder by hindsight, but it is causing tremendous problems at this moment because of the difficulty in changing utilities and the inaccessibility of contaminated ceiling plenums for distribution of services.

2. Omissions

- No emergency power system or uninterruptible power supply for critical systems and equipment.
- No backup of critical filtration in order to facilitate maintenance or accommodate changes.

- No backup fans for maintenance or in case of failure.
- No backup chillers.
- No backup cooling water for expensive equipment.
- No cable tray for distributing data cables.
- No sprinklers, which are very effective in reducing the spread of fire.

3. Downgrading to reduce costs

- Undersizing the HVAC, which causes excessive temperature fluctutations. Inadequate makeup air for fume hoods and no allowance for additional exhaust devices.
- Inadequate filtration, which causes polluted and contaminated laboratory working conditions.
- Low headroom for equipment in the laboratories.
- Inadequate power, distribution system and number of outlets.
- Slab on grade with buried drain lines.
- Not enough space to service equipment.
- Not enough space to use equipment.
- Not enough shut-off valves, which allow maintenance and changes without affecting adjacent laboratories.

4. Decisions that cause hazardous conditions

- Latent heat energy conservation device which introduces contaminants into the air supply.
- Inadequate access to an exit.
- Doors swinging into laboratories classified as hazardous.
- Fume hoods located adjacent to primary exit doors.

1.4 TRENDS N. Watson

1.4.1 Introduction

This section analyzes the trends in laboratory design and the underlying forces of change, looks at changing physical requirements, and explores the emerging fields of science and technology that will impact future laboratory design. Since any specific trend identified today will by definition be moot tomorrow, this section also provides the facility or laboratory planner with a methodology for analyzing future trends. This methodology is similar to the scientific process whereby new knowledge is gained by incorporating informed observations into an existing knowledge base. Business, for example, has successfully used the technique to anticipate consumer demands. The health of the microcomputer industry depends totally upon trend analysis.

For purposes of discussion, it is helpful to consider two classes of laboratory facilities. Laboratories commonly found on academic campuses concentrate on basic, or pure, research.* Those directly funded by the federal government and private industry engage in the full spectrum of basic research, as well as technological development and production.

Trend Analysis

The major task facing a laboratory planner is to design a facility for an activity that is literally driving change. The very nature of research is to discover new ways to render present techniques obsolete and, in turn, render the research facility obsolete. For this reason, the planner must attempt to predict the direction or trend in which the activity is headed, rather than seek an absolute solution.

One component of a trend analysis is informed observations. A significant observation can be made about laboratory-based scientific research: for the most part, laboratory-based research has passed through the "macro" (large) phase to the

---

*Universities also have large numbers of teaching laboratories. This is not an emerging field where new facilities are apt to be developed; however, there is evidence that existing laboratories will require extensive conversions to support the new teaching practices. The trend in laboratory teaching is away from "wet" labs and toward more computer simulations and multimedia—that is, full motion video and sound with computer-controlled interaction.

"micro" (small) phase. Experimentation with genes, viruses, microorganisms, living cells and subatomic particles is accelerating at the same time that experimentation with whole body systems, large organisms and colonies of organisms has plateaued. While there is a considerable amount of research activity at the macro level, the significant trend in the development of new laboratories is at the micro level. The parameters of design for macro-based facilities are well documented and are extensively covered elsewhere in this handbook.

Further evidence supporting the trend toward micro-level research can be found in the emergence of new research technologies such as high-resolution mass spectroscopy, positron emission tomography (PET), scanning ion-conductance microscopy (SICM), scanning "tunneling" microscopy (STM), micro-machines and magnetic resonance imaging (MRI). Most of these technologies were nonexistent 6 years ago, and it is safe to assume that even more complex analytical tools will emerge in the future. While these new, exotic devices require a very specific and uncompromising facility, it is clear that most of tomorrow's equipment will also place stringent requirements on building utilities, structures and environmental control systems. It should also be noted that many new analytical devices which are developed for one field soon find applications in other fields. Medicine, for example, is always seeking devices or methodologies for nondestructive, noninvasive testing. The resultant devices soon find their way into chemistry, physics, aviation, marine biology, oil and gas pipelines and environmental quality.

Having introduced the concept of trend analysis, it is important that the nature of this approach be fully understood. Failure to do so results in colossal failures where retrofitting reigns supreme. Failures fall into two general classes. The first class is characterized by excessive "move-in" costs incurred by the client. Given the pace of equipment development, it is reasonable for the client to expect to make minor modifications such as special service fittings, but not to make

new service runs or to discover that the benches are too shallow for a new piece of equipment. The second class is the facility where the basic utilities design severely restricts the addition of new devices such as fume hoods and biological safety cabinets.

Why does a planner have to anticipate future trends of activities that will take place in a laboratory project? Isn't it just a simple matter of communicating with the principal scientist and documenting the program requirements? The answers will become clear as the underlying nature of scientific research and the spinoff into technology and R&D facilities are explored.

Methodology of Trends Forecasting

As science moves ahead, so must the planning for science facilities. Science as a whole moves ahead by developing paradigms to explain research findings. These findings are the result of designed experiments/observations established on an existing base of knowledge and experience. New findings are usually verified by repetition in a peer laboratory, and finally the results are published or committed to the public domain. In 1989, the public press was filled with news of "cold fusion" in a process where the investigators avoided peer review and came under severe criticism. If the findings are readily accepted, the scientific community moves to another level of investigation. This is often referred to as a "paradigm shift." The process repeats itself, expanding the knowledge base. The quest for knowledge is the goal and the force that drives the process. Technology follows a similar process and searches for solutions to specific purposes or special problems.

The role of the laboratory planner, much like that of the scientific/technologist, is:

- to acquire a knowledge base of existing lab design;
- to critically observe the activity of the client's specific field;
- to synthesize this information into a model which predicts the needs of a particular project.

This is not to suggest that the planner become an expert in a particular scientific or technical field, but simply adopt an informed analytical approach. In other words, the planner must become a *process* expert in order to discover the *appropriate content* that leads to a solution. It is interesting to note that often in the process of building a knowledge base, it is more informative to observe an unsuccessful project than a successful one. The unsuccessful project presents an opportunity for discovery *and refinement* of the content. This is particularly important, since the content or amount of information is expanding so rapidly. So-called experts in any field have an extensive knowledge base but are also process experts.

There is no "cookbook" for tomorrow's successful laboratories. Each new laboratory will be an experimental extrapolation of today's laboratories. Figure 1.4-4 illustrates the process.

1.4.2 Funding Trends

The diverse forces which drive funding for laboratory research and laboratory facilities can be discovered in the various agency requests, the mood of the administration or Congress, the overall economy and the health of certain segments of the economy. Although there is often an interrelation or co-dependency, it is useful to consider three categories of research funding: academic research, industrial R&D, and the federal government.

While private industry receives the bulk of federal funds,† there is a trend to perform more industrial research in the academic environment through technology centers. This is a growing sector on major research-oriented campuses where industry and/or state governments provide startup funds and capital to build facilities. The centers are expected to become self-sustaining on returns from licensing and royalties. These centers were made possible by legislation in 1983 and 1986 which allowed universities to retain patent and licensing rights to research results supported by federal funds. Basic computer technology and genetics have received the most attention up to this point. However, computer applications, medical technology and environmental research will be included in this area of growth.

This is a difficult area in which to predict consistent trends; for example, there are new regulations governing animal research facilities which affect the whole industry. A recent article in *Science* reported that the Office of Management and Budget (OMB) is expected to release new regulations related to animal welfare. These regulations will affect industry, academia, and federal government facilities and operations. According to *Science,* the regulations would cost research institutions about $111 million in capital expendi-

---

†In general, the federal government provides approximately 50% of all R&D funds, while industry provides some 47% and the remaining 3% come from academia. Industry, on the other hand, performs 73% of the work, while government performs about 12% and academia some 15%.

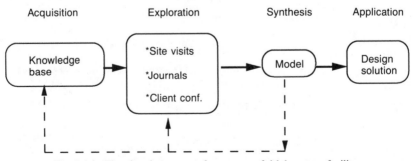

Fig. 1.4-1. The planning process for a successful laboratory facility.

tures for primate facilities and $138 million for dog facilities.

The total cost of the new law to the private sector would be $885 million in initial outlays. Over half of these costs would be borne by private research institutions. The bulk of the funds are to cover improvements to existing facilities. There are 1,277 institutions involved. Actions of this nature are difficult to predict even by experienced congressional and administration watchers.

Academic Research

Table 1.4.-1 shows that direct support for academic research is projected to increase between 7.4 and 7.6%. The distribution method will be the same, through competing grants; however, the consensus is that program projects, or large programs, will be favored over individual grants. This is good news for facilities improvements, since program project leaders tend to have greater clout at the institutional level in competition for local capital funding for new construction and renovations.

The major problem facing academic research is not just the availability of operational funding but the age and condition of the existing facilities where the research is to be conducted. A bill was introduced in Congress in 1987 that called for expenditures of $2.5 billion for repair, renovation or replacement of research facilities at universities and colleges. While many universities have experienced some growth in dedicated research fields, there has been no general infusion of

funds into this area since the expansion years of the mid-1960s. A recent study sponsored by NIH and NSF, "The Status of Biomedical Research Facilities,"‡ revealed that 15% of all biological research facilities need major renovation and 23% need limited renovation. The report goes on to say that 36% of the existing space is suitable for most work and the remaining 26% is of high enough quality to be used for the most sophisticated research. *The Chronicle of Higher Education* (1989) states that nearly three-fifths of all universities planned to start at least one major new project in 1988 or 1989 at a total cost of $2.7 billion. The trend in funding for university-based biological research facilities is definitely on the upswing.

There is mixed support for the 8 to 10 new science and technology centers sponsored by the National Science Foundation. This proposal has been criticized in academic circles as unfairly funding big projects at the expense of individual grants which have been the backbone of scientific breakthroughs. The advisors to the government, in supporting the proposal, have pushed the idea that fields like AIDS research are too complex to be adequately covered by individual researchers and can only be handled by programmed research in larger centers. This will necessitate the construction of new facilities, since most of the existing facilities are heav-

‡Copies of the report are available free of charge from Mary Collins at Westat, Inc., 1650 Research Boulevard, Rockville, MD 20550.

Table 1.4-1. Forecasts of R&D Growth for 1988 and 1989

	1987 Level (Billions of $)	1988 Growth (NSF)	1988 Growth (Batelle)	1989 Growth (Battelle)
Federal gov't.	60.35	7.0%	7.3%	4.3%
Industry	58.57	6.9	6.4	3.5
Academic	2.7	7.4	8.5	7.6
Other Nonprofit	1.45	5.2	6.0	4.2
Total	23.05	6.9	6.9	3.9

Source: National Science Foundation (1988) and Batelle (1988).

ily utilized and cannot make room for large new programs.

Industrial Research

While there are some forecasts that project the growth of industrial expenditures for R&D at 10.8%, the U.S. economy may be too healthy to support that level of growth. The trend in research funding in much of the industrial sector tends to be inversely related to profits. This situation could change if the administration is serious about reconsidering the capital gains tax and the investment tax credit. The only safe thing to do in the short term is to watch the actions of the administration and the health of the general economy. Industrial laboratories are not running at capacity, and there will be a lag between new research startups and new construction/renovations. Aerospace and computing equipment will experience the largest increase in industrial R&D expenditures in 1989–90.

Federal Research

The administration is known to favor big, high-profile projects like the superconducting supercollider, the space station, the Strategic Defense Initiative, and the human genome project. The Reagan administration had called for a $190.5 million budget for research on the global environment. If this represents a trend in research funding, one can argue that a major capital expansion for new facilities to carry out these studies is on the way. These new facilities will require great sums of money and will be highly specific to the project. It is too early to tell how NIH, NSF, DOE and DOA laboratories funding will fair under the Bush administration.

1.4.3 Emerging Fields and Other Indicators

Scientific journals are filled with news about new developments in fetal cell and gene therapy, transgenic animals, superconductivity, and others. It is impossible to predict which of these will ever migrate into the R&D laboratories and ultimately result in a societal benefit.

It is clear, however, that society has elevated expectations for science and technology—be it in medicine, defense, space, education, entertainment, transportation, communications or the economy. Needless to say, the advances to meet these expectations will emerge from increased activity in the laboratory. Due in part to the factors that created the national deficit, society has also come to realize that science and technology are strategic resources and should be managed as such. The rationale is that if these publicly owned resources, or "intellectual properties," get to market, the United States might recover its position in the world economy.

Where do these resources reside? Many scientific advances emerge from the academic community, although academia accounts for only 10% of all working scientists. Federally funded laboratories such as the Los Almos National Laboratory, NASA, NIH and approximately 350 others consume some $20 billion and produce large numbers of visible advances.

This concept is in conflict with the traditional view that academic intellectual property belongs in the public domain, where any person or any country could develop and market the ideas. The debate continues over this issue. However, Congress passed the Technology Transfer Act in 1986 and at the same time strengthened the Federal Laboratory Consortium (FLC) and the Cooperative Research Act of 1984. Basically, Congress has thrown open the door for cooperative R&D between the public and private sectors, a privatization of federal assets.

The proliferation of academic technology transfer centers and Engineering Research Centers (ERC), coupled with the willingness of the federal laboratories to form partnerships with private industry, has significant implications for the future of new laboratory facilities.

There is also reason to believe that a new form of R&D laboratory will emerge that will be a combination of prototyping/production facilities. The input and output of this facility would be coupled directly to the customer, so that changing requirements could be incorporated in the final product. This could be characterized as "niche marketing," where each product exactly meets the customer's unique requirements. There would be no product inventory in the traditional sense. In many ways, the custom computer manufacturers have already achieved this level of prototyping/productivity, where custom boards are designed (CAD) and manufactured (CAM) by a computer. In this instance, it is a laboratory, as opposed to a factory, as every new product is an R&D experience.

1.4.4 Design Trends

Environment

As noted in the introduction to this chapter, the trend in laboratory research is toward the micro phase. This translates into a set of physical requirements that ideally includes an environmentally clean site and an environmentally controlled laboratory. A controlled environment in this context means a controlled atmosphere for the protection of the experiment, the laboratory worker and the surrounding environment. The significance of operating a laboratory in a clean environment became apparent during the search for a cause of Legionnaire's disease. Early studies implicated nickel (carbonless paper was identified as the source) when its presence was discovered to be common in all the victims. However, upon further investigation, it was discovered that the traces of nickel were being deposited by the stainless steel knives used during tissue sectioning. Definitive experimental results depend upon a tightly controlled environment, as well as good laboratory practices. This is one of the hazards of searching with a machine that measures parts per billion.

The down side of a tightly controlled environment is that it places new physical and psychological restrictions on the lab worker. The simple act of entering/exiting a controlled environment can be psychologically stressful. New health risks and the resultant working conditions will play a greater role in future laboratory design and will present the planner with the challenge of making them more inhabitable.

A caveat: Local code administration/enforcement is commonly on the trailing edge of technology, so the planner and/or client must pay particular attention to this area. Local code authorities are also susceptible to community activists, whose reactions are often based on fear. The local and national press contribute to this environment, and many communities are fortunate enough to have articulate science writers. In addition, the new, exotic facilities will require a close working relationship with the local fire department, not only for code compliance and code interpretation but also to minimize the risk to fire fighters. A cooperative, proactive approach is advised to minimize delays and keep projects on target.

Environmental Hazards

It is interesting to observe the *rate* of discovery or the accelerated identification of hazardous materials in the environment. The public press is filled with news of radon, dioxin, Alar, formaldehyde emissions, secondary smoking, and asbestos; the list grows each day. In addition to the identification of existing materials, there is an increase in the introduction of new exotic materials, such as composites, and new chemical processes that are rapidly causing concern.

This trend will intensify as workers and the public at large become more aware and play out the drama in the press and before the courts and Congress. More accurate measuring devices and the growing number of agency workers will contribute to this trend.

This trend has two implications for the laboratory planner. First, an increased awareness is required in the design stage; based on personal experience, copper lines should not be used to supply water to goldfish rearing ponds! Second, the increased research activity means more laboratories.

Equipment

The trend in laboratory equipment is toward more automation with computer-controlled processes and higher orders of resolution that require a vibration-free platform, clean uninterruptable power, a specialized fire suppression system and controlled access for security. Equipment is also being replaced more often. It is typical for three or four analytical devices to be replaced by one very expensive automated machine that produces more reliable results in less time and with less labor. There is also a trend toward leasing of expensive equipment. In the last 2 years, the leasing market for laboratory equipment has grown dramatically. If the leasing trend continues, equipment will be replaced more often, which means that the lab must be more flexible than ever.

Sample preparation, which takes place in the support laboratories, also requires a controlled environment so that the specimens are not contaminated prior to arrival in the analytical laboratory. In order to get the return on investment of the very expensive equipment used in preparation, one would expect the operational hours to be extended, thus putting additional stress on the building's systems. This may also require the addition of nonlab human support areas, i.e., architectural amenities.

The increasing complexity of equipment and operational procedures will likely result in fewer but more specialized professional laboratory workers who will be required to have advanced degrees and more skills. This has implications for the planner. For one thing, the planner can use the laboratory workers as an informed source of information regarding laboratory performance requirements. They represent one of the information sources in the trend analysis methodology.

The capital cost of the new equipment, coupled with the value of the experimental specimens and laboratory data, mandates greater attention to alarms, monitoring and controlled-access systems. The laboratory planner must be aware of the potential threats to laboratory operations.

In many laboratory complexes, the large, expensive equipment and specialized spaces such as containment facilities must be factored into the space allocation program in addition to the traditional square footage per occupant algorithm.

Flexibility

Flexibility is often substituted for comprehensive planning. For purposes of discussion, we will consider three levels of flexibility in laboratory design. The first level means that the occupants are able to rearrange casework and shelving, and use common hand tools to reorder the work flow. In addition, it means that they may adjust or remove sections of lab tops in order to place equipment directly into the work flow. The second level of flexibility means that with minimum disruption of operations, trades personnel can remove or install new equipment and attach to building services in a reasonable amount of time. This may include the addition of a biological safety cabinet. The third level of flexibility means that minor renovations including interior walls, fume hood removal/installation and casework changes can take place without impacting adjoining lab operations or disrupting building services.

Clearly, there is a first cost/life cycle trade-off in flexibility. The client must understand and participate in the final decision regarding the costs, benefits and level of appropriate flexibility.

1.4.5 Summary

There is every reason to be optimistic about the future development of new laboratory facilities and the renovation of existing ones. The new facilities must be appropriately flexible, more heavily equipped, more sterile, more secure, and more expensive and will be operated by more highly skilled and educated personnel. The challenge to the laboratory facilities planner is to build a strong knowledge base of general science, become informed about the successes and failures of today's facilities, assist in the development and analysis of the clients' lab performance requirements, and synthesize this information into a design solution.

GLOSSARY

Magnetic Resonance Imaging (MRI)——uses a combination of radio frequency (RF) and a strong magnetic field to develop high-resolution images of the structure and function of a biological organism. The organism is placed in a strong magnetic field, typically 15,000 gauss. The field is disturbed by small RF pulses which are controlled by the MRI computer. Protons radiate weak energy signals which are characteristic of their molecular structure. The emitted energy is detected and processed into an image which can be viewed in real time or stored in the computer.

Mass Spectrophotometry——a method of identifying molecular structures and compounds by transillumination with laser light and detecting the spectrum associated with the mass-charge ratios. The devices are capable of measuring parts per million and in some applications can be operated in real time.

Micro-Machines——ultrasmall silicone compound devices that convert electricity, sound or electrostatic charges into physical motion. These devices are on the order of 60–120 microns in size.

Positron Emission Tomography (PET)——an imaging methodology for determining in vivo cross-sectional images of positron-emitting isotopes that demonstrate biological function, physiology or pathology. The "light house" geometry of the positron decay is utilized to detect the two back-to-back γ rays emitted simultaneously when the $\beta+$ particle combines with a free electron.

Scanning Ion-Conductance Microscopy (SICM)——utilizes a micropipette filled with a conducting electrolytic fluid to scan the surface structure of biological material. The variations in conductance are reconstructed to provide a map or image of the surface. Mapping of individual atoms is possible.

Scanning "Tunneling" Microscopy (STM)——relies on the detection of electrons that have "tunneled" through the sample material. The methodology defies classic physics and depends upon the probability of electron exchanges between two conducting surfaces in close proximity. In theory, their electron clouds overlap and at times spontaneously tunnel from one material to the other. The electron activity is detected and converted to a visible image with a magnification factor of 3 to 24 million compared to 275 for visible light.

Superconductivity——traditional materials used as electrical conductors have some resistance to electron flow and thus are inefficient. While superconductivity has been known for some time, it was possible only at extremely low temperatures. Recent discoveries have led to superconductivity at ambient temperatures, which is defined as a state in which pairs of electrons of opposite spin and moving in opposite directions form "cooper" pairs that condense into a cooperative electronic state.

Transgenic Animals——animals created with genes from nonparent animals. In April 1988, Harvard University received the first patent on a mouse whose cells were genetically engineered to carry a cancer-promoting gene. Bioengineered animals may prove valuable in toxicology and in molecular farming of useful human or animal protein products.

REFERENCES

Battelle Memorial Institute, 1988. *Probable Levels of R&D Expenditures in 1988: Forecast and Analysis.* Columbus, Ohio.

NSF, 1988. *Sciences Resource Studies Highlights.* March 11. Washington, D.C.

Holden, Constance, 1988. *Science* (1988). Billion Dollar Price Tag for New Animal Rules, Vol. 242, p. 662.

Cordes, Colleen, 1989. *The Chronicle of Higher Education,* 1989. February 15, A-23.

2

Laboratory Facilities Planning

2.1 INTRODUCTION   *T. Ruys*

In Chapter 1, the characteristics, differences and similarities among laboratories were discussed. Common errors in planning were pointed out, and trends that will affect future laboratory layouts were covered.

This chapter covers planning issues and the process, techniques and tools used in laboratory facilities planning. Since almost all laboratories will be new or already exist, we have included sections on how to assess building for use as laboratories and the factors that must be addressed when renovating an existing laboratory facility. Last but not least, this chapter covers the space standards by which the requests for space can be measured; the risks assessment involved in planning laboratories and how to measure these as they affect space and equipment; and the impact that laboratories may have on the community and how to minimize or avoid problems.

2.2 APPROACH TO LABORATORY FACILITIES PLANNING   *T. Ruys*

The phrase coined by Gropius, "Form follows function," should be changed to "Form follows information." Without the correct information, the function of the facility will not be apparent to the design team. Equally important is the approach to planning. Any type of building should be designed "from the inside out" to maximize its functional efficiency, but that is particularly true of laboratories because of their high cost.

Laboratories are equipment intensive, expensive to build and potentially hazardous places in which to work. The arrangement of the equipment has an effect on the efficiency of space layout and work flow; it therefore affects operating and construction costs, and an emergency exit must be provided in case of fire or an explosion. Although several arrangements are possible, these will dictate the building footprint and the appearance of the facade to a large degree. Typically the work proceeds from laboratory module or modules to plan to building footprint to exterior design (see figure 2.2-1); at the same time, the implication of mechanical, electrical, structural and laboratory furniture systems are analyzed.

Another consideration that has a profound effect on the laboratory planning approach is the use of open plans versus closed plans. Open plans generally enhance the users' feeling of well-being, although that is not universally true. They improve supervision and the ability to assist colleagues in case of accidents. Open plans also reduce construction costs and improve the net to gross square feet efficiency, which also affects the cost. Some individuals have a strong preference for traditional closed plans, i.e., walls around every laboratory. The advantages and disadvantages of both should be weighed and a decision made very

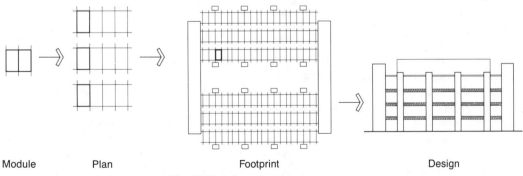

Module   Plan   Footprint   Design

Fig. 2.2-1. Laboratory planning process.

early because of the profound impact on the plan and the fire code application. Closed plans may have non-fire-rated walls or partitions to reduce costs as well. This topic is covered in Section 7.3.

Another consideration that has a large impact on the building configuration is the location of the offices associated with the laboratories. Offices are generally separate from laboratories because of the hazards associated with laboratory operations, but they may be located next to the laboratory, one on one; clustered and in close proximity; or remote from the laboratories in a separate wing. Each choice will have an effect on the ultimate appearance and very likely on the cost of the building.

2.3 THE PROCESS OF DOCUMENTATION OF NEEDS
T. Ruys

2.3.1 Programming the Program of Requirements (POR)

A few words on the process of decision management and decision making are in order. Green (1967) pointed out that (1) every decision can be broken down into steps for analysis and that (2) every decision can be specified in the chronological sequence in which it must be made. For instance, one cannot decide on the arrangement of a given laboratory until it has been determined that it can be built with the budget established.

The first order of business is, of course, to establish who the decision makers are. If the decision steps and sequence can be established, it follows that the decision makers who are qualified and competent to make those decisions can also be selected. This is rarely the case, however. The decision makers are often a collection of people: a building committee, facilities department, administrators, etc. These people are often chosen or appointed for reasons which are not directly related to the decision to be made during the programming and planning phases. This reflects a lack of awareness on the part

of the building owner or institution about the decisions which must be made. Those on the committee often lack the knowledge, competence and power to make the necessary decisions.

If the necessary decisions are identified early on in the sequence in which they must be made and the individual who is to make those decisions is selected, the process of planning will be less likely to be by trial and error and consequently the cost of planning will be lower. Figure 2.3-1 shows the effect of time on the planning cost. The further along the planning process is, the more costly it will be to make changes. During the programming phase, a new idea can be changed simply by changing a 5 × 8-inch card; during the working drawings stage, changing the size of a laboratory will result in changes to architectural plans at different scales, the reflected ceiling plan, mechanical, plumbing, lighting and power drawings at a minimum. A change of this type during construction will also result in change orders to the contract. A change after the building is built will result in a new set of documents, a new contract and possibly demolition of what was already built. The need for a complete program of requirements (POR) cannot be overemphasized. To proceed with the design based on inadequate, invalid and possibly irrelevant information could be a grave error indeed. In summary, the POR's goals are to:

- Avoid redesign later;
- Avoid change orders during construction;
- Avoid problems during and after occupancy.

A POR therefore contains the data necessary to plan and design the laboratory building; provides an understanding of the whys and hows of the operation; documents the goals and objectives of the company or institution; and establishes a budget and a schedule. The process documents the needs; col-

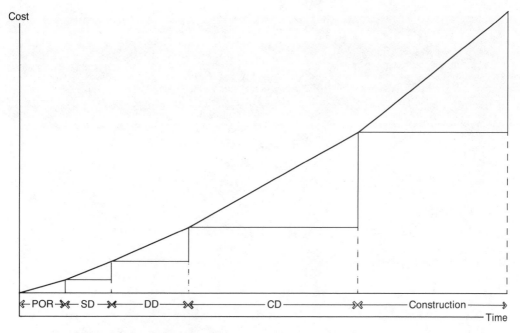

Legend: POR = program of requirements
SD = schematic design
DD = design development
CD = contract document

Fig. 2.3-1. The effect of time on planning costs.

lects and interprets data; resolves conflicts; verifies the adequacy of the budget; establishes quantitative and qualitative measures; builds a consensus; and establishes a framework for implementation.

Necessary conditions for a good POR are an involved building owner (client); an in-depth understanding of the building type; an analytical approach to data collection; an effective process and techniques; and the right tools.

Many books have been written on the subject of programming building requirements. One of the best is *Problem Seeking* (1987) by William Pena. The methodology of data collection discussed in this chapter has been taken from this book and applied to laboratory facilities. Readers are encouraged to purchase their own copy. Pena suggest a process of documenting ideas and data on 5 × 8-inch cards (see Figure 2.3-2), one item of information per card, so that ideas can be

prioritized, added and deleted. The cards are mounted in a matrix of four steps and four conditions. The steps are goals, facts, concepts and needs. The conditions are function, form, economy and time. This information is necessary for the design of a facility.

As Pena points out, programming is preparation, exposure and analysis, while designing is illumination, insight and synthesis. Both are equally important. This book deals with planning, which affects both programming and data gathering, and implementation, which effects design.

The four steps and four conditions are represented in a matrix to implement data gathering. Figure 2.3-3 shows this matrix as it is applied to a typical laboratory facility. Functions deal with people, activities and relationships. Form deals with site conditions, environment and quality. Economy deals with budget, efficiency of operations and life

Fig. 2.3-2. Documenting the program of requirements.

	GOAL	FACTS	CONCEPTS	NEEDS
Function				
Form				
Economy				
Time				

Fig. 2.3-3. Information matrix.

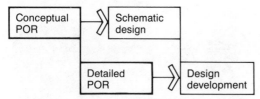

Fig. 2.3-4. Phasing of information flow for schematic design and design development.

cycle costs. Time deals with schedule phasing and time constraints. Goals are quantitative and are established by the building's owner. Facts are quantitative, and must be collected by the planner and provided by the owner. Concepts are qualitative and the results of discussions between the parties concerned, based on as many ideas as can be generated by the group. Needs are qualitative and represent the numerical space needs tested against the budget.

For purposes of laboratory planning, a few deviations from *Problem Seeking* are in order. Because of the complexity of laboratory facilities, two data gathering phases are recommended. The first one, the conceptual POR, documents the information needed for the conceptual design, using the process and tools described by Pena. See Figure 2.3-4. The second one, the detailed POR, documents the information needed for the design development phase. Figure 2.3-5 gives examples of concept program cards and Figure 2.3-6 examples of detailed program criteria.

The traditional methodology of one-on-one meetings, writing memos and designing by trial and error is no longer appropriate, if it ever was. The need to collect design criteria quickly and accurately is acute. This is accomplished by intensive work sessions, with all the decision makers present and involved. These work sessions should be conducted away from the daily routine and with freedom from interruptions, but close enough to the work so that the facilities can be visited in order to illustrate a good or bad condition or feature. In fact, a tour of the clients' facilities is essential to establish a baseline understanding of their frame of mind. It is during these work sessions that conflicts are resolved. Consensus is built, and the adequacy of the budget is verified. Table 2.3-1 lists a number of conflicts that may be discussed. Most require a compromise on the part of the participants. Pena suggests that requested space needs to be documented on brown sheets and these documents used to bring the requests for space by the users of the facility (typically a wish list) in line with the budget. See Figure 2.3-7, which shows the participants in action, and Figure 2.3-8, an example of a brown sheet.

The players in the process and their roles are key to a complete POR and a successful building.

2.3.2 The POR Team Members and Their Roles

The importance of the interactive process was explained earlier. In order to be effec-

Table 2.3-1. Suggested List of Potential Conflicts for Discussion and Reconciliation

Needs	Oppositions		
Building owner's needs	Largest number of NSF	vs.	Regulations, codes and standards
	Lowest cost	vs.	Required sophistication
	Future needs	vs.	Flexibility
Occupant's needs	Containment	vs.	Filtration
	Construction schedule	vs.	Continuity in occupancy
	Multiagency occupancy	vs.	Individual agency needs
Staff needs	Pleasant work environment	vs.	Energy conservation
	Office/lab proximity	vs.	Safety and cost
	Proximity of spaces	vs.	Existing building layout
Public's needs	Operating costs	vs.	Public safety
	Capital costs	vs.	Aesthetics
	Service to public	vs.	Security

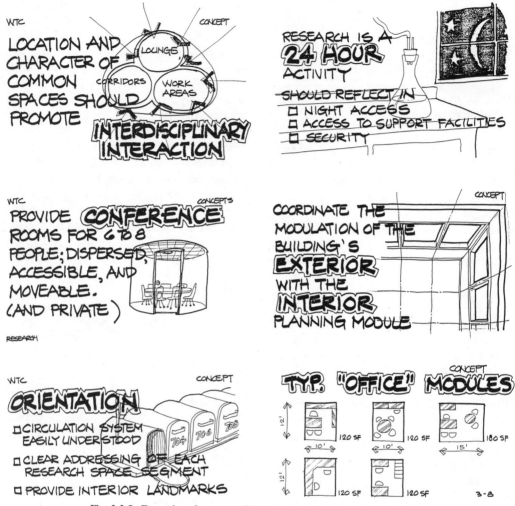

Fig. 2.3-5. Examples of conceptual/POR cards. (Source: The NBBJ Group)

tive, this process must be structured and carefully planned. The building owners' organization (client) is typically made up of a number of specialists who may rely on various consultants or specialists outside their organization. That is also true of the planners' team.

For those unfamiliar with the design process, a short explanation is in order. This handbook deals with the issues and criteria needed to plan and design a laboratory facility. The planning and development of a POR for a laboratory facilities are typically accomplished by a laboratory planner who may be a part of the builders'/owners' orga-

nization, an independent consultant or part of an architectural firm. Quite often the owners' employee assembles the data for the POR. The advantage is that this person is familiar with the operation and knows the individuals who make up the typical wish lists. The disadvantages are that the employee is enmeshed in the organization's politics, may not be trained to know what information is required for the design team and probably already has a full-time job. The disadvantage of letting an architect assemble the data is that there are not many architects who know anything about laboratory facilities.

The criteria established by the POR are

110 V elec. raceway

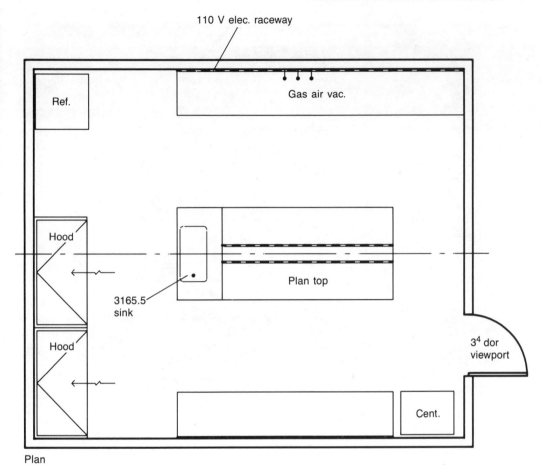

Ref.

Gas air vac.

Hood

Plan top

3165.5
sink

Hood

3⁴ dor
viewport

Cent.

Plan

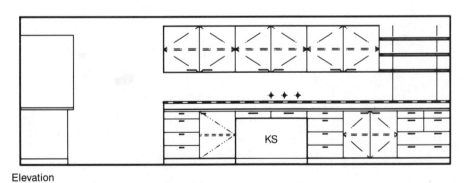

KS

Elevation

Fig. 2.3-6. Examples of detailed program criteria.

Fig. 2.3-7. Participants in the process of bringing space requests in line with budget (Photo: The NBBJ Group).

MICROBIOLOGY—5710 NSF

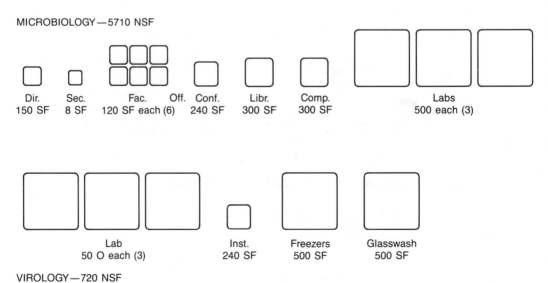

VIROLOGY—720 NSF

Fig. 2.3-8. Example of Brown Sheet documenting space requests to scale in graphic form.

synthesized into a building by a designer, typically an architect who gives them form. The steps in the process are shown graphically in Figure 2.3-9. The contract documents which portray the design in drawings and specifications are, in turn, used to construct the building. There are many ways in which a building can be planned and contracts written. In this handbook, we describe the most common arrangement for purposes of illustration.

The key players and their role in this process are:

- Building owner—authorizes funding for the planning; sets policy; provides information on staffing; establishes the purpose, goals and needs of the organization; approves the final documents; approves the budget; and appoints a representative for day-to-day contact with the planning team.
- Laboratory planner—collects and analyzes data and suggests alternatives; organizes the team's data-gathering process; establishes a schedule; collects data; contracts with consultants in needed specialties and maintains day-to-day contact with the building owner's representative; produces the POR; assists in equipment selection; interprets the POR to the design team; and produces equipment contract documents.
- Owner's representative—guides the tour

through the facilities; organizes meetings with the owner's staff; provides building and site data as needed; facilitates the decision-making process; and keeps the building owner informed.
- Architect—synthesizes the data into a design for the facility; organizes and heads the design team; contracts with consultants in needed specialties; designs and sites the facility; and keeps in contact with the owner's representative for day-to-day decisions. Besides the architect, the architectural team typically consists of mechanical, electrical and structural engineers, a specification writer and a cost estimator.
- Contractor—contracts to assemble a team of suppliers and subcontractors to produce a building from the contract documents provided by the design team.

This information flow from individual to individual and from team to team is typically as shown in Figure 2.3-10. However, the contractual relationship is often as shown in Figure 2.3-11. That has some advantages but can also cause some problems. The advantage is that the teams of planners, architects and contractors are independent and can be selected to be the best in their respective fields. The disadvantage is, of course, the breakdown of communications and lack of coordination between these entities and the potential for disputes among them. It is

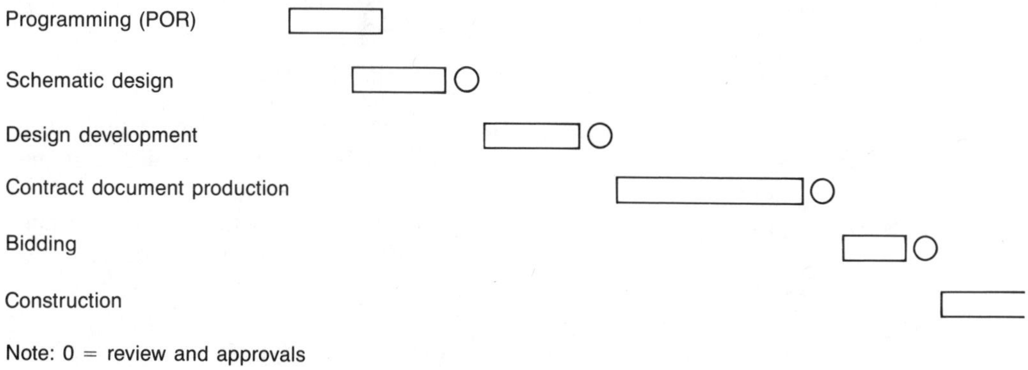

Programming (POR)

Schematic design

Design development

Contract document production

Bidding

Construction

Note: 0 = review and approvals

Fig. 2.3-9. Planning, design and construction steps.

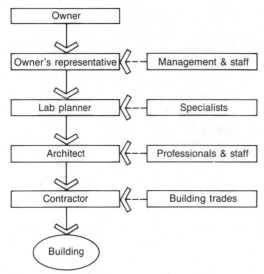

Fig. 2.3-10. Team relationship (information flow).

therefore imperative that everyone involved understand the role of the other contributors to the process.

A few words about leadership styles and the decision-making process are in order. In health care facilities, planners tend to take the role of initiator, i.e., to lead the client in the process of decision making. This seems to be true for two reasons. First, there is much published data on health care planning that derives needed square feet areas from the number of procedures or patients. Second, health care facilities are service institutions and, with few exceptions, there are no nationally recognized individuals heading

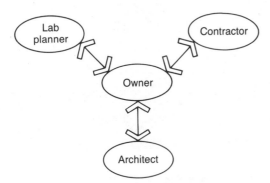

Fig. 2.3-11. Team relationship (contractual).

these institutions that want things done *their* way. The client is often an administrator who is used to delegating some authority to others and relying on outside help.

Laboratory facilities planners, on the other hand, tend to take the role of advisor, i.e., they present alternative solutions for a decision by the owner. This seems to be true for the opposite reasons stated above: There is little published data on research facilities because of the variety and unpredictable nature of these facilities. The nature of research is to change. The client is the investor or is heavily dominated by an investigator (researcher). Except for clinical, quality control and development laboratories, research laboratories are not service oriented and are often headed by a strong, well-known individual. Except for some of the components, there are also very few similarities between research facilities. The laboratory facilities planner therefore usually tends to present alternatives, identify information resources and translate needs into physical facilities, a controlled environment and utility services.

2.4 THE POR—CONTENTS *T. Ruys*

Laboratory facilities, because of their complexity, require two PORs: conceptual and detailed. In order to be effective and complete, a conceptual POR for laboratory facilities must, at a minimum, address the following issues, which are extremely critical to the success of these facilities: flexibility, safety, energy, human needs, cost and reliability. See Table 2.4-1.

2.4.1 Flexibility

Laboratory facilities are renovated frequently, and the state of the art in equipment changes quickly. Many facilities house activities which are unpredictable in nature and must be flexible to accommodate changes. Flexibility includes the following:

- Adaptability—the ability to accommodate changed functions
- Expansibility—the ability to change size

Table 2.4-1. Laboratory Design Issues

Issues	Considerations
Flexibility	Types of flexibility
	Conflicts between various types
	Reasons for flexibility
	Frequency of anticipated changes
Safety	Goal-oriented systems approach
	Emergency protocol
Energy conservation	Exhaust air
	Energy conservation devices
Human needs	Personnel areas
	Communication places
Cost	Construction project cost
	Life cycle cost
Reliability	Equipment selection
	Backup system
	Redundancy

- Versatility—the ability to reuse components

There may be conflicts between different types of flexibility. For instance, the desire for large, column-free spaces to facilitate equipment rearrangement may be incompatible with the need to minimize vibration of the floor slab. Since conflicts are inevitable,

it will be beneficial to document the reasons for various types of flexibility and to set priorities.

The need for flexibility is inversely proportional to the absence of decision-making power. As pointed out earlier, that may be the result of the nature of the activities accommodated and may be difficult to predict. What may be easier to predict is the frequency of changes. See Section 3.2, "Flexibility Considerations," for a more detailed discussion of flexibility.

2.4.2 Safety

Laboratory facilities are potentially hazardous places to work. Section 3.5, "Managing Laboratory Hazards by Design," deals with a response in facilities planning and design to these hazards. The POR must document these requirements. A goal-oriented systems approach will organize these requirements and ensure that all safety issues are covered. See Table 2.4-2.

It is not enough to discuss hazards under normal working conditions. Emergency conditions in case of spills, fire or explosion must be considered, and the protocol for dealing with the emergency must be discussed. This may result in a new set of planning and design issues.

Table 2.4-2. Laboratory Hazards

Nature	Type	Response
Chemical	Toxic	Ventilation and filtration
	Oncogenic	Ventilation and filtration
	Carcinogenic	Ventilation and filtration
	Flammable/combustible	Fire protection, enclosures
	Explosive	Barrier, venting
Biological	Pathogenic	Containment
	Microbial	Containment
Radiation	Alpha	Containment
	Beta	Containment
	Gamma	Lead or concrete shielding
	X-ray	Shielding
Other	Noise	Enclosure or acoustical treatment
	Electrical	Grounding
	Freezing	Equipment design
	Overheating	Ventilation

2.4.3 Energy Conservation

Laboratory facilities are intensive energy users primarily because of the large volumes of conditioned air commonly used for ventilation. A laboratory can be compared to a wind tunnel: insulating has a negligible effect on energy conservation, but reducing the volume of air will likely result in a substantial reduction of energy use.

There are various types of energy conservation devices on the market. Some are suitable for laboratories; others are not. Chapter 6 deals with energy conservation issues and equipment selection in detail.

2.4.4 Human Needs

Protocol prohibits eating and drinking in laboratories. More often than not, laboratories have no windows. There is a need to get away from the work environment, since much of the work is routine. The constant hum of many pieces of equipment and instruments takes its toll. An investment in personnel spaces and amenities creates good will, loyalty and increased productivity. There is also a need for individuals to interact, to discuss common problems, to generate new ideas, to celebrate a birthday, to have a party. Section 3.4 discusses the amenities suggested in greater detail.

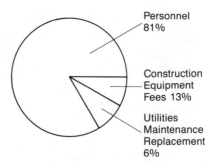

Fig. 2.4-1. Life cycle costs.

2.4.5 Cost

An increase in operational efficiency will pay handsomely over the life of a building. See Figure 2.4-1, which shows a personnel cost of approximately 80% of the total life cycle cost over 25 years. This figure may be somewhat lower for laboratory facilities, since these are in general more equipment intensive and less people intensive.

The quality of construction and finishes must be discussed and documented. Section 3.7, "Architectural Finishes," and Chapter 8, "Cost Issues," will assist in focusing these discussions.

2.4.6 Reliability

Many laboratories are used for research and many others for the analysis of specimens.

	GOAL	FACTS	CONCEPTS	NEEDS
FUNCTION	Building purpose Staffing Public or private Operations	Zoning restrictions Code compliance Regulations Hazard	Flexibility Space standard(s) Security	Net space Gross space
FORM	Growth projections Image Amenities	Site constraints/ survey Sun/wind direction Parking Site utilities	Site use Lab module(s) Functional zones Support cores	Relationships Proximities Links
ECONOMY	Efficiency NASF/GSF Energy use	Budget Building ownership Energy sources Soil conditions	Materials movement System Quality of const. Arch. finishes	Priorities
TIME	Occupancy Life cycle Payback	Component availability Construction schedule Time of operation	Phasing of moves Oversizing	Expansion

Fig. 2.4-2. Information matrix for laboratory facilities.

Room Data Sheet _____

Project _____   Description _____

Job Number _____   Room Name and Number _____

Date _____   Net Square Feet _____

By

Space Function   Key Relationship Critical Dimensions Hours of Use:
                   Major Equipment Occupancy: _____

Equipment	Description Make/Model	Quantities	Status	Description Make/Model	Quantities	Status
	1._____	_____	_____	7._____	_____	_____
	2._____	_____	_____	8._____	_____	_____
	3._____	_____	_____	9._____	_____	_____
	4._____	_____	_____	10._____	_____	_____
	5._____	_____	_____	11._____	_____	_____
	6._____	_____	_____	12._____	_____	_____

Attach Manufacturer's specifications if possible.
Use additional sheets to complete list.

Furnishings		Size	Quantity		Size	Quantity		LF	Quantity
	Desks ____	__	____	Files ____	__	____	Tops ____	__	____
	Chairs ____	__	____	Chalkboard ____	__	____	Drawers ____	__	____
	Tables ____	__	____	Tackboard ____	__	____	Cupboards ____	__	____
	Shelving (length) ____	__	____	Other ____	__	____	Wall cabinet ____	__	____

Finishes	Floor	Comments	Wall	Comments	Ceilings	Comments
	Material ____	____	Material ____	____	Material ____	____
	Finish ____	____	Finish ____	____	Finish ____	____
	Base ____	____			Height ____	____
	Other ____	____	Other ____	____	Other ____	____

Fig. 2.4-3. Room data sheet example (front).

Openings	Door	Comments	Relites	Comments	Windows
	Size		Size		___ Required
	Lock		___ Operable		___ Not Required
	Closer		___ Fixed		___ Not Desired
	Other		___ Draperies		___ Light Control

Electrical	Power	Comments	Lighting	Comments	Communications
	___ 120V ___ 2-8V		___ Fluorescent		___ Telephone
	___ 1∅ 3∅		___ Incandescent		___ Data Process
	___ Emergency		Level (fc)		___ Clock
	___ Grounding		Other		___ Other
	Other				

Mechanical	Ventilation	Comments	Air Conditioning	Comments	Pressure
	___ Mechanical		Min. Temperature		___ Positive
	___ Natural		Max. Temperature		___ Negative
	Exhaust		Min. Relative Humidity		___ Neutral
			Max. Relative Humidity		Control
			Acoustical Control		___ Individual
			Filtering		___ Zone

Plumbing	Piped Service	Quantity	Fixtures	Comments	Fixtures
	___ Oxygen		___ Sink		___ Floor Drain
	___ Nitrogen		Type		___ Eyewash
	___ Air		Material		___ Emergency Shower
	___ Vacuum		Sink Control		
	___ Nitrous Oxide		___ Wrist		
	___ Carbon Dioxide		___ Spray Unit		___ Other
	Other		___ Acid Waste		
	___ Hot/Cold Water		___ Plaster Trap		___
	___ Steam		___ Other		___
	___ Nat. Gas				___
	___ Distilled Water				___
	___ Deionized Water				___

Fig. 2.4-4. Room data sheet example (back).

DEPARTMENT _____

ROOM _____

EQUIPMENT DATA SHEET

DATE _____ JOB _____

CODE _____

STATUS _____ GROUP _____

ITEM DESCRIPTION _____

_____

MANUFACTURER _____ MODEL NO. _____

PURPOSE _____

Further info call _____ Phone No. _____

ELECTRICAL SERVICES						MECHANICAL SERVICES				
V	Amp	KW	HP	PH	Other	STM	HW	CW	W	Other

REMARKS _____

_____

_____

HEAT LOSS _____

SIZE: W = _____ D = _____ H = _____ WEIGHT _____

MAINTENANCE CLEARANCES _____

SKETCH or PHOTO – show service connections – staple additional info to this sheet _____

SERVICE NOTES _____

_____

_____

_____

_____

_____

_____

_____

_____

Fig. 2.4-5. Equipment data sheet example (Sources: The NBBJ Group).

Neither type can afford to lose power and/or ventilation. Equipment must be reliable; therefore, manufacturers of choice must be identified. Redundant or backup systems must be discussed, identified and documented. Chapter 4, "Laboratry Equipment Selection and Testing," and Chapter 5, "Systems," will assist in identifying these needs.

2.4.7 Other Issues

Besides the issues discussed above, a number of other items must be included in the conceptual POR in order to provide adequate information for the design team. These items are shown in Figure 2.4-2 to match Figure 2.3-3. After this information has been gathered, it is often reproduced in its original form and constitutes the conceptual POR.

2.4.8 Detailed POR

Once the conceptual information has been gathered and documented as required for the schematic design, it is time to document additional details for each space to be incorporated in the project. Typically, that includes a description of the space function and, for large spaces, material and people flow; identification of major equipment and benches, their status (existing versus new) and their associated utility services; and an indication of the space environmental controls and finishes. These are documented on room data sheets. See Figures 2.4-3 and 2.4-4.

In addition, diagrammatic plans and elevations must give equipment locations, systems and detailed requirements: See Figure 2.4-5.

A suggested table of contents for a detailed POR is given in Table 2.4-3.

Table 2.4-3. Suggested Table of Contents for a Detailed Program of Requirements

Chapter	Subject
Introduction	
Room Data Sheets	
• Project data	Name, date, space name and number
• Space function	Description and internal relationships
	Hours of use
	Critical dimensions
• Equipment	Size and status
• Furnishings	Tables, chairs, drapes
• Finishes	Floor, wall, ceiling
• Openings	Doors, relites, windows, security
• Electrical	Power, lighting, communications
• Mechanical	Ventilation, air conditioning, pressure
• Plumbing	Piped services, fixtures
Diagrammatic Plans and Elevations	
• Typical modular arrangement	
• Typical casework elevations	
• Typical plumbing plan and elevation	
• Typical mechanical and ceiling grid	
• Typical electrical plan and elevation	
• Typical lighting layout	
Equipment Data Sheets	
• Identification number	
• Item description, manufacturer, model number	
• Size and weight	
• Utility requirements	

2.5 TECHNIQUES AND TOOLS TO GATHER DATA   *T. Ruys*

2.5.1 Introduction

For purposes of clarification, a distinction is made between data-gathering techniques and tools. The techniques discussed include both direct and indirect methods, and the results may vary a great deal, depending on the skills and understanding of the individual applying the technique. Techniques include group interaction and site visits; interviews; observations, time lapse and still photography; role playing; the critical path method (CPM); flow diagrams; scales; cut paper models; and computer modeling. Section 1.3 discusses many of the errors in applying various techniques, and the reader is encouraged to review that material. As pointed out, some errors are the result of the situation in which the data are gathered; others are due to observer or interviewer behavior or status.

Tools for data gathering include instruments such as computers, cameras, recorders and measuring devices, and such aids as questionnaires, checklists, matrices, cards, brown sheets and scales.

The techniques and tools selected for a particular project should be carefully evaluated. The selection depends to a large degree on the ingenuity, skills, and creativity of the individual and on the schedule and budget of the project.

The data gathering should proceed from the general to the specific; from group interaction to random observation during a site visit; and from interview and role playing to CPM, flow diagrams and modeling.

Some techniques use direct methods, some indirect methods and some both. Group interaction, site visits and interviews are examples of direct methods. Time lapse photography, observation and role playing are indirect, and flow diagrams/CPM are both.

It is important to keep in mind that the data acquired must be systematic, measurable, and verifiable. If used for statistical analysis, they must also be adequate, representative and quantitative.

The methods used must be free of embar-rassment or harassment to the individuals dealt with.

2.5.2 Techniques

Group Interaction

This part of the process is probably the most critical. The participants form an opinion very quickly about the leadership, skills, values and general attitude of the data gatherer. Much information is transmitted nonverbally. It is essential to create a level of trust; the best way to accomplish that is to spend time explaining the process, objectives, what is expected, what will be the product and the reason for the exercise. Being unbiased, unopinionated and a good listener with a sense of humor will help. Preparation is essential in order to keep the discussions focused. Visual aids and an agenda are a great help.

The location of the interaction is also very important. It should be away from the daily work environment, with its disruptions and distractions, and ideally in a relaxed, pleasant location conducive to creative thinking and interaction.

Site Visit

There is no substitute for collecting data on site. By "site" we mean the organization's facilities, both external and internal, including laboratories representative of the project. The users must be encouraged to point out the good and bad features and operations, the deficiencies and inefficiencies. This will facilitate subsequent discussions during interviews because it establishes a point of reference and a common vocabulary.

Site visits do not need to be restricted to the participant's facilities. It is very beneficial to visit other similar or appropriate facilities. Some research and discussion with the participants will provide suggestions for facilities to visit. The value of visiting other companies or institutions should not be underestimated for the same reasons given earlier: to establish a common vocabulary and a baseline of acceptability during subsequent discussions.

Interviews

Interviews are of two types: unstandardized and standardized.

The unstandardized interview is completely flexible and very useful in the exploratory stages of interviewing when the broader aspects of the problem are being formulated. The advantage of this type of interview over the standardized interview is that the meaning of any answer is clearer and more true to life than a "yes" or "no" answer. Any interesting and pertinent directions which the interview may take can also be pursued. One must also bear in mind that the respondents may not have an opinion on some issues and should not be forced to give one. Unstandardized interviews will bring out the "don't know" answers.

The standardized interview may be open or closed. Both types follow a predetermined order of questioning, however, to ensure that the intended subject matter is covered. The advantage of this type of interview over the unstandardized interview is that the answers are comparable between different respondents and reliable for statistical purposes; in addition, errors inherent in the interview method can be minimized (see Section 1.3). This type of interview is used at the measuring stage after the exploratory stage.

In order to maximize the respondents' cooperation, it is important to publicize the reason for and objectives of the interview ahead of time. Include a reference to the authoritative source (familiar to the respondents) backing the project, and write a letter with proper credentials. Follow up with a phone call for an appointment. Select an appropriate time which ensures an interview with a minimum number of interruptions. Conduct the interview in private, and assure the respondent that any information given is confidential.

Interviewing methods that achieve maximum cooperation and minimize error, according to Lindzey (1954), depend on a proper manner and bearing in asking the questions. A reserved, dignified manner which takes the respondent seriously is important. The interviewer should show interest without revealing personal attitudes. A friendly permissiveness is most effective, along with the necessary probing questions, such as: "Really, I see your point. That is very interesting. Could you tell me more about that?" Repeated sessions must not weaken the interview by asking the same questions. Gradually approach topics of emotional content. Systematically cover all items. Ask direct rather than devious questions, placing the burden of denial on the respondent. Avoid multiple questions. Crosscheck for accuracy. However, allow the respondent to save face in case of a contradiction in the way the question is phrased: "I want to be sure to get this right; in my notes . . ."

In interviewing a too wordy respondent, the following methods can be used without directly interrupting the individual, which must be avoided: ask a shunt question; avoid a later digression by starting with a general question; ask precise questions.

Visual aids are very important during interviews in facilitating communications in both directions. We cannot assume that the interviewee knows what we are talking about or will admit it. We may also not comprehend the significance of what we are told. Photographs, slides or other illustrations of desirable or undesirable situations or features taken by the space users will facilitate understanding. We may also photograph an existing facility or operation and solicit comments during an interview. Photographs very often solicit strong responses and surprising results. A photograph to identify a specific piece of equipment may result in a remark about the wrong placement of the cabinet above the equipment at 6 feet off the floor, where nobody can reach it, or about its bad quality or appearance, depth, fixed shelves, etc. All of this could otherwise have been easily overlooked.

Observation

Observation is systematic viewing coupled with a consideration of the seen phenomena.

In architectural programming of buildings, the observation method is rarely used to acquire data for quantitative statistical analysis. However, it is important to observe space use. Space occupants are not always able to express likes or dislikes or to state needs, since they suffer from "occupational blindness"; that is, they are so used to working in a certain way that possible improvements do not occur to them. The human adaptation level is phenomenal; people are able to work under almost any conditions. It is up to the architectural programmer to observe and question some of the conditions and propose improvements.

There are several types of field observations. Young (1966) specifies controlled observations, which use such devices as one-way mirrors, movement recorders, sound recorders, motion pictures, etc.; uncontrolled observation with participation; and uncontrolled observation with nonparticipation.

The first of these methods is used for small-group interaction observation, for educational purposes and to minimize the influence of the observer on the results of the study. It has a limited use for architectural programming, except perhaps in cases where motion studies are important, such as the design of a dental cubicle, or to determine the size of a laboratory module. The effect of the observer on the behavior of the respondent is negligible in such cases.

The second type of field observation is designed to win the confidence of the respondent(s) and thus minimize the error due to the presence of the observer. This method is too time-consuming and expensive for architectural programming purposes, except in cases where the programmer also acts as a management consultant and makes a study of the client's organization to recommend necessary changes which will affect the program's items.

The third method is the most practical for our purposes. Data required for program items such as building constraints, activity systems, space requirements and proximity relationships may be acquired in this manner. This method has some limitations, however, which must be recognized (see Section 3.1.3).

Recording methods must be considered in field observations. Before any recording of field observations can take place, the objectives of the observations must be formulated and those aspects which are significant for the purpose must be singled out. This will facilitate standardized observation and systematic recording of observed phenomena.

The criteria for observation are as follows: observe according to a planned technique; observe the larger setting in which the acts occur; describe the social atmosphere, if pertinent; record without delay and without bias; compare findings with other findings on the same subject, if available; if possible, use a control group from experience or other site visits; integrate the observational technique with other suitable techniques such as interviews.

Time Lapse Photography

It has been known for some time that human cognition is limited to a maximum of 8 to 10 objects at any one time and that the attention span fluctuates due to fatigue, boredom and lack of motivation. A camera is a valuable observation tool because it is not subject to these limitations and can record events and objects in great detail, at fixed intervals and over a long period of time.

A camera is most often used to illustrate a finding that has already been decided upon as being significant. Rarely is it used as a recording tool which can standardize and tabulate.

An individual observing the same events and using field notes would be less accurate, and the effort would be more time-consuming. Collier (1967) points out that photographs can be used to record material reality and special relationships, which can be filed, cross-filed, corrected, measured, compared, qualified and used with statistical methods. Another advantage of photographic observation is that it does not depend on an individual field observer's decision on what and how to record. Two different observers typically will record the same event in different ways with field notes because inferences have to be made between the observed fact and the recorded word. These observed facts, however, are subject to errors, as discussed in Section 1.3.

Time lapse photography is a useful technique for recording complex interactions and the flow of people, products and materials in a particular space such as a machine shop, glass wash facility, or media preparation facility. It assists in establishing where equipment and work benches should be located and points out major traffic flows and congested areas. See Figure 2.5-1, a time lapse record of a bank teller's lobby, first at 1-minute intervals and then at 30-second intervals.

Still Photography

In the section on interviews we briefly mentioned the use of photographs as a visual re-

minder to solicit a response; as an aid to discussion; to focus on a subject of interest; or to direct the interview to one topic from a selection of variables.

Still photography can also be used for recording the inventory; for documenting existing conditions that are desirable or undesirable; or for later comparison or discussions with users or outside consultants not present on the site. Photos represent nonverbal evidence of issues brought up at interviews.

Photos often solicit emotionally charged responses from individuals who project their own experiences into the picture as a result of viewing it. A photograph can be a very powerful reminder.

Awareness of the content level will assist in selecting the subject matter that needs to be photographed:

- Record keeping—quantities, inventory, condition

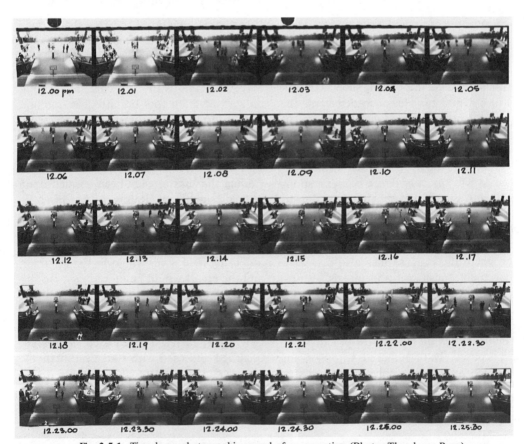

Fig. 2.5-1. Time lapse photographic record of an operation (Photo: Theodorus Ruys).

- Preferences—attitudes, values, pros and cons
- Content—relationships, ergonomics
- Appearance—quality, image, design

Role Playing

This is an indirect method of getting the information needed. At times, interviewees are unable or reluctant to provide answers or do not understand what is needed to plan a space for them. This may be due to the errors caused by interviews pointed out in Section 1.3. Role playing may overcome these problems.

Role playing can be done in two ways: The planner can pretend to be someone else and solicit a response, or the planner can ask the interviewee to act out his or her daily routine and observe.

The first: Acting out someone else's role is useful in conveying our understanding and thus soliciting a response. It also enables the planner to introduce creative, new ways of doing things for discussion.

The second: Asking others to go through their daily routines enables the planner to observe and ask questions about the reasons for the activity and associated space needs. Many things will be overlooked if the activity is only described verbally, particularly in complex laboratory operations.

Scales

Much of the data we seek are qualitative in nature and cannot be quantified. Individuals may be asked to prioritize from a list of options, to make distinctions of degree and/or quality. Scales are useful in this process. There are several types of scales. Those useful for data gathering for a POR are as follows:

- Differentiation Scale: $A = B$ or $A \neq B$ in order to distinguish between comparable situations without measuring quantities. This scale is useful during the initial meetings in order to establish a baseline or common body of knowledge for understanding. This is a method by trial and error. A sketch may

be presented and the interviewee asked: "Is this what you have in mind?"
- Quantitative Scale: $A \geq B$ or $A \leq B$. A cost estimate may be of this nature. Some design solutions cost more than others. $A > B > C$ is another form of this type of scale. Priorities scales are typically of this type. Sometimes references are ranked in order of position. Self-administered scales to measure the strength of a preference are of this nature: "On a scale of 1 to 10, where is your preference?" In questionnaires one often finds a preference checklist as follows: "excellent, good, average, bad, worst" or "strongly agree, agree, undecided, disagree, strongly disagree" when responding to a question. This is a quantitative scale on which the outcome is selected by the respondent. In the opposite situation, the response generates a score on a predetermined scale such as "this is better than that," answered by a number of individuals on a number of subjects.

Cut Paper or Block Models to Scale

A very useful technique commonly used by architects is to cut paper to scale. Each piece represents a space or an object. These pieces can be moved and arranged in various configurations to represent possible solutions and recorded in sketch form or photographically. Several alternative solutions can be arrived at very quickly for detailed analysis or presentation later. The use of different colors will make it possible to comprehend and record complex interrelationships among many components. See Figures 2.5-2 and 2.5-3.

Flow Diagram

The strength of a relationship can be verified by counting the frequency of contact between two points or individuals and recording this graphically on a flow diagram. See Figure 2.5-4. These relationships may have different reasons—personnel communication, supervision or visitors, materials flow,

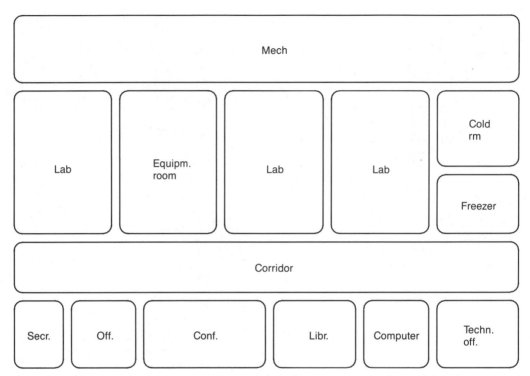

Fig. 2.5-2. Cut paper to scale arranged to study and record two-dimensional relationships.

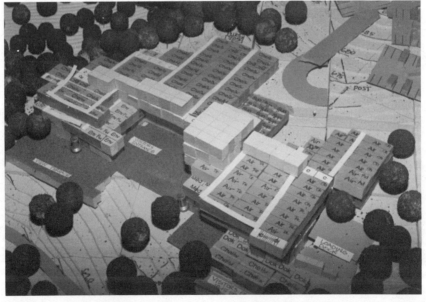

Fig. 2.5-3. Blocks in color, arranged to show three-dimensional relationships (The NBBJ Group).

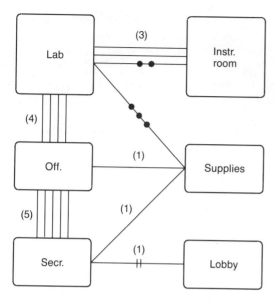

Legend:

— ++ — Visitors
—●●●— Material flow
—●●— Equipment sharing
(1) Number of trips

Fig. 2.5-4. Flow diagram.

sharing of equipment, etc.—which can be distinguished by various line symbols.

The same analysis can be accomplished with a string diagram on a board with colored yarn or rubber bands. See Figure 2.5-5. This technique will establish the most efficient way to operate and verify the strength of the relationship and number of personnel required. The purpose of planning a facility, after all, is to increase productivity with the same number of people or fewer if possible.

Critical Path Method

For many years, the CMP has been used in the construction industry to coordinate activities with schedules. The critical path establishes the order of these activities so that the project can proceed in the most economical and efficient way. This technique can be used to order the decision-making process. For instance, the programs for a particular organization must be established before the staffing projections for a given point in time can be known or assumed, and their activities must be known before space projections

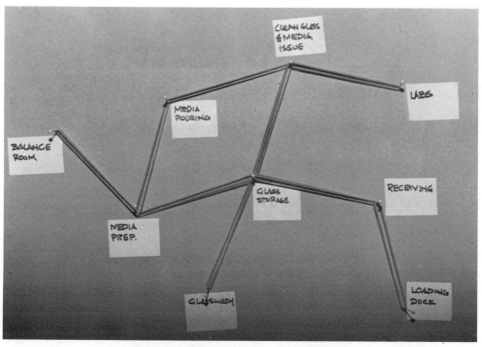

Fig. 2.5-5. String diagram (Theodorus Ruys).

can be made. These projections, in turn, are necessary in order to arrive at a construction cost, which is required to establish a project cost. See Figure 2.5-6. This method will assist in the decision-making process described in Section 2.3, "The Process of Documentation of Needs."

2.5.3 Tools

Cards and Brown Sheets

In Section 2.3 we described Pena's (1987) process of data gathering and bringing the wish list in line with the budget. These tools are illustrated in Figures 2.3-3 and 2.3-8 and included here for completeness.

Relationship Matrix

The flow diagram technique described earlier can also be recorded on a matrix. See Figure 2.5-7. The reason for and strength of the relationship can be recorded on the intersection of the lines leading to the space name. This system has several advantages over the flow diagram and at least one disadvantage.

Advantage: (1) The order of adjacent spaces in a real floor plan can be arranged. There is a limit to the number of spaces that can be adjacent to each other, and this matrix will quickly establish this limit. (2) Because the reasons for the adjacencies are recorded and priorities can be established for them, the flow diagram is a more flexible tool to develop an actual floor plan later on and arrive at a preferred scheme sooner.

Disadvantage: It is more difficult to envision an actual floor plan from this matrix than from a flow diagram because a matrix only provides a list of names, while a flow diagram can provide spaces to scale.

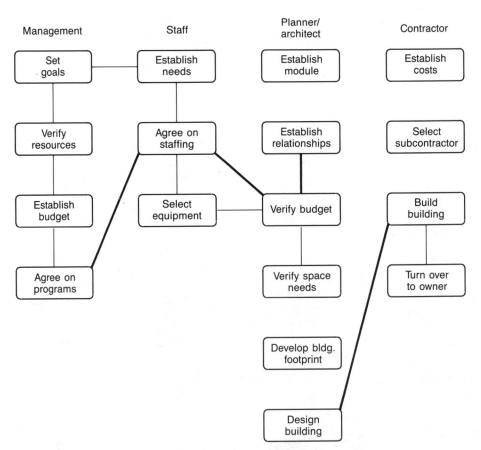

Fig. 2.5-6. CPM applied to decision making.

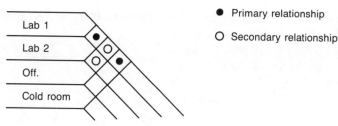

● Primary relationship

○ Secondary relationship

Fig. 2.5-7. Relationship matrix.

Evaluation Matrix

Somewhere in the process of planning, choices will need to be made between alternatives. Not all choices have the same weight, however, and priorities in selection must be included in the system. A good way to accomplish this is to establish a matrix of options, selection criteria and priorities (or multipliers), as shown in Figure 2.5-8. The selection criteria used to evaluate schematic design options A to D have been summarized for function, form, economy and time to conform to the method outlined in Section 2.3, "The Process of Documentation of Needs." In this figure the budget is considered the most critical, so it has been given a multiplier of 4 on a scale from 1 to 4. Time effects cost, so it has also been given a 4, and function and form a 3 and a 2, respectively.

The options are evaluated on a scale based on the number of options—four in this example. Let us assume that the item flexibility gets a score of 2, 3, 4 and 2 for options A to

Selection criteria	Multiplier	Option A	Option B	Option C	Option D	

Function
  Flexibility
  Relationships
  Access
	3	2 × 3	3 × 3	4 × 3	2 × 3	

Form
  Image
  Design potential
  Views
	2					

Economy
  Constr. cost
  Life cycle cost
  Efficiency
	4					

Time
  Constr. time
  Design time
	4					

TOTAL		——	——	——	——	

Fig. 2.5-8. Evaluation matrix.

D, respectively. Each is multiplied by 3. In completing this process and totaling the scores, the best solution based on the criteria and priorities agreed upon will be arrived at.

Checklists

These tools lend themselves well to comparative analysis between answers and to the recording of data quickly and inexpensively. A checklist is a short form of a questionnaire.

Checklists are easy to administer, since these are mostly self-directed, but they are also very limiting since they do not allow for an alternative answer. Figure 2.4-3 and 2.4-4 are examples of a checklist to collect data for each space in a laboratory building.

Questionnaires

Questionnaires are probably the most common tools used for data gathering. It is therefore important to review the types of questionnaires discussed in Section 2.5-2. Errors due to questionnaires have been discussed in Section 1.3.4. Much of the discussion on questionnaires is from Selltiz et al. (1959).

The following checklist may serve as a reminder in questionnaire preparation:

- What is the purpose? What information is sought? Is it adequate? Is it necessary?
- What should be the sequence of questions?
- Should the questionnaire be pretested?
- Should the questionnaire be structured (closed) or unstructured (open-ended)?
- Is adequate space provided for the response?
- Are the questions clear? Are there any double meanings? Does the respondent have the knowledge to answer?
- Do the questions indicate preferences or biases? Are any questions loaded?
- If preferences are solicited, are all alternatives indicated?
- Can the responses be quantified?

Camera (Still and Video)

In reviewing Section 2.5.2, it should be obvious that the camera is a very useful tool to record and analyze objects and/or events. A Polaroid camera is probably the easiest to use because it gives instant results and because the subject photographed can be noted on the print at the time the picture was taken. It also prevents errors due to over- or underexposed film or film that has not been advanced.

On the other hand, a simple 35mm camera with a flash attachment is the easiest, quickest and most useful tool for most photographic recordings, as well as the least expensive. A more expensive camera on a tripod with a zoom lens for wide-angle and telephoto recording is very useful for time lapse photography.

The video camera is also very useful to record complex operations and as an analytical tool. The events recorded can be stopped, advanced and played back to view or discuss.

Measuring Scales

Many observed items of space or equipment have dimensions that can be measured and recorded. Equipment has three dimensions that must be known in order to be accommodated in a laboratory setting and to make sure that adequate headroom and service areas are provided. Existing conditions in terms of linear feet of space for each function should be recorded for later analysis and comparison.

The architectural scale allows items to be recorded to scale on a standard page. Figure 2.4-5 shows the plan and elevations of a particular laboratory on a scale of 1/4th of an inch to 1 foot. Anyone with an identical scale can check equipment sizes and space needs and thus the adequacy of the total space.

Computer

With increased versatility, the computer is a very handy tool not only for recording needs

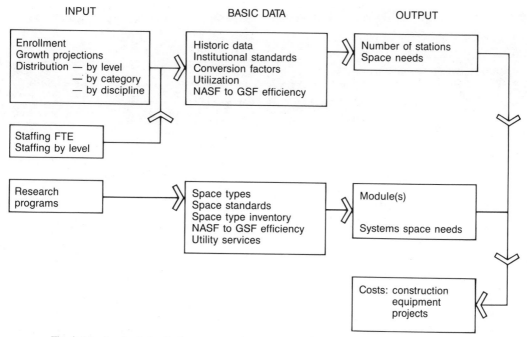

Fig. 2.5-9. Academic institution, suggested computer model to arrive at space needs and costs.

but for comparing them with a data base to arrive quickly at a cost.

Figure 2.5-9 suggests such a computer program for an academic institution and figure 2.5-10 for an R&D facility. Enrollment growth projections or production goals are translated into space needs, and costs from the data base are collected and updated over many projects. The more often the data base is updated, the better it will get.

REFERENCES

Collier, John, Jr., 1967. *Visual Anthropology: Photography as a Research Method.* Holt, Rinehart and Winston, Inc.

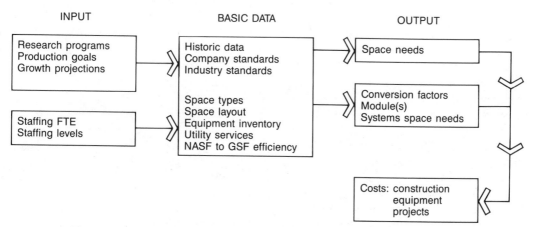

Fig. 2.5-10. R&D facility, suggested computer model to arrive at space needs and costs.

Green, Meg, 1967. Decisions-Making Theory Applied to Architectural Programming, Unpublished paper.

Lindzey, G., 1954. *Handbook of Social Psychology,* Vol. 1, *The Interview: A Tool of Social Science,* pp. 449–484. Cambridge: Addison-Wesley.

Pena, William, 1987. *Problem Seeking.* Washington, DC: American Institute of Architects Press.

Selltiz, C., Jahoda, M., Deutsch, M., and Cook, S.W., 1959. *Research Methods in Social Relations.* New York: Holt–Rinehart and Winston, Inc.

Young, Pauline V., 1966. *Scientific Social Surveys and Research,* 4th ed. New York: Prentice-Hall.

2.6 SPACE GUIDELINES   *D. Paulien and T. Ruys*

2.6.1 Introduction

When an organization believes that it needs additional space, an early concern is how to quantify those needs. Doing detailed planning at this early stage would be very time-consuming and costly, and it is not yet known if the project is feasible. Utilizing rule-of-thumb factors is an important step in defining the scope of a project.

In a university setting there are usually competing demands for space, with different departments asserting their claims for additional space. How can these be evaluated in an appropriate way so that the planner and administrator are assured that reasonable requests and decisions are being made?

What kind of analysis can be produced that allows the planner or administrator to propose a course of action or make a convincing case for a particular course of action to CEOs, top administrators, governing boards, and, in the case of public institutions, legislative bodies?

An important tool in this process is space guidelines. These are based on the experience of companies and institutions, and represent the amount of space determined appropriate by these groups for a specific type of activity. Space guidelines for academic institutions have been developed by governing boards, state coordinating boards, legislative budget review committees and individual universities. Examples are available and are listed in the references on page 102. Guidelines for industrial R&D facilities are more difficult to come by, but some have been proposed based on the experience of a number of planners. This section focuses on the use of space guidelines for teaching laboratories, academic research laboratories, and R&D laboratories. Office space guidelines for researchers will also be covered, so that the total space needs for a laboratory unit can be estimated. The space guidelines in this section are given in net assignable square feet (NASF). Section 8.6 discusses the way to arrive at estimates in gross square feet (GASF).

Guidelines as a Tool in Setting the Project Scope

The type and amount of information available when a project is proposed will vary greatly. In some instances, a particular laboratory unit or department will have done a detailed analysis utilizing whatever method occurred to them to state the case for their perceived need. In other instances, the need statement will be vague, since it is believed that double or triple the amount of space now available is needed. Some units or departments will inflate their estimate because they assume that it will be cut back. Others may have documented the expected growth in personnel based on the program and analyzed their needs on a lab-by-lab, office-by-office basis.

Regardless of the depth of planning, the CEO or planning official faces the task of evaluating, commenting on, and approving or disapproving the perceived need. Space guidelines can be an effective tool in helping the planner justify and explain space need recommendations.

In states where guidelines are enforced by governing or coordinating boards, the public institution planner will know what guideline and methodology must be followed. In other states, the planner must determine which, if any, guideline to utilize.

It is most important that a guideline used

for the first time by a company or an institution be tested against actual cases of occupied space that are considered reasonable in allocation—not too tight, not too generous. The planner must analyze the results and determine whether these guidelines are producing results that are appropriate for the organization.

Some space guidelines were produced for use at major research universities. Others were developed by coordinating boards or legislative bodies. The latter may be more conservative because they were intended to be applied to a broader range of institutions. It is important that the planner understand for what purpose and type of activity the guidelines were intended so that their use will have credibility when the results are presented to reviewing officials both within the organization and externally.

The Role of Space Guidelines in Detailed Facilities Planning

If guidelines have been used to set parameters for a project, the laboratory units or departments involved still should be asked to justify their needs on a lab-by-lab, person-by-person basis. The guidelines will have set an overall parameter for the project, but since that parameter is not based on the specific needs of the unit but rather on the experience of other similar units, it should be tested against the perceived needs of the unit. An evaluation must then be made to ascertain whether the total amount of space requested, if it is more than the guideline suggests, can be justified, or whether the unit should be asked to prepare a reduced estimate using the guidelines as a maximum limit. In those instances where a unit does not justify as much space as the guidelines suggest, the space request should be questioned. Many individuals inexperienced with planning issues may grossly underestimate their space needs and may be penalized for it.

Guidelines alone should never be the only

justification for the space needs for a building, but they are an important tool in setting the project scope.

2.6.2 Academic Facilities Space Guidelines

Academic Teaching Laboratories

In setting guidelines for teaching laboratories, there are two issues which must be considered. The first is the amount of space needed per student station to perform the activities required by a particular course in the academic program. The second is the time utilization expected for the type of laboratory and the subject matter taught.

All university teaching lab guidelines have both of these elements. The first, square feet per student station, is based on an actual determination of the amount of space a student will need in conducting a particular type of laboratory activity. That figure must include adequate circulation space, so that the guideline provides space for the student to work and the instructor to teach.

Example: if 20 students are taught in a laboratory and each requires 50 NASF, a total of $20 \times 50 = 1,000$ NASF will be needed, including the instructor's space and aisles. Most guidelines suggest 20 hours per week of scheduled laboratory usage with 80% student station occupancy when the room is in use. This produces 16 hours/week of 100% station occupancy (20 hours $\times$ 80% occupancy). Dividing the station size by the utilization formula, e.g.,

$$\frac{\text{Station size} - 50 \text{ NASF}}{\begin{array}{c}\text{Utilization 20 hours} \times \\ 80\% = 16 \text{ hours/average} \\ \text{station use}\end{array}} = \begin{array}{c}3.13 \text{ NASF} \\ \text{per weekly} \\ \text{student hour}\end{array}$$

The square feet per weekly student hour factor allows calculation of the space need based on the number of weekly student hours actually generated by certain courses or based on projections.

In some guidelines, a distinction is made between the space in the laboratory itself and assumptions about related service space. For the initial planning of a project, using guidelines which include the service space simplifies the process so that the additional step of quantifying all the support space is avoided and is probably not necessary in this early planning stage of a project.

Tables 2.6-1 through 2.6-5 give space guidelines for academic teaching laboratories based on five different guideline systems. Tables 2.6-6 and 2.6-7 show how these space guidelines were applied to chemistry

Table 2.6-1. Space Guidelines for Academic Teaching Laboratories

	Area per Student Station	Service Space as a Percentage of Lab Space	Total Area per Station	Weekly Room Contact Hours Expected	Percent of Station Utilization*	Sq Ft per SSPO†
Agricultural Sciences						
Agronomy						
Soils	40	28	51.2	20	80	3.20
Soil chemistry, physical microbiology	45	28	57.6	20	80	3.60
Field crops, weed control	45	28	57.6	20	80	3.60
Animal Husbandry						
Chemical analysis	40	24	49.6	20	80	3.10
Feeding and care, meat technology	80	24	99.2	20	80	6.20
Breeding, physiology, nutrition	50	24	62.0	20	80	3.88
Dairy Husbandry						
Chemical analysis	40	30	52.0	20	80	3.25
Feed and care, milking methods	80	30	104.0	20	80	6.50
Breeding, physiology, nutrition	50	30	65.0	20	80	4.06
Forestry and Range Management						
All labs	35	30	45.5	20	80	2.84
Horticulture						
General, lawn management	30	150	75.0	20	80	4.69
Flower arrangement, taxonomy	50	150	125.0	20	80	7.81
Germination and propagation	50	400	250.0	20	80	15.63
Poultry Husbandry						
Genetics	100	30	130.0	20	80	8.13
Nutrition, physiology	45	30	58.5	20	80	3.66
Biological Sciences						
Anatomy and Histology						
Histology, developmental anatomy	35	24	43.4	20	80	2.71
Microscopic anatomy, vertebrate Morphology	45	24	55.8	20	80	3.49
Gross anatomy	60	24	74.4	20	80	4.65
All graduate laboratories	60	24	74.4	20	80	4.65
Bacteriology						
All undergraduate laboratories	45	32	59.4	20	80	3.71
All graduate laboratories	60	32	79.2	20	80	4.95

Table 2.6-1. (Continued)

	Area per Student Station	Service Space as a Percentage of Lab Space	Total Area per Station	Weekly Room Contact Hours Expected	Percent of Station Utilization*	Sq Ft per SSPO†
Biochemistry						
All undergraduate laboratories	50	24	62.0	20	80	3.88
All graduate laboratories	60	24	74.4	20	80	4.65
Biological Science						
General, introductory	35	24	43.4	20	80	2.71
Biophysics						
All undergraduate	45	24	55.8	20	80	3.49
All graduate	60	24	74.4	20	80	4.65
Botany						
Elementary, planet anatomy, tax- onomy	35	25	43.8	20	80	2.74
Morphology, mycology	45	25	56.2	20	80	3.51
Microtechnique, plant physiology	45	25	56.2	20	80	3.51
Pathology	60	25	75.0	20	80	4.69
All graduate	60	25	75.0	20	80	4.69
Entomology						
Elementary, introductory	35	24	43.4	20	80	2.71
All other undergraduate	45	24	55.8	20	80	3.49
All graduate	60	24	74.4	20	80	4.65
Genetics						
Elementary	35	24	45.5	20	80	2.71
All other undergraduate	45	24	55.8	20	80	3.49
All graduate	60	24	74.4	20	80	4.65
Microbiology						
All undergraduate	45	24	55.8	20	80	3.49
All graduate	60	24	74.4	20	80	4.65
Pathology						
All undergraduate	45	24	55.8	20	80	3.49
All graduate	60	24	74.4	20	80	4.65
Physiology						
Pharmacology, chemical physi- ology	45	24	55.8	20	80	3.49
Experimental, animal physiology	100	24	124.0	20	80	7.75
Plant pathology						
Elementary, general	35	24	45.5	20	80	2.71
All other undergraduate	45	24	55.8	20	80	3.49
All graduate	60	24	74.4	20	80	4.65
Zoology						
Introductory, elementary Comparative, anatomy, physiology	35	20	42.0	20	80	2.62
Vertebrate, invertebrate, cytology, embryology, enzymology, parasitology, histology, morphology, ornithography, ecology, limology, taxonomy	45	20	54.0	20	80	3.38

Table 2.6-1. (Continued)

	Area per Student Station	Service Space as a Percentage of Lab Space	Total Area per Station	Weekly Room Contact Hours Expected	Percent of Station Utilization*	Sq Ft per SSPO[†]
Engineering Sciences						
Aeronautical						
All laboratories	150	18	177.0	20	80	11.06
Agricultural						
Electricity	45	18	53.1	20	80	3.32
Soil and water	60	18	70.8	20	80	4.43
Structures	85	18	100.3	20	80	6.27
Farm metal work, shop work	115	18	135.7	30	80	5.65
Farm machinery, equipment	200	18	236.0	30	80	9.83
Chemical						
Instrumentation	30	18	35.4	20	80	2.21
Physical chemistry	60	18	70.8	20	80	4.43
Unit operations	150	18	177.0	20	80	11.06
Civil						
Photogrammetry, surveying	50	18	59.0	20	80	3.69
Soils	60	18	70.8	20	80	4.43
Hydraulics, concrete	88	18	103.8	20	80	6.49
Strength of materials	150	18	177.0	20	80	11.06
Electrical						
Measurements, control systems	45	18	53.1	20	80	3.32
Electronics	45	18	53.1	20	80	3.32
Circuits	75	18	88.5	20	80	5.53
Machines, power engineering	125	18	147.5	20	80	9.22
Geophysical						
Electricity, magnetism	45	18	53.1	20	80	3.32
Circuitry, electronics	45	18	53.1	20	80	3.32
Seismology	50	18	59.0	20	80	3.69
Prospecting, well logging	100	18	118.0	20	80	7.38
Industrial						
Processes, time and motion	65	18	76.7	20	80	4.79
Mechanical						
Machine shop, machines	50	18	59.0	20	80	3.69
Mechanical, thermodynamics	200	18	236.0	20	80	14.75
Manufacturing processes	200	18	236.0	20	80	14.75
Metallurgical						
Microscopy	40	18	47.2	20	80	2.95
Physical metallurgy	70	18	82.6	20	80	5.16
Spectrography	120	18	141.6	20	80	8.85
Mining						
Unit operations, production	125	18	147.5	20	80	9.22
Petroleum						
Refining processes	100	18	118.0	20	80	7.38
Unit operations, production	150	18	177.0	20	80	11.06
Physical Sciences						
Astrogeophysics						
All lower division	40	24	49.6	20	80	3.10
All upper division	45	24	55.8	20	80	3.49
All graduate	60	24	74.4	20	80	4.65

Table 2.6-1. (Continued)

	Area per Student Station	Service Space as a Percentage of Lab Space	Total Area per Station	Weekly Room Contact Hours Expected	Percent of Station Utilization*	Sq Ft per SSPO[†]
Astronomy						
All lower division	25	24	31.0	20	80	1.94
All upper division	50	24	62.0	20	80	3.88
All graduate	60	24	74.4	20	80	4.65
Astrophysics						
All undergraduate	50	24	62.0	20	80	3.88
All graduate	60	24	74.4	20	80	4.65
Atmospheric Science						
All lower division	40	24	49.6	20	80	3.10
All upper division	50	24	62.0	20	80	3.88
All graduate	60	24	74.4	20	80	4.65
Chemistry						
General, elementary	40	25	50.0	20	80	3.12
Beginning quantitative and qualitative	45	25	56.2	20	80	3.51
Beginning organic	45	25	56.2	20	80	3.51
Advanced quantitative and qualitative	50	25	62.5	20	80	3.91
Advanced organic, biochemistry	50	25	62.5	20	80	3.91
Physical chemistry	60	25	75.0	20	80	4.69
All graduate	60	25	75.0	20	80	4.69
Engineering physics						
All lower division	40	24	49.6	20	80	3.10
All upper division	45	24	55.8	20	80	3.49
All graduate	60	24	74.4	20	80	4.65
Geology						
Elementary, general	40	23	49.2	20	80	3.08
Crystallography, mineralogy, paleontology	40	23	49.2	20	80	3.08
Stratigraphy, petrology, petrography	50	23	61.5	20	80	3.84
Mapping, cartography, lithology	50	23	61.5	20	80	3.84
All graduate laboratories	60	23	73.8	20	80	4.61
General Physical Science						
General subjects	35	24	43.4	20	80	2.71
Meteorology						
All lower division	40	24	49.6	20	80	3.10
All upper division	50	24	62.0	20	80	3.88
All graduate	60	24	74.4	20	80	4.65
Physics						
General elementary	40	25	50.0	20	80	3.12
Intermediate, electronics, heat	45	25	56.2	20	80	3.51
Mechanics, optics	45	25	56.2	20	80	3.51
Atomic physics	60	25	25.0	20	80	4.69

*Calculated on the basis of the hours when rooms are in use.
[†]Student station periods of occupancy per week.

Source: A selection from Colorado Commission on Higher Education, *Policy Manual,* Denver, CO, July 1, 1987, pp. III-F.7 to III-F.13.

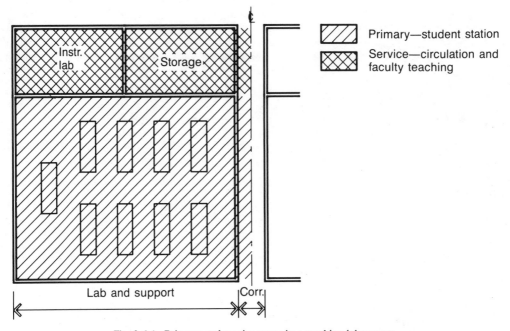

Fig. 2.6-1. Primary and service space in a teaching laboratory.

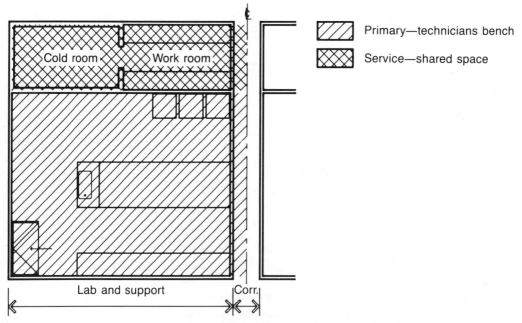

Fig. 2.6-2. Primary and service space in a research laboratory.

Table 2.6-2. Space Guidelines for Academic Teaching Laboratories

Field of Study	NASF per Station Including Auxiliaries	NASF per Weekly Student Hour	
		20 Hours/Week; 80% Station Utilization	24 Hours/Week; 80% Station Utilization
Agriculture			
Agriculture engineering	160	10.00	8.33
Agronomy	70	4.38	3.64
Animal science	160	10.00	8.33
Dairy science	68	4.25	3.54
Food science	96	6.00	5.00
Forestry	65	4.06	3.39
Home economics	100	6.25	5.21
Horticulture	65	4.06	3.39
Plant pathology	65	4.06	3.39
Engineering			
Aeronautical and astronautical engineering	160	10.00	8.33
Ceramic engineering	112	7.00	5.83
Civil engineering	112	7.00	5.83
Electrical engineering	65	4.06	3.39
General engineering	32	2.00	1.67
Mechanical engineering	160	10.00	8.33
Industrial engineering	160	10.00	8.33
Mining engineering	160	10.00	8.33
Metallurgy engineering	160	10.00	8.33
Petroleum engineering	160	10.00	8.33
Nuclear engineering	160	10.00	8.33
Physics	65	4.06	3.39
Theoretical and applied mechanics	160	10.00	8.33
Liberal Arts and Sciences			
Astronomy	50	3.13	2.60
Botany	50	3.13	2.60
Chemistry	68	4.25	3.54
Entomology	50	3.13	2.60
Geography	68	4.25	3.54
Geology-geoscience	68	4.25	3.54
Microbiology	68	4.25	3.54
Physics	65	4.06	3.39
Physiology	68	4.25	3.54
Zoology	50	3.13	2.60

Note: Usage based on facilities being scheduled, as well as classrooms from 7 A.M. to 4 P.M., and 80% station utilization.

Source: Harlan D. Bareither and Jerry Shillinger, *University Space Planning.* Urbana: University of Illinois Press, 1968, Table 8, p. 55.

Table 2.6-3. Space Guidelines for Academic Teaching and Research Laboratories

Academic Unit	Research Allowance ASF	Instructional Allowance Station Service Factor		
		ASF	ASF	ASF/WSCH
Institute of Technology				
Aero. engineering mec.	400	100	44	9.0
Chemical engr. & mat. sci.	350	60	36	6.0
Chemistry	350	54	18	4.5
Civil & mineral. engr.	450	100	44	9.0
Computer science	40	60	0	1.5

Table 2.6-3. (Continued)

Academic Unit	Research Allowance ASF	Instructional Allowance Station Service Factor		
		ASF	ASF	ASF/WSCH
Earth sci. geol. & geophy.	350	40	8	3.0
Electrical engineering	300	60	36	6.0
Mechanical engineering	300	100	28	8.0
Physics & astro. school	350	50	14	4.0
Medical School				
Anatomy	220	40	24	4.0
Anesthesiology	220	40	24	4.0
Biochemistry	220	40	24	4.0
Dermatology	220	40	24	4.0
Lab medicine & path.	220	40	24	4.0
Medicine	220	40	24	4.0
Microbiology	220	32	32	4.0
Neurology	220	40	24	4.0
Neurosurgery	220	40	24	4.0
Obstetrics and gynecology	220	40	24	4.0
Ophthalmology	220	40	24	4.0
Orthopedic surgery	220	40	24	4.0
Otolaryngology	220	40	24	4.0
Pediatrics	220	40	24	4.0
Pharmacology	220	40	24	4.0
Physical med. & rehab.	220	40	24	4.0
Physiology	220	40	24	4.0
Psychiatry	220	40	24	4.0
Radiology	220	40	24	4.0
Surgery	220	40	24	4.0
Therapeutic radiology	220	40	24	4.0
Urological surgery	220	40	24	4.0
School of Dentistry	220	50	14	4.0
School of Pharmacy	220	40	24	4.0
College of Agriculture				
Agric. & applied econ.	20	15	1	1.0
Agricultural engineering	300	80	16	6.0
Agronomy & plant genetics	220	55	9	4.0
Animal science	300	80	16	6.0
Ent. fish wildlife	220	40	8	3.0
Food sci. & nutrition	300	70	10	5.0
Horticultural science	300	55	9	4.0
Plant pathology	220	55	9	4.0
Soil science	220	55	9	4.0
Col. of Biological Sci.				
Biochemistry	300	55	9	4.0
Botany	300	55	9	4.0
Ecology & behav. biology	300	55	9	4.0
General biology program	220	25	7	2.0
Genetics & cell biology	300	40	8	3.0
College of Forestry				
Forest products	300	55	9	4.0
Forest resources	40	25	7	2.0
College of Veterinary Med				
Biology	300	40	8	3.0
Large animal clin. sci.	450	80	16	6.0
Pathobiology	300	55	9	4.0
Small animal clin. sci.	300	70	10	5.0

Source: Minnesota Facilities Model, University of Minnesota, July 1982.

Table 2.6-4. The Ohio State University Academic Teaching Laboratories Student Station Modules

	NASF		NASF
Agriculture		Engineering	
Ag. economics	30	Civil/construction	75
Agricultural education	40	City and regional planning	60
Agricultural engineering	125	Computer and information science	40
Agronomy	65	Electrical/electronics	90
Animal sciences	60	Engineering graphics	50
Dairy science	60	Engineering mechanics	90
Food science	60	Industrial and system engineering	100
Horticulture	50	Landscape architecture	60
Natural resources	35	Mechanical engineering	100
Plant pathology	50	Metallurgical engineering	90
Poultry science	60	Mining engineering	100
		Welding engineering	170
Biological Sciences			
Biochemistry	65	Health Professions (except Medicine)	
Botany	60	Dentistry	60
Entomology	60	Nursing	60
General biology	60	Optometry	70
Microbiology	60	Pharmacy	65
Molecular genetics	60	Veterinary medicine	60
Zoology	60		
		Math and Physical Sciences	
Engineering		Astronomy	50
Aeronautical & astronautical		Chemistry	75
engineering	100	Geodetic science	70
Architecture	60	Geology and mineralogy	60
Aviation	80	Mathematics	30
Ceramic engineering	100	Physics	75
Chemical engineering	90	Statistics	30

Source: Courtesy of the Ohio State University Office of Campus Planning and Space Utilization March, 1989.

Table 2.6-5. Space Guidelines for Academic Teaching Laboratories

CLASS LABORATORY ASSIGNABLE SQ FT PER STATION CRITERIA—ACADEMIC CURRICULA

(1)	(2)	(3)	(4)	(5)
HEGIS Discipline			Assignable Sq Ft per Student Station	
Code	Specialty	Course Levels	Excluding Services	Including Services
0100	AGRICULTURE AND NATURAL RESOURCES			
0101	General	Lower	30–40	50–60
0102	Agronomy, crops	Lower	30–40	50–60
		Upper	40–50	60–80
0103	Soil science	Lower	30–40	50–60
		Upper	40–50	60–80
0104	Animal science			
	Chemical analyses	Lower	30–40	60–80
	Animal practices	Lower	40–80	100–160
		Upper	50–60	100–160
0105	Dairy science			
	Chemical analyses	Lower	30–40	60–80
	Animal practices	Lower	40–80	100–160
		Upper	50–60	100–160

Table 2.6-5. (Continued)

CLASS LABORATORY ASSIGNABLE SQ FT PER STATION CRITERIA—ACADEMIC CURRICULA

(1)	(2)	(3)	(4)	(5)
	HEGIS Discipline		Assignable Sq Ft per Student Station	
Code	Specialty	Course Levels	Excluding Services	Including Services
0106	Poultry science	Lower	30–40	50–60
		Upper	40–50	60–80
0107	Fish, game, wildlife	Lower	30–40	50–60
		Upper	40–50	60–80
0108	Horticulture	Lower	30–40	50–60
		Upper	40–50	60–80
0109	Ornamental horticulture	Lower	30–40	50–60
		Upper	40–50	60–70
0110	Agriculture and farm management	All	30–40	50–60
0111	Agricultural economics	All	20–30	25–35
0112	Agricultural business	All	20–30	25–40
0113	Food science and technology	Lower	30–50	50–65
		Upper	50–60	60–80
0114	Forestry	Lower	30–40	50–60
		Upper	40–50	60–70
0400	BIOLOGICAL SCIENCES			
0401	Biology, general	Lower	30–40	45–55
0402	Botany, general	Lower	30–40	45–55
		Upper	40–60	50–70
0403	Bacteriology	Lower	30–40	50–70
		Upper	40–60	60–90
0404	Plant pathology	Lower	30–40	45–55
		Upper	40–60	50–70
0405	Plant pharmacology	Lower	30–40	45–55
		Upper	40–60	50–70
0406	Plant physiology	Lower	30–40	45–55
		Upper	40–60	50–70
0407	Zoology, general	Lower	30–40	50–70
		Upper	40–60	60–80
0408	Pathology	Lower	30–40	50–70
		Upper	40–60	60–80
0409	Pharmacology	Lower	30–40	40–50
		Upper	40–60	70–90
0410	Physiology	Lower	30–40	50–70
		Upper	40–60	70–90
0411	Microbiology	Lower	30–40	50–70
		Upper	40–60	60–80
0412	Anatomy			
	Developmental	Lower	30–40	45–55
	Gross	Lower	50–60	60–80
		Upper	40–60	60–80
0413	Histology	Lower	30–40	45–55
		Upper	40–60	60–80
0414	Biochemistry	Lower	40–50	55–65
		Upper	50–60	60–80
0415	Biophysics	Lower	40–50	55–65
		Upper	50–60	60–80
0416	Molecular biology	Lower	30–40	50–70
		Upper	40–60	60–80
0417	Cell biology	Lower	30–40	50–70
		Upper	40–60	60–80

Table 2.6-5. (Continued)

CLASS LABORATORY ASSIGNABLE SQ FT PER STATION CRITERIA—ACADEMIC CURRICULA

(1)	(2)	(3)	(4)	(5)
	HEGIS Discipline		Assignable Sq Ft per Student Station	
Code	Specialty	Course Levels	Excluding Services	Including Services
0418	Marine biology	Lower	30–50	60–100
		Upper	40–70	70–150
0419	Biometrics and biostatistics	All	25–30	30–35
0420	Ecology	Lower	30–40	45–55
		Upper	40–60	60–80
0421	Entomology	Lower	30–40	45–55
		Upper	40–60	60–80
0422	Genetics	Lower	30–40	45–55
		Upper	40–60	60–80
0423	Radiobiology	Lower	30–40	45–55
		Upper	40–60	60–80
0424	Nutrition	Lower	40–50	55–65
		Upper	50–60	60–80
0425	Neurosciences	Lower	30–40	50–70
		Upper	40–60	70–90
0426	Toxicology	Lower	30–40	45–55
		Upper	40–60	50–70
0427	Embryology	Lower	30–40	50–70
		Upper	40–60	60–80
0900	ENGINEERING			
0901	General	All	40–70	90–120
0902	Aerospace, aeronautical, and astronautical	All	100–150	130–180
0903	Agricultural engineering			
	Electrical	All	40–50	55–65
	Soil and water	All	50–60	70–80
	Structural	All	80–100	100–120
	Metal and shop	All	100–120	120–140
	Machinery and equipment	All	100–150	130–180
0905	Bioengineering and biomedical	All	40–60	60–80
0906	Chemical			
	Instrumentation	All	30–40	40–50
	Physical	All	60–100	70–110
	Chemical processes	All	100–150	120–170
	Unit operations	All	100–150	150–200
0907	Petroleum	All	100–150	150–200
0908	Civil, construction, and transportation			
	Soils, photogrammetry	All	50–60	70–80
	Hydraulics, concrete	All	80–100	100–120
	Strength of materials	All	100–150	130–180
0909	Electrical, electronics, and communications			
	Measurements, electronics	All	40–50	55–65
	Communications			
	Circuits	All	60–70	80–90
	Machines, power	All	80–100	100–120
0910	Mechanical			
	Machine shop	All	50–60	65–75
	Other	All	100–150	150–200

Table 2.6-5. (Continued)

CLASS LABORATORY ASSIGNABLE SQ FT PER STATION CRITERIA—ACADEMIC CURRICULA

(1)	(2)	(3)	(4)	(5)
			Assignable Sq Ft per Student Station	
HEGIS Discipline		Course Levels	Excluding Services	Including Services
Code	Specialty			
0911	Geological			
	Unit operations	All	100–150	150–200
	Other	All	40–60	50–80
0912	Geophysical			
	Prospecting and well logging	All	80–100	100–120
	Other	All	40–60	50–80
0913	Industrial	All	100–150	120–170
0914	Metallurgical			
	Microscopy	All	40–50	55–65
	Physical	All	70–80	90–100
	Spectrography	All	100–150	150–200
0915	Materials	All	100–150	130–150
0916	Ceramic	All	60–80	100–150
0917	Textile	All	60–100	100–150
0918	Mining and minerals	All	100–150	150–200
0919	Engineering physics	Lower	30–40	45–55
		Upper	40–60	60–80
0920	Nuclear	All	100–150	150–200
0921	Engineering mechanics	All	100–150	150–200
0922	Environmental and sanitary	All	80–100	100–150
0923	Naval architecture and marine	All	100–150	150–200
0924	Ocean	All	100–150	150–200
0925	Technologies	All	75–150	130–180
1900	PHYSICAL SCIENCES			
1901	General	Lower	30–40	40–50
		Upper	40–60	50–80
1902	Physics	Lower	30–40	40–50
		Upper	40–60	50–80
1903	Molecular physics	All	40–50	55–65
1904	Nuclear physics	All	50–60	70–80
1905	Chemistry, general	All	30–40	45–55
1906	Inorganic chemistry	All	40–50	55–65
1907	Organic chemistry	All	50–60	70–80
1908	Physical chemistry	All	50–60	70–80
1909	Analytical chemistry	All	40–50	55–65
1910	Pharmaceutical chemistry	All	40–50	55–65
1911	Astronomy	Lower	25–40	30–50
		Upper	40–60	60–80
1912	Astrophysics	All	40–60	70–80
1913	Atmospheric sciences and meteorology	Lower	30–40	45–55
		Upper	40–60	70–80
1914	Geology	Lower	30–40	40–50
		Upper	40–60	50–70
1915	Geochemistry	All	40–60	50–70
1916	Geophysics and seismology	All	40–60	50–70

Table 2.6-5. (Continued)

CLASS LABORATORY ASSIGNABLE SQ FT PER STATION CRITERIA—ACADEMIC CURRICULA

(1)	(2)	(3)	(4)	(5)
	HEGIS Discipline		Assignable Sq Ft per Student Station	
Code	Specialty	Course Levels	Excluding Services	Including Services
1917	Earth sciences, general	Lower	30–40	40–50
		Upper	40–60	50–70
1918	Paleontology	All	40–50	50–60
1919	Oceanography	Lower	30–50	60–100
		Upper	40–70	70–150
1920	Metallurgy	Lower	30–40	40–50
		Upper	40–60	50–70

The above table guidelines were originally founded upon a similar table in Guideline Procedure and Criteria for Campus Development and Capital Outlay Planning, prepared by the Association of State Institutions of Higher Education in cooperation with Taylor, Lieberfeld, and Heldman, Inc. (April 1964), Table 8-1. However, the authors and their consultants have extensively modified the table to follow the Taxonomy of Instructional Programs in Higher Education of the National Center for Educational Statistics. In addition, the unit floor area values and proportions of service space have been changed, both in the establishment of ranges and in the magnitudes of those ranges. The values reflect the judgment of the authors and consultants based on their experience and the review of many published space inventories and planning criteria documents.

Source: *Higher Education Facilities Planning and Management Manuals, Manual Two.* Boulder, CO: Western Interstate Commission on Higher Education (WICHE), 1971, pp. 127–133.

and biology teaching laboratories for the University of Arizona as prepared by Paulien & Associates.

Table 2.6-7 shows utilization for laboratory courses of the Chemistry and Ecology/ Evolutionary Biology Departments. The student count figures were actual enrollments for the semester in question, as was the number of sections. The average section size was calculated by dividing the student count by the number of sections. The weekly room hours were the actual hours per week each section met, and the weekly student hours were the weekly hours each section met times the enrollment for that course. For example:

Course	Student Count	Sections	Hours per Section
CHEM 102A	292	15	3

Student count (292) × hours per section (3) = weekly student hours (875)
Sections (15) × hours per section (3) = weekly room hours (45)

The balance of this table takes the square feet per weekly student hour factors resulting from each guideline's space and utilization factors for the particular subject matter being reviewed. A previous table in the Arizona study showed each course name, the square feet per station, and the square feet per weekly student hour calculations (Table 2.6-6). This table enabled the University of Arizona to see a range of square footage need for these courses. Table 2.6-8 shows the number of laboratory rooms that would be needed, utilizing the different hour per week assumptions of each of the guidelines.

The second issue dealt with space utilization. The utilization which is expected to be achieved has traditionally been assumed to be on the order of 20 hours per week of scheduled course laboratory time out of an assumed total possible day occupancy of 45 hours/week. This does not include setup and take-down time, but only the time when the students are specifically scheduled to be in the laboratory. It is the authors' belief that rooms serving multiple sections of under-

Table 2.6-6. Comparison of Five University Teaching Laboratory Space Guidelines

Dept. Name	Course Number	Course Title	Colorado Station Size W/O Svc	Colorado Station Size Inc Svc	Colorado Sq Ft/Wkly Stdnt Hour	Illinois Station Size W/O Svc	Illinois Station Size Inc Svc	Illinois Sq Ft/Wkly Stdnt Hour	Minnesota Station Size W/O Svc	Minnesota Station Size Inc Svc	Minnesota Sq Ft/Wkly Stdnt Hour	Ohio State Station Size W/O Svc	Ohio State Station Size Inc Svc	Ohio State Sq Ft/Wkly Stdnt Hour	WICHE Station Size W/O Svc	WICHE Station Size Inc Svc	WICHE Sq Ft/Wkly Stdnt Hour
Chemistry																	
CHEM	0102A	Gen Chem Lab	40	50	3.12	N/A	68	3.54	54	72	4.50	N/A	75	4.17	40	55	2.86
CHEM	0102B	Gen Chem Lab	40	50	3.12	N/A	68	3.54	54	72	4.50	N/A	75	4.17	40	55	2.86
CHEM	0104A	Fund Techn of Chem	40	50	3.12	N/A	68	3.54	54	72	4.50	N/A	75	4.17	40	55	2.86
CHEM	0104B	Fund Techn of Chem	40	50	3.12	N/A	68	3.54	54	72	4.50	N/A	75	4.17	40	55	2.86
CHEM	0105	Fund of Chem	40	50	3.12	N/A	68	3.54	54	72	4.50	N/A	75	4.17	40	55	2.86
CHEM	0243A	Organic Chem Lab	45	56	3.51	N/A	68	3.54	54	72	4.50	N/A	75	4.17	60	80	4.17
CHEM	0243B	Organic Chem Lab	45	56	3.51	N/A	68	3.54	54	72	4.50	N/A	75	4.17	60	80	4.17
CHEM	0245A	Organic Chem Lab	45	56	3.51	N/A	68	3.54	54	72	4.50	N/A	75	4.17	60	80	4.17
CHEM	0302	Sci Glassblowing	50	63	3.91	N/A	68	3.54	54	72	4.50	N/A	75	4.17	60	80	4.17
CHEM	0323	Prin Analysis I Lab	50	63	3.91	N/A	68	3.54	54	72	4.50	N/A	75	41.7	50	65	5.08
CHEM	0326	Analytical Chem Lab	50	63	3.91	N/A	68	3.54	54	72	4.50	N/A	75	4.17	50	65	5.08
CHEM	0400B	Chemical Meas Lab	50	63	3.91	N/A	68	3.54	54	72	4.50	N/A	75	4.17	50	65	5.08
CHEM	0412	Inorganic Prep	50	63	3.91	N/A	68	3.54	54	72	4.50	N/A	75	4.17	50	65	5.08
CHEM	0446	Organic Preparation	50	63	3.91	N/A	68	3.54	54	72	4.50	N/A	75	4.17	60	80	6.25
CHEM	0528X	Adv. Analytic. Inst.	60	75	4.69	N/A	68	3.54	54	72	4.50	N/A	75	4.17	50	65	5.08
Ecology and Evolutionary Biology																	
ECOL	0106	Environ Biology	35	43	2.71	N/A	50	2.60	25	32	2.00	N/A	60	3.33	40	55	2.86
ECOL	0107X	Concepts in Biology	35	43	2.71	N/A	50	2.60	25	32	2.00	N/A	60	3.33	40	55	2.86
ECOL	0130	Natural Hist of SW	35	43	2.71	N/A	50	2.60	25	32	2.00	N/A	60	3.33	40	55	2.86
ECOL	0159AL	Human Anat & Physio	60	74	4.65	N/A	50	2.60	55	64	4.00	N/A	60	3.33	60	80	4.17
ECOL	0181X	Life-Sci of Biology	35	43	2.71	N/A	50	2.60	25	32	2.00	N/A	60	3.33	40	55	2.86
ECOL	0260	Elem Plant Physio	45	56	3.51	N/A	50	2.60	55	64	4.00	N/A	60	3.33	40	55	2.86
ECOL	0302	Fund Ecology & Evol	35	43	2.71	N/A	50	2.60	55	64	4.00	N/A	60	3.33	60	80	6.25
ECOL	0320	Gen Genetics Majors	45	55	3.49	N/A	50	2.60	40	48	3.00	N/A	60	3.33	60	80	6.25
ECOL	0460	Plant Physiology	45	56	3.51	N/A	50	2.60	55	64	4.00	N/A	60	3.33	60	70	5.47
ECOL	0464AL	Human Physiology	60	74	4.65	N/A	50	2.60	55	64	4.00	N/A	60	3.33	60	80	4.17
ECOL	0468L	Comp. Phys. Lab	60	74	4.65	N/A	50	2.60	55	64	4.00	N/A	60	3.33	60	80	6.25
ECOL	0470	Plant Diver. & Evol	35	44	2.74	N/A	50	2.60	55	64	4.00	N/A	60	3.33	60	70	5.47

Note: Three of the guideline systems do not provide a separate per station figure. Their figure is for a student station including service space.

Source: Paulien & Associates. June, 1989.

Table 2.6-7. Comparison of Five University Teaching Laboratory Space Guidelines as Applied to NASF Per Weekly Student Hours for Chemistry and Biology Courses at the University of Arizona

Dept. Course Number	Student Count	Number of Sections	Average Section Size	Weekly Room Hours	Weekly Student Hours	Colorado Comm. On Higher Ed.		University of Illinois		University of Minnesota		Ohio State University		WICHE	
						NASF WSH	Guideline Sq Ft	NASF WSH	Guideline Sq Ft	NASF WSH	Guideline Sq Ft	NASF WSH	Guideline Sq Ft	NASF WSH	Guideline Sq Ft
Chemistry															
CHEM 102A	292	15	19.0	45	876	3.12	2,733	3.54	3,101	4.50	3,942	4.17	3,653	2.86	2,505
CHEM 102B	49	3	16.0	9	147	3.12	459	3.54	520	4.50	662	4.17	613	2.86	420
CHEM 104A	1,139	60	19.0	180	3,417	3.12	10,661	3.54	12,096	4.50	15,377	4.17	14,249	2.86	9,773
CHEM 104B	155	9	17.0	27	465	3.12	1,451	3.54	1,646	4.50	2,093	4.17	1,939	2.86	1,330
CHEM 105	46	3	15.0	18	276	3.12	861	3.54	977	4.50	1,242	4.17	1,151	2.86	789
CHEM 243A	275	16	17.0	48	825	3.51	2,896	3.54	2,921	4.50	3,713	4.17	3,440	4.17	3,440
CHEM 243B	99	5	20.0	15	297	3.51	1,042	3.54	1,051	4.50	1,337	4.17	1,238	4.17	1,238
CHEM 245A	78	5	16.0	25	390	3.51	1,369	3.54	1,381	4.50	1,755	4.17	1,626	4.17	1,626
CHEM 302	6	1	6.0	6	36	3.91	141	3.54	127	4.50	162	4.17	150	4.17	150
CHEM 323	87	6	15.0	18	261	3.91	1,021	3.54	924	4.50	1,175	4.17	1,088	5.08	1,326
CHEM 326	69	4	17.0	24	414	3.91	1,619	3.54	1,466	4.50	1,863	4.17	1,726	5.08	2,103
CHEM 400B	32	4	8.0	24	192	3.91	751	3.54	680	4.50	864	4.17	801	5.08	975
CHEM 412	7	1	7.0	9	63	3.91	246	3.54	223	4.50	284	4.17	263	5.08	320
CHEM 446	5	1	5.0	3	15	3.91	59	3.54	53	4.50	68	4.17	63	6.25	94
CHEM 528X	12	3	4.0	12	48	4.69	225	3.54	170	4.50	216	4.17	200	5.08	244
Subtotal	2,351	136		463	7,722		25,534		27,336		34,753		32,200		26,333
Ecology and Evolutionary Biology															
ECOL 106	124	6	21.0	18	372	2.71	1,008	2.60	967	2.00	744	3.33	1,239	2.86	1,064
ECOL 107X	102	4	26.0	12	306	2.71	829	2.60	796	2.00	612	3.33	1,019	2.86	875
ECOL 130	118	6	20.0	12	236	2.71	640	2.60	614	2.00	472	3.33	786	2.86	675
ECOL 159AL	358	17	21.0	51	1,074	4.65	4,994	2.60	2,792	4.00	4,296	3.33	3,576	4.17	4,479
ECOL 181X	41	2	21.0	6	123	2.71	333	2.60	320	2.00	246	3.33	410	2.86	352
ECOL 260	25	2	13.0	6	75	3.51	263	2.60	195	4.00	300	3.33	250	2.86	215
ECOL 302	37	2	19.0	6	111	2.71	301	2.60	289	4.00	444	3.33	370	6.25	694
ECOL 320	45	3	15.0	9	135	3.49	471	2.60	351	3.00	405	3.33	450	6.25	844
ECOL 460	10	1	10.0	3	30	3.51	105	2.60	78	4.00	120	3.33	100	5.47	164
ECOL 464AL	23	2	12.0	6	69	4.65	321	2.60	179	4.00	276	3.33	230	4.17	288
ECOL 468L	9	1	9.0	3	27	4.65	126	2.60	70	4.00	108	3.33	90	6.25	169
ECOL 470	24	1	24.0	2	48	2.74	132	2.60	125	4.00	192	3.33	160	5.47	263
Subtotal	916	47		134	2,606		9,523		6,776		8,215		8,680		10,082

Source: Paulien & Associates. June, 1989.

Table 2.6-8. Comparison of Five University Teaching Laboratory Space Guidelines to Arrive at the Number of Teaching Laboratories for Chemistry and Biology

Course Number	Target Year Weekly Room Hours	Colorado Comm. on Higher Ed. Hours per Week	Number of Labs Needed	University of Illinois Hours per Week	Number of Labs Needed	University of Minnesota Hours per Week	Number of Labs Needed	Ohio State University Hours per Week	Number of Labs Needed	WICHE Hours per Week	Number of Labs Needed
Chemistry											
CHEM 102A	51	20	2.6	24	2.1	20	2.6	22.5	2.3	24	2.1
CHEM 102B	9	20	0.5	24	0.4	20	0.5	22.5	0.4	24	0.4
CHEM 104A	198	20	9.9	24	8.3	20	9.9	22.5	8.8	24	8.3
CHEM 104B	27	20	1.4	24	1.1	20	1.4	22.5	1.2	24	1.1
CHEM 105	18	20	0.9	24	0.8	20	0.9	22.5	0.8	24	0.8
CHEM 243A	48	20	2.4	24	2.0	20	2.4	22.5	2.1	24	2.0
CHEM 243B	18	20	0.9	24	0.8	20	0.9	22.5	0.8	24	0.8
CHEM 245A	25	20	1.3	24	1.0	20	1.3	22.5	1.1	24	1.0
CHEM 302	6	20	0.3	24	0.3	20	0.3	22.5	0.3	16	0.4
CHEM 323	18	20	0.9	24	0.8	20	0.9	22.5	0.8	16	1.1
CHEM 326	24	20	1.2	24	1.0	20	1.2	22.5	1.1	16	1.5
CHEM 400B	24	20	1.2	24	1.0	20	1.2	22.5	1.1	16	1.5
CHEM 412	9	9	1.0	9	1.0	9	1.0	9.0	1.0	9	1.0
CHEM 446	3	3	1.0	3	1.0	3	1.0	3.0	1.0	3	1.0
CHEM 528X	12	12	1.0	12	1.0	12	1.0	12.0	1.0	12	1.0
Subtotal	490		26.5		22.6		26.5		23.8		24.0
Ecology and Evolutionary Biology											
ECOL 106	24	20	1.2	24	1.0	20	1.2	22.5	1.1	24	1.0
ECOL 107X	18	20	0.9	24	0.8	20	0.9	22.5	0.8	24	0.8
ECOL 130	14	20	0.7	24	0.6	20	0.7	22.5	0.6	24	0.6
ECOL 159AL	63	20	3.2	24	2.6	20	3.2	22.5	2.8	24	2.6
ECOL 181X	9	20	0.5	24	0.4	20	0.5	22.5	0.4	24	0.4
ECOL 260	6	20	0.3	24	0.3	20	0.3	22.5	0.3	24	0.3
ECOL 302	9	20	0.5	24	0.4	20	0.5	22.5	0.4	16	0.6
ECOL 320	9	20	0.5	24	0.4	20	0.5	22.5	0.4	16	0.6
ECOL 460	3	20	0.2	24	0.1	20	0.2	22.5	0.1	16	0.2
ECOL 464AL	6	20	0.3	24	0.3	20	0.3	22.5	0.3	16	0.4
ECOL 468L	3	20	0.2	24	0.1	20	0.2	22.5	0.1	16	0.2
ECOL 470	4	20	0.2	24	0.2	20	0.2	22.5	0.2	16	0.3
Subtotal	168		8.7		7.2		8.7		7.5		8.0

Source: Paulien & Associates. June, 1989.

graduate courses, particularly beginning-level courses, can achieve significantly higher utilization than 20 hours per week. On the other hand, upper-division and graduate-level courses often need a dedicated laboratory during the semester in which they are being taught because of the amount of work and time involved in setting up experiments. Universities in states with state guidelines must attempt to meet the average utilization factor. Their ability to do so may well depend on whether they have a large pool of lower-division students taking beginning science and engineering courses, and on the extent to which their upper-division and graduate level instruction is fully developed and therefore includes a greater number of courses which need dedicated labs. In the authors' experience, it is very difficult for most institutions to meet the campuswide target level of 20 hours/week.

A survey of 25 states conducted by the California Post-secondary Education Commission revealed the following utilization factors (assuming a maximum occupancy of 45 hours/week):

Teaching labs
  Natural sciences—50 to 80 NASF/station
  Engineering—90 to 130 NASF/station
  Utilization—20 hours/week (range, 16 to 30)
  Station occupancy—80% (range, 70 to 85%)
For lower-division teaching laboratories
  Recommended usage 56% of 45 hours/week = 25 hours/week
  Stations occupied—85%
For upper-division teaching laboratories
  Recommended usage 44% of 45 hours/week = 20 hours/week
Stations occupied—80%

The study prepared by Paulien & Associates for the University of Arizona proposed the following planning criteria for teaching laboratories in chemistry and biology:

For chemistry and biological sciences
  40 to 60 NASF/station plus service space = 50 to 80 NASF

Assuming 27 hours/week in the lower division when multiple sections of only one or two courses are taught in one lab
Assuming 20 hours/week in the upper division and the graduate and lower-level divisions without multiple sections, assuming dedicated labs for graduate courses when determined necessary by a departmental analysis
Station occupancy—80%
For upper-division biological sciences
  25 to 60 NASF/station plus service = 32 to 80 NASF
Assuming 27 hours/week in the lower division when multiple sections of only one or two courses are taught in one lab
Assuming 20 hours/week in the upper division and the graduate and lower-level divisions without multiple sections, assuming dedicated labs for graduate courses when determined necessary
Station occupancy = 80%

For institutions without large numbers of multiple sections of one course, 20 hours/week is a reasonable target. Some upper-division and graduate courses need a laboratory dedicated to a single course. This means that some laboratories will be utilized for only 3 or 6 hours/week. The academic unit should be challenged to justify the need for dedicated labs. Every effort should be taken to minimize their number.

As noted, the expectation is that laboratories be filled to 80% of student station capacity during the scheduled hours of laboratory work. This means that if a lab has 20 student stations, it is expected that an average of 16 students will be enrolled in the courses in that laboratory. This is a higher expectation level than the one utilized for classrooms, where the guideline percentage of student occupancy is usually 60 to 67%. The reason is that laboratories have more specialized equipment and are more expensive to construct and operate. Funding bodies stress that departments should make every effort to achieve good station use.

Another challenge during the planning phase is to identify the maximum number of students a department wants to teach and to determine the average laboratory class sizes it can handle. If those average sizes are considerably less than 80% of the maximum size, further analysis of the academic methodology should be undertaken to determine if the new laboratories should be built with fewer student stations or if adjustments can be made in the sectioning practices of the department to achieve better station utilization.

A third method of calculating space needs that is particularly useful in planning whole new institutions is to develop a square feet per full time equivalent (FTE) student factor for each major type of space. The University of California utilized this approach when it was developing a number of new campuses in the 1950s and 1960s. Various models are available, but they are normally not utilized for planning a laboratory building. Their use is usually limited to determining campuswide square foot needs. Therefore, they are not dealt with further in this section.

Components of teaching laboratory space guidelines. Having discussed the elements which make up a teaching laboratory guideline, we will now give an example of how these are combined to produce a figure that will be useful in facilities planning.

Example: Assume a utilization of 20 hours/week at 80% and a student station size of 50 NASF.

That is 20 × 80% = 16 expected average hours/week

$$\frac{50}{16} = 3.13 \text{ NASF per actual weekly student}$$

contact hour

That figure can now be utilized to project square footage needs for the part of the instructional program for which that guideline is appropriate.

The guideline can be applied either on a course-by-course or a department-by-department basis. Both methods have certain bene-

fits. Utilizing the course-by-course approach forces the department involved to evaluate its section size practices, may produce better utilization of facilities, and may help the department assign the faculty more efficiently and effectively by carefully analyzing the possible changes in teaching lab size allowed by new facilities. In a course-by-course analysis, the course hours per week are recorded and multiplied by the number of students enrolled in the course. Therefore,

Course hours per week ×
student enrollment =
weekly student hours

Example: Assume that the course has 20 students enrolled and requires 3 hours/week of laboratory work. The subject is one for which the guideline suggests 3.13 NASF per weekly student contact hour.

20 × 3 = 60 weekly student contact hours × 3.13 NASF per student contact hour = 188 NASF for the laboratory space

The results from other courses for which that guideline is appropriate will be added to this number to produce the total square footage need for this type of laboratory instruction. It will then be compared to the actual need for laboratories.

A word of caution: This use of these guidelines produces total amounts of space. It is not a reliable guide to determine the correct size of an individual lab. Individual lab sizing must be done utilizing the square feet per student per station guideline and the desired number of stations for an individual laboratory. This number should be tested against the guidelines, as shown in Table 2.6-7. In this instance, the author applied six different space guidelines to the space program of a chemistry lab and a biology department at the University of Arizona. The student count data, the number of sections, the average section size, the weekly room hours and the weekly student hours are all shown. The weekly student hours were multiplied by the assignable square feet per weekly student hour factors of each guideline. These were totaled and compared. This allowed the institution to see a range of results from comparable institutions, since it did not have state governing board guidelines to meet.

A second type of analysis, shown in Table 2.6-8, took the weekly room hours and the laboratory utilization targets and determined how many laboratories would be needed for each course and the total for each department. Again, based on several guidelines, this showed a range of results which was useful to the institution in making a final decision about the most appropriate amount of space and number of laboratories for those departments.

In those instances where planning involves a larger number of departments, it is preferable to utilize guidelines which have a single space factor for each department. These, by their nature, are average guidelines. Thus, there is a somewhat greater likelihood that they will overstate the need if a department's course activity is heavily weighted toward the lower division or understate the need if a department's course activity is heavily oriented toward graduate work. This is because analysts lose the sensitivity of the detailed guideline, which often provides more space or expects lower utilization for the same number of graduate hours. However, these guidelines tend to be a good tool in quickly approximating space needs without extensive, detailed calculations. Table 2.6-9 shows departmental laboratory station size and square feet per weekly student hour factors which the author recommended to a midwestern university following the application of a number of different guidelines to campuses in that system. This guideline analysis assumed the 20-hour utilization rate at 80% of station occupancy. Examples of how these data are applied were given earlier.

To apply these departmental guidelines, it is necessary that the weekly student hours for each laboratory course for the department be established in order to provide baseline data. Estimated weekly student hours may be used if a future target year analysis is intended. Normally this information can

Table 2.6-9. Academic Teaching Laboratory Space Guidelines By Student Station (NASF) and Square Feet Per Weekly Student Hour*

Academic Colleges, Schools and Departments	Student Station (NASF)	Sq Ft per Weekly Student Hour
Agriculture	65	4.06
Arts and Science		
Anthropology	45	2.81
Art History & Archaeology	40	2.50
Biology	60	3.75
Chemistry	80	5.00
Computer Science	40	2.50
Geography	45	2.81
Geology	65	4.06
Physics	80	5.00
Psychology	45	2.81
Dentistry	50	3.13
Education	48	3.00
Health & Physical Education	150	9.38
Engineering	90	5.63
Home Economics	55	3.44
Medicine	80	5.00
Mines & Metallurgy	75	4.69
Nursing	60	3.75
Optometry	80	5.00
Pharmacy	75	4.69

*Assumes 20 hours/week utilization at 80% station occupancy.
Source: Paulien & Associates. June 1989.

be acquired from the institutional research office or registrar's office. In some cases, only raw enrollment data will be available; these must be multiplied by the weekly laboratory course hours. The guideline application process is the same as for the course-by-course basis, except that the total number of weekly student hours are multiplied by the square feet per weekly student hour factor shown for that department.

Example: Assuming chemistry teaching laboratories and a need to accommodate 1,000 weekly student hours:
Per Table 2.6-9, a student station is 80 NASF or 5 sq ft per weekly student hour, i.e., 1,000 weekly student hours × 5 sq ft per weekly student hour = 5,000 NASF

Calculating service space. We have discussed guidelines which include a service space factor. In most cases, this factor is based on a percentage of service space to primary laboratory space. It can range from no service space to as much as 230% service space in fields such as atmospheric science, where wind tunnels and other large support facilities may be needed for the laboratories. If an institution has a facilities space inventory, it may be possible to calculate the service space factors. For example, a department may have 12,000 square feet of teaching lab space and 1,000 square feet of teaching lab service such as preparation area and teaching aids storage. The service space is 1,000 square feet divided by 12,000 square feet, or 8%. Caution is needed in converting an existing space result into a guideline. The current space may be totally inadequate or it may be underused. Finding a service space guideline from a related field, or evaluating the existing service space percentage and adjusting it based on the results of the evaluation, are preferable to accepting the existing percentage as a projection tool.

An alternative approach to calculating the amount of service space is to list the typical needs for the type of teaching activity. This information should be provided by the department chair or key faculty and includes the service space needs, including the dimensions of major pieces of equipment and the room dimensions, if critical.

The author has found that the percentage method is accurate enough in most cases at the early planning stage. It should, as noted above, be verified by a detailed analysis of needs during the programming phase.

Specialized lab support facilities. The service space includes the equipment and services that are immediately associated with a laboratory. None of the guideline systems consider animal quarters or greenhouses as service space. These are called "support space." An additional analysis must be made based on the types of animals to be housed in animal quarters and the need for support space such as storage for food and bedding, cage-washing equipment, staff space and procedural space.

For greenhouse space, identifying the needs is based on the types of instructional activity. One of the best sets of teaching greenhouses with which the authors are familiar is the one at Iowa State University. Their College of Agriculture has four greenhouses and a headhouse directly attached to its Agronomy Building. Additional greenhouses serve the horticulture department courses. The agronomy greenhouses are the following:

- Introductory Crop Science, 30 × 40 ft = 1,200 sq ft
- Grain and Forage, 30 × 40 ft = 1,200 sq ft
- World Crops, 20 × 40 ft = 800 sq ft
- Wheat Science/Crop Physiology, 20 × 40 ft = 800 sq ft
- Headhouse, 20 × 40 ft = 800 sq ft

This set of greenhouses provides the variety needed to demonstrate plant materials to introductory crop science students. The introductory crop science greenhouse is split between sand benches, benches with mesh bottoms for pots and soil beds. Soil beds were provided under about one-half of the bench areas to add flexibility to the room. Two hundred students per semester utilize this space to observe experiments as part of a self-paced auto/tutorial approach to this course. Students reach a certain point on the audiotape, stop and go to the greenhouse to observe an experiment.

The grain and forage laboratory provides greenhouse space for a sophomore course taught in conventional laboratory sections. The greenhouse is directly attached to the laboratory. The work in this course consists of both materials for demonstration and actual student experiments where plants are grown. Approximately 100 students per semester are served by this greenhouse.

The world crops greenhouse has one area where the floor is excavated and the ceiling is raised to provide for tall plants such as banana, coffee and sugar cane. This greenhouse is for observation only, and grows a number of crops not normally grown in the United States which need environments quite different from that found in Iowa. The final greenhouse is a weed science/crop physiology greenhouse where various weed plants are grown and physiology students measure leaf expansion and other growth factors.

Adjacent headhouse space is very important. It includes ovens for drying plant materials and storing various fertilizers, silica, and other materials that are needed in the greenhouse itself. Some refrigeration is desirable, as are growth chambers to allow experiments where very tight control of variables is necessary. Growth chambers provide complete light control and heat control.

Instructional greenhouse needs vary widely by program mix and enrollment.

For research greenhouse needs, a Paulien & Associates study with the University of Missouri College of Agriculture resulted in identifying corn genetics and wheat genetics as areas needing more greenhouse space than most other types of agricultural research. This study suggested that 2,500 sq ft per principal investigator be provided for those two areas and that 500 sq ft be provided for all other types of agricultural research. This is a broad-based planning guideline, and individual judgment should be utilized in analyzing the needs for a particular area.

The authors have found that headhouse space for research greenhouses should normally be provided at about 25% of greenhouse space. Some portions may have soil beds or benches dedicated to teaching laboratory courses, while other portions of a greenhouse or other greenhouses are utilized for research.

At most universities, both animal quarters and greenhouses have research as their primary mission, and the housing of animals for teaching laboratory activities is part of the total animal care program.

Self-paced instruction laboratories (auto/tutorial). More and more laboratory activity is self-paced, using computer terminals and/or audiovisual equipment to guide a student through the course material. The laboratory guidelines cannot be applied in the traditional way because there are no scheduled weekly student hours. If the student is expected to spend 3 hours/week in the lab, multiplying the number of students enrolled by 3 hours will produce an imputed weekly student hour figure for that course. Particularly in community colleges where many courses are self-paced, the college must keep accurate records of the use of facilities. Accurate data are necessary in order to arrive at space size. Such detailed record keeping is not common in a 4-year college or university. If data are not available, using the expected utilization for closely related standard teaching laboratory sections would be a reasonable assumption for self-paced course student use.

Knowing how many student hours the laboratory may be occupied is not enough. It is necessary to know how many hours the laboratory is accessible 24 hours/day and 7 days/week or less. In addition to safety considerations, a self-paced facility usually needs a student assistant to check out materials, deal with problems in operating equipment and, in some cases, deal with questions from students.

Once the assumed available hours have been determined, an analysis of the percentage of station use should be made. Since most facilities of this type will be available after normal hours, room utilization rates as high as 48 hours/week may be achievable. The authors recommend that the percentage of station use for the total hours that the facility is open should exceed 75%. The reason is that there will be certain prime hours when there is a heavy demand, and the facility will be 100% occupied. At a higher use rate, the turnaway rate will make student compliance with course requirements difficult and may discourage less committed students. For those courses where the auto/tutorial experience utilizes audiotape, videotape, and perhaps slides, a student station in the range of 30 to 35 sq ft is usually sufficient. The electronic equipment is usually built into a corral-like space so that freestanding equipment is not stolen. If the auto/tutorial work utilizes computer terminals or personal computers, 25 to 40 sq ft per student is usually sufficient, depending on the amount of peripheral hardware such as printers and plotters. If the self-paced instruction involves regular science laboratories, the guidelines shown in Tables for the appropriate subject matter should be utilized.

Academic Research Laboratories

Space guidelines for academic research laboratories vary far more than those for teaching laboratories. When several different research laboratory guidelines are applied to a specific program, it is not unusual for one guideline to provide two or three times as much space as another. Those developed by major universities usually provide more space than those developed by statewide governing or coordinating boards. Therefore, the planning official's task in evaluating a guideline system becomes even more critical.

Alternative methods of determining space needs. Several methods are used to determine space needs for research. The first method is to calculate the NASF per principal investigator. This method makes assumptions about the *average* team size and the amount of space that is needed to conduct research in a particular department or subject *field* for the average principal investigator. The words "average" and "field" must be stressed because, in any situation, providing the same amount of space to all researchers will not produce desirable results. Some researchers will have programs with large budgets, which are equipment intensive or with a large staff, while others will be working with minimal outside funding and employ a very small team or only the principal investigator. Many of the data available are based on actual facilities and are therefore more reliable.

A second method is based on space per individual research function. Some of these guideline systems list one space size for a faculty member and other sizes for professional scientific staff, such as postdoctoral fellows, research associates, visiting scientists, laboratory technicians and graduate students.

A third method is based on the equivalent linear feet (ELF) of bench and equipment multiplied by a factor to arrive at the number of NASF needed and the space to provide access. To this number is added a percentage for access to the space.

A fourth method is based on a ratio of "soft" and "hard" spaces. This method is proposed to check the numbers arrived at by other means and to solicit a response and a justification from users if the numbers are substantially out of line in either direction (too many offices or too many labs). Over time, as experience is gained, this method can become a valuable check.

A fifth method is based on the project funds generated. This method provides an established amount of square footage for each significant increment of grant support—for example, 300 assignable square feet of wet research space for each $25,000 of grant support and 300 assignable square feet of dry research support for each $100,000 of departmental contracts and grant contracts acquired during the previous year. This analysis was developed by the University of Texas Health Science Center in San Antonio.

Each of these approaches will now be described in more detail.

Research space guidelines by principal investigator. This approach is particularly useful for a campuswide analysis. Certain assumptions must be made and agreed on. Typically, the space is per faculty member and therefore can be readily applied with available data. Table 2.6-10 is an excerpt from guidelines that Paulien & Associates developed for the University of Missouri at Columbia in cooperation with Thomas R. Mason of MIRA, Inc. These guidelines should be reviewed if applied at another institution. The average research team size for this application is eight people. The concept can be adjusted for larger or smaller teams. Table 2.6-10 shows the types of research and the

Table 2.6-10. Research Laboratory Unit Floor Area Per Faculty

Staff Category	Staff Number	Biologic	Chemical Analysis	Field Support	Electronic	Heavy Equip.	Info. Analy.	Small Health Science
			Model Research Lab Unit (NSF)					
Faculty rank	1	240	280	120	200	300	80	80
Professional	1	120	140	80	100	200	60	60
Technical	1	60	80	60	80	100	40	40
Support staff	0.50–1	60	60	60	60	60	60	60
Graduate assistants	2	120	160	120	160	200	80	80
Student assistants	2	80	80	80	80	80	40	40
Primary lab model	8	680	800	520	680	940	360	360
Research service ratio		0.70	0.40	0.30	0.40	0.50	0.10	0.10
Service area ASF		480	320	160	270	470	40	40
Average per faculty research		1,160	1,120	680	950	1,410	400	400

Source: University of Missouri–Columbia by Paulien & Associates; MIRA Inc., 1984.

amount of space required for each staff category occupying the research space. In addition to the primary lab space, it makes an assumption based on the authors' experience of how much research service space is needed, on the average, per faculty researcher for each major type of research. The research service ratio is the percentage of service space expected to be needed to support a given amount of primary space in a given discipline. The Colorado Commission on Higher Education Guidelines utilize this concept.

This information is noted in Table 2.6-11 and deemed to be the most appropriate faculty team research space unit for each academic discipline. It produces a research space per FTE faculty member for each discipline. For example, if there are 30 FTE faculty in chemistry, that figure is multiplied by the research space per FTE faculty, which is 1,120 sq ft. This establishes a research space need of 30 × 1,120 = 33,600 NASF for research for the Chemistry Department.

A recent survey by The NBBJ Group of six universities gave an average of 1,206 NASF/faculty research space for arts and sciences and 1,281 NASF/faculty research space for engineering. The available space of 1,068 and 844 sq feet, respectively, at the

University of Washington was considered inadequate (see Tables 2.6-12 and 2.6-13). Again, as noted earlier, this does not suggest that every faculty member should be given the same amount of space, but it does indi-

Table 2.6-11. Academic Divisions Research Space Per FTE Faculty

Academic Colleges, Schools and Departments	Research Space per FTE/ Faculty Unit (NASF)
Agriculture	1,160
Arts and Sciences	
Anthropology	680
Art History & Archaeology	680
Biological Sciences	1,160
Chemistry	1,120
Computer Science	0
Geography	400
Geology	1,120
Geosciences	760
Physics	950
Psychology	780
Education	400
Health & Physical Education	1,160
Engineering	1,180
Home Economics	760
Medicine	1,160
Health-Related Professions	400
Nursing	400
Veterinary Medicine	1,160

Table 2.6-12. College of Arts and Sciences Research Space Comparison With Other Institutions (NASF/faculty)—University of Washington

	Total Department Space			Research Space		
	University of Washington		Competitive Institutions*	University of Washington		Competitive Institutions*
	NASF	NASF/ Faculty	NASF/ Faculty	NASF	NASF/ Faculty	NASF/ Faculty
Math sciences						
Computer sciences	19,900	830	2,300	9,900	400	900
Physical sciences						
Chemistry	106,300	2,360	3,800	62,800	1,400	2,200
Physics	73,000	1,460	2,050	50,000	1,000	1,050
Astronomy	11,700	1,170	1,825	3,500	350	400
Earth sciences						
Geology/geophysics	60,700	2,050	2,300	12,400	1,000	1,150
Atmospheric sciences	25,000	1,900	1,800	16,900	1,000	650
Biological sciences						
Biology+	29,000	—	—	5,000	—	—
Botany	58,900	3,050	3,500	32,200	1,690	1,500
Genetics	24,600	2,050	2,600	18,000	1,500	1,650
Zoology	46,600	1,550	2,400	38,100	1,270	1,350
Range		830– 3,050	1,800– 3,800		400– 1,690	650– 2,200
Average		1,824	2,508		1,068	1,206

*Represents average NASF/faculty for five institutions considered peers of the University of Washington: University of California, San Diego; University of California, Los Angeles; University of California, Berkeley; University of Michigan; and University of Illinois.

+Graduate faculty in biology are primarily from other departments. The program is not comparable to other programs; therefore, NASF/faculty ratios for evaluating space needs are not appropriate.

Source: The NBBJ Group, 1988.

cate that the total could be an initial planning target for that department.

Research space guidelines by individual research function. The Colorado Commission on Higher Education utilizes an approach which provides an amount of space per faculty member, professional and technician involved in the research program and a lesser amount of space for each graduate student (see Table 2.6-14). Therefore, if this guideline is being applied on a departmental basis, the total number of people in each of these two categories must be determined. Next, the subject field of the specific research is selected and the amount of space is calculated. Continuing the chemistry example:

Assuming 30 FTE faculty + 20 professionals & technicians + 100 graduate students

Table 2.6-14 gives 100 NASF/faculty, professional and technician and 75 NASF/graduate student

$(30 + 20) \times 110 =$ 5,500 NASF

100×75 $=$ 7,500 NASF

    Subtotal   13,000 NASF of primary space

Table 2.6-14 assigns a service space factor of 29%:

$13,000 \times 29\%$ $=$ 3,770 NASF

    Total   16,770 NASF research space

Table 2.6-13. College of Engineering Research Space Comparison with Other Institutions (NASF/faculty)—University of Washington.

	Total Department Space			Research Space		
	University of Washington		Competitive Institutions*	University of Washington		Competitive Institutions*
	NASF	NASF/ Faculty	NASF/ Faculty	NASF	NASF/ Faculty	NASF/ Faculty
Engineering						
Aero. & astronautics	34,000	2,200	2,200	23,000	1,000	1,150
Bioengineering	18,000	1,000	2,050	10,200	600	600
Chemical	34,000	2,300	3,250	21,600	1,450	2,200
Civil	65,800	1,600	2,250	37,700	900	1,200
Electrical	49,400	900	2,600	19,600	450	1,300
Materials science	25,800	1,500	2,600	14,100	800	1,500
Mechanical	64,700	1,850	2,100	26,400	750	1,000
Nuclear	10,700	1,300	2,300	3,700	800	1,300
Range		900 – 2,300	2,050 – 3,250		450 – 1,450	600 – 2,200
Average		1,581	2,419		844	1,281

*Represents average NASF/faculty for five institutions considered peers of the University of Washington: University of California, San Diego; University of California, Los Angeles; University of California, Berkeley; University of Michigan; and University of Illinois.

Source: The NBBJ Group, 1988.

Table 2.6-14. Academic Research Space Guidelines by Individual's Research Function

Subject Field	Primary Space NASF/Person		Service Space as a Percent of Primary Space
	Faculty, Professional and Technician	Graduate Student	
Agricultural sciences			
Agronomy	110	70	122
Animal husbandry	120	80	122
Dairy husbandry	110	70	122
Dairy manufacturing	120	80	120
Farm management	110	70	100
Horticulture	110	70	111
Ornamental horticulture	110	70	111
Poultry husbandry	110	70	233
Forestry and range management	100	60	100
Watershed management	110	70	100
Biological sciences			
Biological science	110	70	0
Biology, general	110	70	67
Botany	110	70	84
Zoology	110	70	74
Anatomy and histology	110	70	67
Bacteriology	110	70	67
Biochemistry	110	70	33
Biophysics	110	70	33
Entomology	110	70	100
Genetics	110	70	67

Table 2.6-14. (Continued)

Subject Field	Primary Space NASF/Person		Service Space as a Percent of Primary Space
	Faculty, Professional and Technician	Graduate Student	
Pathology	110	70	122
Plant Pathology	110	70	67
Physiology	120	80	67
Microbiology	110	70	67
Mathematical sciences			
Applied mathematics	20*	+	+
Computer science	20*	+	+
Mathematics	20*	+	+
Statistics	20*	+	+
Physical sciences			
Physical science, general	100	60	54
Astrophysics	110	75	54
Astrogeophysics	110	75	54
Atmospheric science	100	60	233
Chemistry	110	75	29
Geology	110	75	62
Physics	110	75	60
Engineering physics	110	75	54
Astronomy	110	75	54
Engineering sciences			
Agricultural	120	80	33
Architectural	90	60	33
Chemical	110	70	33
Civil	100	60	33
Electrical	100	60	33
Geological	100	60	33
Geophysical	100	60	33
Mechanical	100	60	33
Metallurgical	110	75	33
Mining	110	75	33
Petroleum	110	75	33
Petroleum refining	110	75	33
General, engineering science	100	60	33
Industrial	100	60	33
Social sciences			
Anthropology–archeology	110	70	233
Geography	100	60	233
Psychology	110	70	29
Health professions			
Dentistry	+	+	+
Medicine	+	+	+
Nursing	+	+	+
Pharmacy	110	70	100
Veterinary medicine	120	80	150
Occupational, physical, speech therapy	110	70	122
Premedicine, predentistry, prenursing	+	+	+

*This could be applied either as a supplement for research within offices or as separate departmental research room(s).

+Needs vary so widely that a guideline quantity cannot reasonably be established.

Source: Colorado Commission For Higher Education, July 1987.

This does not include office space for faculty, technicians and students.

The Colorado Commission on Higher Education makes it very clear that "room layout sketches accompanied by supporting documentation will supersede their guidelines in situations where the guidelines can be shown to be inappropriate."

For comparison of the data presented, let us assume one faculty member, with five technicians and four graduate students. Using Table 2.6-14:

Faculty 1 × 110	=	110
Technicians 5 × 110	=	550
Graduate student 4 × 75	=	300
Lab space subtotal		960 + (29% × 960) = 1,238 NASF
Faculty office		120
Technician (in lab)		0
Graduate students (50 each)		200
Secretary		80
Office space subtotal		400
Total research space		1,638 NASF/ faculty

This figure is higher than the 1,120 NASF from Table 2.6-11 and the 1,400 NASF for the University of Washington from Table 2.6-12 but lower than the 2,200 NASF average from five other institutions. A shared conference/library, copying machine and computer may be added.

Equivalent linear feet of equipment space. This method is based on the equivalent linear feet (ELF) of benches, sinks, fumehoods, storage and floor-mounted equipment. This number is multiplied by 5 ft, which is the space required to provide space for those items, including half of an access aisle. See Figure 2.6-3. From 10 to 15% is added to that amount for space required to exit from these spaces. This number is divided by the number of staff members, and the resulting NASF/staff is compared with similar numbers arrived at by other methods.

The number of ELF is arrived at by measuring the length of existing items for each department. If that information is not available, the following guidelines may be used (for biomedical research, this does not apply to engineering):

NIH suggests that every technician requires at least 16 LF of bench.

Assuming four technicians for each 500 NASF laboratory (see Figure 2.6-4), that means approximately 88 ELF available: 88 − (4 × 16) = 24 ft for fumehoods, sinks and floor-mounted equipment, or 24/4 = 6 feet for each technician.

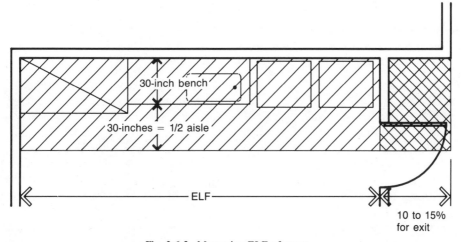

30-inch bench

30-inches = 1/2 aisle

ELF

10 to 15% for exit

Fig. 2.6-3. Measuring ELF of space.

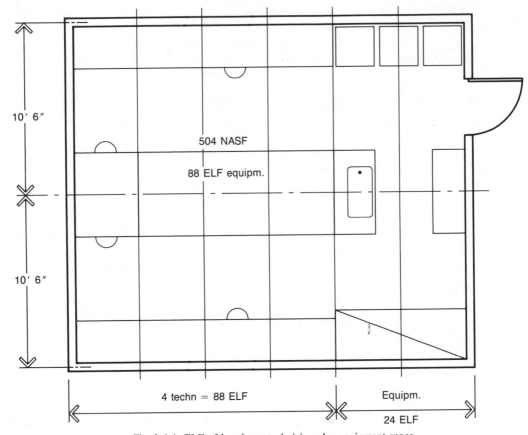

Fig. 2.6-4. ELF of bench per technician plus equipment space.

In summary: 16 LF of bench + 6 ft of floor mounted equipment for each technician.

The NASF arrived at does not include research office space, which must be added. A typical research office is 120 NASF or 24 ELF.

Example: Continuing the chemistry research lab example, assuming one faculty member, five technicians, and four graduate students: Figure 2.6-4 shows for four

technicians	504
The additional technician and faculty half as much	252
Graduate students half as much as technician	252
Lab space subtotal	1,008 NASF

Faculty office	120
Technician (in lab)	0
Graduate students (80 each)	320
Secretary	80
Office space total	520
Total research space	1,528 NASF

Ratio of soft space to hard space. In this method, soft spaces include faculty offices, secretary/receptionist areas, library/conference room, copying machine space, storage space, and spaces without extensive utilities. Hard spaces are laboratories and support spaces. See Table 2.6-15. The facilities shown in this table were considered inadequate, so the numbers should be applied with some caution; however, experience has shown soft spaces to be in the range of 25 to 30% of hard spaces for the total of all labor-

Table 2.6-15. Ratios of NASF For Soft Versus Hard Space—University of Washington Science Buildings

Bldg. No.	Building	Soft Space* NASF	%	Hard Space† NASF	%	Remarks
224	Atmos. sci. geophys.	15,777	37	27,179	63	
117	Bagley—chemistry	22,158	24	69,944	76	
235	Guthrie—psychology	13,985	45	17,135	55	
241	Hitchcock—biology/botany/zoology	31,498	36	56,315	64	Combined Bldgs. 241 & 106
231	Kincaid—zoology	7,561	20	30,925	80	
101	Physics	22,359	38	36,784	62	
103	Guggenheim—aero. & astro. appl. math.	11,539	51	10,891	49	
232	Aero. & engr. research	5,588	27	14,929	73	
214	Benson—chem. engr., nucl. engr.	10,758	33	22,041	67	
162	Electr. engr.	15,270	45	18,407	55	
190	Mech. engr.	12,534	32	26,745	68	
140	More—civil	16,303	43	21,712	57	
157	Fisheries Center	20,564	41	29,548	59	
172	Henderson—applied physics	22,286	47	25,553	53	
213	Marine Sciences—oceanography	8,840	28	22,506	72	
148	Health Sciences—J Wing Biochemistry-genetics	19,101	23	63,760	77	
149	Health sciences—RR Wing Mental retardation/child dev.	28,843	40	43,737	60	Includes animal fac/surgeries
		Range 23–51%			49–80%	
		Average 36			64	

*Including research offices, secretary/reception areas, conference room, copying area, storage.
†Research laboratories and support, not including animal facilities, class labs, class rooms, and lounge.
Source: The NBBJ Group, 1988.

atory-intensive academic departments. This in itself is not a measure of NASF for academic research facilities, but it has been proven to be a valuable check on data arrived at by other means. Some departments require more paper-oriented laboratories in addition to offices, and others require a great deal of wet laboratory space, so some judgment and experience are needed to use this measure.

Example: Continuing with the chemistry research space arrived at earlier:

	Lab Space	Office Space	Total	Office/ Lab (%)
First calculation	1,238	400	1,638	25/75
Second calculation	1,008	520	1,528	34/66

This ratio favors soft spaces compared with the figures for the chemistry department at the University of Washington noted in Table 2.6-15, so a justification or check may be in order.

Research space guidelines by amount of project financial support. This method, developed by the University of Texas Health Sciences Center in San Antonio, assigns NASF to an individual or program depending on the amount of support funding generated. Data from institutional records need to be collected to establish the amount of grant support that is available to the department. Let us assume that $6 million of support has been received by the department, and that 80% of the research is in wet labs and 20% in dry labs. Let us further assume that 300 NASF is justified for each $25,000 of net research lab space and 300 NASF for each $100,000 of dry research space.

Example: $6,000,000
Wet labs: 80% of $6 million = $4,800,000
    ÷ $25,000 = 192 modules
Dry labs: 20% of $6 million = $1,200,000
    ÷ $100,000 = 12 modules
Wet labs: 192 modules × 300 NASF =
    57,600 NASF
Dry labs: 12 modules × 300 NASF =
    3,600 NASF
    ‾‾‾‾‾‾‾‾‾‾‾
    61,200 NASF

Another rule of thumb is that $100,000/ year in support justifies 500 NASF for four to five faculty members and technicians. These calculations do not include research offices and related spaces.

Applying research laboratory space guidelines. At this point, it is appropriate to bring up the concepts of validity and reliability again. See Section 1.3.2 for details. In order to use these guidelines, it is important to ascertain that they apply. As experience is gained, these guidelines can and should be modified.

The best way to ensure reliability is to use several methods of measuring and to compare the results.

It should also be pointed out that all methods that arrive at an NASF/faculty or student measure space needs at a specific point in time; that is total space needs depend on the number of faculty and/or students. That seems logical enough, but it is often ignored. Figure 2.6-5 gives an example of how student enrollment over time affects crowdedness.

Example: Let us assume that the student count for chemistry in 1986 is 2,351, as noted in Table 2.6-6, and that the enrollment is projected to increase by 100 students/year for 4 years and by 20 students/year thereafter. A new facility is being planned for completion in 1989. The weekly student hour number is not anticipated to change.

Table 2.6-9 gives 80 NASF/student station for chemistry, which is noted on Figure 2.6-5 as a horizontal line. The university's chemistry teaching laboratories are crowded at 60 NASF but will get even more crowded until 1989, down to 53, when the new laboratories come on line. However, with the new laboratories completed, the student station space is 87 NASF. By 1996 it will be back down to 80 NASF, where it should be when the next cycle of planning for space should start, not when it is back down at 60 NASF.

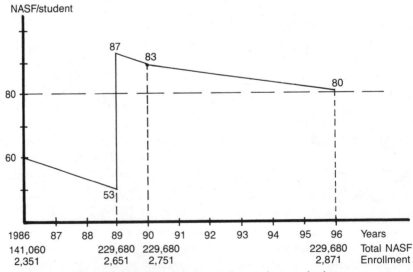

Fig. 2.6-5. Available space per student station—projections.

Equipment Space Utilization

Type of equipment. It is clear that academic science space requirements are equipment driven. In touring many facilities, very few individuals were seen in these laboratories, support facilities and shops.

The first question that comes to mind is: Is this equipment necessary and is it used? According to a study by the National Science Foundation (1987), the answer is yes.

The next question is: Who is using it? We posed that question to deans, faculty and staff. In order to answer it, we must first differentiate between various types of equipment:

- *Standard laboratory equipment* such as lab benches and fumehoods, which are used to prepare, manipulate, try out at smaller scale, as layout space, and for parts storage including chemicals. The fumehood is an extension of the lab bench for those manipulations that are toxic and flammable or in general hazardous to health. More and more chemicals fall into that category each year; consequently, more and more hoods have to be available even if they are not used all the time.
- *Research equipment that performs a specific task,* such as centrifuges, balances, counters, refrigerators, freezers and incubators. This equipment needs to be readily accessible because it is used frequently, and its usefulness does not end because it will always be needed.

  There is also equipment that, because of its size or cost, is shared, separate from the labs and located centrally, such as cyclotrons, electron microscopes and magnetic resonance imagers. This equipment is heavily used intermittently, depending on the programs, availability of the skilled operator, etc. Some of this equipment becomes outdated but is still very useful for teaching purposes, and more space is required to house the latest version for research.

  Within this category is also equipment used to scale up from the bench experiment to larger quantitites in order to study problems on a larger scale such as pilot plants, experimental surgeries, decompression chambers, etc.

- *Research equipment that requires a special environment.* Some of the equipment mentioned earlier falls into this category. The special environment may involve closer temperature and humidity controls, such as equipment rooms for computers, balances and counters. It may be vibration resistant and/or darkened for electron microscopes, film processing or microscopy.

  There are also special controlled environments such as cold rooms, hot rooms, controlled environmental rooms, freezer, growth chambers and sound chambers. These are prefabricated, purchased rooms which are considered equipment and require space.

  In addition, there is standard equipment that, because of the hazardous or clean nature of the work for which it is used, must be located in special rooms such as benches and special hoods in radioisotope, biohazardous containment facilities and clean rooms.

  Equipment that supports the research effort is also part of this category. Some equipment is not used for research or teaching at all, but is needed to produce the instrumentation required for research, such as that found in machine and electronics shops. This instrumentation cannot be bought and is itself the product of the research effort.

  Within this category are also central glass wash and media preparation equipment such as washers, dryers, sinks, autoclaves and sterilizers, which require their own space because the activity produces heat, noise, high humidity and, on occasion, bad odors.

Equipment utilization. Now that we have answered the question "Is the equipment needed?" and "Is it used?", the next questions are: How much equipment is needed?, What is the utilization? and Why can't equipment be shared more?

There are several explanations, some subjective and some objective. The objective ones are as follows:

- Much of the equipment is specialized to perform only a certain function, such as for surgeries and x-ray rooms, or is modified for a certain discipline only, such as lasers. It is of not much use to others.
- Some of the equipment may be underutilized but needs to be in fairly close proximity to the lab bench work, such as cold rooms, freezers, and incubators for reasons of safety, security and efficiency. This means that there will be duplication.
- Some equipment is utilized so much that it cannot be shared, such as lab benches and some fumehoods. The space standards discussed in this report address the bench length and individual equipment space per investigator.
- Some equipment is tied to a specific grant or donor and cannot be used by any other program.
- Some equipment is experimental in nature and, although used infrequently, is modified over time to advance the state of the art. Therefore, it cannot be disposed of.
- Some equipment is for teaching. As the state of the art advances and the desire to teach more interdisciplinary courses increases, the need to store more and more equipment grows exponentially.

The subjective explanations are as follows:

- Some equipment has historic value and is kept to show the evolution of the state of the art for educational purposes.
- Some equipment belongs to a faculty member who is about to retire or has in fact retired but is still active.
- There are cases of territoriality, a lack of trust; a need to have equipment available at short notice, which makes sharing impossible; and variations in working style, which make sharing difficult.

- The fear of letting go. The nature of research is unpredictable, and it is often difficult to predict whether a certain piece of equipment will be needed again in the future.
- In the research environment, space means status and power, up to a point and for a while until the funding dries up. Equipment occupies space, and its utilization and need are often not questioned.
- Research is a personal endeavor. Research programs are subjective and promoted by the individual investigator. This person sells the idea, gets the funding and looks for the physical facility to house the program and equipment. This individual is recruited by the university with promises or a contract for space for equipment and staff. That equipment is rarely shared and may be underutilized, but that fact is an integral part of attracting and keeping first-class investigators.

There is a third explanation that makes it appear that equipment is underutilized. It is a matter of schedules. Many faculty members and their staff and graduate students also teach, and often can be found in their research facilities at night and on weekends.

Conclusion. There is no denying that:

- some equipment can and should be shared;
- some equipment can be disposed of;
- some equipment can be temporarily or permanently located in less expensive space.

What is needed are management systems and policies.

Management systems might include the following:

- *An equipment management system.* Each piece of equipment is tracked for ownership, location, age, condition, initial cost, replacement cost, utilization and research program. Much of this information is usually available. If a piece of equipment is no longer used, it can be employed for teaching, stored off campus or disposed of. The off-campus storage facility must be secure. It must also keep track of ownership and if desired, pick up, deliver and maintain equipment, which may also be leased to other departments or industry to offset the cost of storage.

- *A better security system.* If equipment is checked out to individuals in order to create accountability, more sharing would be possible.
- *A better housekeeping system.* Many investigators will not share equipment because they ''don't want to clean up after someone else.'' They also won't let sanitary engineers (janitors) enter their labs. If some janitors were trained to keep equipment clean and running, they could become a part of the equipment security/checkout system.
- *A better quality control system.* A few years ago, few researchers accepted the idea of central facilities. That attitude has generally been eliminated by federal mandates and regulations. There is also a movement to centralize glasswashing and media preparation, centralize cold/freezer storage and create an equipment pool. No one questions the need to share an electron microscope or cyclotron because of the equipment's cost. The initial construction cost, operating cost and maintenance cost of space are very high, and researchers must now get used to the idea of sharing this commodity called ''space.'' It is thus imperative that quality control be ensured. No one is going to use a central glasswash that does not wash and consequently creates the wrong research readings.
- *A different system of teaching.* If (1) all the teaching laboratories were centralized, (2) they could be assigned based on needs and (3) could be used for various disciplines. That would require laboratories that could be cleaned out and re-supplied quickly; where benches could be raised, lowered or removed quickly, easily and with a minimum of storage for the components; and, above all, where student traffic and service traffic are separated. That is exactly what was done at a number of institutions in the 1970s. They are called ''multidisciplinary'' teaching facilities. The advantages are obvious. These facilities will increase the utilization of teaching labs and reduce overall space and equipment needs. The disadvantages are more subtle. The faculty needs to travel between office/research and teaching labs, although that may be a fraction of their time. Another often raised objection is that students are less exposed to research activities. That may be a self-serving argument because many faculty members do not want large groups of undergraduate students passing their offices and research labs. If exposure is desirable, it can be provided at the graduate level and/or through internship programs.

To make the suggested systems work certain policies will be necessary:

- A policy to establish an accounting system to track the cost of housing, maintaining, securing and moving equipment versus replacing if it is reactivated.
- A policy of space allocation, based first on national averages as a baseline; second on program and funding; and third on seniority and rank. This is the proposed order of testing space allocation, not of testing the importance of a function or program.

None of these suggestions may seem practical, but let's remind ourselves of what Samuel Johnson said: ''Nothing will ever be attempted if all possible objections must be first overcome.''

The time has come to become leaner and thereby more competitive. The best way seems to be to reduce the cost and increase the productivity of research and teaching.

Table 2.6-16. Average Laboratory Staffing at NIH Per Discipline and NASF Per Person, Not Including Offices

	Single Module*		Double Module*	
	Number of Staff Average[†]	NASF/Person Average	Number of Staff Average[†]	NASF/Person Average
Biochemistry	1.8	140	3.2	155
Pathology	1.5	170	4.0	140
Physiology	1.7	145	3.0	155
Virology	2.2	120	3.8	130
Immunology	1.6	155	2.0	185
Biophysics	1.5	205	3.0	170
Multidiscipline[‡]	1.8	145	3.2	155

*Modules vary between 180 and 334 NASF; single module average, 220 NASF; double module average, 440 NASF.

[†]Including investigator.

[‡]Discipline frequency-weighted values.

Source: U.S. Public Health, Monograph No. 71-1963. Wash. D.C.

2.6.3 Nonacademic Laboratories Space Guidelines

Very little data are available for these types of laboratories, and those noted in this section should be used with some caution; they are intended as guidelines only. Every effort has been made to collect data for identical or similar categories, as noted in the tables. However, as the reader will quickly see, the categories are for a wide variety of laboratories or disciplines and are given in ranges for NASF and GSF.

The square feet ranges are based on a sample of laboratories at a specific point in time. Since space is static and the process of construction adds space incrementally, it should be noted that space in every company or institution fluctuates with every staff member added or deleted.

It should also be noted that space per person has increased over the years. Table 2.6-16 shows the average space per person at

NIH in 1963 as 145 to 155 NASF for a single and a double module, respectively, not including support space or offices. In 1974, the NIH *Space Manual* gave 165 NASF/person but added the following information: 235 NASF/person for lab support and 140 NASF/person for office and office support, for a total of 540 NASF/person; see Table 2.6-17. This number appears high by other standards and probably includes administrative offices, central animal facilities, pilot plants and building support. None of the other tables in this section include these types of spaces.

In 1972, the National Bureau of Standards (NBS) conducted a survey of 15 major laboratories (see Table 2.6-18), including laboratory support and laboratory offices; the range was 125 to 528 NASF/person. The average for the ranges given was 306 to 337 NASF/person, including offices and support. These averages are very comparable with an average range of 340 to 370 NASF/

Table 2.6-17. Space Standards for Laboratories

Office NASF/Person	Office Support NASF/Person	Laboratory NASF/Person	Lab Support NASF/Person	Total NASF
115	25	165*	235	540

*Irrespective of the type of work.

Source: *NIH Organizational Space Manual.* NIH Division of Space Management, January 1974.

Table 2.6-18. Space Standards for Laboratories—National Bureau of Standards Survey

Office NASF	Lab & Supp. NASF	Total NASF	Remarks
125–140	250/person	375–390/person	Inadequate
75–150/scientist	250–300/scientist	400 min/scientist	
Desk in lab	125–165/chemist	Lab only w/desk in lab	
	150–200/scientist and electronics engr.		
Included in support	165/person, all disc.	400	Lab only
	235/person		Support only
	275/person, all disc.		
648 (3 people)	624	424/person	Tot: 1,272/section manager
216 (2 people)	312	264/person	Tot: 528/branch manager
—	312	312/exp. scientist and staff	
108–216	156–312	254–528/contributor	
Range, 75–216		125–528	
Average, 156–172		306–337	

Source: Responses to questions on space management from 15 major laboratories, compiled by the Management and Organization Division, National Bureau of Standards, August 1972. Gaithersburg, MD. Duplications and data that were not comparable are deleted from the table; remaining sample is 13 for offices and 12 for total.

person, including laboratory office and direct support, reported by Haines Lundberg Waehler (HLW) for laboratories planned between 1980 and 1984. See Table 2.6-19. Only the space for electronics and telecommunications is substantially lower at 200 NASF/person.

Flad and Associates conducted a survey of U.S. industrial research laboratories but noted their findings in GSF. See Table 2.6-20. A later survey of 11 petrochemical research facilities produced a range of 280 to 816 GSF/staff and an average of 655 GSF/person. In order to compare the GSF of Table 2.6-20 with the NASF of Tables 2.6-18 and 2.6-19, we have taken an average of the

numbers in Table 2.6-20 and assumed a NASF to GSF of 55 to 60% (see Section 8.6) and have noted these figures in Table 2.6-21. The Flad and HLW surveys, both based on industrial research laboratories, are very comparable but somewhat higher than the NBS survey for governmental laboratories; this finding may be expected.

A recent survey by The NBBJ Group, noted in Table 2.6-22, confirms the slightly lower NASF and GSF for regulatory/governmental laboratories and biomedical laboratories.

All the tables include laboratory offices, which are directly related to the work in the laboratory, but the sizes may vary. Tables

Table 2.6-19. NASF Per Person Per Discipline

Research Activity	Technicians (Labs Only)	Technicians & Scientists (Lab and Office)	Total Lab Area, Including Direct Scientific Support
Basic discovery	190	180	370
Chemistry and analytic	200	175	345
Pharm. formulation & devl.	175	150	340
Chemical	220	180	—
Electronics & telecommunications	—	—	200

Source: Stark (1985).

Table 2.6-20. GSF Per Staff* of Total Space

	GSF per Person		
Discipline	Staff Range 100–249	Staff Range 250–499	Staff Range 500–999
Drugs	465	416	528
Food	752	734	—
Petro. and coal	519	505	505
Organic chem.	680	675	528
Inorganic chem.	695	505	500

*Based on median staff size and median NASF in each sample; first and fourth quartiles were deleted in order to control partially for exceptional conditions.

Source: Capital Spending Study of Research and Development Laboratories, Flad and Associates, 1982.

2.6-23 and 2.6-24, from two different sources, have been provided as an aid to laboratory planners. The first four categories in Table 2.6-23 and the first two categories in Table 2.6-24 should be deleted, since these are administrative offices.

Conclusion

As pointed out earlier, all the spaces per individual, whether NASF, GSF or averages, are based on a specific point in time. These guidelines must therefore be applied with some caution. Figure 2.6-6 illustrates graphically how the GSF per person changes over time with a facility that has not been changed or expanded. Figure 2.6-7 gives the same scenario for a facility that is being

Table 2.6-21. GSF Average to NASF Per Person*

Discipline	GSF/Person Average	NASF/Person Range
Drugs	470	259–282
Food	743	409–446
Petro. and coal	510	281–306
Organic chem.	628	345–377
Inorganic chem.	567	312–340
Petrochem.†	655	360–393

*NASF to GSF efficiency assumed to be 55 to 60%.

†From a separate survey.

Table 2.6-22. NASF and GSF Averages to NASF Per Person

Discipline	NASF/Person	GSF/Person
Regulatory agency	282–306	465–516
Biomedical research	208–272	322–435

Source: The NBBJ Group, 1986 and 1988.

Table 2.6-23. Laboratory Offices—Space Standards

Category	NASF	Remarks
Division director	288–450	
Deputy & assoc. dir.	192–375	
Assistant dir.	255	
Assistant to dir.	150	
Branch chiefs	150–300	
Secr. to dir (2)	112–150	
Stenographic personnel/ clerical	75–100	Average
Admin. & professional	115	
Research assoc.	192–225	
Research scientist (2)	96–100	
Supervisor	96–100	
Drafsmen	75–100	Individual or group
Research engineers/ scientists	48–50	

Source: Responses to questions on space management from 15 major laboratories compiled by the management and organization division, National Bureau of Standards, August 1972—modified and summarized.

Table 2.6-24. Laboratory Offices—Standards

Category	NASF
Executive	250–350
Administrator	150–250
Manager	125–150
Supervisor/professional	95–150
Working professional	95–110
Technical professional	95–125
Technician clerk	70–120
Clerical supervisor	75–110
Clerical	60–100

Source: *California State Administrative Manual*, Section 1402, May 1979.

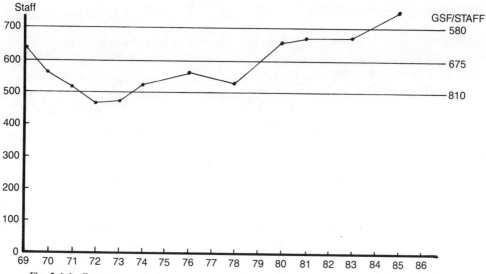

Fig. 2.6-6. Gross square feet per person—actual over time (Industrial chemical R&D facility).

planned in 1988 for the future, with projected staffing over two 5-year periods. The new addition will come on line in 1991. The existing NASF/staff in 1988 was 226, and the 10-year goal is 316 NASF/staff in 1998.

The authors have found these guidelines very useful in arriving at ballpark NASF figures based on programs and staffing projections. Their use, together with the aid of Section 8.6, quickly produces a reasonably accurate conversion to GSF and construction cost.

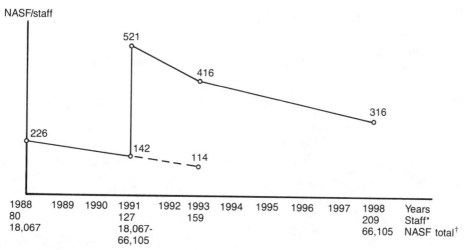

*Projected increase of 16 staff/year for the first 5 years and 10 staff/year for the next 5 years.
†Building addition of 48,038 NASF increases total from 18,067 to 66,105 NASF.

Fig. 2.6-7. NASF per staff—projected (Regulatory Agency Laboratory Facilities Program—BOHM-NBBJ, 1987).

GLOSSARY

Full-Time Equivalent (FTE)—students and staff are measured in FTE. Normally this is a full academic load for a student (typically 15 credit hours per semester) or for a full-time worker in staff analysis. This figure is used in data and formulas to arrive at occupancy ratios and square feet.

Net Assignable Square Feet (NASF)—see Section 8.6.

Primary Space—rooms used for primary teaching or research space—in this context, the laboratory. See Figures 2.6-1 and 2.6-2.

Principal Investigator—the individual who is the primary space generator, such as a faculty member or funded researcher.

Service Space (see *Primary Space*)—space occupied by equipment or activities supporting the primary activity, often located adjacent to the primary space. Examples are cold rooms, balance rooms and darkrooms.

Support Space (see *Service Space*)—the space occupied by equipment or activities which indirectly support the teaching or research activities and are usually shared by several faculty members or researchers, such as greenhouses, animal quarters, centralized stockrooms, shops and storage.

Unit—used interchangeably with the term "research laboratory unit" or "academic teaching or research unit."

Weekly Room Hours—the number of scheduled hours per week that laboratory sections use a laboratory. Most guidelines expect 16 to 20 hours of scheduled use per week for an academic laboratory. Sometimes called "room utilization" or "room contact hours."

Weekly Student Hours—the enrollment in each laboratory section multiplied by the number of hours per week that the section meets (e.g., a lab with 20 students meets for 3 hours per week; that produces 60 weekly student hours). This figure is utilized as the multiplier for square footage guidelines to determine the amount of space needed for a certain amount of instructional activity. Sometimes called "student contact hours," "weekly student contact hours," or "student-station periods occupied."

REFERENCES

Bareither, Harlan D., and Shillinger, Jerry, 1968. Space Guidelines for Academic Teaching Laboratories, Urbana: University of Illinois Press, Table 8, p. 55.

California Post-secondary Education Commission, 1986. *Time and Territory. A Preliminary Exploration of Space and Utilization Guidelines in Engineering and the Natural Sciences.* Commission Report 86.2 Sacramento.

California State Administrative Manual, 1979. Section 1402, May. Sacramento.

Colorado Commission on Higher Education, 1987. *Policy Manual.* Denver: pp. III-F.7 to III-F.13.

Flad & Associates, 1982. *Capital Spending Study of Research and Development Laboratories.* Madison, WI.

Higher Education Facilities Planning and Management Manuals, Manual Two, 1971. Boulder, CO: Western Interstate Commission on Higher Education (WICHE), pp. 127–133.

Minnesota Facilities Model, 1982. University of Minnesota. Minneapolis, MN.

National Bureau of Standards, 1972. Responses to Questions on Space Management from 15 Major Laboratories, Compiled by the Management and Organization Division. Gaithersburg, MD.

National Institutes of Health, 1974. *Organizational Space Manual.* Division of Space Management. Bethesda, MD.

National Science Foundation, 1987. *Academic Research Equipment in the Physical and Computer Sciences and Engineering: 1982 and 1985.* Report SRS 87-D6.

The NBBJ Group/TRA, 1988. *Science and Engineering Facilities Planning Study.* Seattle, WA: University of Washington.

Snow, Donald, 1963. *Space Planning Principles for Biomedical Research Laboratories,* US Public Health Service. Monograph No. 71. Public Health.

Stark, Stanley, 1985. From Program to Design. *Architectural Technology,* Summer, 1985, p. 24.

2.6.4 Clinical Laboratory Space Guidelines   *T. Ruys*

Introduction

In contrast to the scarcity of data on academic and industrial research facilities, much has been published about clinical laboratories space guidelines. In fact, so much has been written that there is conflicting information and potential causes of confusion:

- Some methods arrive at laboratory sizes which include automated procedures; others include only nonautomated procedures.
- Some methods include space for special services such as autopsy rooms and morgues.

- Some methods arrive at space needs based on the number of annual procedures, others based on the number of beds served.
- Most methods arrive at the total size of the laboratory. Some break down the total area into departmental space needs.
- Multipliers to derive departmental GSF from NASF vary.

To make matters worse, clinical laboratory planners have introduced another concept not used in planning academic and industrial laboratory facilities: that of departmental gross square feet (DGSF). The reader is referred to Section 8.6 for a detailed discussion of NASF and GSF. DGSF is NASF, plus surrounding and internal walls and partitions, plus internal circulation space, but not the public corridors serving the laboratory and other functions.

$$DGSF = NASF$$
$$+ \text{ partitions}$$
$$+ \tfrac{1}{2} \text{ access corridor}$$

Except for commercial laboratories, most clinical laboratories are part of a larger building, so that the concept of DGSF makes a great deal of sense in determining the area occupied by the laboratory. However, additional space must be provided for stairs, elevators, toilets, corridors, and mechanical systems to arrive at building gross square feet (GSF).

Each clinical laboratory operation is unique and highly variable. It is not the intent of this section to provide a survey of the literature on clinical laboratory space guidelines, but rather, for planning purposes, to provide a quick way to arrive at the total size of a clinical laboratory from readily available data:

- Based on the number of beds served
- Based on annual procedures performed

The more detailed analyses of tests per admissions or tests per patient day have not been covered.

The size of the laboratory area depends primarily on the number and type of procedures performed. However, many variables affect these numbers, and these must be considered in using the calculations suggested in this section.

- Type of institution or function
  The most common clinical laboratories are found in general hospitals, but the number of outpatients and the size of the intensive care unit must be considered.
  Teaching hospitals require roughly twice as many procedures as general hospitals (source: CAP 1985, Figure E-10).
  Children's hospitals require roughly four times as many DGSF per bed as general hospitals (source: NACHRI 1978).
  Commercial laboratories require roughly twice as much NASF per staff as general hospitals (source: CAP 1977, Appendix D).
- Types of procedures
  Are specimens collected in the laboratory?
  Are an electrocardiogram and an electroencephalogram included?
  Are a stat lab, blood bank, autopsy and morgue included?
- Types of patients
  The specialty of the hospital affects the type and number of procedures.
- Number of patients served
  Size of the hospital. Larger hospitals tend to be more efficient than smaller ones, which increases the number of procedures per technician and reduces the square feet required per procedure or bed.
  For commercial laboratories, the market share must be estimated and provided for both at present and for the future.
- Other functions accommodated in the laboratory
  Teaching and training functions will increase laboratory size.

The existence of satellite labs will reduce the central lab size but increase the overall size per procedure.
Length of time specimens are kept in storage.

- The size of the staff
  This affects the number of offices and the size of locker rooms, lounge and conference room/library.
- The degree to which support functions are provided by the hospital. Commercial laboratories must provide their own:
  Central supply; chemical and gas cylinder storage and receiving.
  Waste disposal and handling.
  Locker rooms, lounge.
  Housekeeping functions.
  Repair shops.
  Central glasswash, decontamination, media prep.
  Animal facilities.
  Computer facilities.
  Billing, accounting, management, personnel.
- Utilization of workstations and equipment
  The extent of multipurpose workstations.
  The hours per day and days per week of occupancy.

There are also a number of variables that affect the square feet per procedures, which must be considered in using the calculations suggested in this section:

- Types of procedures
  The complexity will affect the time per procedure, as well as the number of procedures that are sent to outside laboratories.
- Degree of automation
  The speed and capacity of automated equipment will affect the square feet per procedure per year.
- Efficiency of operation
  Larger labs tend to be more efficient (economies of scale).

- Projected growth
  It takes time to plan and build facilities. Space needs should be estimated for at least 5 years into the future.

Considering the above requirements, it is imperative that the planner verify programs, workload, equipment and staffing projections for immediate and future needs. In addition, with litigation on the increase, the number of tests per patient, and therefore the total number of procedures, will increase. However, automation will also increase, with an overall reduction in space.

Presently there is a trend toward an increase in the number of tests per patient per year. That is not going to be the case forever, but what is the critical mass for an efficient clinical laboratory? Too large a laboratory is just as bad as one that is too small, considering the cost of operating a laboratory.

In summary, this section outlines ways to arrive at a clinical laboratory size in NASF based on the number of beds served and the number of procedures performed. The NASF must be translated into a DGSF and support functions added. The nest requirement is to make the space as adaptable as possible to minimize the results of errors, unforeseen events and changes, and hope for the best.

Several methods to arrive at space requirements have been outlined. All should be applied and the results compared in order to increase the reliability of the answers.

Guidelines

Guidelines draw on data from the past and project these into the future. It is for that reason that "dated" information has been included. It also appears that smaller general hospital laboratories have not changed to the same degree as larger, more fully automated laboratories, so these data may be useful.

A number of methods have been proposed. The reliability of the answers will increase with the number of methods used and the number of results compared.

All methods arrive at NASF or DGSF per

Table 2.6-25. Laboratory Square Feet Per Bed—Comparison for General Hospitals

Source (Year)	Number of Beds*									
	100–300		300–500		500–700		700–1,000		Average	
	NASF	DGSF	NASF	DGSF	NASF	DGSF	NASF	DGSF	NASF	DGSF
Rappoport (1961)									15	20–25
USPHS (1961)	16–10	—								
Wheeler (1964)		26–18		24–16						
Steinle (1969)[†]									20.8	24.9
Wheeler (1971)[‡]		28–19		24–18		31–16		36–19		
Little (1975)[†]										26.6
California (1975–1977)[†]		35–31								
NACHRI (1978)[†]										22
Simmons (1983)		27–23	22							

*Note higher values for lower number of beds.

[†]Without morgue.

[‡]3 GSF deleted for morgue.

unit. This unit, however, may be per bed, per technician, per procedure or per piece of equipment.

Most methods arrive at the number of technicians first and apply an NASF/technician ratio as a multiplier.

We have arbitrarily organized the following information on laboratory size based on the number of beds served and the number of annual procedures performed.

Laboratory size based on number of beds served. As early as 1961, Rappoport suggested that 15 NASF or 20 to 25 DGSF per bed should be provided for laboratory space. Several other sources from 1961 to 1977 reported their findings; these are given in Table 2.6-25. It should be noted that the higher values are for the lower number of beds in each range.

It is also interesting to note that Wheeler (1971) increased the DGSF/bed from 1964 to 1971 for the larger hospitals.

Later information from the CAP *Manual for Laboratory Planning and Design* (1977) gave substantially higher values for DGSF and associated NASF per bed. See Table 2.6-26. These values, however, include autopsy and other support spaces not covered in Table 2.6-25. It is worthwhile to note that the areas became smaller over time with increased automation, but after 1974 increased again due to the increased number of procedures per bed.

Table 2.6-26. Laboratory Square Feet Per Bed*

Year	Sample Size	NASF/Bed	DGSF/Bed	Automation
1971	1	51.6	65.4	20%
1973	3	37.1	49.4	36.6%
1974	3	26.0	31.2	52%
1975–1977	7	27.2	35.1	55.6%

*Average for all functions (including morgue) in general hospitals with laboratories over 10,000 NASF.

Note: It appears that the NASF became smaller per staff because of automation, but after 1974 increased again due to an increased number of procedures per bed.

Source: *Manual For Laboratory Planning and Design.* Skokie IL: College of American Pathologists, 1977, Appendix D.

Table 2.6-27. Suggested Laboratory Square Feet Per Bed*

Number of Beds	100–300	300–500	500–700	700–1,000	Average
DGSF/bed	36	30	34	40	35
NASF/bed	28	23	26	31	27

*Total lab space including morgue. Based on 55% automation.

Based on these data, we suggest that the NASF and DGSF per bed noted on Table 2.6-27 be used.

Laboratory size based on annual procedures performed. There are several ways that annual number of procedures can be converted to NASF and DGSF:

1. *Staff driven (personnel)*
   This method assumes that the staff is known and can be projected.

NASF/technician (non-automated) × number of technician	= ___ NASF
NASF/technician (automated) × number of technician	= ___ NASF
Total	= ___ NASF
NASF × DGSF multiplier	= ___ DGSF

Available data: Table 2.6-28 makes a comparison of the NASF/technician from various sources. Table 2.6-29 gives the same from the CAP *Manual* (1977). Based on these data, we suggest the following:

297 NASF/technician (nonautomated)
116 NASF/technician (automated 55%)

This is a wide range. The planner is expected to use judgment about the degree of automation and the number of beds.

More recently the College of American Pathologists and the Canadian Association of Pathologists developed a method to measure the production time of the staff for various procedures. The "CAP workload recording" method was the result. It is expressed in "unit values per procedures," popularly known as "CAP units." These are expressed in minutes per procedure. The total time for all procedures is divided by the units per hour and again by the hours per staff per year to arrive at the number of staff expressed in FTE. This does not include nontest time, however.

Table 2.6-28. NASF Per Technician—Comparison

Source	NASF	Comments
Owen et al. (1958)	300	All activities plus internal circulation
Rappoport (1960)	217–180	150–450 beds
	228–250	450–600 beds
	228	600+ beds
Wheeler (1964)*	510–440	100–200 beds
	370–310	300–400 beds
	275	500+ beds
Elin et al. (1982)	110	Chemistry in teaching hospitals
Simmons (1983)	420	220 beds
	235	450 beds
Chi Systems (1989)	200	Chemistry and microbiology

*Including MBR, electrocardiogram and electroencephalogram, but without autopsy/morgue or blood banking.

Table 2.6-29. NASF Per Technician*

Year	Sample Size	NASF/ Technician	Automation (%)
1971	1	343.7	20
1973	3	244.7	36.6
1974	3	121.9	52
1975	7	115.8	55.6

*Average for all functions (including morgue) in general hospitals with laboratories over 10,000 NASF.

Source: *Manual for Laboratory Planning and Design.* Skokie, IL: College of American Pathologists, 1977, Appendix D.

CAP unit = minutes per procedure

Sum total of procedures × equivalent CAP units = total unit value

$$\frac{\text{Total unit value}}{\text{Units per hour}} \div \frac{\text{number of hours per}}{\text{staff per year}} = \text{FTE}$$

This can be applied to the NASF per technician, noted earlier, and the procedure repeated to arrive at DGSF.

Health and Welfare Canada (1980) proposes a method which arrives at DGSF directly from total unit values as follows:

$$\frac{\text{Total annual unit values}}{\text{620 to 460 units/DGSF}} = \text{DGSF}$$

This wide range (620 to 460) requires some judgment. The figure of 620 units should be used for the larger and more efficient laboratories.

Dr. M.D.D. McNeely (1989), Secretary-Treasurer of the Canadian Association of Pathologists, expressed great concern about the use of the workload recording system. It is extremely difficult to apply this system to a theoretical setting and come up with workload units which are realistic. The best use of the workload recording system is to examine over a long period of time the changing direction of workload requirements in a specific setting.

Available data: Although the workload recording system was originally developed by the Canadian Association of Pathologists, it

subsequently evolved into a federal government function. The Canadian Association of Pathologists is no longer directly involved in the development and administration of this workload recording system. Readers are advised to contact Miss Anita Jensen, National Hospital Productivity Improvement Program, Workload Measurement System, c/o Ottawa Civic Hospital, 1053 Carling Avenue, K1Y4E9.

Another source of information is the College of American Pathologists. Telephone: 312/966-5700; address: 5202 Old Orchard Road, Skokie, IL 60077.

2. Procedures driven (workload)
This method is based on circular reasoning, since it relies on some of the same data as method 1, but it is useful in checking staff numbers against procedures.

Some institutions may be under- or over-staffed. Most institutions report annual billed procedures, not counting quality control or setup procedures, which may add 20 to 25% to the workload. For purposes of these calculations, it is assumed that only "productive" procedures are counted.

$$\frac{\text{No. of procedures per year}}{\text{Procedures per technician}} = \frac{\text{No. of technicians}}{\text{(Remainder same as for method 1)}}$$

Available data: 8,000 to 11,000 annual procedures/person (nonautomated). Table 2.6-30 makes a comparison of annual procedures per technician as reported by various sources. We suggest an average of 8,000 to 11,000 annual nonautomated procedures per technician. Commercial laboratories and large hospital clinical laboratories are assigned the higher figure, since these are more efficient.

Table 2.6-33 gives the annual automated procedures per technician for various pieces of equipment.

Other data are reported in terms of procedures per DGSF, as shown in Table 2.6-31. This eliminates the circular reasoning noted

Table 2.6-30. Annual Tests Per Technician—Comparison

Source	Nonautomated	Comments
Coll. Am. Pathol. (1960)	10,190	
USPHS (1961)	11,935–12,373	Median, including electrocardiogram and blood bank for 100- to 200-bed general hospital
California DPHL (1961)	11,400	Average by professional staff
Hudenburg (1967)	11,000–11,883	
Hosp. Survey Comm. (1974)	8,299	159.6 per week
Simmons (1983)	7,143–7,424	

above. If converted to DGSF per procedure this information is much more useful, since most readily available data are give in terms of annual procedures. Therefore, we have taken the information from Table 2.6-31 and created Table 2.6-32 so that procedures can directly be converted to DGSF.

Our suggestion is to use the following:

0.022   DGSF per annual procedure (nonautomated)

0.001   DGSF per annual procedure (automated)

3. *Equipment driven (nonautomated)*

This method is based on actual or anticipated equipment and operator space needs. Equipment includes benches, fumehoods, floor-mounted equipment, storage cabinets and space for carts and emergency shower/eyewash. See Figure 2.6-3. This may be the best procedure to arrive at space needs because it has the fewest number of variables.

Large, automated equipment should be figured separately because of the greater depth and operator space required.

This method is used to check DGSF arrived at by other means and to lay out individual spaces.

Linear feet of benches + linear feet of equipment

×

5 feet for equipment depth and access

+

10 to 15% for space access

×

DGSF multiplier = required DGSF

Available data: actual measurements.

4. *Equipment driven (automated)*

Automation has changed the makeup and size of the clinical laboratory more than any other factor. The easiest way to handle this variable is to calculate nonautomated procedures as in the past, account for automated procedures separately, and add the results. Table 2.6-33 gives the space requirements for the more common automated equipment found in the clinical laboratory.

Available data: Table 2.6-33 or manufacturers' catalogs.

5. *Program driven (function)*

All the methods discussed so far arrive at a gross approximation of the square feet required for the clinical laboratory. Method 5

Table 2.6-31. Number of Procedures Per DGSF—Comparison

Source	Number of Procedures per DGSF		
	Lower	Median	Upper
Rappoport (1960, 1961)		45	
USPHS (1961)		42	
Hosp. Survey Committee (1974)	46.88	51.88	56.88

Table 2.6-32. Laboratory DGS Per Procedures—Comparison*

	Number of Procedures Per DGSF		
Source	Lower	Median	Upper
Rappoport (1961)		0.0222	
USPHS (1961)		0.0238	
Hospital Survey Committee (1974)	0.0176	0.0193	0.0213
DHEW (1977)	0.020	0.023	0.025

*Note that the upper numbers in Table 2.6-32 becomes the lower numbers in Table 2.6-33, and vice versa. Higher procedures/DGSF become lower DGSF in space needs.

Table 2.6-33. Automated Equipment—NASF and Maximum Number of Procedures

Equipment	Area* (w × d)	Utilities	Remarks
Coulter S. Plus IV (counter model)	9' × 11' = 99 SF	120V 20 A, drain	Hematology
Coulter STKS (counter model)	Similar	Similar	Hematology
Technicon H-6000	6' × 8' = 48 SF	Deionized water drain; 120 V 30 A, (UPS)	Hematology
Technicon H-1 (counter model)	6' × 6' = 36 SF	120 V 20 A, (UPS)	Hematology
Dupont ACA IV (mobile unit)	6' × 6' = 36 SF	120 V (UPS)	Chemistry
Instrumentation laboratory IL 1302/ 1306 (counter model)	7'6" × 5' = 38 SF two plus gas cylinders for calibration	120 V (UPS)	Chemistry
Hatachi Automatic Analyser 737 (floor mounted)	9' × 8' = 72 SF	208 V, 30 A (UPS) CW, drain 1320 # weight	Chemistry
Hatachi Automatic Analyser 736 (floor mounted)	9' × 17' = 153 SF	208 V, 30 A (UPS) CW, drain 3100 # weight	Chemistry
Beckman ASTRA-8 (mobile unit)	7' × 6' = 42 SF	110 V (UPS) drain	Chemistry
Technicon SMAC II (floor mounted)	15' × 9' = 135 SF	Air, CW, drain, electrical (UPS) 208 V, 30 A 208 V, 20 A	Chemistry
Beckman Synchron CX4 (mobile)	6' × 7' = 42 SF	Deionized water, drain 120 V (UPS)	Chemistry
Technicon RA-1000 (counter model)	4' × 6' = 24 SF	110 V (UPS)	Chemistry
EPICS CS Flow Cytometer (floor mounted)	12' × 10' = 120 SF	208 V 3∅ 120 V, 15 A (UPS)(2) CW, drain, nitrogen	Histology
Instrumentation Laboratories IL Monarch 2000 (mobile unit)	4' × 5'6" = 22 SF	208 V, 30 A 1∅	Toxicology
Perkins Elmer Atomic Absorption Spectrophotometer 603 (counter model)	6' × 6' = 36 SF	Air, Acetylene 120 V exhaust	Toxicology
Hewlett Packard 5890 GC/MS (counter model)	8' × 6' = 48 SF	120 V (UPS) cylinder gases	Toxicology
Becton Dickenson BACTEC NR-660 Automated blood culture machine (counter or floor model)	6' × 6' = 36 SF	120 V (UPS)	Microbiology
MacDonald Douglass VITEK (counter model)	8' × 6' = 48 SF	110 V (UPS)	Microbiology

*Including access space for service and space for operator.

Table 2.6-34. Breakdown of DGSF by Function—Level 2

Function	Annual Units	Divided by	Units/DGSF =	DGSF
Clinical chemistry	———	divided by	1,140 =	
Hematology	———	divided by	1,280 =	
Immunochematology	———	divided by	710 =	
Surgical pathology	———	divided by	460 =	
Cytology	———	divided by	425 =	
Immunology/serology	———	divided by	570 =	
In Vitro nuclear medicine	———	divided by	570 =	
Microbiology	———	divided by	850 =	
Other	———	divided by	500 =	
Total primary activity area				——— DGSF
× 1.82 for support & admin.				———
Total				——— DGSF

Source: Health and Welfare Canada, 1980, Level 2 Method.

Table 2.6-35. Multipliers to Arrive at Department GSF from NASF—Comparison

Source	Multiplier
Steinle (1969)	1.195
Modern Hospital (1973)	1.5
Baer (1984)	1.3
The NBBJ Group	1.43

gives a number of approaches to arrive at a more detailed breakdown.

Health and Welfare Canada (1980) suggests a method to divide the annual units for each laboratory function by units per DGSF, as noted on Table 2.6-34. These numbers were developed by Chi Systems, Inc., based on actual numbers of procedures performed in a given laboratory space and from a survey of Canadian and American hospitals. Although some of the numbers may be outdated due to more recent changes in technology, equipment, configurations, and possible laboratory restructuring, the overall approach can be used to develop a comprehensive, room-specific space program. These areas are totaled and multiplied by 1.82 to provide for laboratory support and administration areas. Primary laboratory areas are roughly 55% of the total laboratory area. The *Laboratory Planning Manual* can be acquired from Chi Systems, Inc.

Multipliers

The various methods proposed have been summarized in Table 2.6-36. Some of the methods arrive at NASF and some at DGSF. To derive DGSF from NASF, we suggest the

Table 2.6-36. Summary of Methods to Arrive at Space

Base Data	Suggested Value	Space in NASF	Space in DGSF	Multiplier Net to Gross
No. of beds	Table 2.6-28	X	X	
Space for technicians	297 (nonautomated)	X	X	1.43
	116 (automated)	X	X	1.43
Annual unit values (CAP units)	620–460 units/DGSF		X	
No. of annual procedures	0.022 (nonautomated)		X	
	0.001 (automated)			
No. of annual procedures technician	11,000 (nonautomated)	Indirect		
	Table 2.6-34 (automated)	Indirect		

Table 2.6-37. Checklist of Spaces in the Clinical Laboratory and Suggested Areas

Space	NASF (no. of Persons)	NASF (93)	NASF (144)
Laboratories (clinical pathology)			
General chemistry	300	1,350	2,050
Hematology	150	1,100	1,415
Urinalysis	150	200	250
Microbiology	—	950	1,380
Biochemistry	150	370	650
Serology	150	250	350
Blood banking	—	1,000	1,455
Bacteriology (parasitology, mycology)	200	325	450
Virology	—	100	275
Radioimmunoassay	—	—	450
Cold storage	—	—	130
Laboratories (anatomic pathology)			
Histopathology	150	750	1,270
Cytology	—	300	600
Electron microscopy	—	—	285
Photomicrography	—	—	—
Autopsy	450	750	1,370
Cytogenetics	—	—	—
Blocks, slides, tissue storage	—	170	390
Laboratory support			
Quality control	—	120	125
Microscopy support	—	120	250
Balance room	—	—	—
Glasswash/decontamination	250	190	240
Media preparation	—	—	—
Tissue culture	—	—	—
Morgue	150	(1)	(1)
Administration/Records			
Pathologist offices	100	750	1,415
Specialists' offices	—	149	675
Secretary/reception	200	180	275
Conference/library	—	470	1,140
Clerical workroom/admin. storage	—	370	520
Accessioning	—	420	825
Computer	—	400	500
Specimen storage	—	200	300
Patient support			
Waiting	100	100	100(2)
Venipuncture	50	125	200
Exam	100	120	120
Specimen toilet	50	80	80
Employee support			
Lounge	—	250	540
Locker room	100	300	410
Toilet/shower	50	170	205
Education and training			
Conference/classroom	—	200	600
Special procedures			
Stat Lab	—	(3)	(3)
EKG, EEG, BMR	—		

Table 2.6-37. (Continued)

Space	NASF (no. of Persons)	NASF (93)	NASF (144)
Subtotal	2,850 NASF	12,320 NASF	21,290 NASF
Other Circulation/structure/mechanical shafts	350 DGSF	1,850 DGSF	3,195 DGSF
Total	3,200 DGSF	14,170 DGSF	24,485 DGSF
Procedures/year	150,000	1,140,000	2,050,000

Notes: 1. The morgue is included in the autopsy area.
2. There is an outpatient drawing, therefore, requiring less space in the lab.
3. The stat lab is included in the accessioning, chemistry and hematology areas.

Source: Garikes Wilson Atkinson, Inc. (1989), and Hospital Survey Committee (1974).

multiplier of 1.43 used by The NBBJ Group. Other multipliers have been proposed by other sources, as noted in Table 2.6-35.

Primary Space and Secondary Space

It may be useful for the planner to have a checklist of spaces found in a clinical laboratory and a suggested size, if appropriate. See Tables 2.6-36 and 2.6-37.

The reader is referred to Health and Welfare Canada's *Evaluation and Space Programming Methodology Series #16 Laboratory* (1980) for a detailed method to arrive at a breakdown of spaces which is outside the scope of this handbook. This can be obtained from CHI Systems, Inc., as noted earlier.

These spaces usually operate 8 hours/day, 5 days/week except for the stat lab, which operates 24 hours/day, 7 days/week.

REFERENCES

Baer, Daniel M., 1984. Laboratory Design for Automated Instruments. *Journal of Clinical Laboratory Automation,* Vol. 4, No. 4, 271–274.

Block, Louis, 1966. Hospital Planning Today—An Inbuilt Growth Factor Is Essential in Laboratory Planning. *Hospitals, JAHA,* Vol. 40, pp. 103–108.

California State Department of Public Health, 1961. *Local Public Health Laboratory Report.* Berkeley, CA.

———, 1977. *Statewide Average Number of Square Feet per Licensed Bed, January 1, 1975–December 21.*

Canadian Schedule of Unit Valves for Clinical Laboratory Procedures. Canadian Association of Pathologists (latest edition). Victoria, BC.

College of American Pathologists, 1977. *Manual for Laboratory Planning and Design.* Skokie, IL: College of American Pathologists.

College of American Pathologists, 1985. *Medical Laboratory Planning and Design.* Skokie, IL: College of American Pathologists.

Elin, R.J., Robertson, E.A., and Sever, G., 1982. Workload, Space, and Personnel of Clinical Laboratories in Teaching Hospitals. *American Journal of Clinical Pathologists,* Vol. 78, No. 6, pp. 839–846.

Garikes, Wilson. Atkinson, Inc., 1989. Unpublished data. Birmingham, AL.

Health and Welfare Canada, 1980. *Evaluation and Space Programming Methodology Series #16, Laboratory.* Chi Systems, Inc., Ann Arbor, MI.

Hospital Survey Committee, 1974. Cost Containment and Financing of Hospital Construction. Philadelphia, p. 8.

Hudenberg, Roy, 1967. *Planning the Community Hospital.* New York: McGraw-Hill.

Little, A.D., 1975. *Evaluation of Hill Burton Standards.*

McNeely, M.D.D., 1989. Private letter. Secretary-Treasurer Canadian Association of Pathologists.

Mercy Medical Center, 1979.

NACHRI, 1978. *Study to Quantify the Uniqueness of Children's Hospitals.*

Owen, Seward E., Finch, E.P., and Byers, W.H., 1958. Good Design Steps Up Laboratory Production. *Modern Hospital,* Vol. 91, No. 3,

Rappoport, Arthur E., 1960. *Manual for Laboratory Planning and Design.* Chicago: American College of Pathologists.

Rappoport, Arthur E., 1961. As reported by Hudenberg (1967).

Rappoport, Arthur E., Taylor, Wilbur R., and Gaulin, Richard P., 1973. What the Modern Laboratory

Must Include and Where to Put It. *Modern Hospital,* pp. 55–63.

Simmons, H.J., 1983. The Extramural Laboratory, *Human Pathology* Vol. 14, No. 2, pp. 104–107.

Steinle, John G., 1969. Consultants Corner, *Hospital Topics,*

U.S. Department of Health, Education and Welfare, 1977. *Preliminary Hospital Evaluation Form, Clinical Laboratory.* Washington, DC.

U.S. Public Health Service, 1961. How to Plan the Laboratory for the General Hospital, *Modern Hospital,* Vol. 96, No. 6, pp. 83–86.

Wheeler, Todd E., 1964. *Hospital Design and Function.* New York: McGraw-Hill.

Wheeler, Todd E., 1971. *Hospital Modernization and Expansion.* New York: McGraw-Hill.

USEFUL SOURCES OF INFORMATION

College of American Pathologists
5202 Old Orchard Road
Skokie IL 60077
312/966-5700

National Hospital Productivity Improvement Program
Workload Measurement System
Miss Anita Jensen
Ottawa Civic Hospital
1053 Carling Avenue
Ottawa, Canada K1Y4E9

2.7 ASSESSING BUILDINGS FOR USE AS LABORATORIES   *T. Ruys*

2.7.1 Introduction

Many states, cities, and universities are getting on the high-technology bandwagon as a way of increasing employment and their tax base. Many high-technology research parks are being developed as a result of this new emphasis.

With an increase in the number of research laboratories in the near future, many developers will build research laboratory "spec" buildings or lease existing buildings planned for reuse as laboratory buildings.

This section provides a convenient checklist for individuals who must evaluate these buildings for use as research laboratories. Most of the same features apply to teaching laboratories as well. These checkpoints need to be adjusted based on needs. They are intended as general guidelines only.

The evaluations are broken down into major areas of concern in the order of their impact on costs if changes were made. These major areas are structural, mechanical, plumbing, power, lighting, and architectural. See Table 2.7-1.

The information provided in this checklist is discussed in greater detail elsewhere in this handbook but is summarized here for the convenience of those who need to assess buildings for use as research laboratories.

2.7.2 Structural Evaluation

- What is the design's live load? Research laboratory buildings typically are designed for 150 pounds/sq ft but may need as little as 100 pounds/sq ft or as much as 200 pounds/sq ft, depending on the equipment and density used. Any live load capacity below 100 pounds/sq ft will limit the usefulness of the building for research. A typical wet bench chemistry lab uses 150 pounds/sq ft live load. See Figure 2.7-1.

- Will vibration be a potential limitation? Steel and precast concrete structures may vibrate to such a degree that the use of vibration-sensitive instrumentation and processes is restricted. Long structural spans may have the same effect. Vibration can also be caused by inadequate isolation of mechanical equipment and by vehicular traffic in the vicinity of the building.

- Is the floor-to-floor height adequate? Research buildings, because of a minimum ceiling height of 8 ft 6 in. and space needs for the distribution of ducts and piping, should not have a floor-to-floor height less than 12 ft 6 in. See Figure 2.7-2. If interstitial mechanical space is required, the floor-to-floor height is even greater.

- What is the structural bay size? Research laboratories are typically laid out in a modular fashion in order to standardize, thus reducing costs and increasing efficiency. Module sizes may

Table 2.7-1. Checklist—Items to Consider in Evaluating Buildings for Use as Laboratories

Category	Item	Evaluation	Remarks
Structural			
	Live load < 100 lbs/sq ft	Reject	Limits location of equipment
	100–200 lbs/sq ft	Review needs	Consider equipment needs
	Vibration		
	Steel structure	Possible reject ⎫	Review vibration-sensitive
	Precast concrete	Possible reject ⎬	equipment
	Long spans	Possible reject ⎭	
	Floor-to-floor height < 12'6"	Reject	Inadequate mechanical space
	Bay size	Review module	20 ft minimum on center along window wall
	Vertical penetrations	Piping, power, etc.	Access for changes
	No crawl space: evaluate available drains	Avoid disruption later	
Mechanical			
	Ventilation, recirculated air	Reject ⎫	Not acceptable for many
	Ventilation rate < 8 to 10 changes/hr	Reject ⎬	types of research
	No cooling	Reject ⎭	
	Filtration < 80%	Reject	
	Thermostats zone control	Reject	Many instruments require close tolerance
	Systems redundancy absent, fans, filters, power	Review needs	Also needed for maintenance
	Air intake location	Relation to other building exhaust pollutants	Evaluate
Plumbing			
	Site utilities—water	Adequacy, location avail-	Size for fire protection
	gas	ability	Consider propane
	Utilities distribution	See structural backflow	
	Potable water	prevention	
Waste			
	Drainlines	Material and size	
	Treatment	Capacity	Site or municipality
Power			
	Capacity	Transformer—watts/GSF	Allow for growth Switch gear
	Distribution	Subpanels 200 amps/lab	Spare capacity Bus duct
	Special power	Clean power	Evaluate need
		Emergency power	Evaluate need
	Redundancy	Two sources	
Lighting			
	Level < 75 foot-candles	Reject	Ideal parallel & above bench
	Location	Can fixtures be moved in a grid?	
	Type	Fluorescent cool white	Color corrected for some
	Switching	Each module has own switch	
Architectural			
	Fire zones	Evaluate code compliance	
	Exiting	Evaluate code compliance	
	Ceiling heights < 8'6"	Reject	Too low for some equipment
	Door sizes to labs < 3'4"	Reject	

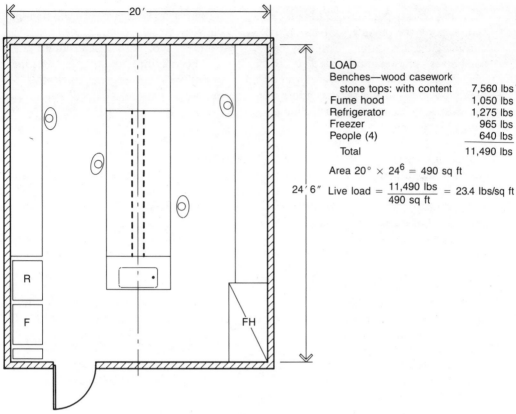

LOAD
Benches—wood casework
   stone tops: with content   7,560 lbs
Fume hood   1,050 lbs
Refrigerator   1,275 lbs
Freezer   965 lbs
People (4)   640 lbs
   Total   11,490 lbs

Area $20° \times 24^6 = 490$ sq ft

Live load $= \dfrac{11,490 \text{ lbs}}{490 \text{ sq ft}} = 23.4$ lbs/sq ft

Fig. 2.7-1. Live load—typical wet chemistry lab (configuration of the lab is for this example only).

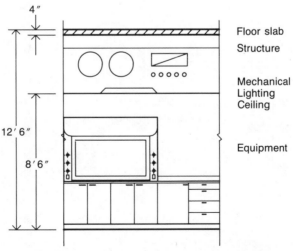

Floor slab
Structure

Mechanical
Lighting
Ceiling

Equipment

Fig. 2.7-2. Floor-to-floor height—research building (diagrammatic).

vary, but a bay spacing of 20 ft on the center along the outside wall should be considered a minimum. Columns can sometimes be accommodated if the structural grid and the laboratory module do not overlap, but there is a loss of useful space. Partitions need to line up with exterior columns or window mullions. See Figure 2.7-3. The cost of this reduction in space efficiency must be weighed against the lease, operating, and maintenance costs.

- Are vertical penetrations possible? Research laboratories require utilities, power, and communication links. Space is needed. Horizontal distribution can be accommodated in the floor-to-floor heights noted above. Vertical penetrations, if not provided, may be expensive or impossible to accommodate, depending on the structural system.
- Is a crawl space available? Drain lines run below the floor they serve. For the ground floor, that may create a problem if there is no space where drain lines can be rearranged, changed, enlarged or connected to. A so-called slab on grade can be cut into to accommodate new drain lines but is very disruptive for buildings that are occupied. All utilities can run down from the ceiling of the ground floor. The exception is steam lines, which like drain lines, are located below the floors they serve because the steam condensate return flows down.

2.7.3 Mechanical Evaluation

- Is the exhaust air from the laboratories recirculated? Recirculating air is not acceptable for many types of laboratories. Clean air is critical to many types of research. A spec office building typically has 80% recirculated air with 30% filtration. If that is acceptable initially, it may not be later on when research needs become more sophisticated. Changes of this nature are very costly.

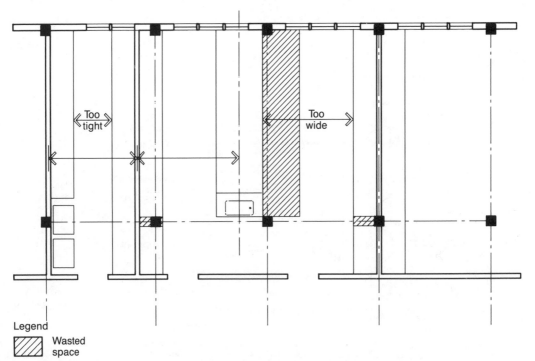

Legend
▨ Wasted space

Fig. 2.7-3. Reduction of space efficiency when structural grid and laboratory modules don't match.

- What is the ventilation rate in changes per hour? Typically a research laboratory has a ventilation rate of 8 to 12 changes per hour, which is required to keep contaminants at a low level and to keep the temperature at the level needed for instrumentation. If the ventilation rate is below 10 changes per hour, rejection should be considered because it limits future growth potential. Adding air volume later is very expensive.
- Is cooling provided with the mechanical system? Cooling is essential to maintain room temperatures for many types of research and instrumentation, not to mention human comfort. A range of 68° to 72°F is common for research laboratories. Individual laboratory air conditioning package units are often added, but these pose special problems. Lack of maintenance causes the filter media to become a growth area for pathogens, thus increasing the level of contaminants over time. These units are also noisy and take up space in the laboratory.
- Is the filtration adequate? For many research laboratories, filtration should not be less than 80%. Some types of research require even more. Increasing the level of filtration later on is expensive.
- Does each laboratory have its own thermostat? Individual thermostats in laboratories are highly desirable. Laboratories vary in their need for cooling. Some need close tolerances; others can vary greatly in order to save energy. Some accommodate many heat-producing objects such as people and ovens; others are empty or not in use. On the other hand, offices typically operate on zone controls.
- Do the systems have built-in redundancy? The need for redundancy in systems must be evaluated. Is any research or material lost due to failure of the fans, cooling, power, water or any other utility? Is it an irreversible loss? What is the cost in person-hours, dollars or competitiveness (see Section 2.9 on risk assessment). Some systems must be redundant in any case for maintenance reasons or in order to accommodate changes needed during summer and winter months. Boilers, fans and filters often come in pairs for that reason.
- Where is the air intake for the building located? Effluent exhausted from the building must not find its way back into the building air intake in order to avoid recirculating contaminants. The wind directions of the site must be known: both the prevailing winds and the microclimate created due to surrounding structures. The air intake must also be remote from intermittent and seasonal pollutants such as parking lots, loading docks, vegetation and dust. Air intakes should also be remote from hot surfaces so that the coolest outside air is taken in. See Figure 2.7-4.

2.7.4 Plumbing Evaluation

- Are site utilities adequate? Present and future needs must be considered for water, gas and sewage. Water source must be adequate for fire-fighting needs to meet construction codes and insurance requirements. Natural gas, if needed and not available, may be replaced by bottled or tanked propane gas.
- Are utilities distributed adequately? Needed utilities should be distributed to each laboratory module and valved and capped at that point to provide the capability to install service fixtures to each lab later on without discontinuing service to other laboratories. If utilities are not in place, the space needed for distribution must be evaluated. (See ''Structural Evaluation'' above.)
- Is the water source protected? A backflow preventer must be installed to protect the water source from contamination by laboratory operations. The water for drinking water fixtures and bathroom lavatories must be independent of the laboratory water system. See Figure 2.7-5.

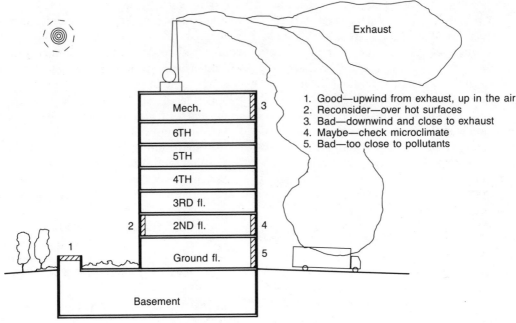

1. Good—upwind from exhaust, up in the air
2. Reconsider—over hot surfaces
3. Bad—downwind and close to exhaust
4. Maybe—check microclimate
5. Bad—too close to pollutants

Fig. 2.7-4. Building air intake conditions.

2.7.5 Waste Evaluation

- Are drain lines adequate? The size and material of drain lines must be evaluated. Typical spec buildings have undersized drain lines which may not be acid resistant. Laboratory waste lines must be separate from sanitary waste and storm drains.

- Where is the waste treated? Waste treatment may be on site or provided by a municipality. Either way, the capacity must be adequate to handle the volumes of waste expected. Many reviewing

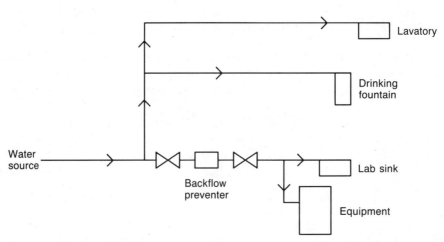

Fig. 2.7-5. Location of a backflow preventer in a laboratory water system.

agencies require acid dilution tanks in the laboratory waste line.

2.7.6 Power Evaluation

- Is the capacity adequate? Power needs for research typically far exceed those for office buildings. See Chapter 6 for rules of thumb for power needs for receptacles, mechanical equipment and lighting. Is spare capacity available for growth?
- Is power distribution adequate? Many buildings have an adequate source of power, but the distribution is inadequate, so that power is not available where needed in the laboratory, too few electrical receptacles are available at the bench, and/or too many adjacent receptacles are on the same circuit.
- Is special power available? Some instrumentation with a high amperage or clean power needs bypass subpanels and must be connected to the transformer as directly as possible. Adding a conduit later can be very disruptive. Adequate space must be provided for changes and additions. Emergency power as required by building codes for exit lighting can often be provided by battery-operated lights. However, emergency power for elevator exits for handicapped persons, freezers, refrigerators, incubators and animal life support systems is rarely provided and must be considered.
- Is power redundancy provided? Emergency power needs may be provided by a second source of supply taken from another power grid. Transformers should be provided in groups of three and sized such that any two can take the total load.

2.7.7 Lighting Evaluation

- Is the light adequate? Research laboratories typically require 100 foot-candles at the benchtop level. Because of energy conservation pressures and local energy codes, that level of illumination is rarely provided. A level below 75 foot-candles for general illumination should be rejected. Laboratories are not work stations and do not lend themselves to task lighting.
- Where are lighting fixtures located? They should be located parallel to the laboratory bench and above the front edge (see Figure 2.7-6). This could be considered a form of task lighting. Fixtures perpendicular to the bench length cause hot spots and glare. Fixtures mounted below wall cabinets are no substitute for ceiling-mounted fixtures because they fix the cabinet in place and cause glare on the benchtop surface. Some ceiling grids allow light fixtures to be moved; this capability should be verified.
- What type of lighting is provided? Few buildings now have incandescent fixtures; however, among fluorescent fixtures, there is a wide variety of styles and quality of illumination. Fixtures should minimize glare and maximize efficiency. Sound rated ballast is desirable in quiet areas, and color-corrected tubes should be considered in areas where simulating daylight is important.
- Is switching adequate? Two switches per laboratory module (see Figure 2.7-6) is considered a minimum because one side of the lab can be darkened for certain operations. Switching for each lab is important for energy conservation as well.

2.7.8 Architectural Evaluation

- Does the building meet exiting requirements? This section cannot provide an exhaustive treatment of this subject. Local codes vary widely. The intent is to alert the evaluator to the most obvious and glaring discrepancies. Are there two ways out of laboratories over 500 square feet? Are there at least two ways to exit a floor? Are corridors fire rated to provide access to an exit such as an outside door or stair? Are there any dead-end corridors? Do doors swing in

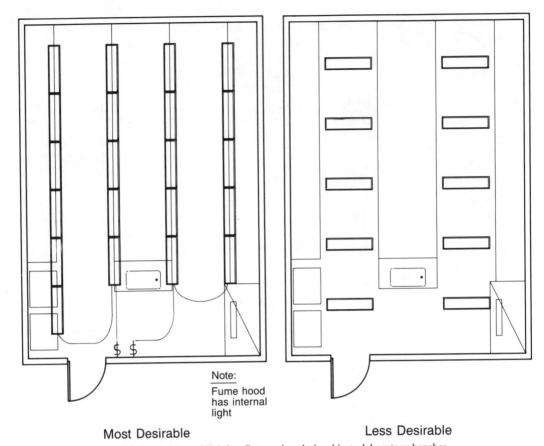

Most Desirable   Less Desirable

Fig. 2.7-6. Location of lighting fixtures in relationship to laboratory benches.

Note:

Fume hood
has internal
light

the direction of exit from the lab to the outside?

- Is the amount of space adequate? A typical research laboratory building requires more space for mechanical and electrical needs than a typical office building for the same NASF. This varies with the complexity of the research conducted, the safety requirements and the number of people. See Section 8.6 for guidelines about the NASF to GSF ratios in various laboratories. Future growth must also be considered.

- Are ceiling heights adequate? Ceilings, if required, and/or lighting fixtures are typically placed at 9 ft but can be as low as 8 ft 6 in. to accommodate most laboratory equipment. Ceilings higher than 9 ft are wasteful because they require higher lighting intensity for the same foot-candles on the bench and because

greater air volume must be exhausted for the same air changes per hour.

- Are door sizes adequate? Most laboratory equipment will fit through a 3 ft 4 in. door, but not through the 3 ft doors typically provided.

- Are finishes adequate? For most laboratories a vinyl floor, enamel paint on gypsum wallboard, and a 2- by 4-ft grid lay-in ceiling is satisfactory. These spaces are relatively dust free, easy to maintain, and reasonable in appearance. See Section 3.6 for a discussion of the finishes used in other applications.

2.7.9 Conclusion

If the evaluator is satisfied that a building fulfills most of the requirements, it is time to engage an architect/engineer team to check out the building's systems in greater detail.

Local codes vary greatly, and the local authorities must be consulted. The cost of modifying the existing building to accommodate research needs may be the final governing factor to make the go/no-go decision.

2.8 LABORATORY RENOVATION AND CODE UPDATE   T. Ruys

The Society of College and University Planning, in a survey of colleges and universities titled *The State of College and University Facilities,* stated that "Among the most serious, and least recognized, of the problems currently facing institutions of higher education is the condition of their physical plants" (Helpern 1987).

All building owners must update and renovate their property sooner or later. That can be accomplished piecemeal only up to a point. This section assists the decision-making process by pointing out how code officials view renovations and by listing the major areas of review.

Most building officials treat existing buildings under a "grandfather" clause, which means that the owners do not need to meet code requirements which came into being after the building was built. However, if a major renovation is planned, the building must usually comply with present codes. Codes vary depending on the local jurisdiction, so it is advisable to check with your local building department.

If the decision is made to consider renovation, the following areas of major changes must be anticipated. They are listed in order of the greatest anticipated expense.

2.8.1 Structural Update

Particularly in areas of the country where seismic codes are in effect, a structural update can become a major expense. The reader is advised to engage a structural engineer. For older buildings, the lateral force-resisting system probably must be upgraded.

2.8.2 Life Safety

Building construction, distance to adjacent buildings, exit width of corridors and stairs,

number of stairs and their relative location, and rated corridor walls, including doors and hardware, are all subject to review.

Unprotected open stairwells and dead-end corridors must be eliminated. Automatic fire protection systems may be required in some code jurisdictions or may offer relief from stair and corridor restrictions and be cost effective. New rapid-response fire detection, alarm and emergency communications systems may also be advisable or required.

2.8.3 Mechanical Update

In research laboratory buildings, fumehood requirements have increased over time. Very often fumehoods have been added, but no additional makeup air has been provided. This causes the building to be under excessive negative pressure, which causes outside pollutants and dust to be drawn into the laboratories. Buildings may also begin to leak through outside walls. If the building is fairly airtight, there will not be enough makeup air for the fumehoods to work properly, and an unsafe condition may exist.

Fumehood additions often have the fan located on top of the hood, which causes the exhaust duct to the outside to be under positive pressure. If leaks develop in the duct—and they will in time—the effluent from the hood exhaust may enter occupied spaces.

In older buildings, fire dampers in the ventilation ducts are often not provided. If fire-rated portions are added, fire dampers must also be provided. However, an exception is made for fumehood exhaust ducts (see Section 4.4).

In some areas of the country, seismic bracing is required for major mechanical equipment.

2.8.4 Plumbing Update

Plumbing upgrades generally focus on two areas: the systems and the adequacy of facilities for occupants.

The system review focuses on proper venting of fixtures, backflow prevention, separation of laboratory waste from sanitary waste and storm drains. Waste treatment will also be reviewed.

The facilities checked are the toilets, urinals, lavatories and drinking fountains.

Seismic bracing is required in some areas.

2.8.5 Electrical Update

Electrical needs in laboratories have changed more than any other need. Capacity and distribution are often inadequate. Emergency power requirements for exiting and exits for the handicapped have changed capacity needs.

Lighting levels have been reduced, but more energy-efficient light fixtures should also be considered. Individual room switching should be added, if not available, for energy conservation.

2.8.6 Energy Update

Many municipalities have their own energy codes, with formulas which allow credit for certain items as long as the total stays within prescribed limits. Items considered are reduced heat gain and energy loss. These are controlled by the type of glass, coatings and glazing layers, and by insulation in walls, floors and ceilings.

2.8.7 Asbestos Abatement

At present, there is no law requiring removal of asbestos, but there are regulations on how asbestos should be stabilized or removed. Major renovation typically includes asbestos removal, which is considerably easier and less costly in buildings without occupants. Few buildings are without asbestos in one form or another. The most obvious materials containing asbestos are structural fireproofing and pipe insulation, but asbestos is also found in floor tile, plaster, transite ducts, colorlith and colorceran laboratory benchtops and fumehood liners.

2.8.8 Other Considerations

Renovation on a major scale causes other concerns. Laboratory facilities that have been used for many years may contain high levels of hazardous materials in ducts, piping and drains. Two recent examples illustrate this point.

Perchloric acid was widely used in the past. Only recently was it realized that it can create explosive compounds when in contact with organic substances. In an attempt to re-

Table 2.8-1. Checklist—Items to Consider in Renovating Laboratory Facilities

Category	Item	Evaluation
Structural	Seismic upgrade	Engage structural engineer
Life safety	Construction	Review with code officials
	Exiting	
	Setbacks	
	Fire protection	
Mechanical	Air balancing	Engage mechanical engineer
	Seismic bracing	
Plumbing	Laboratory waste	Engage mechanical engineer
	Venting	
	Seismic bracing	
Electrical	Wiring upgrade	Engage electrical engineer
	Emergency power —	
	Exit lighting, critical systems	
Energy	Mechanical system	Engage conservation engineer
	Electrical system	
Asbestos abatement	Insulation	Engage asbestos abatement or removal company

move a fumehood duct, a construction worker was killed by such an explosion. Building owners should investigate their past fumehood use and alert construction teams to the proper procedures for removing perchloric acid residues and perchlorate compounds.

Polychlorinated biphenyls, like asbestos, were once considered a miracle product. They reduce the likelihood of fires in certain applications and were introduced in gas piping for that reason. Gas piping should therefore be checked for polychlorinated biphenyls before they are changed or removed.

Major renovations will also probably require an environmental impact statement.

2.8.9 Conclusions

When a major renovation is planned, it will cause other reviews that are typically retroactive and require updating at any time, but that may have been missed or ignored by the authorities having jurisdiction. Two that come to mind are compliance with the Occupational Safety and Health Act (OSHA) and the standards for the handicapped. These are covered in greater detail in Sections 7.2 and 7.5.

The major factor in renovation is the cost. In most cases, renovation on a large scale is prohibitively expensive and may not be worth the cost.

REFERENCES

Helpern, David Paul, 1987. *The State of College and University Facilities.* Society for College and University Planning. Ann Arbor, MI.

2.9 RISK ASSESSMENT   *R. Zalosh*

2.9.1 Introduction

Risk assessment is a hazard evaluation approach that accounts for the probability of a loss or injury occurring, as well as the magnitude of the loss or injury. Classical risk assessment, or risk management, relies on historic incident data for both probability and consequence estimates. Modern risk assess-

ment, or engineering risk analysis, uses systematic predictive procedures for applications that lack sufficient historic data. Some of these procedures are described in this section, and simple examples involving laboratory design considerations are offered.

Modern risk assessment techniques were first developed in the 1960s for analyzing the safety and reliability of aerospace vehicles. When nuclear power plant safety analysts adopted and extended these techniques in the 1970s (Levine and Rasmussen, 1975), the engineering and safety communities and, to a lesser extent, regulatory authorities and the general public, reacted with a healthy mixture of interest and skepticism. Several widely publicized catastrophic chemical plant accidents in the 1980s have now motivated the chemical industry to make extensive use of modern risk assessment techniques. Many other industries have started using risk assessment methods to assist in making safety decisions about new products and processes, hazardous material usage, transport and disposal, and cost effectiveness trade-offs in alternative facility protection systems.

It is clear from the preceding rundown of modern risk assessment problems that risk assessment is most often utilized when:

1. there is no previous experience to evaluate the risk/hazard; or
2. there is a new appreciation of the magnitude or probability of loss; or
3. there is a threat of regulatory intervention without a well-founded basis for the proposed regulation, code or standard.

The use of contemporary risk assessment as an alternative to regulatory/consensus codes and standards is particularly appealing to scientists because of their appreciation of systematic, logical reasoning in reaching conclusions. Therefore, these techniques should appeal to laboratory scientists and laboratory directors working in new disciplines or with new and potentially hazardous materials or processes.

Two important disadvantages of modern risk assessment are the time and effort required to obtain useful quantitative results and the likelihood that two good risk assessors will arrive at two or more different conclusions. In other words, a significant amount of time, effort, and subjective judgment are inevitably required to answer the following four generic questions, which form the framework for contemporary risk assessment methodology: What can go wrong? What are the effects and consequences, and are they acceptable? How often will it happen? How are the frequency and consequences affected by the use of various protection measures?

2.9.2 Risk Assessment Methodology

The following is a cursory overview of the more popular modern risk assessment techniques. It is intended to develop the reader's interest in and appreciation for these techniques, but stops far short of providing him or her with all the tools and information needed to be a serious risk assessor. More complete descriptions and instructions can be found in Levine and Rasmussen (1975), Henley and Kumamoto (1981), Vesely et al. (1981), Department of Defense Military Standard (1984) and Battelle Columbus Division (1985).

Preliminary Hazard Analysis

A preliminary hazard analysis (PHA) is implemented at the conceptual design stage of a new project or facility in order to identify major hazards, potential safety systems, and the need for more detailed hazard evaluations. It consists of a simple tabulation of potential hazards, their causes and effects, and possible preventive or corrective measures. The PHA is entirely qualitative, and can be conducted by one or two engineers or architects with a safety background and a basic understanding of laboratory design and operating criteria for the facility in question.

The PHA format shown here is the one suggested by the Department of Defense

Military Standard (1984) and the AIChE Center for Chemical Plant Safety (Battelle Columbus Division, 1982). An example is shown in Table 2.9-1 for a laboratory clean room in which experiments will be conducted with equipment and material vulnerable to contamination when exposed to an ordinary or dirty atmospheric environment. As shown in Table 2.9-1, contamination seems to be the outstanding threat or hazard in a clean room laboratory. The three listed causes of contamination are (1) ventilation system failure (insufficient air velocity, plugged filter, etc.), (2) fire with associated smoke, and (3) a corrosive liquid spill. The third column in Table 2.9-1 lists the major consequences of each source of contamination. Potential protection measures to prevent or limit each form of contamination damage are listed in the last column of the table.

One other hazard listed in Table 2.9-1 is excessive pressure in the clean room as a result of a ventilation system imbalance or an explosion. Room pressure warnings and interlocks to shut down operations are suggested preventive/corrective measures, along with flammable vapor detectors and explosion suppression systems. The list of hazards and protection measures in Table 2.9-1 is far from complete and is offered for illustrative purposes only.

If the PHA identifies novel or severe hazards not previously considered, additional evaluation is usually needed before a decision can be made about protection measures. Specific scenarios leading to the hazard and their likelihood of occurrence should be considered. This can be pursued in a thorough yet qualitative manner by conducting a failure modes, effects, and criticality analysis.

Failure Modes, Effects, and Criticality Analysis

A failure modes and effects analysis (FMEA) is a technique used by reliability engineers and product designers to identify and tabulate systematically the ramifications of various component failures in a system,

Table 2.9-1. Sample Format for Preliminary Hazard Analysis—Clean Room Laboratory

Hazard	Causes	Major Consequences	Corrective or Preventive Measures
Contamination	1. Ventilation system failure	a. Vulnerable equipment damaged	(a-1) Warning and shutdown on ventilation system failure
		b. Experiments interrupted	(a-2) Minimize in-room storage
			(b-1) Expedite repair or replacement of ventilation system
			(b-2) Alternative facilities available
	2. Fire	a,b. Above	(c-1) Use less flammable materials
		c. Injuries	(c-2) Sensitive smoke detection system
		d. Equipment damage in adjacent rooms	(c-3) Automatic fire suppression system
	3. Corrosive liquid spill	a–c. Above	(a-2) Above
			(d-1) Use corrosion-resistant materials
			(d-2) Limit container size for corrosive liquids
Excessive pressure in room	1. Ventilation system imbalance	a. Structural failure	(a-1) Differential pressure interlock
	2. Explosion	a. Above	(a-1) Above
		b. Injuries	(a-2) Flammable vapor detector
		c. Equipment damage	(a-3) Explosion suppression

product, or process. Contemporary risk assessors have adopted and extended the FMEA to identify the seriousness or criticality of component failure modes and their relative probability of occurrence. The extended FMEA with criticality considerations included is called a "failure modes, effects, and criticality analysis (FMECA)."

The FMECA is usually conducted on an equipment level once the equipment detailed design is available and its operation and interaction with other equipment are established. It is best conducted as a team effort with equipment designers, operators, and system safety personnel participating. The FMECA should result in a thorough listing of all system components, failure modes, and their consequences for equipment operation and personnel safety. Since it can be a time-consuming effort for complicated equipment, the FMECA is not conducted for all equipment, but is definitely appropriate for equipment containing hazardous materials or critical safety components such as ventilation/exhaust systems and fire protection systems.

A sample format for an FMECA tabulation is shown in Table 2.9-2. The procedure for filling out the table is to start by systematically considering and listing each system component and operating mode. Possible failure modes are then identified for each combination of component and failure mode. The resulting effects of each failure mode are then listed, along with their relative probability of occurrence (low, medium, or high) and criticality category. The four criticality categories suggested in the AIChE Hazard Evaluation Guidelines (Battelle Columbus Division, 1985) are (1) no hazard; (2) minor hazard, no equipment or process shutdown required; (3) significant hazard, orderly shutdown required; and (4) immediate hazard requiring emergency shutdown.

As an example, consider a laboratory fumehood. One critical component of the fumehood is the exhaust ducting. Two potential exhaust ducting failure modes are corrosion and obstruction. A subtle form of obstruction discussed by Diberardinis et al. (1987) and experienced in this author's laboratory facilities is airflow imbalance on man-

Table 2.9-2. Sample FMECA for a Laboratory Fumehood

Component	Operating Mode	Failure Mode	Effects	Probability	Criticality	Corrective Action
Exhaust duct	On	Corrosion	Leakage	Depends on duct material and vapor corrosivity	Minor or significant	Possible shutdown
Exhaust duct	On	Obstructed	Flow stoppage or reversal	Medium or high	Significant or immediate	Possible shutdown
Front face	Setup	Stuck open	Incorrect ventilation	Low	None or minor	Remove hazardous material
Front face	On	Slides down	No air inflow	Low	None or minor	Possible shutdown
Others						

ifolded ducting connecting multiple hoods. The imbalance can cause reverse flow into one or more hoods and emission of toxic gas or vapor into surrounding laboratories. Based on personal experience, there is a medium to high probability of this imbalance occurring and producing the kind of hazard and disturbance that would entail an orderly shutdown of laboratory operations. The most direct and permanent corrective action is to install a dedicated exhaust fan, duct, and/or scrubber for each new fumehood. Since this is a potentially expensive solution, it may warrant justification by quantifying the frequency and consequences of fumehood flow reversal.

Systematic completion of the FMECA should result in a failure mode tabulation that can be used for both equipment design modification and further hazard assessment.

The next step in a comprehensive risk assessment would most likely be a fault tree analysis.

Fault Tree Analysis

A fault tree is a graphical representation of an accident or hazard caused by combinations of specific equipment failures, human errors, and environmental events. Fault tree analysis (FTA) is the process of deductive reasoning that identifies all possible combinations of independent failures/errors/events resulting in the accident or hazard. Quantitative FTA is the process of calculating the probability and frequency of occurrence of the accident from the failure rates and probabilities of the contributing basic events.

Figure 2.9-1 shows a sample fault tree for

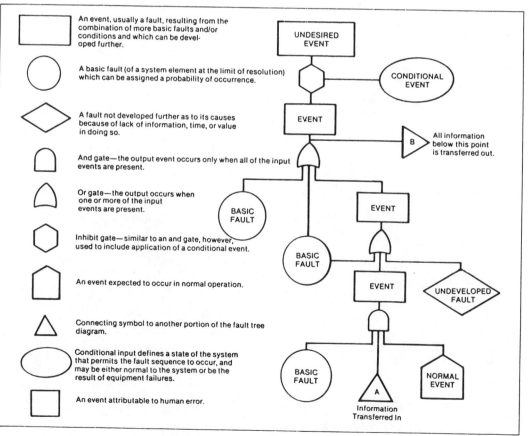

Fig. 2.9-1. Fault tree symbols for an undesirable event.

some undesired event or accident at the top of the tree. The symbols in the tree, which are defined in the figure, represent contributing events/faults and "gates" indicating how these events/faults are combined to lead to some resulting event. Construction of the tree begins with the top event and works backward or downward, level by level, until the basic events/faults are established. A basic event/fault is one which can be assigned a probability or failure rate.

Qualitative analysis of the fault tree usually entails determining minimal cut sets. A cut set is a combination of events which can lead to the top event in the tree. A minimal cut set is a collection of basic events that must occur simultaneously for the top event to occur. If any basic event is eliminated from the minimal cut set, the accident will not occur in that particular scenario. In other words, a minimal cut set is a funda-

mental scenario for the accident or hazard being studied. By identifying the basic events in each scenario, FTA can suggest how these scenarios can be avoided or rendered less likely to occur.

Examples of cut sets and minimal cut sets are given in Figure 2.9-2 and Table 2.9-3, respectively. Figure 2.9-2 is an example of a fault tree used by a chemical company during a safety review of a proposed laboratory expansion and relocation (Le et al., 1988). The laboratory processes toxic gases (arsine, phosphine, and diborane) in a ventilated hood equipped with a nitrogen dilution line leading to a scrubber connected to the hood ventilation fan. The fault tree drawn by Le et al. is in the form of three alternative cut sets leading to the top event: toxic gas release in the laboratory. Each of the 16 minimal cut sets listed in Table 2.9-3 could produce a toxic gas release if the basic events occurred

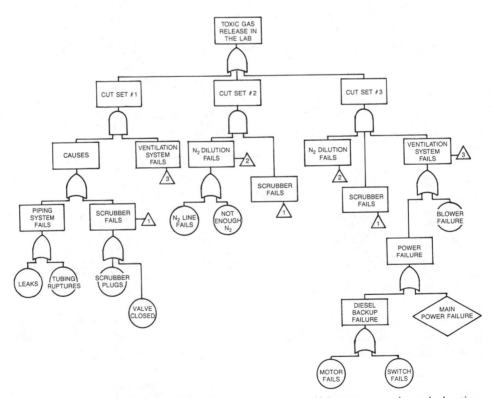

Fig. 2.9-2. Example of a fault tree for a safety review of a proposed laboratory expansion and relocation (Le et al., 1988; reproduced with permission of the American Institute of Chemical Engineers).

Table 2.9-3. Minimal Cut Sets for Fault Tree in Figure 2.9-2

Min Cut Set	Event 1	Event 2	Event 3	Event 4
1-1	Leaks	Blower fails	—	—
1-2	Tube rupture	Blower fails	—	—
1-3	Scrub plugs	Blower fails	—	—
1-4	Scrub valve	Blower fails	—	—
1-5	Leaks	Main power	Diesel motor	—
1-6	Tube rupture	Main power	Diesel motor	—
1-7	Scrub plugs	Main power	Diesel motor	—
1-8	Scrubber valve	Main power	Diesel motor	—
1-9	Leaks	Main power	Diesel switch	—
1-10	Tube rupture	Main power	Diesel switch	—
1-11	Scrub plugs	Main power	Diesel switch	—
1-12	Scrub valve	Main power	Diesel switch	—
2-1	N2 line	Scrub plugs	—	—
2-2	Not enough N2	Scrub plugs	—	—
2-3	N2 line	Scrub plugs	—	—
2-4	Not enough N2	Scrub plugs	—	—

simultaneously, e.g., a leak along with a ventilation blower failure. The fact that the blower failure occurs in four two-event minimal cut sets suggests that it should be particularly reliable or supplemented with an on-line backup blower.

This qualitative FTA is limited in that it does not account for either the probability of an event occurring or its effect on the severity of the top event. In the case of Figure 2.9-2, Le et al. (1988) pointed out that a tubing rupture produces a much more severe toxic gas release than a leak. They calculated the magnitude of the release and the subsequent gas concentrations and decided to limit the size of the toxic gas cylinders allowed in the laboratory.

Quantitative analysis of the fault tree itself entails mathematical manipulation of basic event/fault probabilities through rules of Boolean algebra. These manipulations can become complicated and tedious for large trees and are often conducted by computers. Lee et al. (1985) reviewed the various computer codes and methods available for FTA as of 1984. More recently, some new PC codes such as IRRAS (Russell et al., 1987) have become available.

FTA could be employed in a laboratory environment to analyze both tangible and intangible hazards. For example, FTA is a logical approach for identifying the causes and probability of an accidental release of a potentially dangerous microbiological agent from a biotechnology laboratory. It can also be used to identify the causes and probability of losing valuable experimental data. Results of the analysis would suggest the most effective preventive measures for both types of hazard.

Event Tree Analysis

An event tree is a graphical representation of the possible sequence of events that might occur following an accident initiation event. The initiating event could be a specific equipment failure such as the failure of a vacuum pump during an experiment, or it could be a generic event such as a fire or a flood in the laboratory. Construction of the event tree entails consideration of the likely success or failure of the personnel response and the safety system response called upon in chronological succession following accident initiation.

Event trees are often used for initiating events that could readily lead to a wide variety of consequences, depending on the effectiveness of emergency procedures and safety systems. The AIChE Hazard Evaluation Guideline (Battelle Columbus Division,

1985) recommend that the event tree analysis (ETA) be conducted by a team of two to four people, of which at least one is an experienced risk analyst, one is knowledgeable about detailed operations and emergency procedures at the facility in question, and one is expert on the effectiveness and reliability of installed safety systems.

Quantitative ETA includes estimates of the expected probability of success of each accident response measure. The resulting probability of each event sequence, i.e., each branch in the event tree, is then calculated by multiplying the probabilities of occurrence of all the events in the sequence. These sequence probabilities can then be examined to assess the adequacy of existing safety systems and emergency response procedures. This type of analysis can be particularly useful in comparing the potential effectiveness of alternative designs and operating procedures.

Figure 2.9-3 is a simple example of an event tree in which the initiating event is a fire in the laboratory. The subsequent three events, in sequence, are fire detected, fire controlled, and fire spread to other laboratories. Fire detection is assigned three alternatives: immediate detection, prompt detection, or delayed detection. Some of the fire incident data discussed in Section 2.9.3 use these detection categories. Fire control (which means either suppression or confinement) and fire spread to other laboratories both have binary outcomes: yes or no.

Probabilities are indicated at each branch of the event tree in Figure 2.9-3. The probability of fire control is assigned different values, depending on how soon the fire is detected. The outcome of each path through the tree is indicated as a product of the relevant event probabilities on that path. Each path results in one of the three alternative outcomes indicated, i.e., controlled fire, uncontrolled fire in the laboratory, or fire spread to other labs. The three paths in Figure 2.9-3 resulting in a controlled fire are the product of only two probabilities because the probability of fire spread to other labs is

assumed to be zero if the fire is successfully controlled in the lab of origin.

The probability evaluations required to quantify Figure 2.9-3 depend on the specific fire scenario and whether the laboratory is equipped with automatic sprinklers, smoke detectors wired to an attended station, and/ or effective fire walls, as called for in NFPA 45. Data sources for determining appropriate probabilities are described in Section 2.9.3.

As another example, consider the issue of storage of hazardous chemicals inside or outside of a chemical laboratory. Proponents of inside storage might argue that there is a greater hazard in frequent trips into and out of the laboratory with the chemical than there is in storing a quantity of the chemical in the lab. Proponents of outside storage might argue that the dire consequences of an accident within the lab dictate outside storage despite the need for more frequent trips to bring the chemical into and out of the laboratory. Event trees can be constructed for each situation.

Figure 2.9-4 shows a simple event tree for a volatile chemical spill while transporting the chemical into the laboratory or back to the storage area. The spill-initiating event is indicated as the first event on the left-hand side of the figure. The second event designates whether or not the spill occurs in or near an occupied area of the laboratory such that high vapor concentrations develop in the occupied area. The third event, "Rapid Egress Successful," indicates whether laboratory personnel (both the person transporting the chemical and personnel in the exposed area) can safely evacuate without injury. Assuming that the spill can be treated with a sorbent or containment material to reduce vaporization rates, the next "event" is the availability of this material at the laboratory. The fifth and final event in the tree is the effective treatment of the spill with this material.

Branch points corresponding to each event after initiation in this example have binary outcomes designated as Yes or No in the

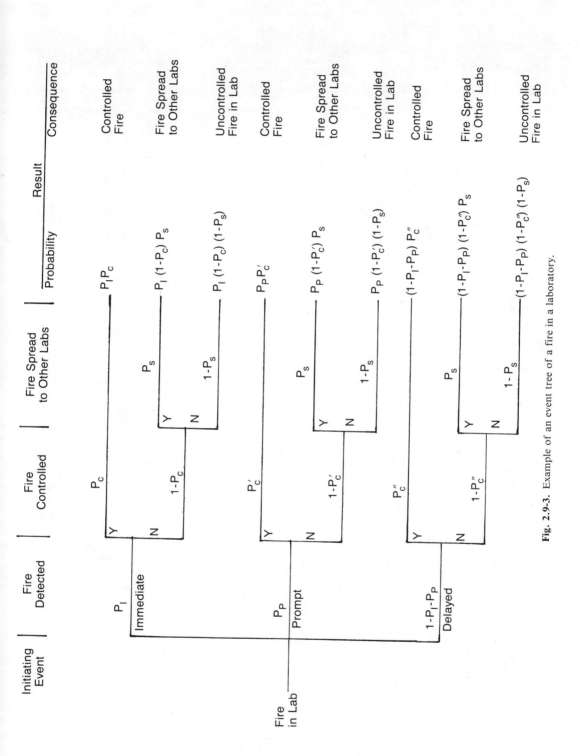

Fig. 2.9-3. Example of an event tree of a fire in a laboratory.

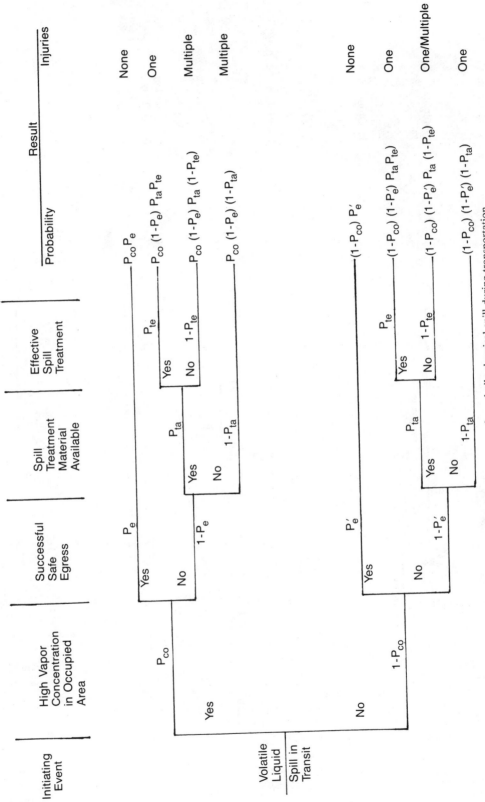

Fig. 2.9-4. Example of an event tree of a volatile chemical spill during transportation.

event tree. Probabilities of the Yes branches are denoted as p_{co}, p_e or p'_e, p_{ta}, and p_{te}, such that probabilities of the No branches are $1 - p_{co}$, etc. These are actually conditional probabilities in that they depend on the course of the accident at that point. Thus p_e denotes probability of successful egress of everyone in an occupied area, and p'_e denotes successful escape without injury of the person transporting the liquid. In some branches of the tree, the outcome in terms of expected injuries does not depend on successive events, so that successive branch points are omitted. For example, if everybody successfully evacuates without injury, there is no need to consider the availability and effectiveness of spill treatment.

The outcome of each path of the tree consists of its probability (computed as the product of individual events on the path) and its consequence, which in this case is the expected number of injuries. Two of the eight paths in Figure 2.9-4 lead to no injuries, three or four paths result in a single injury (the liquid transporter), and two or three paths result in multiple injuries. The uncertainty in the outcome of one path is due to the uncertain need to treat the spill effectively in an unoccupied area to prevent multiple injuries.

The corresponding event tree for an accident initiated with a leak of toxic vapor from a container stored inside the laboratory is shown in Figure 2.9-5. The four subsequent events determining the consequences of this accident as envisioned in Figure 2.9-5 are:

Lab occupied during the leak (p_{oc});
Vapor odor threshold less than danger threshold (p_{ot})
Vapor detector installed and functioning (p_{vd})
Detector triggers evacuation or leak containment (p_d)

In constructing the tree, it has been assumed that personnel smelling the toxic vapor at a concentration between the odor threshold and the danger threshold would realize that they have to stop the leak or evacuate. On the other hand, the presence of the vapor detector may not necessarily trigger the same response, depending on the detector's reliability, its alarm threshold, and the response of laboratory personnel who may not hear the alarm or may choose to ignore it.

Four of the eight paths through this tree lead to no injuries, two paths lead to a single injury (the first person entering the area in which the leak occurs), and two paths lead to multiple injuries (assuming that the laboratory is occupied by more than one person). Of course, the number of paths in each category is not as important as the probability of each category, which is the sum of the probabilities of all the paths in that category. For example, the probability of multiple injuries given this initiating event is

$$p_{oc}(1 - p_{ot})(p_{vd}(1 - p_d) + (1 - p_{vd}))$$

Readers with a mathematical bent may want to verify that the sum of the probabilities of all the outcomes is unity in both Figure 2.9-4 and Figure 2.9-5.

Many other events and safety features could influence the outcomes of the accidents shown in Figures 2.9-4 and 2.9-5. The presence of an effective emergency ventilation system, self-contained breathing apparatus, and a well-trained emergency response team significantly affect the number and extent of injuries in both cases. Addition of these features to the event trees would complicate the event trees and probability calculations significantly. Their inclusion for quantitative ETA would be warranted, provided that there is a basis for assigning probabilities of effectiveness and provided that a consistent level of detail is maintained in trees for comparable accidents. Data sources for estimating event probabilities and consequences are discussed in Section 2.9.3, and risk comparison and acceptance criteria are discussed in Section 2.9.4.

2.9.3 Data Sources for Quantification

Quantitative FTA and ETA requires that data be available for equipment failure rates,

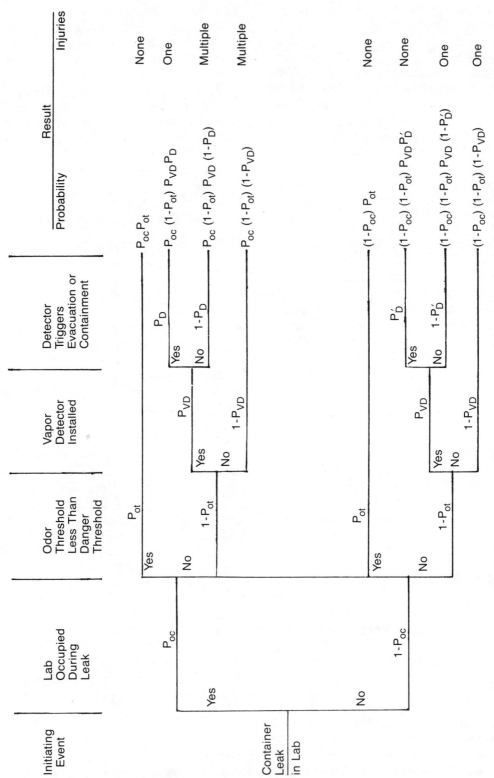

Fig. 2.9-5. Example of an event tree of a toxic vapor leak from a container in the laboratory.

human error probabilities, and incident occurrence. Generic data of this type exist but almost inevitably must be supplemented by subjective judgment when the data are incomplete or not directly applicable to the environment (such as a hospital laboratory) in question. Relevant data sources and systematic techniques for incorporating expert judgments and adjusting the generic data to a specific environment are summarized here.

Perhaps the best source for laboratory incident data is the organization responsible for operating the laboratory, particularly if it is a large organization with a centralized safety department. Many of the larger chemical and pharmaceutical companies maintain company proprietary accident databases with annual tabulations. Some of the trade associations also compile accident statistics based on member company voluntary surveys, but survey responses are usually incomplete. Insurance companies also have incident databases based on claims, but these databases are company confidential and primarily account for incidents in which the loss exceeded the deductible.

A few public domain incident databases are maintained by government agencies and public interest organizations. The Occupational Safety and Health Administration (OSHA), for example, has a database that can be accessed by Standard Industry Code or by material involved. The Department of

Transportation's Materials Transportation Bureau issues annual reports on hazardous material transportation incidents. In the case of fire incidents, the National Fire Protection Agency (NFPA) maintains the National Fire Incident Reporting System (NFIRS) based on reports received from public fire departments. The NFPA has graciously provided this author with the following breakdown on fires in different types of laboratories. All figures in Table 2.9-4 are annual averages of fires in laboratory structures during the period 1982–1986. In addition to these, the NFPA reports an annual average of 938 fires in laboratory rooms not located in laboratory structures. These 938 laboratory room fires annually result in an average of 57 civilian (non firefighter) injuries and $14.2 million in property damage.

Two other fire incident data sources can be used to quantify the event tree example shown in Figure 2.9-3. The Factory Mutual Research loss database includes data on any reported delay in fire detection. According to these data on 22 sprinklered laboratory fires during the past 5 years, detection was immediate in 6 incidents (27%), prompt in 10 fires (46%), and delayed in 6 fires (27%). The corresponding figures for 19 unsprinklered laboratories are: immediate detection: 4 (21%), prompt detection 4 (21%), and delayed detection 11 (58%). Thus, the probability of delayed detection is more than twice as high in unsprinklered laboratories as in

Table 2.9-4. Fires in Laboratory Structures, 1982–1986

Type of Laboratory	No of Fires (Annual Avg.)	Injuries	Property Damage
General research	268	6	$1.3 M
Chemical or medical	132	9	$3.4 M
Physical materials testing	74	0	$0.6 M
Electrical/electronic	73	12	$1.1 M
Unknown	53	2	$0.3 M
Unclassified	30	3	$0.4 M
Agricultural	23	0	$0.2 M
Radioactive materials	10	0	$0.1 M
Psychological	3	0	$0.0
Total	666	32	$ 7.4 M

Source: National Fire Protection Association

sprinklered laboratories. Fire control probabilities for sprinklered laboratory fires can be estimated from the data of Marryatt (1971), which indicate that in Australia and New Zealand, automatic sprinklers successfully controlled all 60 laboratory fires as of 1950. Thus, p_c would be less than 1/61 (0.018) for sprinklered fires. Factory Mutual Research data indicate a somewhat higher value for p_c (depending on the criterion selected) because many successful sprinkler actuations are not reported.

Generic equipment failure rate data are available from several sources, including the U.S. Department of Defense (1979), the Institution of Electrical Engineers, London and New York (1981), and the "IEEE Guide" (1984) for electronic equipment; Reliability Analysis Center (1978) for mechanical equipment; Henley and Kamamoto (1981) and Lees (1980) for chemical plant equipment and instrumentation; and Levine and Rasmussen (1975) for nuclear plant equipment and instrumentation. Private subscription databases for generic data, such as SYREL and the AIChE Center for Chemical Process Safety, new generic database for chemical process equipment, are also available to member companies.

Some of the databases (e.g., "IEEE Guide, 1984) are based primarily on the collective opinion of a panel of experts. Expert opinion failure rates are often expressed either as a range of values or as probability distribution functions. In the latter case, the minimums and maximums and best estimates of the panel of experts are used to determine parameters in assumed distribution functions, such as the log normal distribution. Mosleh et al. (1986) and Apostolakis (1982) provide guidance and a formal mathematical procedure for determining these distribution functions. The procedure involves the use of Bayes' theorem from the theory of probability. Bayes' theorem can serve to develop a plant-specific failure rate distribution from the generic failure rate distributions and a limited amount of site-specific data or judgments.

Human error rate data correlations for risk analysis calculations are divided into two categories. The first category pertains to routine operations, and the second category pertains to accident or emergency situations. In the case of routine operations, a compendium of suggested error rates is available (Swain and Guttmann, 1983; Swain, 1987) for different types of errors of omission (failure to initiate a required task) and errors of commission (incorrect performance of a system-required task). For example, errors of omission in tasks with written checkoff procedures, such as the periodic testing of a toxic/flammable vapor detector, have a suggested error rate in the range 5×10^{-4} to 5×10^{-3}, depending on operator skill, experience, etc. These rates and the many others given in the references just cited are the judgments of the authors based on their expertise in experimental and engineering psychology and their experience with the operation of complex systems.

In the case of errors during accident or emergency situations, the NRC's *Handbook of Human Reliability Analysis* (Swain and Guttmann, 1983) provides curves of the error probability as a function of the time available for action. For example, the probability of laboratory personnel realizing that they should evacuate the building upon hearing a toxic vapor detector alarm will depend on the time available between detection and incipient injury due to vapor inhalation, i.e., on the difference between the vapor detection/alarm threshold and the injury/debilitation threshold. Apostolakis et al. (1988) have reviewed the use of the NRC handbook data together with generic estimates of the probability of a task's being completed as a function of the time divided by the median completion time for the task. For example, the probability of successful evacuation can be ascertained by knowing the time available for evacuation in a specific accident scenario (with a specified toxic vapor concentration) and the median time needed for a person to evacuate the building. Other techniques for estimating human errors during emergencies have also been critically reviewed by Apostolakis et al. (1988).

2.9.4 Risk Comparison and Acceptance Criteria

We assume at this point that the risk assessors have persevered in using appropriate failure/incident rate data to obtain quantitative results for a specific FTA or ETA. Now it is important to present the results in a form that will facilitate decision making. Decisions involve comparisons between alternative courses of action and judgments as to whether an acceptably low level of risk can be achieved with the course selected.

Risk comparisons are facilitated with a "picture" or graph of the likelihood versus consequence results of the risk assessment. To illustrate this process, consider the event tree examples in Section 2.9-2 for the alternative methods of storing volatile toxic chemicals for use in the laboratory. The ETA in Section 2.9-2 described calculations of the probabilities of different numbers of injuries given an accident-initiating event. In the case of external storage and transport, the initiating event was a spill during transport. In the case of in-laboratory storage, the initiating event was a container leak. We now wish to estimate the expected frequency of occurrence of the two initiating events.

The expected frequency of spills in transit depends on the spill probability per trip, p_{st}, and the expected number of trips per year, N. If p_{st} is a small number (such that Np_{st} is much less than 1), the annual frequency of spills is $N \times p_{st}$. The expected frequency of container leaks would best be calculated using an FTA. If we assume, for simplicity, that the most prevalent leak scenario is associated with incomplete closure of the container following usage, the expected leak frequency would be $n \times p_1$, where n is number of container openings and closings per year and p_1 is the probability of leakage per closing (assumed to be small to invoke small probability approximation theory).

Now the expected frequency of each injury category can be calculated by multiplying the probability per incident by the expected frequency of incidents. For example, the expected frequency of multiple-injury accidents due to a container's inadvertently being left open in the laboratory is

$$np_1 p_{oc}(1 - p_{ot})(p_{vd}(1 - p_d) + (1 - p_{vd}))$$

After the frequencies for all three injury categories (none, single, and multiple) are calculated in this manner for both initiating-

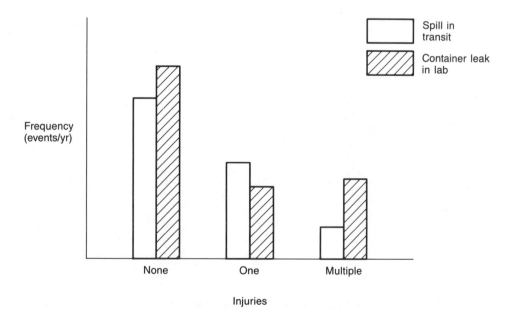

Fig. 2.9-6. Comparison of frequency–consequence results for two accident scenarios.

event scenarios, the results can be plotted as a bar graph, as shown in Figure 2.9-6. The bar graph indicates at a glance which scenario would produce a greater frequency of multiple-injury accidents, single-injury accidents, and no-injury accidents. Since these calculations have not actually been performed, the relative sizes of the bars in Figure 2.9-6 are merely for illustrative purposes, without actually indicating which scenario produces a higher frequency in each injury category. Furthermore, the calculations should be repeated with other initiating event scenarios, such as the release of a flammable vapor with the subsequent fire and explosion threat. Injury frequencies for each scenario would be added to obtain an overall injury frequency bar graph for the two alternative storage options. Refinement of the consequence calculations to estimate the actual number of injuries rather than injury categories would result in a frequency versus injury histogram (or even a continuous plot) instead of a bar graph.

If one scenario resulted in a lower ex-pected frequency for all three injury categories, and for other hazard consequence measures such as fatalities, property damage, and lost data/time, one storage option would have a clear risk advantage over the other. More often, one option is advantageous for low-consequence (e.g., no-injury) accidents, while the other option provides a reduction in the frequency of high-consequence (e.g., multiple-injury) accidents. In these cases, most decision makers will opt for the alternative that minimizes the risk of catastrophic accidents, provided that the costs of the two options are comparable.

Figure 2.9-7 shows a similar conceptual comparison of the probabilities of various fire consequences in a laboratory with automatic sprinklers versus one without sprinklers. The relatively high probability of controlled fires in the sprinklered laboratory is due in part to the prompt detection of fires in an unoccupied laboratory and in part to the relatively high probability of fire control upon detection. Although these results are scenario dependent, they should be represen-

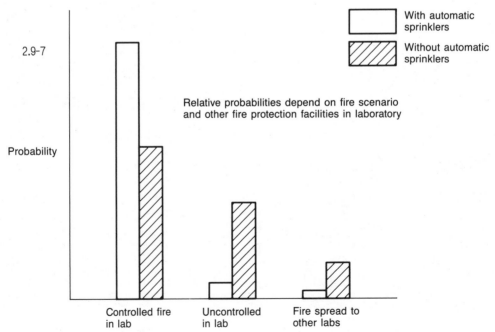

Fig. 2.9-7. Probabilities of alternative outcomes of a fire in a sprinklered laboratory and an unsprinklered laboratory.

tative of the majority of flaming fire scenarios.* The exception would be a laboratory processing chemicals, such as sodium, that react violently with water.

When the costs of alternative actions differ significantly, the traditional risk management approach has been to perform a cost-benefit analysis, or discounted cash flow analysis, in which the total annual cost of protection plus expected damages is calculated for the two alternatives. This traditional approach should be tempered by the realization that there are often hidden costs beyond the direct property damages and injury claims. These hidden costs include poor morale and lost time and data.

The Center for Chemical Process Safety's "Guidelines for Chemical Process Quantitative Risk Analysis" (1988) describes other methods of measuring and comparing risks recommended for use at chemical facilities. One potentially applicable risk measure for laboratory personnel is the maximum individual risk, defined as the frequency of accidents resulting in a fatality to the person closest to the accident, presumably someone working in the laboratory. Other risk measures more applicable to societal risk, as described in the "Guidelines," may be useful for laboratory managers responsible for discussing laboratory risks with local officials and neighbors.

Readers interested in utilizing these risk assessment techniques and methods of interpretation should realize that the subject is anything but an exact science. Treatment of the uncertainties inherent in the application of these techniques is an essential aspect of presenting the results. Thus the reader should not expect to determine with certainty that Option A is preferable to Option B from a risk perspective. A more accurate and rigorous statement of results would report that there is a certain probability (expressed as a percentage) that Option A is

preferable to Option B with regard to the risk comparison measure selected. Appreciation and acceptance of this type of conclusion may not be forthcoming immediately but should become more viable in the future as management, the scientific community, code writers, and public officials become more sophisticated in risk assessment methods.

REFERENCES

Apostolakis, G., 1982. Data Anslysis in Risk Assessments, *Nuclear Engineering and Design,* Vol. 71, 375–381.

Apostolakis, G.E., Bier, V.M., and Mosleh, A., 1988. A Critique of Recent Models for Human Error Rate Assessment, *Reliability Engineering and System Safety,* Vol. 22, 201–217.

Battelle Columbus Division, 1985. "Guidelines for Hazard Evaluation Procedures." American Institute of Chemical Engineers (AIChE) Center for Chemical Process Safety. New York.

Department of Defense Military Standard, 1984, "System Safety Program Requirements," MIL-STD-8828. Department of Defense

Diberardinis, L.J., et al., 1987. *Guidelines for Laboratory Design: Health and Safety Considerations.* New York: Wiley.

"Guidelines for Chemical Process Quantitative Risk Analysis," 1988. AIChE Center for Chemical Process Safety. New York.

Henley, E.J., and Kumamoto, H., 1981. *Reliability Engineering and Risk Assessment.* Englewood Cliffs, NJ: Prentice-Hall.

"IEEE Guide to the Collection and Presentation of Electrical, Electronic, and Sensing Component Reliability Data for Nuclear Power Generating Stations," 1984. IEEE Standard 500. Institute of Electrical and Electronic Engineers. New York.

Le, N.B., Santay, A.J., and Zabrenski, J.S., 1988. Laboratory Safety Design Criteria, *Plant/Operations Progress,* Vol. 7, No. 2, 87–94.

Lee, W.S., et al., 1985. "Fault Tree Analysis, Methods, and Applications—A Review," *IEEE Transactions on Reliability,* Vol. R-34, No. 3, 194–203.

Lees, F.P., 1980. *Loss Prevention in the Process Industries.* London: Butterworths.

Levine, S., and Rasmussen, N. eds., 1975. "Reactor Safety Study," Report WASH-1400 (NUREG-75/014). Washington, DC: Atomic Energy Commission.

Mosleh, A., Kazarians, M., and Gekler, W., 1986. "Development of a Risk and Reliability Data Base for Chemical Facilities," Pickard, Lowe, and Garrick, Inc. Paper presented at the AIChE Summer National Meeting, 1986.

Reliability Analysis Center, Rome Air Development

---

*By contrast, smoldering fires would not normally generate sufficient heat to activate sprinkler heads. Smoke detectors would be a useful supplement for automatic sprinklers in coping with smoldering fires.

Center, 1978. "Nonelectronic Parts Reliability Data," NPRD-1. Department of Defense.

Russell, KD., et al., 1987. "Integrated Reliability and Risk Analysis System (IRRAS) User's Guide—Version 1.0," NUREG/CR-4844, EGG-2495. National Technical Information Service, Springfield, VA

Swain, A.D., 1987. *Accident Sequence Evaluation Program Human Reliability Analysis Procedure,* NUREG/CR-4772. Nuclear Regulatory Commission. National Technical Information Service, Springfield, VA

Swain, A.D., and Guttmann, H.E., 1983. *Handbook of Human Reliability Analysis with Emphasis on Nuclear Power Applications,*NUREG/CR-1278. Nuclear Regulatory Commission. National Technical Information Service, Springfield, VA

"SYREL—System Reliability Service Data Bank." U.K. Atomic Energy Authority, Culcheth, Warrington, WA3 4NE, United Kingdom.

The Institution of Electrical Engineers, London and New York, 1981. "Electronic Reliability Data: A Guide to Selected Components." Surrey: Gresham Press.

U.S. Department of Defense, 1979. "Military Standardization Handbook: Reliability Prediction of Electronic Equipment," MIL-HDBK-217C. Department of Defense

Vesely, W.E., et al., 1981. "Fault Tree Handbook," Report (NUREG-0492). National Technical Information Service, Springfield, VA

2.10 ASSESSING THE IMPACT OF THE LABORATORY FACILITY AND THE COMMUNITY ON EACH OTHER *T. Ruys*

2.10.1 Introduction

A laboratory facility, whether existing or proposed, is a sensitive issue in a community. Community and public favor or acceptance can no longer be taken for granted. In fact, the opposite is true: opposition must be assumed unless proven otherwise.

There are many reasons for this attitude. Recent revelations and bad publicity about toxic waste, the fear of genetic engineering, an increased awareness of and concern about cancer-producing agents and the advent of animal rights groups have created an adversary relationship.

The resistance is not confined to new facilities. Many laboratory facilities that change or expand their scope and operations find that they are classified as bad neighbors,

which tarnishes their image. As a result of these deteriorating relationships, restrictive measures have been enacted by many communities.

Because of these restrictive measures, land available for laboratory facilities is becoming increasingly scarce. To get around this problem, land developers have created "research parks" in many locations where land is still available. Generally these parks are located close to research centers such as colleges and universities, with a pool of needed skilled labor and communities with available fire and police protection, utility services, family resources and recreation facilities.

This section does not deal with the selection of the best location to establish a new laboratory or all the nuances of community and public relations, but only with the regulations that restrict the selection of a site for a new building. Assessing the impact on the community is a very cost-effective effort if it can prevent litigation, long delays and bad press. Assessing the impact of the laboratory requires an understanding of the regulations existing in most locations, forthcoming regulations and the review process. The best defense is early involvement.

Regulations fall into a few general areas; the most important ones, for the purposes of this handbook, are zoning ordinances and environmental impact statements or assessments (EIA). The best defense, of course, is to acquire a copy of the local ordinances and read them. The following sections emphasize some of the points which often are the cause of contention.

2.10.2 Zoning Ordinances

The main thrust of zoning is to set limitations on use and to protect adjacent properties, the public and the general welfare of the community. Land classifications and lot coverage are examples of the former; property setbacks, pollution control and minimum parking requirements examples of the latter.

Land Zoning Classification

Zoning ordinances vary from location to location, are enacted by local legislatures and are reviewed and enforced by local planning officers.

A laboratory facility typically is classified as office/research or industrial, depending on its use. A health care facility laboratory, an academic laboratory on a college campus or a research/industrial park may be covered under different standards.

If the land use or building type does not meet the zoning classification, a variance can be requested. This typically requires a formal submittal and a review by a zoning board. The review period may vary from a few weeks to several months. The likelihood of being accepted depends on the degree to which the variance differentiates from the existing classification, the mood of the community, the size of the project and the local economy. A public hearing may be required.

Lot Coverage

An often overlooked limitation is the maximum allowable lot coverage in many zoning ordinances. Many projects encounter problems sooner or later. When the net (usable) square feet are translated into GSF, it becomes apparent that a laboratory facility requires a larger ''footprint'' than a typical office building. Laboratories also invariably need to expand because, unlike offices, they are expensive to move to another location. Growing vertically is not always possible because many zoning ordinances also have a height limitation. Even if allowed, vertical expansion in laboratory buildings is both disruptive and expensive; it is difficult to move, change and add fumehood and exhaust stacks and plumbing vents. In some ordinances, lot coverage includes parking, service yards and roads, which reduces the available area for laboratories even further.

Property Setbacks

Zoning ordinances typically require setbacks for structures from the property lines. In addition to the lot coverage and height restrictions, these setbacks may severally limit the size of the laboratory facility.

Other setback restrictions may supersede the zoning setback requirements—for instance, those imposed by fire separation in hazardous occupations. Therefore, it is prudent to check all applicable codes and regulations and to evaluate the most restrictive limitations.

Minimum Parking Requirements

Many ordinances require one parking stall for a specified number of GSF of floor area. This may vary from 300 to 500 GSF/stall. However, many laboratories are equipment intensive and therefore have a low occupancy density, which results in more parking stalls than there are occupants and visitors. Since parking areas may be counted as lot coverage, it is important to check this relationship and inquire about the possibility of a variance.

Other Legislation

There are a number of other ordinances or acts that are not peculiar to laboratory facilities but are worth mentioning:

- The Shorelines Management Act, which becomes effective for building or site improvements within a specified number of feet of a body of water, whether an ocean, lake, river or creek. The U.S. Army Corps of Engineers reviews and enforces this act.
- The Clean Air Act
- The National Energy Code

2.10.3 Environmental Impact Assessment (EIA)

Many municipalities require an EIA in order to evaluate the impact on the community, the land, the adjacent properties and the environment. Typical items covered are:

- Existing site condition such as soil, topography, geology, vegetation, wildlife, surface water, subsurface water, unique scenic and historic features, and artificial structures such as buildings, roads, fences, etc.

- Surrounding environment such as existing land use, drainage, transportation network, utilities such as water, power and sewage.
- Proposed methods to minimize the use of resources such as water, power and energy.
- Proposed controls to be employed to minimize or eliminate erosion, runoff, sewage disposal, noise, fire/explosion hazards, odors and air emissions.
- Proposed improvements of on-site and off-site structures, roads, parking and utilities.
- Impacts, both positive and negative, of the proposed facility on drainage, surface water quality, groundwater quality and quantity, sewage disposal, solid waste disposal, vegetation, wildlife, historic and scenic features, air quality, noise levels, energy utilization, neighborhood, public services/transportation/schools/fire/police protection and traffic.
- Ordinances, codes, standards and regulations to be complied with and variances, licenses, permits and other approvals needed or required by law.

2.11 LEGAL CONSIDERATIONS IN PLANNING LABORATORY FACILITIES *A. DeVoe Lawler*

2.11.1 Introduction

Hazardous materials used in laboratories may gravely affect health and safety and have become a source of great public concern. Reports of medical wastes turning up on beaches, toxic ''bombs'' forming in sewer systems, and virulent organisms escaping from research laboratories have exacerbated public fears. Until recently, government oversight of hazardous materials in the research environment was almost nonexistent. With the proliferation of research facilities across the country and the consequent increase in the number of accidents related to the use of hazardous materials, federal, state and local governments have become increasingly involved.

Professionals who design and plan laboratory projects should be aware that health and safety issues arise from the use of hazardous materials at these facilities. These issues may dictate certain planning and design requirements for a laboratory facility. Before beginning the planning of a laboratory facility, the professional should question the client regarding the intended use of the facility. Laboratory processes, types of materials to be used, and proper storage and disposal methods are among the myriad areas about which the design professional should inquire. The responses to this inquiry should be documented in the form of a confirming letter or memo. Improper planning may expose the design professional to claims for damages from the client and from third parties injured or damaged by activities at the laboratory resulting from improper design.

This section summarizes some of the legal considerations of which laboratory planners should be aware. General contractual issues are discussed to the extent that they could be affected by these concerns. Also discussed are issues of particular relevance to the laboratory setting. This section also includes a brief overview of some of the laws affecting the activities of the client in a laboratory setting. This overview will help place in context some of the contractual issues that are discussed.

2.11.2 General Contractual Issues

A good, tight, comprehensive contract between the planner and the client is critical. This should set the stage for work to be performed, the time line for performance, compensation, who is to perform the work, the standard of care regarding performance and what happens if things go wrong. When preparing a contract, or if a planner uses a standard printed form of agreement, be aware that the enforceability of certain contractual clauses may vary from state to state. ''Common law'' rules that govern the interpretation of contracts (i.e., judge-made law that evolves from cases that go to trial and then are appealed) are different in each state. Similarly, ''statutory law'' (i.e., statutes, laws, ordinances, rules and regulations) which impacts contractual issues varies from state to state.

Basic contractual provisions that may deserve additional thought in order to address potential issues regarding hazardous substances are as follows.

- *Scope of Services to be Provided by the Planner:* This should be as specific as possible, particularly when spelling out responsibility for designing any part of the facility where hazardous materials will be located, stored or handled. Specialized or additional services beyond what would normally be provided should be spelled out. This section should also include a schedule for the performance of the work.

- *Owner's Responsibilities.* This section should spell out what information and services will be provided by the owner. With respect to the siting and planning of specialized laboratory facilities, the owner should be required to furnish all applicable information about the types of materials (i.e., hazardous, radioactive or infectious) to be involved in the facilities; what permits are required for that type of work; what local, state or federal laws, rules and regulations apply to that work and will impact the planning and design of the facility; and what specialized needs the owner is hoping to achieve and satisfy in its design and use of the site and building. A related concern that may be set forth is the owner's responsibility to provide the necessary community and local governmental input regarding the siting and design of the facility. Citizens who live and work near these facilities, and local governments that issue the necessary permits for their construction and operation, increasingly have their own agendas, which may dramatically affect the facilities's external appearance and location.

- *Assignment.* The agreement should state that it cannot be assigned by either party without the consent of the other party. From the owner's perspective, this ensures that the planner will not as-sign its duties and responsibilities to another planner who may be unacceptable to the owner. Similarly, the planner is protected from the owner's assignment of the agreement to another party for whom the planner may not want to agree to perform the work. It also allows the planner to ensure that any assignee of the owner, if otherwise acceptable to the planner, expressly assumes all responsibilities of the owner under the agreement. In the absence of a clause prohibiting assignment without the other party's consent, the law in many states is that the contract is freely assignable. This right could be of particular importance if the owner is an artificial entity such as a partnership or corporation. If the client ultimately is liable to the planner for any damages, costs, fees or penalties the planner has incurred or stands to incur relating to hazardous waste issues, the planner wants to know that it is dealing with a solvent owner. These damages could be very significant.

- *Arbitration.* A planner may choose to include a clause requiring that any dispute between the parties will proceed to arbitration. Unless this clause contains language stating that the arbitration decision shall be final and binding on all parties, the arbitration may not be the final resolution of the issue. In some states, parties unhappy with the result of arbitration may still be able to take the matter to court. Some planners prefer not to include an arbitration clause for this reason. They perceive that arbitration does not necessarily ensure a more speedy or less costly process. Planners also should consider inserting a requirement that the arbitrator be well versed in laws dealing with hazardous substances, laboratories and planning in general.

- *Governing Law.* The contract should specify the laws that will govern the interpretation of the contract. For example, the governing laws could be the laws of the state in which the facility is being planned, the laws of the state of the planner's home office, or the laws of the state of the owner's home office. Which law governs could affect the planner's potential liability. As discussed below, there are federal laws governing hazardous substances. Many states have also adopted their own versions of these laws. These laws differ from state to state in many details. These differences could become very important in establishing the standard of care to which planners will be held and/or in establishing who will be responsible for the design of facilities handling hazardous substances. For example, one state may have a law that imposes statutory liability on planners for improper design of a facility where hazardous substances will be handled. The common law of each state which will govern the interpretation given to clauses in the contracts also may differ regarding the enforceability of some of the specialized provisions discussed in this section.

- *Attorneys' Fees.* The agreement should state that attorneys' fees and costs are recoverable by the prevailing party in any lawsuit or arbitration proceeding. In some states, these fees and costs will not be recoverable unless they are agreed to in the contract. This could be important, for example, if a planner is found liable to the government or to a third party for damages as a result of improper design which resulted in a release of hazardous substances. If the planner is able to recover from the owner the sums the planner has had to pay, the planner also will want to try to recover its attorneys' fees and costs. Recovery of these fees may not be possible through a statutory right of contribution action. The planner may have to file a separate action under the terms of its agreement with the owner. Success in that action will depend upon the terms of that agreement.

- *Invalidity.* An invalidity clause states that any provision in the agreement that proves to be invalid or illegal will be stricken but that the remainder of the agreement will remain intact. This is particularly important if the contract by the planner is proposed for use in a number of states. The planner may find that some contractual provisions will not be enforceable in other states.

- *Warranty of Authority.* An agreement may include a clause stating that each person who signs the agreement on behalf of the owner and planner is authorized to do so. This is important if either the owner or the planner is an artificial entity such as a corporation or partnership. The planner may also want to consider having an officer, shareholder or partner sign the agreement individually. These individuals would thus be signing as guarantors. This is important if the planner is concerned about the solvency of the owner in light of the risks the planner is assuming.

2.11.3 Special Contractual Provisions Affecting Laboratories

In addition to the foregoing general contractual terms, the planner should consider including a number of the following specially tailored contractual provisions. These deal with limitation of liability, the standard of care to which the planner will be held, insurance coverage, indemnification and hazardous substances.

- *Limitation of Liability.* Increasingly, planners and similar consultants are including limitation of liability clauses in their agreements to attempt to limit the potential claims and damages that could arise from their negligence or other actions on the site or from performance of their services. In some instances, this is required by the planner's professional errors and omissions insurance coverage (E&O insurance). Each planner should examine the requirements of its E&O insurance policy.

A planner who seeks to include this type of provision in its agreement also should understand that it may not be enforceable in some states. Planners also should be aware that certain clients will not agree to sign a contract containing this provision. It is a provision that generally will be the subject of heated negotiation. An example of a limitation of liability section is as follows:

Notwithstanding anything to the contrary set forth in this Agreement, Owner agrees that to the fullest extent permitted by law, that the Planner's total liability to Owner for any and all injuries, claims, damages, losses, costs, or expenses whatsoever arising out of or in any way related to the project or to the Planner's performance or nonperformance of its obligations under this Agreement, or to any breach of warranty or misrepresentation, shall not exceed the compensation to be paid to the Planner pursuant to the terms of this Agreement.

In some instances, it should be noted that insurance carriers will allow the planner to increase the lid on the limitation of liability in certain increments in return for additional payments by the owner.

• *Insurance Coverage.* Adequate professional E&O insurance coverage is essential in planning laboratory facilities. As alluded to above, the insurance carrier may have requirements for the planner regarding limitations of liability sections.

Another issue to examine with respect to insurance is the nature of exclusions from policy coverage. One exclusion that is now found in almost all insurance policies is the "pollution exclusion" clause. It says, in essence, that the insurance company will not defend the insured/planner or pay any claims resulting from any actual or threatened release, discharge, dispersal, spill or escape of any pollutants, or with respect to any governmental directive requiring the planner/insured to take any action

with respect to any pollutants. This exclusion clause will affect planners who plan laboratory facilities that will be using, handling, storing or disposing of any substances that are deemed to be toxic, hazardous or dangerous by any state, local or federal laws, rules, regulations or statutes.

The insurance companies' concerns arise out of the myriad laws enacted within the last 10 years governing the use, storage, disposal, transportation, generation and cleanup of these substances. The general theme running throughout all of these laws is that society does not want its environment to be polluted, and that any polluted areas are to be cleaned up. In many cases, the laws provide that parties who are involved with these substances have liability that is strict (meaning without fault or negligence) as well as joint and several (meaning that any one of a number of potentially liable parties may be liable for *all* costs associated with this problem). The Superfund laws state that the current owners and operators of the property, together with past owners and operators, are strictly, jointly and severally liable for the costs of solving these problems.

• *Overview of Federal Laws.* A brief review of some of the federal laws potentially influencing the use and operation of laboratory facilities will be useful to help planners understand why insurance coverage contains these pollution exclusion clauses and why certain "pollution" or "hazardous substance" paragraphs should be included in contracts.

The bulk of federal regulation of hazardous substances involves the handling, storage and disposal of hazardous and toxic wastes. The Resource Conservation and Recovery Act (RCRA) of 1976, 42 U.S.C. §§6901-91h, is the primary federal statute dealing with the generation, transportation and disposal of hazardous wastes. The general purpose of this law is to provide "cradle to grave" management of hazardous substances. The statute sets forth detailed requirements for storing and handling hazardous substances; permits for disposal and use of hazardous substances; transportation of hazardous substances; and disposal requirements. Improper methods by which hazardous materials are stored and disposed of in the laboratory environment may involve RCRA liability, which can result in criminal as well as civil sanctions or penalties.

The federal Superfund law, the Comprehensive Environmental Response Compensation and Liability Act, 42 U.S.C. §9601, *et seq.,* and the state equivalents thereof govern who, when and how cleanup of improperly disposed of hazardous and toxic substances will occur. Cleanup activities which arise as the result of spills, releases or unauthorized disposal into waterways or water supplies may also, or alternatively, be subject to the terms of the Clean Water Act, 33 U.S.C. §1251–1387, or the Safe Drinking Water Act, 42 U.S.C. §330f–330j-11.

A new area of regulation with a potentially significant impact on laboratories involves infectious and medical wastes. Federal regulations are being imposed on a trial basis in several states to deal with the problems of improper storage, handling, containment, transportation and disposal of infectious and medical wastes. The range of wastes covered is broad. Several local jurisdictions recently have passed, or are considering passing, similar legislation.

The Toxic Substances Control Act, 15 U.S.C. §2601–2654, regulates a number of chemical substances, including radioactive substances.

• *Hazardous Waste Clauses.* The planner's responsibilities should not include giving any advice regarding hazardous or toxic substances or asbestos. Those subjects are dealt with by consultants with entirely different training and background. To clarify that the plan-

ning consultant will not be offering any expertise or advice in this area, the planner should consider including a section similar to the following:

The Owner and the Planner understand and mutually agree that the project, the design of a laboratory facility, is a complex and highly technical undertaking. The Owner and the Planner further mutually agree and understand that the Owner possesses special expertise in the characteristics, storage and handling of the materials to be used in the laboratory facility. As a result of this special expertise and notwithstanding language in the articles appearing below, as well as attachments to this Agreement, it is understood and agreed between the Owner and the Planner that (a) the Owner shall provide the Planner with the information necessary to allow the Planner to design the facility for the Owner's needs with respect to the handling, storage and use of materials to be used in the laboratory facility and that (b) the Owner shall review and approve all of the Planner's work accomplished pursuant to this contract for the express purpose of the Owner's assuming responsibility for the adequacy of the Planner's services in these areas. The Owner further agrees to indemnify, hold harmless and defend the Planner from any and all actions, costs, expenses, claims, fees, penalties or damages of any kind or character whatsoever arising out of and from the Planner's work which (i) is based upon information and expertise provided by the Owner or (ii) has been reviewed and approved by the Owner to provide for the safe and proper handling, storage and use of materials within the laboratory facility.

Another hazardous waste clause that should be considered for inclusion would cover any release of any hazardous substances on the project site. This clause clarifies that as between the owner and the planner, the owner will be responsible for the results of that activity.

If during the course of the Planner's work on the project site there is a release, discharge, spill or escape of any substances that are found to be hazardous, toxic or dangerous by any state, federal or local law, rule or regulation, now in effect or hereinafter adopted, in that event, the Owner agrees to indemnify, defend, and hold the Planner harmless from and against any and all damages, claims, liabilities, costs, expenses, penalties and fees incurred by the planner as a result thereof.

In these clauses, as well as in any other clauses setting forth indemnification rights, the planner should review the laws of the state in which the work is performed, as well as the laws of the state under which the contract is interpreted, to see how or if these indemnification clauses will be enforced. In some states, these types of clauses may not be enforceable unless the indemnification specifically carves out, and does not cover, any liability for damages caused by the planner through its own acts, omissions or negligence.

• *Standard of Care.* Planners, like other consultants, are increasingly reviewed as professionals from a legal liability perspective. This means that planners may be held liable for the results of their own negligence in the performance of their services. If this results in substantial property damage and/or personal injury by third parties, the damages can be quite high. The limitation of liability clauses and hazardous waste clauses discussed above will assist in narrowing the scope of damages for which a planner otherwise might find itself liable. An additional step to be taken is to define the standard of care to which the planner must perform. An example is as follows:

In performing its services in accordance with the terms of this Agreement, the Planner shall be held to the standard of care of other Planners in this industry performing substantially the same duties and responsibilities within the [local geographic] region.

This clause attempts to establish the level of expertise that is required for the job. By incorporating a regional focus, it lets planners know that if they are working in San Francisco, for example, that they will not be held to the standard of care exercised by planners in the New York area. This standard of care can be narrowed further by specifically calling out the types of duties and responsibilities of the planner against whom the planner will be compared, such as "planners involved in the planning of laboratories for cancer research."

2.11.4 The Planner as an Independent Contractor

In an employment situation, the "master" is liable for the unlawful acts of his employee, or "servant." However, independent contractors are treated differently under the law, and an owner is not necessarily liable for an independent contractor's activities.

In determining whether a master–servant or independent contractor relationship exists, courts will consider the amount of control the owner has over the other person. In situations where very little control is exercised, courts will generally not hold the owner responsible.

A planning professional's status as either an employee or an independent contractor may have important consequences in allocating responsibility for third-party injuries or damages. In most situations, planners render professional services which are not subject to sufficient control to fall under the master-servant category. However, in projects which require substantially all of the planner's time and are subject to the direct supervision and control of the owner or a professional employed by the owner, employee status may be available to insulate the planner from third-party liability.

Similarly, if a planner subcontracts certain elements of the planning process, he or she may or may not be liable for unlawful or negligent acts committed by the subcontractor if the subcontractor is determined to be an independent contractor rather than an employee of the planner.

2.11.5 Conclusion

Planners involved in planning laboratory facilities face a number of the same contractual and legal issues facing other design professionals. They also should expect to encounter issues dealing with characteristics unique to laboratories, including problems associated with hazardous and toxic materials. As discussed above, the planner should work to craft its contract with the owner to define the scope of work and liabilities as specifically and narrowly as possible. To the extent possible, the planner should seek to include sections in the agreement which specifically carve out and delegate to the owner any responsibility for issues related to hazardous, infectious and toxic materials.

The planner's success in negotiating a contract that satisfies all of these concerns, and that limits the planner's liability as narrowly as possible, ultimately will be decided by the relative bargaining power of the parties. The ultimate enforceability of these suggested specialized clauses in the contracts will depend upon the choice of laws for the interpretation of the contract.

This section is not intended to be legal advice. Contact your attorney to determine how the issues discussed impact you.

3

Laboratory Design Principles

3.1 MODULAR DESIGN *U.M. Lindner*

3.1.1 The Need for Modules

Laboratory space is expensive when designing a new building and even more so when remodeling an existing building. Rather than quote actual dollar figures, which will differ from year to year and from location to location, a comparative value might be more appropriate: compared to the average office building, a laboratory building will cost 2 to 2.5 times as much.

What is the reason?

Laboratory buildings require many utility services. They require systems and controls not normally found in other buildings, or at least not to the same degree. It is the functional interaction of all the required systems that makes such laboratory space and its fu-

ture adaptability highly complex and expensive. Systems, and the functions they control, for effective laboratories are as follows:

- Electrical systems: power, lighting, communication, controls, alarms;
- Mechanical systems: heating, ventilation, temperature and humidity control;
- Plumbing systems: hot water, cold water, pure water, cooling water, potable/nonpotable water, fire protection water;
- Various gas distribution systems: central distribution or local systems;
- Vacuum systems;
- Air systems;
- Drainage systems: sinks, cupsinks, floor drains, funnel drains;
- Ceiling systems: ceilings or no ceilings;
- Wall systems: open labs, enclosed labs,

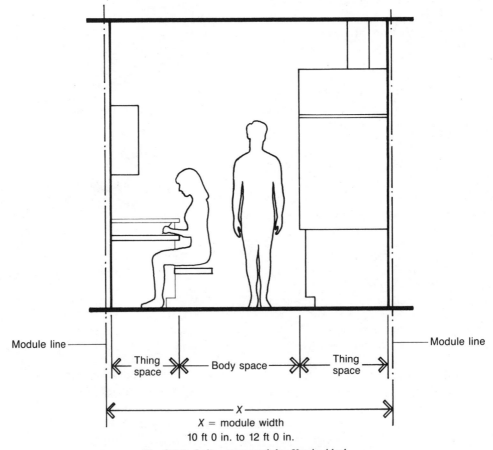

Fig. 3.1-1. Laboratory module, *X* axis: ideal.

fixed walls, movable walls, various materials;

- Furniture systems: casework, storage units, benchtops, safety cabinets, fumehoods, desk spaces, reagent shelving.

All of these systems must interact effectively with the placement of equipment and apparatus. The general work process, safety, security, and no-barrier access must provide future adaptability and, most important, access for maintenance. It stands to reason, then, that coordination through organization is one of the most important considerations. In laboratory design, "a place for everything and everything in its place" is a phrase coined by the grand master of laboratory design, Earl L. Walls. To facilitate this organization, we approach laboratory design on a modular basis.

3.1.2 The Selection of a Planning Module

A planning module is a series of invisible space divisions that predetermines, for the present and the future, the places where things happen. Partitions, drainline drops, services from either above or below, and service or maintenance access will all occur at known locations.

Does one module become the universal module, satisfying all present and future needs? Possibly, but it is much more likely that a good module for animal facilities is not a very economical module for research laboratories or that a module for research space may not work for pilot or scale-up labs. Research space and teaching space generally function with the same module. The designer must become familiar with the work process, traffic patterns and equipment use

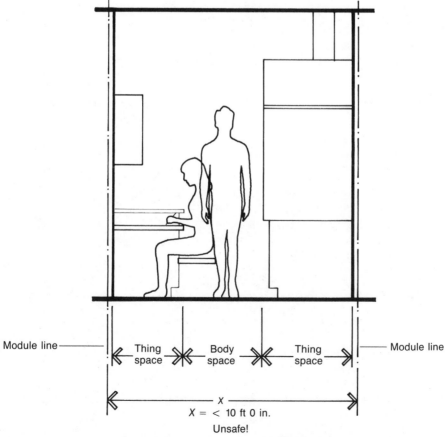

Fig. 3.1-2. Laboratory module, X axis: too tight.

before recommending a specific module or modules for a certain project. Starting with simple ergonomics, we find that the X axis of a space module (in laboratory design) is composed of a circulation space or "body space" and two (back and front) "thing spaces." See Figure 3.1-1. This dimension X lies generally in a range of 10 ft 0 in. center line to center line to 12 ft 0 in. center line to center line. If this dimension becomes larger than 12 ft. 0 in., the circulation space becomes too large and tends to accumulate objects (e.g., tables, refrigerators, or instruments), thereby defeating the purpose of a safe circulation (working) space. See Figures 3.1-2 and 3.1-3.

It is much more difficult to determine a dimension for the Y axis of a space module. Other variables must be considered, such as:

- Work flow
- Internal traffic pattern
- Open or enclosed lab
- Where the offices are located
- Where the desk spaces are located
- The exiting pattern
- Where the hoods are located
- If the main doors in an enclosed lab are recessed
- What equipment must be accommodated
- Where the support space is located
- How much equipment (e.g., refrigerators, incubators), must be accommodated
- How many people the space accommodates

The designer must study and investigate present conditions and work patterns or ob-

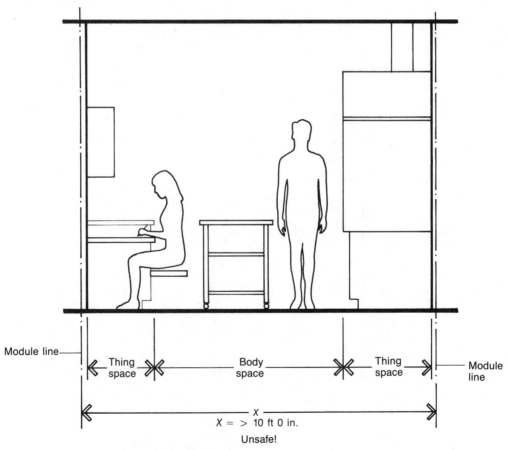

Fig. 3.1-3. Laboratory module, X axis: too generous.

serve similar laboratory operations. A combination of both is usually more helpful.

Depending on the outcome of the studies
and interviews, the Y dimension could be
anywhere from 25 ft. 0 in. to 35 ft 0 in. With
dimensions less than 25 ft 0 in., it will be extremely difficult to set up a sensible ratio of
thing space or working space to body space
or circulation space. There should be 10 to
12 linear ft of uninterrupted, usable work
top for each investigator. See Figures 3.1-4
and Fig. 3.1-5.

Conversely, if the Y dimension is longer
than 35 ft 0 in., circulation becomes cumbersome and points of common use will be too
far apart. See Figure 3.1-6. A single X by Y
module will also have the wrong architectural proportions, giving the impression of
working in a corridor.

3.1.3 Aggregate or Divide Modules

A "module" is a three-dimensional (repeated) planning unit composed of a specific
floor space for laboratory work in a direct
proporational relationship with other building system elements.

- Modules are combined and divided into
  viable fractions to satisfy programmatic
  space needs.
- Modules represent planned and identified locations for partitions, ceiling and
  lighting systems, supply and exhaust air
  systems, plumbing and piping systems,
  and electrical power distribution.
- The modular unit enables the designer
  to develop building systems requirements in a rational manner.
- Modular space planning enables the designer to apply principles of value engineering from the beginning of the design process.
- Modular space permits safe, cost-effective modification of support systems
  when the inevitable changes to laboratory space occur.

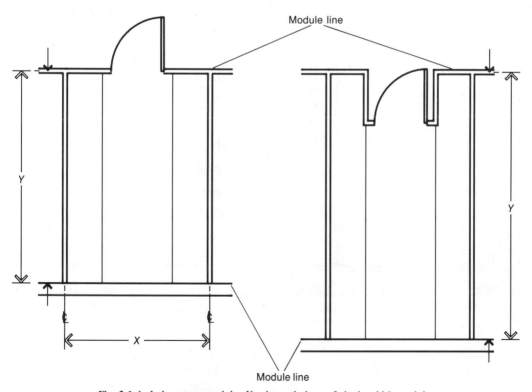

Fig. 3.1-4. Laboratory module, Y axis: variations of single width modules.

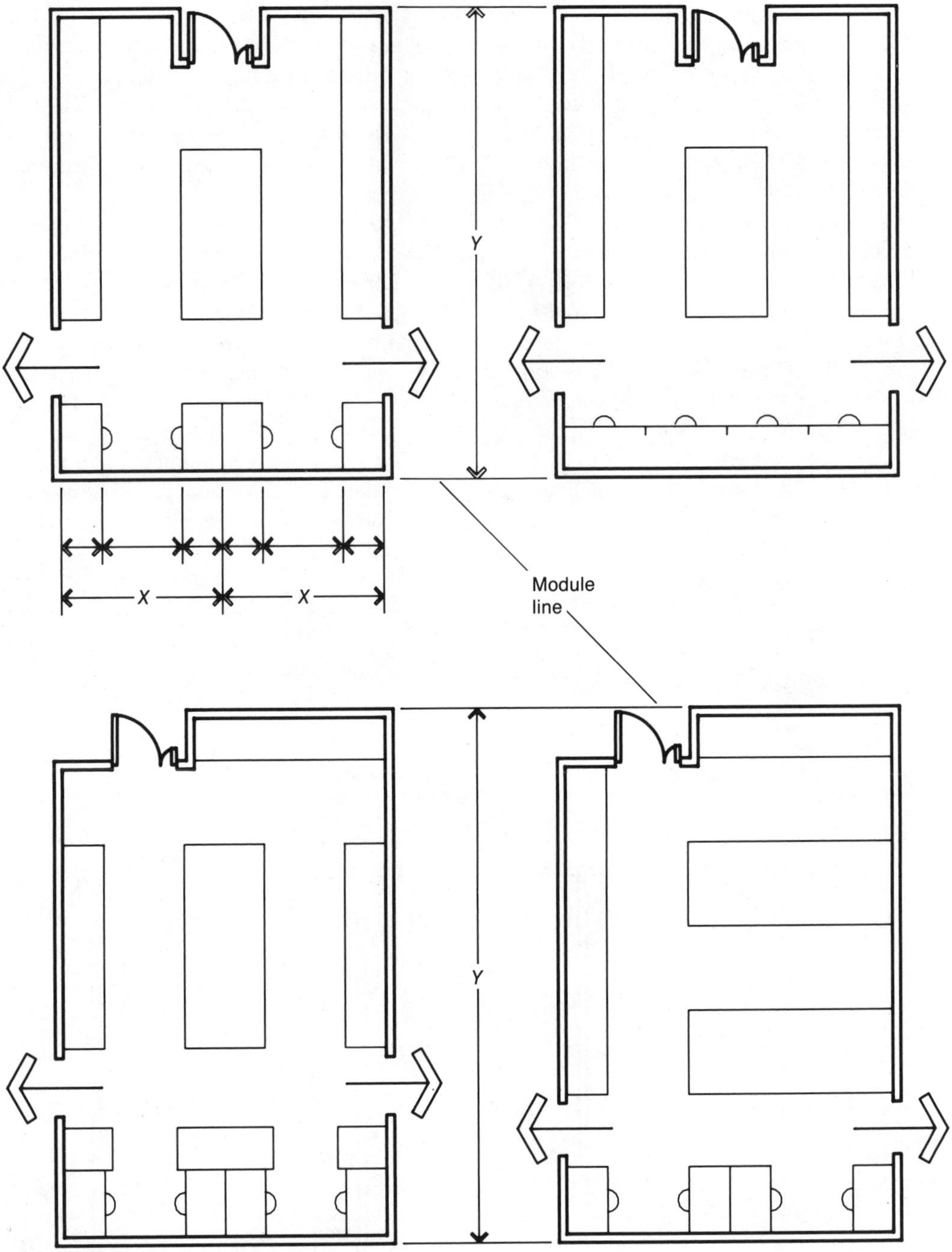

Note: X dimensions center line to center line of the partition; Y dimensions face to face of the partition.

Fig. 3.1-5. Laboratory module, Y axis: variations of double width modules. X dimensions center 1 line to center line of the partition; Y dimensions face to face of the partition.

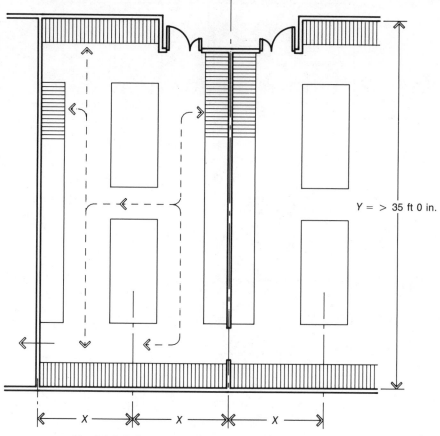

$Y = > 35$ ft 0 in.

Fig. 3.1-6. Laboratory module, very deep lab becomes inefficient.

Viable fractions of the module are those in which a space is equally usable whether entered from the end or the side and ordinarily are quite close to the basic module width. The space need is then expressed as 1/3, 1/2, 2/3, 1, 2, 3, etc. So, all spaces are multiples or viable fractions of the illustrated module. See Figure 3.1-7.

Many different arrangements of modular space are possible and, when left to the skill of the designer, are always coupled with the needs of the researcher, keeping in mind the people who have to maintain the systems and spaces and, of course, the budget. The budget should never compromise safety and efficiency. The mark of a good lab design is that efficiency, safety and economy complement each other.

Mention of the 5 ft 0 in. X dimension, often used, has been purposely avoided. This dimension will not work efficiently in lab de-

sign. Looking again at Figure 3.1-1 and our definition, it can be seen that 10 ft 0 in. is a minimum feasible work space. However, 1.5 modular X dimensions are quite feasible, as shown in Figure 3.1-8. Remember, once a module is established, *it must not be compromised!* From wall to wall, from floor to floor, one must have a place for everything and everything in its place.

Laboratory offices can be accommodated in the chosen module or in a separate module. The project designer may reassess this need during the design process and may prefer to treat office space in an entirely different manner.

3.1.4 Floor-to-Floor Heights

The floor-to-floor height is the third dimension of the three-dimensional module. This Z dimension includes functional space and

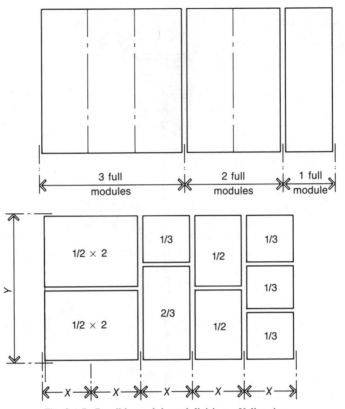

Fig. 3.1-7. Possible modular subdivisions, Y direction.

systems (mechanical, electrical and structural). Constant tracking of early space assumptions is advised as the structural and mechanical engineers refine their calculations. Frequently these refinements lead to floor-to-floor height adjustments.

Early designs should be based on an assumed ceiling height or on the height of the bottom of the light fixture above the finished floor. This height varies from 8 ft 0 in. to 11 ft 0 in. above the finished floor. The low ceiling height of 8 ft 0 in. will largely depend on the size of the space. Heights of 11 ft 0 in. and higher will, again, depend on the size of the space and will affect lighting calculations. The right height depends on the size of the space and the height of the equipment that must be accommodated.

Early assumptions could be based on Figure 3.1-9, keeping in mind that this is a rule-of-thumb guideline only. It must be finalized by involving the project engineers as early as possible.

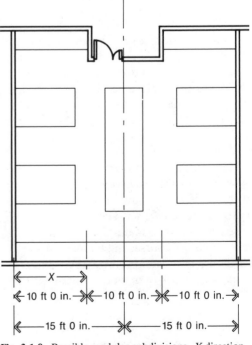

Fig. 3.1-8. Possible modular subdivisions, X direction.

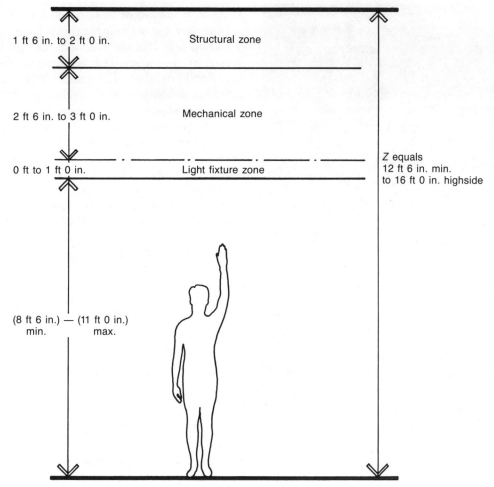

1 ft 6 in. to 2 ft 0 in.   Structural zone

2 ft 6 in. to 3 ft 0 in.   Mechanical zone

0 ft to 1 ft 0 in.   Light fixture zone

Z equals
12 ft 6 in. min.
to 16 ft 0 in. highside

(8 ft 6 in.) — (11 ft 0 in.)
   min.   max.

Fig. 3.1-9. Laboratory model, Z axis.

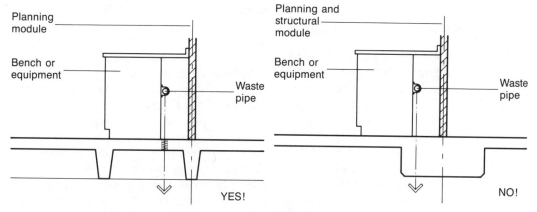

Planning
module

Bench or
equipment

Waste
pipe

YES!

Planning and
structural
module

Bench or
equipment

Waste
pipe

NO!

Fig. 3.1-10. Potential conflict of module and structural system.

Fig. 3.1-11. Utility corridor providing easy access to utilize services, power and cable tray on a modular grid (Edwards Calderon).

Buildings have been, and will continue to be, designed and built with lower floor-to-ceiling heights, but the difficulty of installing and maintaining systems must be weighed against an increase in the initial construction cost. The main loss will be space for mechanical, electrical and plumbing systems, affecting initial and future access for installation and maintenance.

3.1.5 Services for Modular Buildings

Access to utility services is part of the module. However, services in a laboratory building are unlike services in any other kind of facility. A great deal of coordination between designer and engineers is required to provide horizontal and vertical pathways for the ducts and pipes required for HVAC, plumbing, communications and electric power. The location of these pathways is determined by the building's function, systems access and cost.

Many, if not all, of these schemes require access space not only during the original installation but also for maintenance, additional services and remodeling during the life of the building. Early involvement in the engineering design process of engineers representing the engineering disciplines is strongly advised. While there are many ways of servicing or providing pathways for services in laboratory buildings, there are only a few basic approaches. Chapter 5 describes the advantages and disadvantages of basic servicing schemes for laboratory buildings.

It is very important for the designer to keep in mind that the lab planning module and the structural system could potentially be in conflict and impair proper routing of utility services and drainlines during original installation, as well as during future changes. See Figures 3.1-10 and 3.1-11.

3.2 FLEXIBILITY CONSIDERATIONS
M. Wodka

3.2.1 Types of Flexibility

Definitions of Flexibility

During this century, laboratories have become one of our most complex facility types. The pace at which science, research and development is changing caused one commentator to describe these facilities as "the architecture of the unpredictable" (Barnett, 1965). A facility manager at a major university talks about planning for the "X factor" when he discusses laboratories. As it becomes increasingly uncertain what will be done, or how it will be done in a time frame as short as five years into the future, everyone from the scientist to the facility manager sees salvation in flexibility.

Unfortunately, this term lacks consistent meaning for the various participants in the planning process. For some, flexibility means that the parts used to build the laboratory are readily movable or replaceable. For others, it means that the laboratory is relatively fixed but is generic enough to allow many diverse and changing activities to come and go. These diverse and often conflicting interpretations of flexibility must be broken down in some functional way before flexibility can be converted into a working plan.

General types of flexibility. Pena et al. (1977) developed some very useful subdivisions to help us understand alternative types of flexibility. They defined flexibility broadly as the capacity to adjust and modify in some way to respond to a change in activities or functions. They described these adjustments in terms of versatility, convertibility and rearrangeability.

"Versatility" is the ability of the environment to accommodate different functions without physical change—the multiuse place. For example, a given room could accommodate microbiology studies one year and analytical chemistry another year without any changes to benching, hoods, utilities, walls or ceilings. At a larger scale, a given building, if truly versatile, could begin as a center for biological study and then shift to chemical studies with no renovation or physical changes. The only changes would be the type of science being practiced, the equipment brought in and the people doing the work. See Figures 3.2-1 and 3.2-2.

In the "rearrangeability" approach,

change is accommodated by moving and rearranging equipment or furnishings such as tables, chairs, benches, hoods, carts, walls and light fixtures within a given room or space. The individual pieces of equipment or furniture serve the same function and do not change in size or capacity wherever they are located, but the way they are laid out in the plan can be changed to fit new activities. See Figures 3.2-3 and 3.2-4.

In the "convertibility" system, changing functions or activities are accommodated by reassembling interchangeable subcomponents into new spatial configurations, new functional assemblies or both. This may be called the "tinker toy" or "systems" approach. Here we find products such as system furniture, modular walls, modular utility systems or modular ceilings. All of these provide the capacity to adjust for functional variation of the assembly by changing size, shape or capacity, as well as location. For example, a modular ceiling provides both the ability to locate light fixtures at various points and the ability to change the number of light fixtures in the ceiling. At a larger scale, modular building subcomponents can even allow for changes in fenestration, door placement, HVAC loading or zoning, utility distribution capacity, or footprint through the addition, subtraction and relocation of the modular subcomponents. The biggest distinctions between convertibility and rearrangeability are a matter of scale and the number of building elements that can use one type or the other. Convertibility allows finer adjustments and more often includes the ability to change the capacity and location of major building elements such as the mechanical, HVAC and plumbed services. Convertibility adds more complexity compared to rearrangeability but allows adjustments that rearrangeability can't provide. See Figure 3.2-5.

Clearly, any building element can be designed to fit the criteria of any of the flexibility types. In most cases these flexibility options are mixed, depending on how the programming defines the need. A utility system may be a mix of versatility and converti-

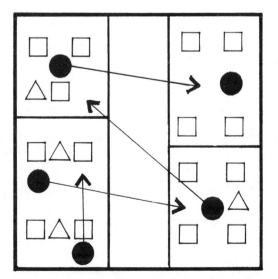

Fig. 3.2-1. Versatility. Change is accommodated by relocating the task within a fixed environment.

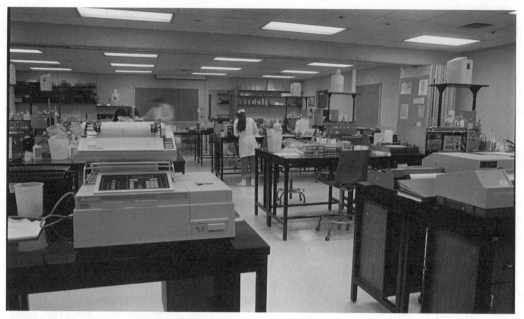

Fig. 3.2-2. Example of versatility. Different courses can be taught in the space without changing the environment because enough space, petcocks, electricity, work surface, etc. are provided to accommodate many kinds of lab courses.

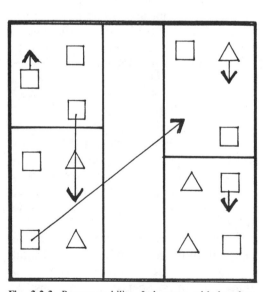

Fig. 3.2-3. Rearrangeability. Lab room with benches that can be skidded from place to place in the room or carried to other rooms.

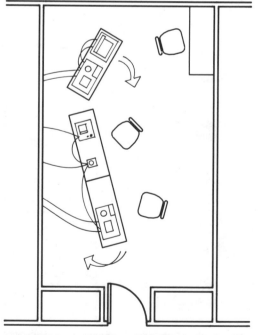

Fig. 3.2-4. Example of a rearrangeable lab. Lab room with benches that can be skidded from place to place in the room or carried to other rooms.

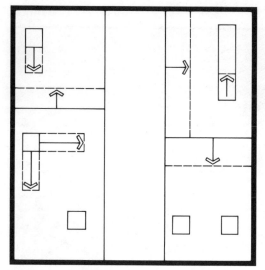

Fig. 3.2-5. Convertibility. Change is accommodated by reconstructing the environment using systems built into the facility.

bility. The system may be versatile at the head end, allowing many services to be distributed without any changes in primary plumbing or distribution. However, at the point of use in lab rooms or in interstitial space, a convertible approach may take over, allowing relocation, addition or subtraction of any service each time a change occurs. The question is, what is the best type of flexibility for a particular element? This is not an easy question to answer unequivocally. These alternative definitions of flexibility are useful in that they provide all parties with a standard vocabulary to use in the planning process when discussing flexibility. Without this common understanding, the discussion of flexibility often ceases with the offhand statement that flexibility is required. The rest of the discussion, defining what type of flexibility is best for each building element, is not conducted in the depth necessary with these common definitions in mind.

3.2.2 Construction Approaches to Achieve Flexibility

Once it has been decided which flexibility approach will be applied to each building element, discussions on appropriate construc-

tion approaches can be conducted. While many conditions can be handled with traditional on-site methods, there are the additional approaches of modular system assemblies, portable parts and mobile components.

Modular Systems

The use of modular systems is the most elaborate construction approach to achieve flexibility. It works best in support of convertibility or rearrangeability. Modular systems are a collection of premanufactured subcomponents that are dimensionally related and functionally different, with common connector systems. See Figure 3.2-6. This allows larger assemblies to be made out of the subcomponents. These larger assemblies, such as benches, walls, utility runs, or even structural parts, allow the users and owners the fullest range of physical change in response to organizational change. If a given assembly's function can remain the same but its physical location should be changed, the assembly can be moved intact. If its function must change but the location is acceptable, this change can also be made. Both the functional configuration and the location can be changed as needed within the limits of space and inventories of subcomponents.

Portable Parts

Portable parts is the second most elaborate approach and probably the approach best suited to flexibility based on rearrangeability. Portability provides prefinished assemblies, each supporting particular functions which can be grouped and regrouped into functional ensembles. See Figure 3.2-7. While the portable parts may be modular in dimension to one another, unlike the modular approach, they cannot be broken down into interchangeable subcomponents. This means that new arrangements are limited by the number of portable assemblies that perform a certain function. For example, since portable parts are prefinished assemblies, one cannot usually convert a bench with six drawers into one with none, as one can with

components, and material handling
components.

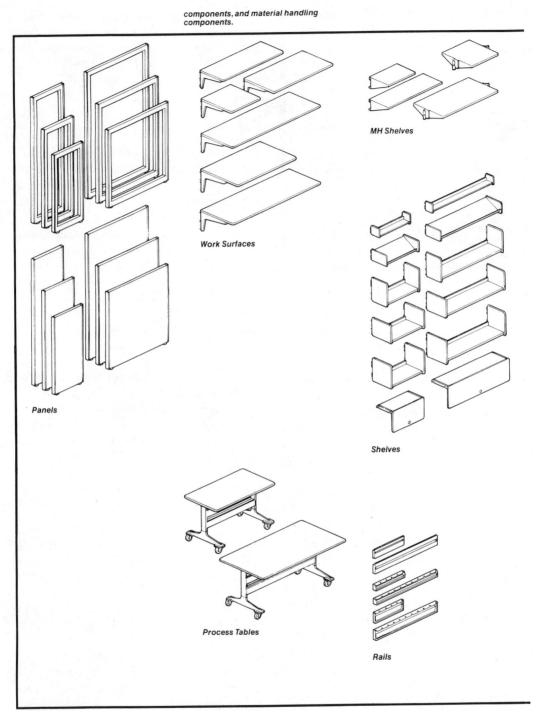

Work Surfaces

MH Shelves

Panels

Shelves

Process Tables

Rails

Fig. 3.2-6. Modular system. It can be assembled into walls, storage units, benches, carts and workstations. (Herman Miller, Inc.).

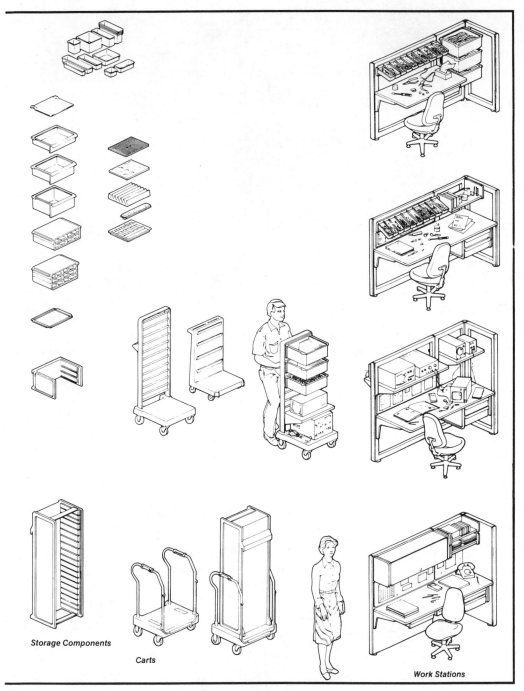

Storage Components

Carts

Work Stations

Fig. 3.2-6. (continued)

Fig. 3.2-7. Portable tables set up around a service spine (Edwards Calderon).

modular parts. A wall panel with no glazing can't be changed into one with partial glazing. One must have the particular finished assembly to fit the new needs.

Mobile Parts

Mobility consists essentially of placing portable elements on wheels. This increases the speed and reduces the physical effort needed to achieve new physical arrangements. See Figure 3.2-8.

In most projects, some combination of these construction approaches is usually employed to assemble the flexibility type and construction methods into a useful package. In addition, in many cases given products combine approaches. For example, a bench

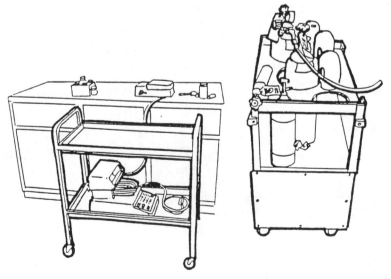

Fig. 3.2-8. Mobile equipment. It allows the location of specialized equipment to be shared or added to experiments. (Herman Miller Research Corp).

may be essentially portable but can have modular drawers or even wheels, making it mobile as well. The important issue is to define the primary construction approach in order to determine how well it fits the need. If a mixed approach is available and works, it should be the option of choice.

3.2.3 Value of Flexibility

The choice of flexibility type and construction approach should be tied to some value for both users and owners in order to offset the increased cost often associated with flexibility.

First-Time Customization

One important advantage of any type of flexibility is the ability to make adjustments before the facility is even finished. There are obvious advantages to each type of flexibility in achieving first-time customization.

Versatility allows a great degree of customization regarding alternatives in assignment but not in physical change. Assuming that the versatility planned really exists, shifts in personnel or equipment location assignment in the lab should be easily absorbed without plan and construction changes. However, if changes are radical, a versatile approach won't absorb the change without extensive revision of the physical plan.

Using rearrangeability or convertibility provides a wide range of first-time design options. These approaches to flexibility also allow changes in the program to be made by physically changing the plans with a minimum of construction penalties. Compared to the versatile approach, the exactness of first-time customization is somewhat greater with rearrangeable or convertible flexibility using modular and portable construction methods. The compromises compared to those of custom-built construction are usually insignificant. Given the increasing likelihood that even during construction needed changes will render a custom approach using built-in-place construction incapable of absorbing the revisions that often occur, choosing manufactured components is usually a good decision.

Future Adjustment

The various types of flexibility also offer their own advantages in the future. Versatility offers the ability to absorb operational changes without making physical adjustments. Since the environment, if designed well, accommodates all likely changes, the facility should only require the reassignment of places to handle future needs. The obvious problem here is the degree of certainty that is necessary in planning for future change. The versatile lab is probably our most common model from the past. Projects like the Nuffield (1961) studies of the late 1950s and early 1960s are examples of the versatile lab, which is far less applicable to today's increasing volatility. The idea that a given room can absorb all the likely instrumental and experimental variety that will occur is today becoming implausible. Add to that the potential shifts in fields of study in corporate R&D, and it becomes virtually impossible to conceive of a lab building or room that will not require major physical re-planning during its life.

In most cases, a mix of rearrangeability and convertibility is seen today as the option of choice. This is especially true of building elements like space delineation, benching, and, where possible, utility distribution.

Investment to Deal with Uncertainty

Some additional dollar investment in flexibility must be made if a lab facility is to have any hope of keeping pace with change. To help determine the value of the investment in flexibility, a return on investment or life cycle cost analysis should be attempted. This exercise helps all parties to sharpen their insights and often reveals that what everyone thinks of a particular flexibility decision may not be as valid when analyzed in terms of some of the factors that a financial investment study demands.

Two important issues to consider when doing this sort of study are the rate of anticipated change and the speed at which a given change should take place. For example, some fields of study require new benching arrangements at relatively long intervals—

such as every 4 to 6 years. But once the need arises, it is advantageous to accomplish that change in 2 days in any given room. These interactions give "value" to certain investments even though the first cost differentials are high.

3.2.4 Issues that Impact Flexibility

Electronic Equipment

To an increasing degree, electronic instrumentation and computers in the lab are now a driving force in flexibility decisions. Yet, there has not been a corresponding response in planning for these changes. Scientists in all types of disciplines must acquire the latest versions of instruments or risk becoming obsolete or uncompetitive. In a 1968 study, both scientists and facility managers rated the introduction of new instrumentation as the first or second most important change factor. Manufacturers of these instruments are partly to blame for the problem. While miniaturization has reduced some of the components of a given instrument, manufacturers have added a variety of peripherals (processors, plotters, etc.), which has increased the size of most equipment with a corresponding increase in profit margins. See Figure 3.2-9.

Growth in various lab types. Each lab type has experienced a rapid increase in electronic hardware. In basic science labs, the electronic hardware is often the experimental apparatus. The days when discoveries were made by pouring liquids from one beaker to another are gone. Equipment such as electron scanning microscopes has taken over the space, replacing benches and bench-top instruments. This forces a rethinking of space delineation, electrical services and benching needs.

In many applied research and invention labs, electronic instrumentation is often modular. This allows the researcher to "assemble" instruments by combining modules to solve different data-gathering problems. However, this equipment consumes available bench space and electrical capacity. See Figure 3.2-10. From the scientists' perspective, the lack of bench space to assemble both electronic instrumentation and experimental apparatus is a severe problem. With labs designed primarily for bench top experimental apparatus, the addition of these electronic devices often overcrowds available space on the bench. In addition, common linear plans that seem to work well for manually observed apparatus cause problems for electronic gear. They tend to work better in arrangements that form a U or an L, allowing easy readout and shorter interconnections between instrument modules.

Of all the lab types, the analytical lab is experiencing probably the greatest impact from computers and electronic instruments. See Table 3.2-1 and Figure 3.2-11. Both scientific and clinical analysis are being performed by ever more accurate, large and automated instruments which replace bench top apparatus. This trade-off of benches for equipment is a problem if traditional benching and utility distribution is used, since benches are hard to remove. Also, as in the other labs, the traditional bench performs work less and less successfully as more electronic hardware is employed, since the electronic instruments often form workstations of their own. The flow of samples into and out of these spaces is no longer as efficient as it could be if only linear planning is available.

These changes require new thinking about providing flexible ways of accommodating

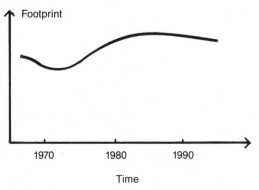

Fig. 3.2-9. Trend for the footprint of individual pieces of electronic lab equipment over the next few years.

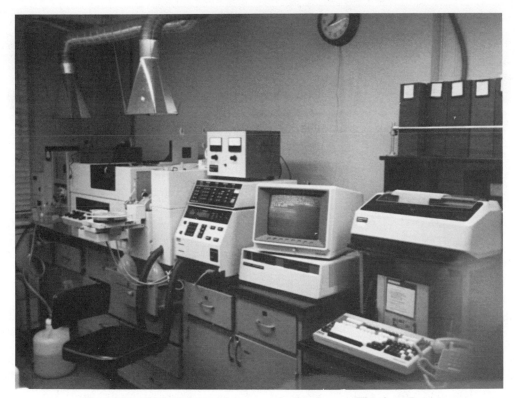

Fig. 3.2-10. Electronic instruments consuming bench space (Theodorus Ruys).

Table 3.2-1. Mean Number of Instruments in Clinical Analytical Laboratories

Equipment	Large Hospital	Small Hospital	Private Lab	Group Practice
Random access chemical analyzer	2.5	1.4	1.6	1.1
Continuous flow chemical analyzer	1.0	.4	.6	.4
Urine chemistry analyzer	1.0	.4	.3	.4
Automated hematology analyzer	2.4	1.5	1.2	1.4
Automated microbiology system	2.2	.7	.4	.7
Blood gas analyzer	2.6	1.2	.6	.8
Therapeutic drug analyzer	2.5	1.1	1.1	1.1
Floor model centrifuge	3.9	1.8	1.8	1.1
Bench centrifuge	6.7	4.9	3.9	3.9
Automated strainer	1.9	.9	.5	.7
Gamma counter	1.3	.7	1.1	.8
Differential microscope	3.0	2.1	2.2	1.9
Other microscopes	6.7	5.0	2.9	2.7
Chromatograph	1.3	.1	.6	.3
Spectrophotometer	2.5	1.5	2.3	1.0
Personal computer or terminal interdependent from instruments	3.6	1.4	2.3	1.0
Refrigerators	6.7	6.2	4.6	3.6

Source: The Clinical Laboratory: *User Needs, Choices and Options.* Chicago: Herman Miller Research Corp.

Fig. 3.2-11. Bench top analyzer typical of equipment moving into analytical and clinical labs (Herman Miller Corp.).

this hardware. Bench top racking is one new feature. At the larger scale, many instruments replace benches entirely. Room plans that allow for arrangements other than linear layouts of equipment will become important (see Section 1.2).

Effects on benching revisions and space. Electronic instrumentation increases the likelihood of bench revision. Trading benches for instruments may require more space to handle new configurations of instruments and remaining benches. Another impact is the desirability to share instruments and the expert operators often necessary to use this gear. This suggest mobility in many cases. This leads to a rethinking of lab layouts and spaces that allow equipment to be brought in and taken out without problems in maneuvering, egress safety or useful placement.

Impact on staffing and space. Another change caused by new instrumentation is on staffing and space needs. Overall staffing tends to go down as instrumentation use goes up. However, requirements change from space for benches and people to more space for instruments, often floor models. Fewer people work in the lab rooms, but the floor space may well be consumed by instruments and their peripherals.

Impact on cabling/wiring access and utility distribution. Finally, laboratory automation leads to radical revisions in utility distribution. Most of the traditional plumbed utilities are not necessary. Yet, new needs arise for local use of exotic gases which are unique to given electronic data gathering situations. Electrical requirements for "clean," uninterruptible power and data networking are also increased over traditional approaches. This seems to increase the need to modify these utilities personally as experiments evolve, and therefore the demand for more physical access that is safe for the scientist to change and reorganize. See Figure 3.2-12.

Project Demand

Project duration as a flexibility determinant. As a flexibility determinant, a lab's project duration is another key element. Project duration can mean the actual length of an R&D project or phase, or it can mean the length of time a particular analytical procedure remains set up and operating. The studies cited earlier showed that as the project duration increases, the ability to reconfigure lab layouts becomes increasingly important. This includes changes in lab size as well as bench arrangement. A project duration of less than 6 months increases the de-

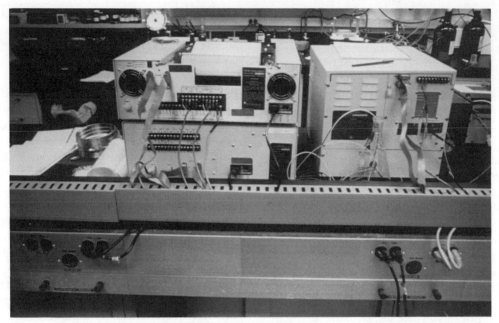

Fig. 3.2-12. Bench wiring and plumbing for new electronic instruments. This example allows users to rearrange utilities to supply instruments with both electrical and special gases through flexible tubing. The electrical chase is above the plumbing chase. Both are mounted at the rear of the bench.

sire to adjust a small variable like bench height, drawer location or work top location, as well as to accomplish larger lab reconfigurations. See Table 3.2-2.

This suggests that rearrangeable and/or convertible approaches are dominant in areas like benching, lab room utility distribution and, where possible, wall systems. There is a shift to the modular system/convertible approach as the project duration

Table 3.2-2. Flexibility Choice Option By Lab Project Duration

Choice option	Duration (Months)	
	< 6	> 6
Change bench height	33	13
Reconfigure lab layout	38	32

Note: As lab project duration increases, the desire to reconfigure lab layouts remains high, while the desire to make small adjustments like changing bench height goes down substantially.

Source: The Clinical Laboratory: *User Needs, Choices and Options*. Chicago: Herman Miller Research Corp.

drops below 6 months. Here small adjustments like work surface height and utility receptacle locations are made as often as the room layout is changed.

Evolution rate of experimental procedures as a flexibility determinant. Like project demands, differing changes in experimental procedures cause different impacts on flexibility requirements. The biggest change has already been discussed: the shift from bench top apparatus to electronic gear. However, in applied research and invention labs, the need to respond to field problems often requires more than one procedure to be set up in a given room. The mix of procedures at any one time is unpredictable. The ability to reconfigure benching at will is a desirable feature with this kind of random experimental evolution.

Need for flexibility by lab type. Of the types of labs described in the classification scheme from Section 1.1, applied and invention labs favor convertible and rearrangeable approaches to flexibility, while basic science and routine analytical labs prefer versatility, opting to adjust apparatus to fit the space. When users are compared to facility managers on this issue, there are small differences which result from the pressure to execute changes. Facility managers see the need for further convertibility and/or rearrangeability in some classes of labs because they receive the demands for change and realize, more clearly than users, how much more difficult versatile labs are to change physically. These difficulties include longer time, more capital expense and the possibility of higher design/planning fees. See Figure 3.2-13.

Basic science laboratories generally tend to favor the versatile approach to flexibility. Basic scientists, by nature, seem more willing to rearrange apparatus than architectural components. Their interests are so focused on the practice of science that rearranging the experimental components is easier than changing the physical space. This preference may also be influenced by the fact that most basic science is practiced in the university. Funds for physical renovation are limited compared to corporate R&D funds and are often tied to grants. Spending this grant money on the experiment seems more productive than spending it on the facility even though there is an improvement in conducting the research. Finally, as basic science must delve into ever more minute and specialized areas of study to make new discoveries, the equipment used often becomes the majority of the lab furnishings. This equipment really needs general versatile space for installation and removal. Traditional benching and utility distribution are of little value.

In *applied and invention* laboratories, the demands for rearrangeability and convertibility are most prominent. The reason for this distribution seems to be based on two factors. The first is project duration. In applied R&D and invention labs, project duration is 6 to 9 months. This rate of project turnover seems to create more pressure for rearranging to fit new programs or procedures as projects shift, leading to a desire for more modular convertible environments.

While basic science labs and some analytical labs have project durations averaging 9 months or more, typical scientists spend less time actually working at the bench. In these situations they act as managers, which keeps them from working directly on the experiments. This is the second factor. It appears that the scientists working in applied research and invention labs spend more time actually working in their labs and develop a taste for rearranging both the experiments and the environment. They may also have more ways of justifying these changes in terms of research efficiency and effectiveness, which can be converted to cost savings for the corporation. This their associates in basic science cannot often do.

Because the rate of output is the critical factor in most *analytical* laboratories, the need for rearrangeability dominates. The setup of these labs is based on efficiency of data production. Therefore, the ability to arrange the space for the most efficient use of people and equipment leads to the need to reconfigure benches as new equipment comes in or as procedural change is initiated to improve output. However, these changes occur at rather long intervals, 1 year or more, which makes investment in modular convertible equipment less attractive than investment in portable hardware.

When users discuss flexibility, they focus on the need to:

- Deal with the continuous rearrangement of electronic instrumentation and experimental apparatus, leading to higher demands for direct access to utility systems, especially electrical service;
- Reconfigure, add and especially subtract benching;
- Change room size to accommodate shifts in instrumentation for experiments or project type.

Rates of change. Over the years, an increasing amount of the total space has been revised in labs. In a study by Wodka (1981), an average of 10% of lab rooms in R&D facilities in any given year underwent a change

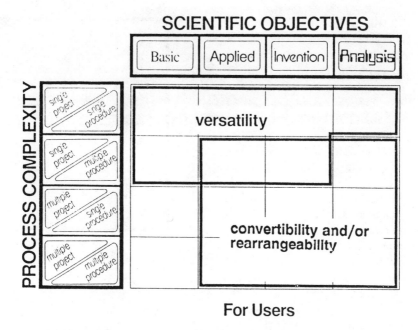

For Users

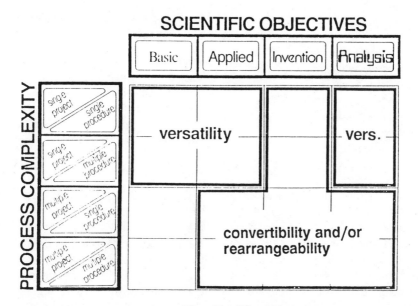

For Facility Managers

Fig. 3.2-13. Typical clustering of flexibility types based on users' and facility managers' perceptions (Herman Miller Research Corp., 1981).

which required bench, utility or wall revisions. In a follow-up study of a similar sample of labs by Levy and Wodka (1986), the rate of change had doubled.

With this increase, there are two key factors which must be considered in trying to determine how flexible the environment should be: the churn rate and down time.

Churn rate: The first factor is the likelihood that changes requiring the environment to be revised will be made. This rate of change, or facility churn, can be classified as (1) hardly ever (3 years or more), (2) regularly (1 to 3 years), or (3) often (8 to 10 months or less). As the churn rate moves toward "Often," use of rearrangeability or convertibility to maintain facility responsiveness becomes more critical.

Down time: The second factor is down time. In any discussion of change, how fast an identified change should occur must be stated explicitly. Can the organization afford a rather slow change (3 months or more), or does it require a faster change (1 month)? Or should the change take place even faster— say, in a matter of days? While these time frames are somewhat arbitrary, they form a background for discussion to determine the best investment for the flexibility desired.

For example, a utility system that allows total bench relocation or removal in 1 work day may be conceptually possible and desirable. However, a realistic review of operations may disclose that change occurs in this lab on a slow cycle, perhaps every 4 to 6 years. In addition, when it occurs, there is ample time before a new program starts up allowing time for construction. These factors point to a less complex utility system which allows for bench removal but a much better cost/benefit ratio.

Impact on flexibility: To make effective use of this interaction, the rate of facility change, or churn, and the speed at which change should occur can be diagrammed on a mapping grid. See Figure 3.2-14. If you take each facility element, from the structural package, skin, walls, etc., down to the furnishings and instruments, and ask (1) should it be able to physically change?, (2) If so, how often might you change that element? and (3) when changed, how fast should/could the change be executed?, you can locate a position on the grid which corresponds to your answers. See Figure 3.2-15. The elements that fall within the "often/fast" quadrant are better candidates for flexibility based on convertibility and mobility, while those that fall within the "hardly ever/slow" quadrant are probably best han-

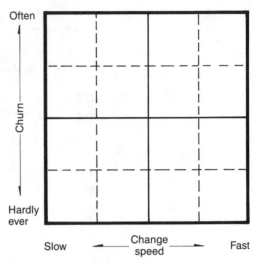

Fig. 3.2-14. Example of change rate "map."

dled with versatility combined with built-in-place construction methods.

3.2.5 Conflicts Between Flexibility Types

While flexibility offers the chance to deal with organizational change effectively over time, inevitable conflicts arise during planning that can render flexibility choices useless unless resolved. Those conflicts fall into two categories: physical and management.

Physical Conflicts

The physical conflicts between flexibility types that can develop in a typical lab plan are enormous. The most common problem stems from attempts to blend flexibility types to work most appropriately with given building elements. Type interaction, assembly agreement, or modular fit and tolerance are the physical conflicts that usually develop.

Type interaction. The most common problems of type interaction happen in trying to blend versatility with convertibility or rearrangeability. Problems occur, for example, in trying to combine a versatile structural system with a rearrangeable room layout and a convertible utility distribution approach. Large spans allow rearrangement of rooms

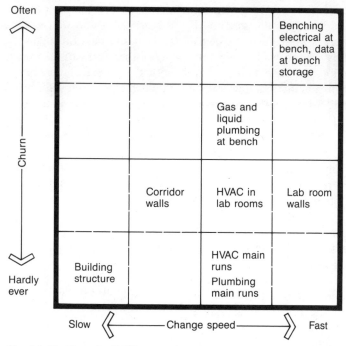

Fig. 3.2-15. Example of filling out the map to help define flexibility requirements and criteria.

but may create vibration and structural loading problems. Vibration-sensitive or heavy equipment must also be freely relocated during room rearrangement at increased cost. Usually the structural system must be strengthened to accommodate this degree of rearrangeability. Otherwise, a decision must be made to limit the rearrangement of certain equipment, restricting it to areas specially designed to support high loads or dampen vibration. In that case, costs are lowered but the structural systems' versatility is significantly reduced.

Misfits can also develop in mixing versatility and convertibility when the utility system consisting of plumbing and electricity is designed for versatility, while walls and benches are to be convertible. The utilities are designed and therefore distributed to provide permanent petcocks and receptacles throughout all the lab rooms. However, the choice of and investment in convertible benches have been made to allow room size, bench function and/or location to be changed easily. If walls are moved, the utility system, which was not designed to move, may not fit the new configuration. The fixed location of the versatile utilities dominates the space usage. If changes of benches or walls don't fit the utility layout, costly construction is required to relocate the utilities on a new grid or to change the petcock/receptacle layout.

Assembly agreement. While the selection of the various flexibility types may be resolved, the issue of assembly methods must also agree, at least in terms of the ease by which it is accomplished. There is little sense in having one system that can be relocated or reconfigured quickly if it must work with other elements that are slow and difficult to change. A bench system that is easily and quickly rearrangeable into new ensembles does little good if the utilities needed to support the experiments cannot be changed just as easily. Assembly methods are a "weakest link" issue. As another example, a convertible modular wall and benching system allowing very rapid changes in function is wasted if the benching system cannot be assembled as quickly as the wall relocations can be made. Flexibility types may agree but, if the change requires many building trades, timing conflicts will arise, reducing the overall success of the flexibility choices.

Modular fit. The conflicts that develop in this case usually involve center lines. When convertibility and rearrangeability are used, some form of dimensional modularity usually must accompany the design. Often what one party considers a module is not exactly what another sees even though similar dimensions are used. Wall systems are a good example, especially where they are expected to fit into a versatile building structural module that is set for the life of the building. Some wall systems are based on the size of the actual panel, which often matches the building module. See Figure 3.2-16. Therefore, there is an addition to the length of the run every time an intersection is created because a connecting post must be added. See Figure 3.2-17. Other systems incorporate the ability to place an intersection at any panel joint without a change in overall length. See Figure 3.2-18. Both approaches are convertible and modular, but the second will be easier to coordinate with the building structural module because the overall center line of the wall system agrees with the building modules. Utility systems made up of modular parts have a similar problem if they are not

based on the same modular dimensions as the benching and wall systems that they attach to and pass through.

Another form of this problem can occur with the fitting of benches which are rearrangeable. If room walls are built center line to center line, and if the benches are specified as a part of that module, they will not fit evenly inside the rooms. See Figures 3.2-19 and 3.2-20. The bench module must be based on the interior finished size or must be specified as a module that compensates for wall thickness if modular fit is to be achieved.

Management Conflicts

Conflicts between flexibility types produce management problems in two areas: supporting service and safety.

Supporting service. As systems become more convertible, facility management tasks increase unless changes can be turned over to the scientists and technicians working in the lab. In many situations the provision of convertibility, especially at the bench or utility system level, goes just far enough to wet the users' appetite for change, but not far enough to make the change occur on time or without an increased facility service force. As with many of the direct physical problems, the problem is usually one of timing. Changes can be made but not as quickly, precisely or cost effectively as the user expects. On the other hand, easy-to-change ap-

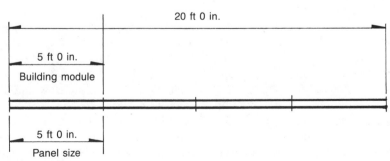

Fig. 3.2-16. Panel run using panel-to-panel joint. Without intersections, panel run stays on module.

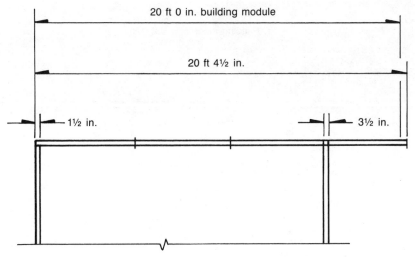

Fig. 3.2-17. Panel run with intersections. Addition of intersections adds module creep.

proaches, based on mobility for example, allow users much more freedom but demand more management tracking to establish ownership or to locate those things that move from place to place. If modular componentry is used to support a combination of convertible and rearrangeable flexibility, there are also problems of inventory management to be considered. Space must be available to store unused parts in a way that makes them available as needed. The inventory mix must also be carefully considered during design to ensure that a reasonable number of parts to

fit the variety of user requirements is in stock.

Since inventory should be purchased at the time of construction to take advantage of the best vendor pricing, there are questions of purchasing to be resolved as well. Should inventory be part of the contractor's package, or should the owner purchase it separately? These are questions that the facility management group should be involved in answering. Finally, for managers, there are the questions of charging for changes. Whether these are part of building costs of operation or

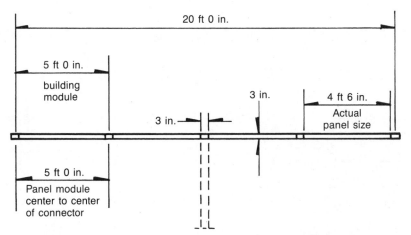

Fig. 3.2-18. Panel run using four-way between panels. No module creep occurs because the four-way connector compensates.

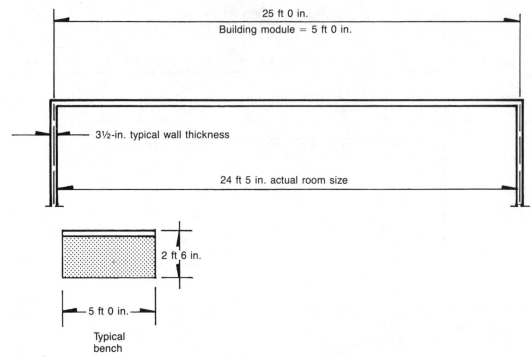

25 ft 0 in.

Building module = 5 ft 0 in.

3½-in. typical wall thickness

24 ft 5 in. actual room size

2 ft 6 in.

5 ft 0 in.

Typical
bench

Fig. 3.2-19. Example of module mismatch. Five benches will not fit inside this room built on a 5 ft 0 in. building module.

project costs can affect users' decisions on flexibility needs and choices. Typically, the more costs are considered part of project costs, the more the scientific project managers want good cost value analysis to justify flexibility investments. When these costs are part of building costs, scientific management often demands flexibility, with less concern for value justification.

Safety. One of the most difficult flexibility conflicts involves safety. As the ability to alter parts of the environment physically increases, the opportunity to create safety

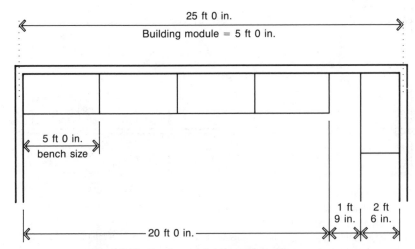

25 ft 0 in.

Building module = 5 ft 0 in.

5 ft 0 in.
bench size

1 ft
9 in.

2 ft
6 in.

20 ft 0 in.

Fig. 3.2-20. Bench module mismatch turning corners.

problems runs parallel or even ahead. One of the appeals of versatile utility distribution systems is that they are intended to remain where they are located. The available outlets are hooked up to experiments and disconnected, but the system is not continuously altered. However, there are increasing user demands for the ability to change. The management dilemma is one of trust in the user and the changeable hardware to create safe assemblies versus trust in a nonchangeable system installed by trained professionals at the expense of lost R&D time. Similar problems exist for contamination containment and air quality management. The ability exists to create easily relocated and convertible components like hoods and wall systems. But if that becomes easy enough for individual users to do on their own, will there be enough built-in safety control to ensure proper application and connection?

3.2.6 Summary

Laboratory flexibility involves four simple issues that must be considered in relation to building the physical structure. These are the flexibility type, the speed with which a change should be accomplished, the rate at which changes are likely to occur and the most appropriate construction approach to satisfy flexibility needs.

The Flexibility Matrix

To help all the persons involved in making these decisions, it is suggested that these issues be charted against the various elements that make up the laboratory. For simplicity, Figure 3.2-21 shows four primary building elements arranged against four flexibility issues. The building elements are:

- The structure, which is made up of the structural system, exterior skin, roof, etc., and all load bearing elements.
- Utilities, which consist of the primary and secondary distribution of gases, air, electricity, data and liquids.
- Space delineation, which consists of all non-load-bearing walls, interior surface finishes that are attached to the structure, raised floors and dropped ceilings.
- Furnishings, which include all movable equipment, benches, hoods and storage cabinets that are not part of the structural or space delineation elements.

The flexibility issues discussed earlier are:

- Flexibility type.
- Rate of change.
- Speed of change.
- Construction approach.

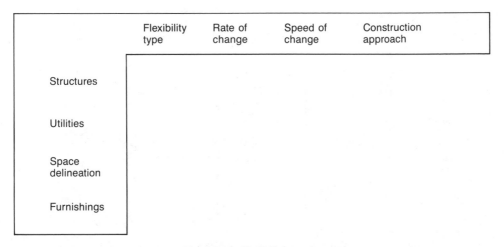

Fig. 3.2-21. Flexibility matrix.

Each of these building elements can be described in as much detail as needed on the matrix.

To use the matrix, the planning team can take its programming information on change rates and speed of change, plus other pertinent information, and fill in the most appropriate flexibility type and the proposed construction approach. Figure 3.2-22 shows the matrix with all the options shown, and Figure 3.2-23 shows a hypothetical example of a matrix filled out for a particular project. Once the matrix is filled out, the team can search for flexibility conflicts and review the overall program for flexibility with users and facility managers.

Rules of Thumb for Flexibility

Structure and utility issues are as follows:

- Create space that allow at least two-dimensional planning by maximizing net usable square footage with a minimum of fixed subdivisions.
- Plan for the greatest plausible demand when specifying utilities. Reserve expansion space at both the front end of the systems and the points of use.
- Plan for easy utility system access. Most cities provide better access to utility distribution than many lab buildings. Yet, getting into these systems is usually the

critical issue in allowing conversion and rearrangements to occur with a minimum of down time, which is usually an important criterion of flexibility.

- Provide for the ability to vary lighting conditions. This means that the ceiling should be analyzed in terms of being a readily convertible plane, with easily relocatable light fixtures to fit lab layout changes.

Space delineation and furnishing issues are as follows:

- Be sure that there is modular agreement. Since most building structural systems are fixed, their modules guide the fit of furnishings and space division if they are relocatable and modular. The overall assembly dimensions must agree, but not necessarily on the same grid (see Chapter 5) to maximize the ease of fitting furnishings and walls into the structure without special fillers.
- Propose change scenarios to ensure appropriate construction approach choices. For example, a change scenario could be a description of past events that led to a major or minor renovation. Or it could consist of descriptions by various scientists of how projects create the need for change as a general flow of

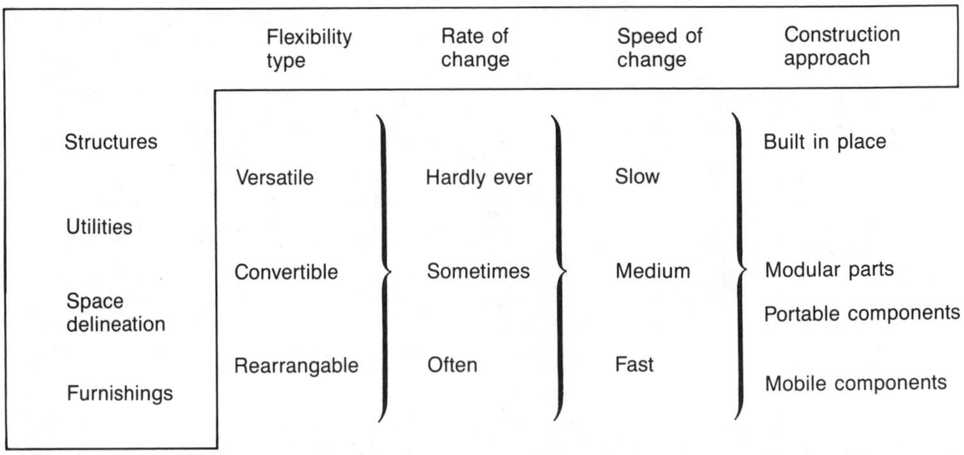

	Flexibility type	Rate of change	Speed of change	Construction approach
Structures				Built in place
	Versatile	Hardly ever	Slow	
Utilities				
	Convertible	Sometimes	Medium	Modular parts
Space delineation				Portable components
	Rearrangable	Often	Fast	
Furnishings				Mobile components

Fig. 3.2-22. Flexibility matrix with all the options shown in each column.

	Flexibility type	Rate of change	Speed of change	Construction approach
Structures	Versatile	Hardly ever	Slow	Built-in place
Utilities	Versatile, convertible	Sometimes to often	Medium to fast	Modular parts
Space delineation	Rearrangeable	Sometimes	Medium	Portable components
Furnishings	Convertible, rearrangeable	Often	Fast	Modular parts, portable components, mobile components

Fig. 3.2-23. Hypothetical example of a completed flexibility matrix.

events both historically and as estimates of the future. These scenarios should, therefore, include the first use and likely changes over the total life of the facility as well as they can be projected.

- Think of furnishings as part of the lab apparatus. The apparatus can be arranged to fit the experiment. It is often portable and/or mobile, which allows it to accommodate varying experimental conditions. Furnishings looked at this way can better fit the experimental needs of the lab.

Corollaries of Flexibility

As in any area, what appears true today may not be so tomorrow. Flexibility, especially in terms of convertibility, will cost more to provide. Yet it may be rendered useless in the future as more sophisticated electronics, which reduces the need to convert and rearrange space, affects more and more experimental situations. However, the typical 10 to 15% investment increase that flexibility requires may still be an excellent investment to absorb the new technology, even though only the utility distribution system is adjusted in the future.

Finally, keep in mind that on this subject the last word is: *There is no last word*. This is true because lab planning and design are based on the unpredictability of science and

technology. These tested and workable recommendations need to be continuously reviewed and updated to help direct the process of providing labs that will work now and in the future.

REFERENCES

Barnett, Jonathan, 1965. Laboratory Buildings, *Architectural Record,* 173–196.

Levy, David, and Wodka, Michael, 1986. *The Industrial Laboratory: User Needs, Choices, and Options.* Ann Arbor, MI: Herman Miller Research Corporation.

Nuffield Foundation, 1961. *The Design Research Laboratories.* New York: Oxford University Press.

Pena, William, Caudill, William, and Focke, John, 1977. *Problem Seeking: An Architectural Programming Primer.* Boston: Cahners Books International.

Wodka, Michael, 1981. *Laboratory Management and Environment Analysis.* Ann Arbor, MI: Herman Miller Research Corporation.

3.3 WORKSTATIONS AND ACTIVITY CENTERS   *T. Ruys*

3.3.1 Introduction

Laboratories are generally thought of as spaces that contain benches and equipment. Utility and power requirements generally are considered first and human needs last.

There is no doubt that laboratories are equipment driven, but with the increasingly specialized skills and associated costs of laboratory technicians, it behooves us to look at laboratories as activity centers with workstations within them.

Activity centers, as their name implies, are spaces or areas that are planned and designed to accommodate certain activities. A workstation, on the other hand, is planned and designed to accommodate an individual, with or without a piece of equipment.

Interestingly enough, if one looks at prints and paintings from before the year 1850, it is clear that laboratories looked like kitchens which included a number of activity centers. The alchemist had a place to grind, heat, mix, write and store things. Laboratories earlier in this century were designed more like workstations with utilities every 4 ft and a drain trough down the middle of the bench for easy disposal from any point.

Three things changed the laboratory's configuration and our thinking about laboratories:

- The increased complexity and scale of laboratory activities, which resulted in multiple tasks per person over a large work area.
- The increased use of instrumentation which had a life of its own because of the required sustaining systems.
- The increase in safety consciousness, which required certain activities to be isolated or contained.

The switch from old to new thinking was very subtle. The response was to make laboratories modular to reduce costs and more adaptable to frequent changes.

The purpose of this chapter is to explore whether we have gone too far in our emphasis on equipment needs, modularity and flexibility, and to concentrate on the individual in order to focus on the design of activity centers and workstations, i.e., to integrate humans and machines.

3.3.2 Workstations

Workstations most often consist of a place where an individual performs a task. At times, multiple tasks are involved or the station is mostly occupied by a large instrument which performs the human function but still requires a number of manipulations to enter samples and solutions and extract data.

Workstations are needed either because the activity is specialized or because the individual spends a great deal of time at that location. Table 3.3-1 shows examples of both equipment- and person-driven workstations.

These workstations require a number of things to support the activity:

- Wireways for communications and power. These can come from the top and must be integrated with the ceiling system, or from the bottom and must be integrated with the flooring or structural system. The top access approach is easier to change but may be unsightly. The bottom access approach often requires a high initial investment. Wireways must also be integrated with the casework system (see Figure 3.3-1) for benches with multiple electrical cords and even for tubing from gas cylinders to instruments.
- Task lighting. Workstations generally, because of the nature of the tasks, require better illumination than the laboratory itself. This lighting system may be part of the casework system or may be independent.
- Comfort. Since individuals are of different sizes, the ability to adjust work surface height, reach distance and posture is very desirable both when changing station occupants and for the same occupant over time (see Figure 3.3-2).
- Security. Many workstations include expensive components or personnel items which should be secured. A drawer or cupboard with a lock is often highly desirable.
- Storage. Many workstations also often need certain supplies. Storage for these must be planned for the size and volume of items to be stored.
- Utilities. Workstations may need a wide variety of electrical and piped services.

Table 3.3-1. Workstation Examples

Type	Equipment Driven	Person Driven	Bench Height (in.)	Environmental Requirements	Utilities Required
Balances	X	X	30	No draft, vibration control	Electrical (see Figure 3.3-5)
Microscopy	X	X	Adjustable	Dimmer, vibration control	Electrical; dimmer control, access
Tissue culture		X	30	Filtered air supply	Gas, cold water, cupsink; electrical, UC refrigerator
Media pouring		X	36	Filtered air	None (see Figure 3.3-6)
Chemical bench		X	36	Standard for laboratories	Electrical; access to gas, water; perhaps vacuum and air
Fumehood	X		36	Varies with type	Same as chemical bench
Biological safety cabinet		X	30 or 36	Varies with type (Section 4.3)	Electrical; perhaps gas; rarely water, air or vacuum.
Teaching laboratory		X	30 or 36	Standard	Electrical; others as needed
Necropsy: large animals		X	36	Downdraft hood	Water, suction; electrical
Small animals		X	30	Backdraft hood	Electrical (see Figure 3.3-7)
PC	X	X	30	Dimmer	Electrical
Handicap	X	X	34	Standard for laboratory	See Figure 3.3-10
Automated analyzers		X	Various	Temperature control	As required

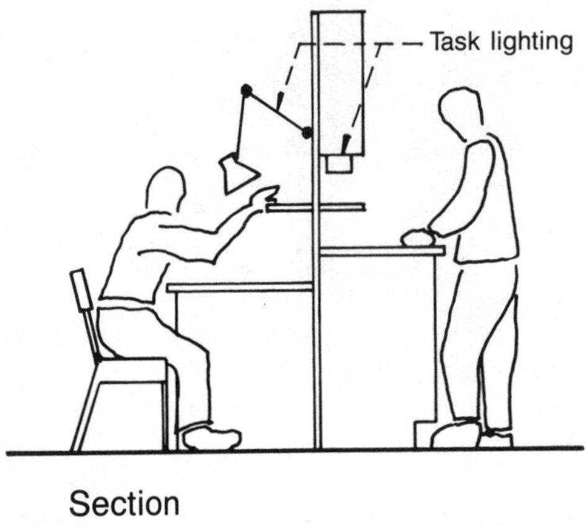

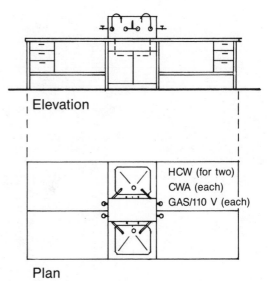

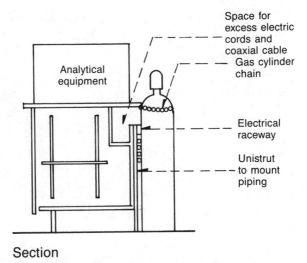

Fig. 3.3-1. Adjustable-top heights and a variety of shelving and cabinets.

Fig. 3.3-3. Multidisciplinary teaching station for four students.

That is particularly true of stations for analytical equipment or teaching (see Figure 3.3-3 and 3.3-4).

A number of special workstations are worth mentioning because they reduce costs, save space or include some special feature:

- A low-cost balance station made up of layers of brick and cardboard topped with a precast concrete reinforced slab (see Figure 3.3-5).
- A media pouring bench with multiple tops so that the floor area may be reduced (see Figure 3.3-6).

- A necropsy workstation with a down-draft air exhaust system to minimize or eliminate noxious and potentially biological hazards to personnel (see Figure 3.3-7).
- A gross anatomy station with a number of features including a voice-activated dictating system (see Figure 3.3-8).
- Many automated analyzers that include, besides the analyzer itself, a keyboard, printer, reagents and sometimes a power

Fig. 3.3-2. Analytical equipment bench.

Fig. 3.3-4. Multidisciplinary teaching station for medical, dental and nursing students (Edwards Calderon).

source. The shape of this type of station is dictated by equipment accessibility, and a linear configuration, common for bench chemistry operations, is not appropriate (see Figure 3.3-9).

Many types of analyzers require maintenance service from the back. Space can be provided behind the equip-

ment for access, which is typically 30 in. Alternatively, in order to reduce floor space, reagents, power units and analyzers can be mounted on heavy-duty, mobile tables with lockable casters (see Figure 3.3-10).

• A handicap station may be unusual but is often required, particularly in teach-

Fig. 3.3-5. Low-cost balance table made up of bricks, cardboard and a reinforced concrete slab (Theodorus Ruys).

Fig. 3.3-6. Media pouring bench with multiple hinged tops (Theodorus Ruys).

ing laboratories. This type of station has been covered in Section 7.5 in some detail but is included as a photograph in Figure 3.3-11.

- Specialized workstations are, of course, the chemical fumehood and the biological safety cabinet designed to prevent the individual from inhaling hazardous chemicals or biological agents. Fumehoods are covered in some detail in Section 4.4. Laminar air flow hoods designed to protect the work against contaminants in the environment are also covered.

Mobility and interchangeability are important characteristics of many workstations:

- They allow reconfiguring of a linear arrangement into a U or L shape (see Figure 3.3-12). These mobile units can be carts or tables on casters.
- Interchangeability includes the ability to remove or change components, such as work surface height, shelving and cabinets. Components must be reusable elsewhere and many break down into units which can be stored easily.

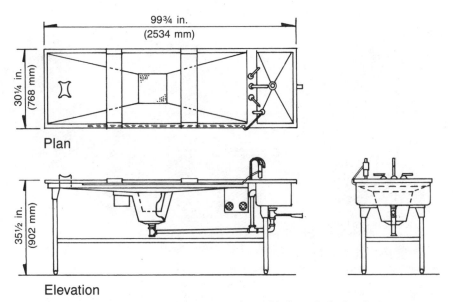

Plan

Elevation

Fig. 3.3-7. Large animal necropsy stations with down-draft air exhaust.

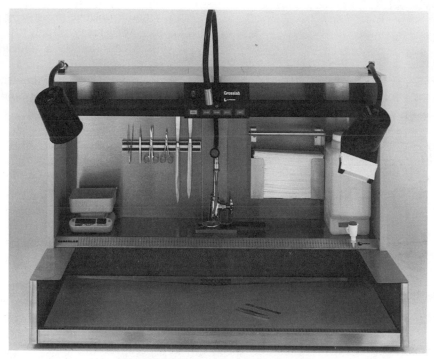

Fig. 3.3-8. Gross anatomy station (Lipshaw).

3.3.3 Activity Centers

These are areas designated, furnished and equipped for certain activities. Within these areas may be several workstations.

Activity centers may be designed for thinking/writing (office), data access, display, storage and retrieval (computer work room), manipulation (glasswash/decontamination), automation (analytical instruments) and assembly (electronics shop), to name a

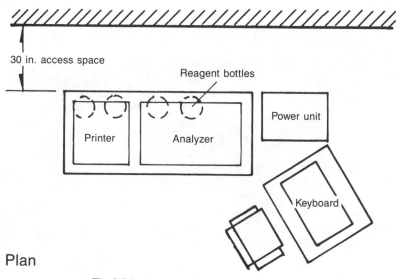

Fig. 3.3-9. Automated analyzer station—fixed.

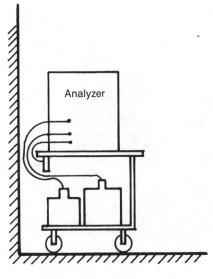

Section

Fig. 3.3-10. Automated analyzer station—mobile.

few. Examples of activity centers and the reason for their existence are:

• Weighing rooms with a number of balances. This space protects the expensive balances from corrosive atmospheres, dust, drafts and theft. The room is typi-

cally under positive pressure, has a filtered, low-velocity supply air and is locked. Vibration is a concern, and these spaces are not occupied full time.

• Microscopy. This space has the same features as the balance room but, in addition, needs a dimmer light for certain types of microscopy.

• Glasswash rooms. These come in various sizes, but they have certain features in common. There must be stations for disassembling soiled glassware, disposing of waste, prerinsing, washing and drying. At times, soaking tanks with detergent and acid solutions are also required. The washing and drying station is very often a washer and dryer, and may include a separate pipette washing station. This space is under negative pressure, requires a high rate of exhaust air to remove the moisture and is usually occupied full time. Washers and dryers generate a great deal of heat and are therefore best recessed. See Appendix J.

• Decontamination areas. These are very similar to glasswash areas, except that items are sterilized by autoclaving or

Fig. 3.3-11. Handicap workstation for a chemistry teaching laboratory (Theodorus Ruys).

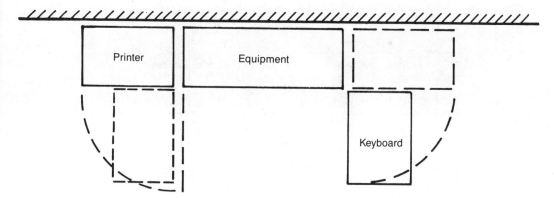

Plan

Fig. 3.3-12. Mobile units allow reconfiguring of a linear arrangement into an L- or U-shape station.

other means and washers are replaced by autoclaves.

- Media preparation also needs autoclaves, but these require clean steam. See Section 4.6. Much space is required for preparing media and for storing glassware and finished media. Media are easily contaminated, and a high-efficiency particulate air (HEPA) filtered air supply and positive pressure are recommended. Maintaining a distance from glasswash and decontamination is advisable to prevent cross-contamination.

- Tissue culture also requires a clean environment to prevent cross-contamination. A HEPA filtered air supply, positive pressure and sliding doors are recommended. Sliding doors slice the air and cause less air turbulence than hinged doors. Tissue culture cubicles often have a refrigerator and/or incubator within the space. For very critical work, a laminar air or biological cabinet may be installed inside the tissue culture room (see Figure 3.3-13).

- Dispensing rooms for flammable liquids and other types of chemicals. Section 3.5 has a good discussion on the equipment and layout required.

- First aid stations, including long-term showers to aid accident victims, are also covered in Section 3.5.

- Environmental control rooms are considered equipment and are covered in Section 4.7.

- Clean rooms, radioisotope laboratories, X-ray, shielded and electromagnetic shielded rooms, because of their complexity, are covered in appendices.

There are a number of activity centers that, because of their size, are better classified as suites. Examples are computer suites, green house/head house, electron microscope suites, animal facilities, surgical and X-ray suites, nuclear magnetic resonance suites, cyclotrons and machine/electronics

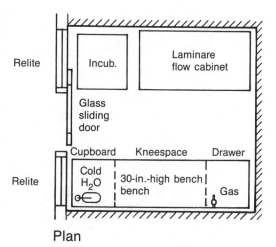

Plan

Fig. 3.3-13. Tissue culture cubicle.

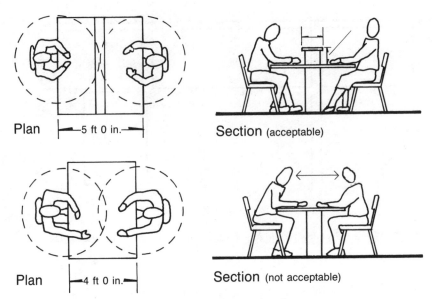

Fig. 3.3-14. Face-to-face workstations.

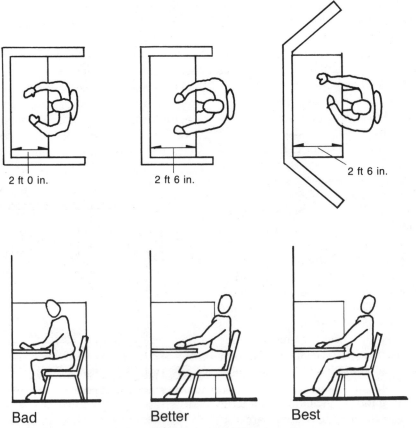

Fig. 3.3-15. Workstation along the wall.

shops. These are not covered in this handbook.

3.3.4 Enclosures

Activity centers may be open, partly enclosed or totally enclosed. The need for barriers depends on a variety of reasons, which are listed in Table 8.7-2.

But in addition, there are some human needs involved. Locating workstations face to face, without visual and physical separation, is generally not considered desirable. The invisible space bubble that surrounds every person has the shortest tolerance in front (see Figure 3.3-14). A 4-ft-wide stand-up bench with a reagent shelf seems to be acceptable, but a 4-ft-wide bench without a reagent shelf is not.

Similarly, a 2-ft-deep bench against the wall is uncomfortable for most people because they cannot stretch their legs without touching the wall in front and they face each other too closely. That discomfort is lessened if the bench is 2 ft 6 in. deep, like a standard desk, or if there is adequate space on either side (see Figure 3.3-15).

A totally enclosed space, particularly a small one such as a cubicle, also creates problems. Opening up this type of space with windows, relites, and/or glass in the door is highly desirable (see Figure 3.3-13).

3.4 THE AESTHETICS AND AMENITIES OF LABORATORY DESIGN   *B. Leathley*

3.4.1 Introduction

Kevin Roche (1973) has stated:

> In a general sense, architecture is a situation in which the viewer who approaches will get varying degrees of satisfaction, depending on the level of sophistication or awareness that he brings to it as viewer. It's easy to bring everyone along, if you start with neon signs, or colorful little things of plastic, or psychedelic effects, or whatever. It's easy to bring the masses along to a certain point, and then you go ahead and do architecture. Having brought the people along, you then do something else. I feel

> you must go the whole way. You must, in fact, deal with every man. However, it hasn't been the tradition of modern architecture to do so. . . . I think you must speak to everyone, but in an understandable way which will appeal to him, and which he will enjoy. . . . One has to find that vocabulary and, at the same time, carry the environment and architecture along at a much higher level. (p. 89)

This section briefly addresses the aesthetic concerns of laboratory space and the amenities that might be considered in the design of that space. The discussion is not exhaustive or academic. It is, rather, a lay person's presentation of thoughts and ideas on the subject that may stimulate a response or at least raise a flag of concern in the next project. The issue of the aesthetic of space and the presence of amenities in a technically focused workplace is current and, hopefully, is here to stay.

3.4.2 Aesthetics

The perception of space, in all of its varied qualities, leads each individual to form an opinion about it. Some, who have similar backgrounds or interests, may come to similar conclusions, or at least evaluate the space from the same perspective. Some may view it for its isolated existence, like a piece of art, while others find it impossible to separate it from its physical and social surroundings. Each of these perceptions is valid to the individual experiencing it, and that perception is in essence the aesthetic of space.

Why is the discussion of the aesthetic of space important in a book about the rigorous practice of technical facility design? Aren't there enough quantifiable and demanding elements on each project to contend with as it is? Are the realities of modern practice such that there is simply no time or money to deal purposefully with aesthetics? The answer to each of these questions is obviously "no." Every built space is evaluated to some degree by its viewer, and the messages it conveys can be very powerful. Technical buildings are not immune from the rigors of this aspect of good design.

The various constituents of space give rise to human perceptions and reactions. They can have an uplifting effect or be depressing; any number of feelings may be evoked by the simple manipulation of space. Isn't that important in an environment that supports research? How do people feel about their workplace? Is it fresh, airy, professional, academic, cloistered? Is there an aesthetic inherent to research settings by virtue of the furniture and equipment it must house, or does it go beyond that? Is it right to think that there may be some qualities of architecture that are absolutely necessary to create a "functional" scientific environment, and therefore that a scientific aesthetic already exists? Is what lies ahead for the designer the simple manipulation of the same environment in reaction to evolving technology?

Obviously, this discussion is leading to the opinion that architects who accept the challenge of designing a technically demanding building must also accept responsibility for the qualities of space that affect the people working in them. The crux of the discussion is where and how to do it. In addition, this discussion offers a plea to designers to reconsider their perspective in designing the scientific workplace.

3.4.3 Amenities

Amenities are a reflection of an aesthetic. They are some of the images or environmental componentes that we as designers hope will bear the burden of conveying a message about how a user is to interact most directly with a building. They can be thematic, eclectic, disjointed or not present at all. Consider comments like "Boy, was that place sterile!" or "The colors were overwhelming. I got a headache just looking at them."

Amenities can play many roles other than visual pleasure, e.g., as direction givers, signals of appropriate activity or mood, security, safety and containment. In the hands of a thoughtful and skilled designer, they quickly leave the realm of "fluff" and take their place as vital operational elements in a project worthy of the discussion and respect

given to something generally considered serious, like a chemical fumehood.

Where do amenities begin to find their way into lab design? A simple imagination tour through just part of your lab will begin to suggest ideas:

The front door: What are the impressions you want to convey? What are the activities you want to encourage/discourage at that point? Are there visual clues that lead you to believe that you should go no farther without an escort, that the lab is part of a large and successful corporation, or that you've just entered a place that takes its science *very* seriously?

Public spaces like the front door, the main circulation system and gathering spaces provide most of the opportunity for effective use of amenities. They communicate their message to those in their presence, and those in their presence will likely, over time, choose to be in that space, provided that it's well designed, because the message matches what they are trying to do. This is a good first indication that the essence of research can be tied directly to design, that is, design of space, including the amenities that communicate best with people and are central to successful research. The connection is communication between persons *and* between persons and their environment.

Discussion

An example of how others have addressed these issues might be helpful. Who can forget the ethereal feeling one has at sunset as one gazes down the center of the open court toward the Pacific from the far end of the Kahn's Salk Institute above La Jolla? This impresses us as being a special place to work, to aspire to a productive and fulfilling scientific career. The building's interior is impressive, too: the melding of outside light with the highly flexible and technical spaces and the office pods.

Undoubtedly this project is successful by virtue of the orchestration of persons from a number of disciplines who cared about the outcome of their efforts. Such an effort takes more than just the architect. But the architect has perhaps the best opportunity to offer the leadership required to develop a certain aesthetic for each project. He can try to develop the qualities of space in such a way that a certain response will be elicited from the building's user.

Work in the programming process should uncover criteria that the owner/user feels are appropriate or desirable for certain segments of the building's population, covering concerns like security, safety, communication, and privacy and feelings like austerity or opulence (rare!). A direct discussion with the client about the aesthetics of a building, inside and out, is necessary and should involve as many of the different client groups as possible.

The discussion doesn't have to be confusing or inconclusive. There should be some vehicle to elicit the experiential qualities appropriate to each project from the client, and the framework needs to be flexible and gentle enough to promote a synergism between the designer and the client free of the confusing jargon of the profession.

While it may seem simplistic, one method of talking with a client might be simply in terms of the qualities of the five senses. These senses are the receptors of environmental stimuli and usually are easy to talk about. The following list is offered as an outline or a framework to use in thinking about the subject at hand. It is assumed that the designer will consider them prior to the conversation and have specific questions and comments prepared for each participant.

Sight
    Light
    Form
    Color
    Pattern
    Texture
    Rhythm
    Symbol
Hearing
    Volume
    Clarity
    Longevity
    Repetition
Feeling
    Form
    Weight
    Temperature
    Texture
Smell
    Strength
    Persistence
    Savory/sweet
    Fresh/stale
Taste
    Subtlety/robustness
    Savory/sweet/spicy
    Fresh/stale/saucy
    Aftertaste

This list suggests a framework for the designer. Some of the senses are more easily dealt with by certain fields of design than others. Taste and smell are harder to control and are probably best left for the appropriate moment; for instance, a retail display designer may use the smell of bayberry in a department store's exhibits during the Christmas season. Conversely, it might be argued that taste and smell can be enhanced by the quality of the space in which they are experienced. Witness the wine cellar.

That leaves us with sight, sound and touch. Certainly sight is the single most powerful sense in our perception of and reaction to any sort of built environment. Hall (1966) stated:

There is a general relationship between the evolutionary age of the receptor system and the amount and quality of information it conveys to the central nervous system. The tactile, or touch, systems are as old as life itself; indeed, the ability to respond to stimuli is one of the basic criteria of life. Sight was the last and most specialized sense to be developed in man. Vision became more important and olfaction less essential when man's ancestors left the ground and took to the trees. . . . The amount of information gathered by the eyes has not been precisely calculated. . . . Since the optic nerve contains roughly eighteen times as many neurons as the cochlear nerve, we assume it transmits at least as much information. Actually, in normally alert subjects, it is probable that the eyes may be as much as a thousand times as effective as the ears in sweeping up information. . . . (p. 40)

If this is indeed true, then, for sighted persons, the manipulation of the visual field is foremost in creating a place. Sound and touch may be likened to adjectives or adverbs in their role of qualifying the scene with additional information. This suggests that creating specific environments to accomplish a certain aesthetic starts with the qualities of basic sight: form, light, color, pattern, and texture. Accompanying these elements are all the learned aspects of perception, the historical basis for qualities we assume that certain sights embody, e.g., the "elegance" of polished marble. The authors who have written about the qualities of human perception and reaction are too numerous to mention, but let it be said that there are ways of tearing down a visual experience and analyzing what affects the formation of an opinion. These studies offer a wealth of information for the designer who is interested in best accomplishing the effect he's set out to achieve.

It is reasonable to expect designers, on a day-to-day basis, to use all the sensory design tools available to them to create the proper environment, but also to realize that other priorities and limited fees will dictate the degree of success given the talent of the design team. Often, though, the needs of certain user groups will be similar enough that certain aspects of safety and function can be expeditiously addressed and little time need be spent confirming or adjusting them. It is the next series of tasks that can "flavor" a project, starting with the overall questions: How does the project fit within the context of its neighborhood? Is their a hint or suggestion arising from its special character that can translate into some organizing theme or system that will guide the rest of the design? Are there anticipated activities that can drive the design of any of the spaces? What will it take to really make the place enrich the experience?

It is beyond the scope of this discussion to address the creative process as it brings forth combinations of ideas that create a place that, coupled with an occasion, provide an experience. However, examples that can support the discussion of aesthetics and amenities might stimulate others with better ideas to put them to work.

Getting Started

One of the foremost issues facing research teams today is communication. They live in an age of information, and the process they use to control and direct that information will have a great effect on how well they work. As designers, we look at the scientific workplace and see a number of settings that support critical communciation experiences. The factors to be considered in designing these spaces are the specific functional and aesthetic needs of the various individuals involved in their roles as productive members of their team and the best space for them to accomplish their tasks. There are occasions for the casual imparting of knowledge, for the seclusion of the individual so that he can best communicate with himself, and for the coming together with others as a group to reaffirm, build on and celebrate their existence as a body. Corridors are often maligned for their drabness, yet they serve as an important casual communication space. Offices can provide retreats, but separation from others can be awkward. The reception desk may be the only single space common to every building user's daily experience, and yet how often is it frequented by the group as a whole?

Visualizing the same space but assigning different names to them might allow a greater feeling of freedom in how we address these design problems. Let creativity and innovation start to redefine state-of-the-art thinking about these spaces. Call the corridor "Main Street" and think about what makes walking along such a street a stimulating experience. Call the office the "situation

Table 3.4-1. Spaces, Amenities and Communication

Space Name	Possible Spatial Qualities	Administrator to Administrator	Administrator to Scientist	Scientist to Scientist	Scientist to Technician	Technician to Technician	Technician to Administrator
Niche	Extended view Comfortable seating with coffee table Open access, but not a thoroughfare Background lighting Carpeting	○	●	●	●	○	○
Situation room	Local view, if any Work table and chairs Whyte board/pinboard and supplies Open-ended enclosure Well lit Tile floor	○	●	●	●	●	○
Working street	Whyte board Standing only For spontaneous, short encounters	○	●	●	●	●	○
Piazza	Statement of identity Breeding ground for corporate culture The great equalizer Relaxed refuge Fun Large, open Variety of seating and standing "Textured" local view Comfortable seating	●	●	●	●	●	●

● = excellent; ○ = good

Fig. 3.4-1. Niche (The NBBJ Group).

Fig. 3.4-2. Piazza (The NBBJ Group).

room," and suddenly a certain vitality imposes itself on the user of that room. Call the lobby the "piazza," and not only is the space inhabited at 8 A.M., 12 noon and 5 P.M., but it also becomes the sociocultural heart of this scientific community. These words can reshape the form and proximity of these elements by virtue of the occasion they now support. The qualities of their design will create an aesthetic that can be carefully manipulated to meet the aesthetic requirements so carefully laid out in earlier discussions. Here is where an active discussion of each of the five senses will begin to have an effect.

We have illustrated four basic architectural examples that may accommodate and

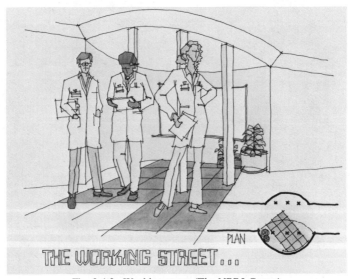

Fig. 3.4-3. Working street (The NBBJ Group).

Fig. 3.4-4. Space for technical staff to talk informally or niche (Karl Bischoff).

encourage effective communication. Those ideas are presented in Table 3.4-1 and in Figures 3.4-1 through 3.4-6.

Table 3.4-1 is designed to stir the designer's imagination and raise questions. The de-

signer needs to understand the communication patterns of his client. These, as much as anything else, establish a culture for a lab environment. It can be as informal or controlled as can be imagined, each for all the

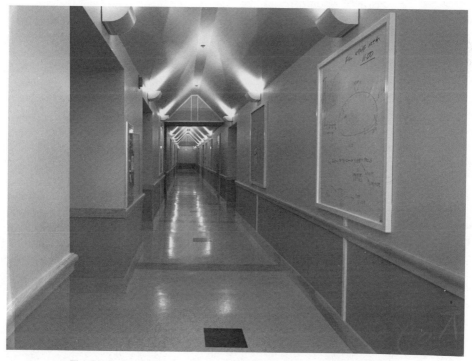

Fig. 3.4-5. Breaking up space in a corridor or main street (Karl Bischoff)

Fig. 3.4-6. Open stair acting as the hub of activity or piazza (Paul Warchol).

right reasons. The aesthetic should respond accordingly. The amenities will reflect that culture. In this case, we are obviously suggesting that a lab should have both hard and soft spaces to be effective and promote interaction.

Such amenities can often afford a chance to develop a special character or feeling of the building—one that contrasts with the required hard surfaces of a testing facility or laboratory. Carpeting, comfortable chairs, wall coverings and a change in the type of lighting can quickly transform an ordinary space into one that is sought after and used frequently. Attention to the details of actual laboratory space can produce similar results, especially with the design of entries, the placement and treatment of paperwork areas, and the simple manipulation of color and pattern on the various room surfaces.

It seems appropriate to end with a quotation from Kevin Roche (1973): "I think that one should have the sense of responsibility, one should have the vision to see the dimen-

sion of the problem. One should accept all that is and do the best he can do in response to these realizations" (p. 89).

REFERENCES

Hall, Edward T., 1966. *The Hidden Dimension*. Garden City, NY: Doubleday.
Roche, Kevin, 1973. In J.W. Cook and H. Klotz, *Conversations with Architects*. New York: Praeger.

3.5 MANAGING LABORATORY HAZARDS BY DESIGN*
N. V. Steere

3.5.1 Introduction

The laboratory planner can help owners provide effective means of managing laboratory hazards if the facilities design provides appropriate space, equipment and building systems to control the hazards. The laboratory planner cannot rely completely on regulatory standards or national consensus standards to provide necessary guidance because such standards often cannot keep pace with scientific and technological innovation and the safety and health problems that often accompany such innovation. Although there are some standards to guide the laboratory planner, he or she will need to have the owner identify the hazards to be controlled and define the results to be achieved. The owner may have specific performance requirements which exceed the minimums contained in regulatory standards or for which there are no established and published standards. The laboratory planner or the owner may need to seek expert advice on safety and industrial hygiene early in the planning and incorporate it in the functional program statement. This information will help the laboratory planner achieve design solutions that will provide a safe working environment in an economical and functional manner.

Managing laboratory hazards by design includes six major areas: contamination con-

---

*This section is copyrighted by Norman V. Steere & Associates, Inc., and is reprinted with permission.

trol, access and egress, ventilation, chemical storage and dispensing, fire protection and emergency equipment. This section will discuss hazards and principles for their control, some of the standards that may apply, and recommendations for exceeding the standards.

3.5.2 Laboratory Ventilation

Laboratory ventilation systems are critically important for protecting the safety and health of laboratory users and the condition of the laboratory facilities. However, the laboratory planner must determine the owner's performance requirements, obtain early and continuing input from the mechanical systems designers and provide adequate space for efficient operation of the systems. To ensure the design of effective laboratory ventilation systems, it must be able to remove airborne materials that are irritating, flammable or toxic, supply clean air, and control temperature and humidity within the limits needed for laboratory equipment and animals.

Since adequate space for ventilation ductwork and equipment is absolutely crucial for its maintenance, modification and economical operation, the laboratory planner needs to be sure that the budget is adequate and that no last-minute cost cutting is allowed to reduce the size or height of areas needed for the ventilation system. Such changes will increasae the life-cycle cost of the building by permanently increasing the difficulty and hazards of servicing the equipment and by decreasing the performance and cost effectiveness of the system.

Difficulties are encountered in designing an effective and economical laboratory ventilation system if visual aesthetics come before safety in selecting the height of hood exhaust stacks above the roof or the locations of air intakes. If the laboratory planner allows the owner to shorten or screen exhaust stacks so that they do not project above the building, the discharge is not likely to be dissipated effectively and the building may inhale its own exhaust.

The NFPA Fire Protection Standard for Laboratories Using Chemicals (NFPA 45-1986) and the *Industrial Ventilation Manual* published annually by the American Conference of Governmental Industrial Hygienists (ACGIH) provide important design guidance for laboratory ventilation systems.

NFPA 45 includes key principles regarding the design of air intake, supply systems, recirculation and discharge. NFPA 45 specifies that the location of fresh air intakes be chosen to avoid drawing in hazardous chemicals or products of combustion coming either from the building or from other structures and devices, such as vehicles stopped with engines running.

Air supply diffusion devices must be selected and placed so that they do not adversely affect the performance of laboratory hoods or other exhaust systems or of fire detection or extinguishing systems. It is crucial to introduce the air at low velocity to minimize interference with laboratory hoods or individual workstation exhaust devices. The ACGIH *Industrial Ventilation Manual* provides specific recommendations for maximum throw velocities.

Although not a code requirement, it is important for the laboratory planner to design and have installed a ventilation system that will capture vapors, gases, aerosols or other effluents that may be irritating, sensitizing, flammable or toxic wherever they may be released in significant quantities. Choices for control of airborne material within a laboratory include enclosures and capture devices. Enclosures may include glove boxes, biological safety cabinets and laboratory hoods, and capture devices may include canopies, slot exhausts and elephant trunks.

New and remodeled laboratories should have ventilated storage cabinets provided as needed so that laboratory hoods will *not* be used for storage.

Exhaust fans for laboratory hoods and other special exhaust devices must be located on the roof or in a penthouse so that the exhaust duct systems are at negative pressure relative to occupied areas. This code requirement is intended to prevent laboratory exhaust from leaking through ductwork into the building.

NFPA 45 specifies that exhaust be discharged above the roof at a height and velocity sufficient to prevent reentry in order to reduce the likelihood that exhaust from laboratory hoods and special exhaust systems will be brought back into the laboratory. Straight vertical discharge stacks should be provided on each hood exhaust; rain entry can be minimized or eliminated by addition of a section of larger-diameter duct which catches rain and drains it off. (See the ACGIH *Industrial Ventilation Manual* for details.)

NFPA 45 also specifies that air exhausted from laboratory hoods and other special local exhaust systems must *not* be recirculated. Ventilation systems should also not recirculate air that is exhausted from laboratory work areas or other rooms where toxic, irritating or flammable vapors or gases are released. Offices, meeting rooms and other spaces that are built with conventional air handling systems which recirculate a major part of the air in the rooms should not be used for laboratory work areas unless the ventilation system can be modified to exhaust all contaminants released within the rooms.

Odors from laboratory activities in one work area may become apparent in other areas because there is no exhaust device, the exhaust system is not adequate or not operating properly, weather conditions may cause the odors to reenter the building, or natural convection currents within the building may carry the odors up or down through floor openings or stairwells.

3.5.3 Contamination Control

The laboratory planner will need guidance from the owner as to whether special measures are needed to prevent contaminants from entering laboratory work areas or escaping from such areas. In either case, space will be needed for decontaminating personnel or equipment, which may otherwise carry contamination into clean areas.

In the first case, "clean room" facilities and airlocks are needed to prevent contamination from entering work areas and interfering with analytical or research work. Special work areas and space for contamination control may be needed for laboratory activities which must be protected against contamination by any interfering organism, particle or chemical. Examples are cell cultures, semiconductor fabrication, and extremely sensitive analytical procedures.

In the second case, facilities are needed to prevent toxic or pathogenic materials used in the work area from escaping and causing injury to humans or the environment. Special work areas and space for contamination control may be needed for preventing the spread of highly infectious organisms, contaminating dusts, carcinogens or highly toxic chemicals.

In any laboratory facility that handles infectious organisms or toxic materials, adequate and conveniently available space should be provided outside of laboratory work areas for desk activities, smoking and consumption of beverages and food.

In all laboratory areas in which personnel may become contaminated by contact with hazardous materials or infectious organisms, handwashing sinks should be provided and equipped for convenient use. Foot-operated controls for water and detergents will minimize contamination of faucets and dispensers.

Whenever employees are required to wear protective clothing because of the possibility of contamination with toxic materials, Occupational Safety and Health Administration (OSHA) standards require that change rooms be provided for storage of street clothing and protective clothing (29 CFR 1910.141 (e)). Change rooms should also be provided if protective clothing is used because of possible contamination with infectious materials.

Desk Space and Data Transmission

Desk space should not be located in laboratory work areas where hazardous or infectious materials are present. Separate desk space should be provided to protect personnel and records. A system for autoclaving or decontaminating records or for transmitting information electronically may be needed in laboratory work areas where biohazards, radioactive material, hazardous waste, and highly toxic material must be confined.

Storage and Consumption of Food

OSHA standards specify that no employee shall be allowed to consume food or beverages in any area exposed to a toxic material, and no employee should be allowed to consume food or beverages in any area exposed to infectious material (29 CFR 1910.141 (g)). If the laboratory planner provides break rooms at convenient locations, laboratory occupants will be able to follow recommended safe practices and not risk contamination by having coffee, lunch or a cigarette in a potentially contaminated work area. If break areas are close to work areas, these activities are more likely to be kept out of the laboratory.

Space should also be provided for storage of lunches and beverages so that they are not placed in laboratory refrigerators used for storage of samples or reagents.

Containment Areas for Handling Highly Hazardous Materials

The following criteria should be used for the design of containment areas for handling regulated carcinogens or highly hazardous materials. These criteria are based on the principles set forth in OSHA standards (29 CFR 1910.1000), which include establishment of a "regulated area," control of air flow, handwashing and showering at the end of each workday.

The facility should be designed so that there are double sets of doors between the containment laboratory and the rest of the facility to help control air balance.

The facility should be designed so that access can be limited to authorized personnel. Three separate areas should be provided within the containment laboratory:

- Clean area—for storing protective clothing and supplies, changing out of street clothing and into special protective clothing, storing street clothing, changing back into street clothing, and toilet facilities
- Decontamination area—for changing out of used protective clothing, storing dirty clothing, and handwashing and showering
- Dirty area—for all necessary functions involved in working with regulated or highly toxic materials

Air supplied to the containment laboratory should be:

- Fresh air taken in from a location as remote as possible from exhausts
- Conditioned as necessary for analytical procedures and equipment
- Conditioned as needed for the heat load of work in protective clothing
- Delivered in a manner that will not interfere with hood performance
- Slightly less in volume than that removed by laboratory exhaust systems, to create negative air pressure in the space so that contaminants are less likely to leak out

Laboratory hoods or glove boxes should be provided for chemical handling:

- Opening of containers and samples
- Preliminary analysis
- Preparation and packaging of dilute samples for subsequent analysis outside of the containment laboratory
- Repackaging of original materials and samples

Hoods should be stainless steel, with a combination sliding sash (horizontal panels in a vertical sash) to allow laboratory personnel to minimize easily the size of the hood face openings. Hoods and glove boxes should be mounted so that laboratory personnel can sit down to work conveniently for extended periods.

Additional exhaust ventilation should be provided for cabinets used to store highly toxic or odorous chemicals and for any equipment or operation that may discharge toxic or flammable gases, vapors, aerosols or dusts.

The laboratory planner should obtain guidance from the owner on the possible need for control measures to reduce emissions that may be infectious or potentially hazardous. For example, it is possible to remove particulates by providing high-efficiency particulate air (HEPA) filters, to remove organic contaminants by carbon filters, and to reduce acid mists and gases with scrubbers. If such emission control devices are provided, some means should be included for measuring their performance, such as pressure gauges or sampling lines. Filters should be located on the roof or in a penthouse where they can be reached for service safely, conveniently and without contaminating laboratory work areas. The design of the area in which the filters are located should provide sufficient space for servicing the filters and a means of removing and replacing the filters safely and conveniently, with minimum contamination of the service area.

Exhaust air should be discharged straight up from the building at a height and velocity designed to minimize reentry into fresh air intakes.

In all work areas where the owner anticipates that liquid wastes cannot safely enter the building or public sewer without special treatment, because of safety reasons or discharge limits, sinks should be equipped with a holding tank so that wastes can be held for analysis before discharge. Another alternative that has been used successfully to prevent discharge of hazardous wastes from sinks is to equip the sinks with a normally closed valve that is motor controlled to allow users to discharge the sink to the waste line or to a separate outlet for intercepting prohibited discharges.

Laundry facilities should be provided on site for reusable clothing.

Flooring should be provided that is seamless and coved at the walls.

Storage space should be provided within the laboratory facility for certain types of activities. Separate space should be provided for activities that are incompatible. Activities that need storage space are:

* Incoming materials awaiting opening and unopened containers
* Materials in process and materials awaiting analysis
* Laboratory chemical standards
* Analytical apparatus, glassware, and supplies
* Used laboratory reagents and liquid waste
* Waste packing material received with incoming materials

Space should be provided for storing cylinders of compressed breathing air, with outlets provided in the work area for connecting air-line respirators, so that laboratory users will have a capability for safe cleanup of spills in the work area.

Special safety equipment should be provided *in* the laboratory, including emergency eyewash; spill control material for small spills; an automatic fire extinguishing system; fire extinguishers; and emergency lighting.

Special safety equipment provided *outside* of the laboratory should include a hand-held drench hose and safety shower; a pair of self-contained breathing apparatus and spare cylinders; and protective clothing and equipment for rescue and spill control.

3.5.4 Access and Egress

Building Access

Walkways, ramps and corridors should be designed to accommodate convenient access for several reasons. Access for the handicapped is generally required by law, and any pathway that will accommodate movement of wheelchairs will facilitate movement of pedestrian traffic and delivery carts. A well-designed ramp will make it possible for equipment and supplies to be moved into or out of a building more easily and safely as well.

In areas where ice or snow may accumulate on an exposed ramp, provision should be made for heating it because any degree of slope can be hazardous if it is slippery—even a gradual slope not exceeding a change in elevation of 1 ft per 12 ft of horizontal run.

Movement within a Laboratory Building

Traffic will move more smoothly if corridors are wide enough to accommodate the amount of pedestrian traffic which can occur and designed to avoid obstructions by drinking fountains, safety equipment and out-swinging doors. If doors cannot be offset from the corridor by their full width, there are other alternatives. Figure 3.5-1 shows a commonly encountered hazardous condition when doors swing into the corridor. Figures 3.5-2 and 3.5-3 show how a 45-degree recess can allow the doors to swing outward without obstructing the corridor.

Fig. 3.5-1. Hazardous conditions created by doors swinging into the path of an exit (Theodorus Ruys).

This arrangement also meets the standards for access of the mobility handicapped.

The minimum width recommended for corridors to allow two people to pass each other safely is 5 ft (60 in.).

Movement within the laboratory is also facilitated by having storage space for movable carts, deliveries, supplies, glassware awaiting use or washing and waste materials to be picked up. Storage space should be provided outside of the laboratory for equipment that will be used only periodically.

If laboratory facilities are built with service corridors wide enough for deliveries of hazardous materials, there will be less conflict between different types of traffic and less likelihood of hazards such as a spill blocking the main means of egress.

Corridor design should provide easily maintainable access to emergency devices such as eyewash and safety showers, fire extinguishers and other emergency equipment. Such devices should be clearly identified. If respiratory protective equipment is to be installed, provide space in areas not likely to be involved in chemical spills, leaks or fires.

Corridors, stairwells and other egress components should be increased in width beyond code requirements if two-way pedestrian traffic is expected to be heavy (as in a teaching laboratory) or if corridors may be obstructed by carts. Code requirements for means of egress are minimal and are designed for rapid evacuation of all occupants of a building in case of fire.

Location of Exit Access Relative to Hazards

Exit access must be so arranged that it will not be necessary to travel toward any area of high-hazard occupancy in order to reach the nearest exit, unless the path of travel is effectively shielded from the high-hazard location by suitable partitions or other physical barriers.

The NFPA Life Safety Code defines high-hazard occupancy as those buildings having high-hazard materials, processes or contents.

Fig. 3.5-2. Recessed, out-swinging doors that do not obstruct the path of the exit or cart traffic (Theodorus Ruys).

It defines high-hazard contents as "those which are liable to burn with extreme rapidity or from which poisonous fumes or explosions are to be feared in the event of fire." In contrast, "ordinary-hazard" contents are defined as those which are liable to burn with moderate rapidity and give off a considerable volume of smoke, but from which neither poisonous fumes nor explosions are to be feared in case of fire.

Furniture and equipment in laboratory work areas must be arranged so that access to an exit may be reached easily from any point. This is a requirement in NFPA 45, the Fire Protection Standard for Laboratories

Using Chemicals. Figure 3.5-3 shows a good arrangement which provides direct access through the door to the corridor.

Number of Exits from a Laboratory

Two means of egress are required as a minimum for "every building or structure, section, or area thereof of such size, occupancy, and arrangement that the reasonable safety of numbers of occupants may be endangered by the blocking of any single means of egress due to fire or smoke." The means of egress should be remote from each other and "so arranged as to minimize any possibility that

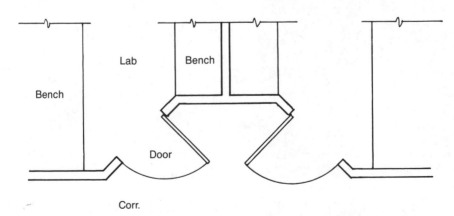

Fig. 3.5-3. Plan of the recessed door shown in Fig. 3.5-2.

both may be blocked by any one fire or other emergency condition'' (NFPA 101).

A second means of access to an exit must be provided from a laboratory work area (per NFPA 45) if any of following situations exist:

- A laboratory work area exceeds 500 sq ft within a laboratory unit that is classified as Class A or high hazard based on the quantities of flammable liquids present.
- A laboratory exceeds 1,000 sq ft within a laboratory unit classified as Class B or Class C (intermediate or low hazard).
- A hood in a laboratory work area is located adjacent to the primary means of exit access.
- Safe egress could be prevented in the event of accidental release of a hazardous compressed gas or liquified gas in use in the work area. This would apply only if a compressed gas cylinder in use is larger than lecture bottle size (a short cylinder about 2 in. in diameter) or if the liquified gas is in a cryogenic container, and if the gas is flammable or has an extreme or severe health hazard (meeting the NFPA definition of Health Hazard Rating of 3 or 4).
- A laboratory work area contains an explosion hazard as specifically defined in NFPA 45) so located that an incident would block escape from or access to the laboratory work area.

Whether or not it is required by a code, a second means of access to an exit is recommended as an additional precaution for every laboratory work area, particularly if fire or explosion hazards may be present. If a second means of access to an exit is not required, it can in most cases go through an adjacent laboratory.

Exit Access Doors and Direction of Swing

A door from a room to an exit or to a way of exit access must be of the side-hinged, swinging type. (Vertical-rolling doors and horizontal-sliding doors may be used to provide a fire-resistant barrier in some locations, but they are *not* permitted in exit routes.) The exit door or doors of a room must swing out in the direction of exit travel if the room is used for a high-hazard occupancy or is large enough to be occupied by more than 50 persons (NFPA 101). The required exit doors of all laboratory work areas in Class A or Class B laboratory units must swing in the direction of exit travel (NFPA 45).

The 1988 Uniform Building Code requires educational laboratories using hazardous materials and occupancies classified as H1 and H2 to have two exits from a room if it is larger than 200 sq ft.

3.5.5 Storage and Dispensing of Chemicals

The laboratory planner can design efficient, safe storage and dispensing facilities only if the owner provides information on the quantities and hazards of the chemicals that will be stored and dispensed. With adequate information, the laboratory planner will be able to identify aisles and storage rack locations so that the owner can set up a system for specifying storage locations.

Information that the laboratory planner will need from the owner includes:

- Hazards of and precautions for all chemicals to be stored
- Quantities and container sizes to be stored
- The number and size of individual rooms or separate storage areas needed
- A list of chemicals which will be dispensed from bulk and what dispensing facilities will be needed

Storage

Three factors that should be considered in designing safe and efficient storage of hazardous chemicals are compatibility, optimum use of storage space, and convenience of storage and retrieval.

Compatibility. In storage areas, provide the separation required to prevent hazardous reactions between incompatible chemicals. Some guidance is provided in NFPA 49, Hazardous Chemicals Data, and some may be provided in NFPA 30, Flammable and Combustible Liquids Code, or in local codes. Figure 3.5-4 shows an example of good practice.

Laboratory facilities will usually require a separate, fire-protected room used only for storage of bulk quantities of flammable and combustible liquids. If these liquids are to be dispensed from bulk containers, a separate room should be provided and should be used exclusively for dispensing such liquids.

Additional rooms or separation may be needed for large containers and quantities of chemicals that are oxidizers, mineral acids, alkaline, water-reactive, heat-sensitive or hazardous in other unique ways.

Separation may be needed within stockrooms or laboratories for storage of hazardous chemicals.

Optimum use. Storing large and small containers on the same shelf can make retrieval difficult and bottle breakage likely. Deep shelves spaced vertically for gallon bottles or 5-gallon cans should not be provided for storage of small containers. Shelves should be sized and spaced appropriately for storage of compatible materials by container size, and drawers can be used for storage of small bottles.

Convenience of storage and retrieval. Table 3.5-1 shows an example of a convenient chemical inventory and locator system. In the table, FLAM indicates the room for storage of flammable and combustible liquids, and ALK designates the room for storage of alkaline materials. OXID indicates the room in which oxidizers and mineral acids are stored, and SPEC refers to the room for storage of special hazards such as carcinogens. As an example of how information in such a table could be used, the inventory list shows that 1-nitronaphthalene is stored in the FLAM room, Aisle 12, Rack 7, on Shelf 4 in Row 5 at Position C.

General Recommendations for Chemical Storage

Storage racks and shelves should be designed to prevent breakage or leakage, which might

Fig. 3.5-4. Separate storage rooms for incompatible chemicals (Theodorus Ruys).

Fig. 3.5-5. Exterior explosion venting for flammable liquids storage vault. The path of the explosion is over the lawn area (Theodorus Ruys).

cause damage or endanger those who enter or work in the storage area. Ventilation should be provided to prevent corrosion or dangerous concentrations of vapor. The storage facility should be separated and protected so that a spill or fire there is not likely to spread beyond that area.

Regulations and code-enforcing authorities can provide some important guidance for designs that will minimize fires, explosions and contamination of the environment. However, they usually cannot address all the safety and health aspects of chemical storage, particularly as new chemicals come into more common use and new hazards are discovered.

Since code requirements generally were written for storage of large containers and

Table 3.5-1. Example of a Chemical Inventory and Locator System

Chemical Name	C.A.S. Number	Room Name	Aisle Number	Rack Number	Shelf or Drawer Number	Row Number	Position In Row
Acetic acid	64-19-7	FLAM	1	1	A	1	A
Acetone	67-64-1	FLAM	1	1	A	1	B
Ammonium hydroxide	1336-21-6	ALK	2	2	C	3	A
Anhydrone	See magnesium perchlorate						
Magnesium nitrate	10377-60-3	OXID	4	4	2	7	D
Magnesium perchlorate	10034-81-8	OXID	1	2	B	2	C
o-Methoxyphenol	See Guaiacol						
p-Methoxyphenol	150-76-5	FLAM	7	3	12	8	A
1-Naphthylamine	134-32-7	SPEC	1	1	1	1	D
1-Nitronaphthalene	86-57-7	FLAM	12	7	4	5	C
Sodium hydroxide	1310-73-2	ALK	7	2	6	3	E
Sulfuric acid	7664-93-9	OXID	8	5	3	4	E

industrial quantities, some requirements may not be appropriate for storage of chemicals in small or break-resistant containers.

The material and size of containers to be stored will affect the need for special storage practices and safety procedures. For example, if containers of flammable liquids are no larger than 5 gallons in size, there is no requirement for ramps or special construction to prevent liquid flow out of the storage area.

Ventilation is needed for chemicals and containers which may release dangerous or damaging quantities of vapors or gases which are flammable, corrosive, irritating or toxic. Ventilation may also be needed for containers and chemicals which may produce annoying odors.

Doors to chemical storage areas should be identified with the hazards of the materials stored in the area. Some NFPA standards require specific identification and use of the hazard signal system described in NFPA 704.

For every storage area, there should be an evacuation alarm and emergency equipment to be used in case of a leak, spill or fire in the room.

Other important safety and health considerations for storage areas include lighting for finding containers and reading labels; strength, stability and corrosion resistance of shelving; and aisles and storage arrangements that provide for safe access, such as sturdy, movable steps to reach storage areas above eye level.

It is recommended that corrosive liquids in glass containers not be stored above eye level or about 48 in. above the floor.

Location of Storage Facilities

Storage facilities should be located where they will be safe, convenient and economical. The hazards, inconveniences and cost of transport chemicals increase as storage is located farther away from the areas where chemicals are used. On the other hand, the cost of building storage space generally decreases as it becomes less specialized and farther from laboratory areas.

Within laboratory work areas, storage for working quantities should be provided on or in laboratory benches or in the immediate vicinity. Such storage should be limited to chemicals which are used frequently, quantities that are the minimum necessary and container sizes that are the minimum convenient.

Storage in cupboards, cabinets and closets near the immediate work area should be limited to the quantities necessary.

Stockrooms or similar accessible supply areas should be provided for frequently needed chemicals that are not stored in laboratory work areas. Separate or detached areas should be provided for bulk quantities which cannot be stored safely or economically in stockroom areas or inside the building.

Separation, Segregation and Isolation

NFPA 49 and other NFPA codes regulating the storage of hazardous materials will often specify separation, segregation or isolation as a basic means for preventing fire and hazardous reactions between stored chemicals. Since the costs of storage facilities will be greater for segregation than separation, and greater yet for isolation, the laboratory planner should be told by the owner what degree of protection will be required. Whether or not the chemicals to be stored in the new facility are regulated, the laboratory planner should seek guidance from the owner for the design of storage areas that separate, segregate or isolate incompatible chemicals so that leaking or broken containers will not result in unintentional mixing and hazardous reactions.

The need for separation, segregation or isolation will depend on the size and breakage-resistance of storage containers, the total quantities stored, the potential for leakage and the hazards of the chemicals. For example, if large containers of sulfuric acid and sodium hydroxide (both corrosive) were stored in a single area and the containers broke, a hazardous chemical reaction could result from the accidental mixing.

"Separation" is defined by NFPA 49 as storage within the same fire area but separated from incompatible materials by as much space as practicable or by intervening storage. For example, NFPA 49 recommends that sulfuric acid be stored separately from combustible materials and that acetic acid be stored separately from oxidizing materials.

"Segregated" storage is generally defined by NFPA as storage in the same room but physically separated by space from incompatible materials. NFPA 43A requires sills, curbs or intervening storage to maintain spacing. NFPA 43C specifies separation by at least 20 ft (6.1 m).

"Isolation" is defined by NFPA 49 as storage away from incompatible materials in a different storage room or in a separate and detached building located at a safe distance.

The 1988 Uniform Fire Code also contains segregation requirements for hazardous chemicals.

Flammable and Combustible Chemicals

NFPA codes and OSHA regulations which limit the allowable quantities of unprotected flammable and combustible liquids stored in a single fire-resistant area within a building generally allow additional quantities to be stored within the area if the liquids are kept in a storage cabinet that meets NFPA standards.

Under OSHA regulations, quantities in a fire area are generally limited to 25 gallons of Class IA liquids (such as ethyl ether and pentane) and 120 gallons of Class IB, IC, II, and IIIA liquids. (Class IA, IB and IC liquids have different boiling points, but all have flash point temperatures below 100°F and are defined by NFPA and Department of Transportation [DOT] regulations as flammable liquids. Class II and IIIA liquids are combustible liquids with flash point temperatures between 100° and 200°F.)

Additional quantities are permitted in a fire area if stored in an approved storage cabinet or storage room. The NFPA Flammable and Combustible Liquids Code,

NFPA 30, has a similar requirement for industrial occupancies.

In assembly, office, educational and institutional occupancies, the NFPA Code establishes a combined limit for Class I and II liquids of 10 gallons not stored in safety cans and a limit of 25 gallons stored in safety cans. The corresponding limit for Class IIIA liquids is 60 gallons. Larger quantities of Class I, II, and IIIA liquids must be stored in storage cabinets or storage rooms.

Special storage is commonly required for flammable liquids and certain combustible liquids in quantities which exceed the limited amounts permitted in approved storage cabinets. Liquids which require such storage have flash point temperatures at or below 200°F; this includes every liquid identified as a flammable liquid, an ignitable liquid (EPA definition) or a combustible liquid in Classes II or IIIA.

Some acids are combustible liquids; therefore it is appropriate to store them with other combustible liquids in either an approved storage room or a storage cabinet. Examples of common organic acids which are combustible materials are shown in Table 3.5-2.

OSHA standards and the NFPA Flammable and Combustible Liquids Code, NFPA 30, spell out the requirements for storage of flammable and combustible liquids. Both sets of standards allow storage of significant quantities of such liquids within laboratory buildings in rooms that are specially separated from the rest of the building so that a

Table 3.5-2. Common Organic Acids Which Are Combustible

Acid	Class
Acetic	Combustible liquid, Class II
Butyric	Combustible liquid, Class IIIA
Crotonic	Combustible liquid, Class IIIA
Oleic	Combustible liquid, Class IIIB
Stearic	Combustible liquid, Class IIIB
Toluenesulfonic	Combustible (DOT label is corrosive)

spill or fire in the room is not likely to spread to the main building.

Generally, the only other combustible materials that require special storage are combustible gases and a limited number of materials that are classified as flammable solids. Storage requirements for combustible gases will be discussed later in the section on "Compressed Gases."

The 1988 Uniform Fire Code specifies storage conditions, and for some storage rooms it also requires automatic sprinklers.

Flammable and Combustible Liquid Storage Rooms

An inside storage room for flammable and combustible liquids will meet or exceed OSHA and NFPA 30 standards and be reasonably safe if it meets the following requirements:

- Size, Construction and Fire Protection. An inside storage room that does not exceed 150 sq ft in floor area is permitted to contain up to 2 gallons of flammable and combustible liquids per square foot of floor area if the room is separated from the building by construction having at least 1-hour fire resistance and if all openings between the room and the building are protected by assemblies having a fire resistance rating of 1 hour. If it is desirable to increase the allowable storage capacity of such a room, the capacity can be increased to 5 gallons per square foot by providing the room with an automatic fire extinguishing system.

An inside storage room that does not exceed 500 sq ft in floor area is permitted to contain up to 4 gallons of flammable and combustible liquids per square foot of floor area if the room is separated from the building by construction having at least 2-hour fire resistance and if all openings between the room and the building are protected by assemblies having a fire resistance rating of 1.5 hours. If it is desirable to increase the allowable storage capacity of such a room, the capacity can be increased to 10 gallons per square foot by providing the room with an automatic fire extinguishing system. See Table 3.5-3.

- Ventilation. An inside storage room must be ventilated to prevent accumulation of flammable concentrations of vapors from container leaks or spills. Recommended ventilation is from the floor level, with a capacity of 1 cu ft per minute of exhaust for each square foot of floor area in the room, with a minimum of 150 cu ft per minute. (If there is dispensing in the room, there should be provision for ventilating the dispensing operations close to the points at which vapors are emitted.)

- Barriers and Drainage. If the containers of flammable and combustible liquids are no larger than 5 gallons in size, it should *not* be necessary to provide barriers to prevent spills in the room from spreading to the main building. If containers of Class I or II liquids are larger than 5 gallons in size, there is a need for curbs, ramps, scuppers or special drains. Drainage capacity is required

Table 3.5-3. Flammable and Combustible Liquid Storage Room Requirements

Room Size (Sq Ft)	Location	Allowable Quantities (Gal./Sq Ft)	Fire Separation (Opening)	Automatic Fire Protection
150 max.	Inside building	2	1 hour (1 hour)	No
Same	Same	5	Same	Yes
500 max.	Detached	4	2 hours (1.5 hours)	No
Same	Same	10	Same	Yes

for all the water which could be discharged from an automatic fire extinguishing system and from fire hose streams which may be applied by the fire department, although this may not be physically possible.

Drainage should be to a safe location where burning liquids will not cause further fire damage and where liquids can be kept from entering surface or ground water supplies. Drainage from storage rooms for flammable and combustible liquids must be kept separate from drainage from any other storage area which contains incompatible materials.

- Electrical Wiring. Wiring and electrical fixtures located in inside storage rooms must be suitable for the hazards. Explosion-proof (Class I, Division 2) electrical equipment is required to prevent explosions if flammable liquids (Class I) are being stored or dispensed. If only combustible liquids are being stored or dispensed, general-use wiring is acceptable.
- Exterior Wall. If an inside storage room has an exterior wall, it will be classified by the NFPA Flammable and Combustible Liquids Code (NFPA 30) as a "cut-off room," for which there are two additional requirements. First, exterior walls are required to provide ready accessibility for fire fighting. Second, if Class IA or Class IB liquids are dispensed or if Class IA liquids are stored in containers larger than 1 gallon, the exterior wall or roof is required by NFPA 30 to be designed to provide deflagration venting. Information on deflagration venting is provided in NFPA 68; if such venting is provided, NFPA 68 gives details of other safety considerations required.

Explosion venting or deflagration venting may not actually be needed in a small room used only for storage, or in a well-ventilated dispensing room, according to informal opinions expressed by experienced fire protection engineers. Before designing explosion venting for storage rooms, laboratory planners may wish to consult the authorities having jurisdiction and the latest revisions of NFPA codes.

Flammable and Combustible Liquid Storage Cabinets

Storage cabinets are permitted to contain no more than 60 gallons of Class I and Class II liquids and no more than 120 gallons of Class IIIA liquids. Except in industrial occupancies, no more than three storage cabinets may be located in a single fire area. In industrial occupancies, additional cabinets may be located in the same fire area if individual cabinets or groups of no more than three cabinets are separated by at least 100 ft.

Limits on the number of storage cabinets seem intended to limit the total quantity of liquids in the area, and a greater number of cabinets may be permitted if the total quantity limit is not exceeded. In a large laboratory, many small cabinets at points of usage could reduce hazards and travel time without exceeding the total quantity allowed in the area.

NFPA 30 permits storage for industrial and educational laboratory work to comply with NFPA 45.

NFPA 45 establishes limits for the quantities of flammable and combustible liquids permitted to be located in laboratory units, depending on the construction and fire protection provided. The basic quantities of flammable and combustible liquids permitted in open or unprotected storage can be doubled if they are stored in safety cans or storage cabinets. Quantities can also be doubled if the area is provided with an automatic fire extinguishing system. Quantities can range from 1 gallon per 100 sq ft in a low-hazard educational laboratory to 40 gallons per 100 ft or a maximum of 1,200 gallons in a sprinklered, high-hazard laboratory unit.

- Protection Provided by Cabinet Construction. Storage cabinets built to meet the specifications of NFPA 30 are designed to insulate their contents so that in case of a fire outside the cabinet, the internal temperature will not exceed 325°F for 10 minutes.

Double-walled metal storage cabinets are available to provide the minimum protection required by OSHA and NFPA standards, and some have been tested at Factory Mutual Engineering Laboratories. Most of the commercially available metal storage cabinets have a 60-gallon capacity, although cabinets with a 30-gallon capacity are available.

Storage cabinets constructed of 1-in. exterior grade plywood are also presumed to meet the fire exposure test described in NFPA and OSHA standards. Fire tests by the Los Angeles Fire Department have shown that the thermal insulation provided by 1-in. plywood greatly exceeds that provided by double-walled metal construction.

Plywood storage cabinets have the advantages of providing greater fire protection and being readily fabricated to meet varying quantity needs and to fit conveniently within a new or existing laboratory. Plywood cabinets are commercially available, and one brand has passed fire tests and is listed by Factory Mutual Engineering Laboratories. The Uniform Fire Code requires wooden cabinets to have a 2-in. deep liquid retention capabity and to be painted with intumescent paint.

Specially made storage cabinets which have fire resistance ratings of 30 minutes or longer have become available recently. Records protection cabinets with fire resistance ratings of 60 minutes or longer can be used if there is a need for extended fire protection of unique materials.

• Ventilation of Storage Cabinets. Ventilation of storage cabinets is not required by NFPA standards. If it is considered desirable or necessary to ventilate a storage cabinet in order to control odors or corrosion or to prevent flammable concentrations of vapors, there should

be a mechanical system to provide an effective exhaust of the cabinet, and the duct should be as fire resistant as the cabinet. Ducting of plastic, aluminum or copper with sweated joints is not likely to provide 10 minutes of fire resistance, equal to what a cabinet is expected to provide, and a ventilating duct may reduce the insulation provided for the contents.

• Closers on Cabinet Doors. The Uniform Fire Code requires cabinet doors to be self-closing and provided with a latch. However, automatic closers can be hazardous if they act so rapidly or forcefully that they interfere with safe use of the cabinet.

Oxidizers

Oxidizers must be stored to avoid contact with incompatible materials such as ordinary combustibles, flammable liquids, greases, and other materials, including other oxidizers, that could react with the oxidizer or catalyze its decomposition.

Mineral acids, including those recognized as strong oxidizers, such as nitric acid, perchloric acid and sulfuric acid, should be separated from flammable and combustible materials. Such mineral acids should be stored in separate rooms or separate cabinets, or in break-resistant containers if large glass bottles have to be stored in proximity to combustible materials. In order to prevent oxidation of wooden storage shelves (or corrosion of metal shelves), acid-resistant trays or mats should be provided under bottles of nitric, perchloric and sulfuric acids.

• Gaseous Oxidizing Materials. Mechanical exhaust ventilation must be provided for an enclosed storage area if the owner anticipates that the laboratory facility will store and use gaseous oxidizing materials, which are generally irritating, toxic and highly reactive. (Natural ventilation is adequate for open storage areas.)

The Code for Storage of Gaseous Oxidizing Materials, NFPA 43C, applies to oxidizers in cylinders or other containers with an aggregate capacity in excess of 100 lb (45 kg) when in storage or connected to a manifold system. The standard applies to chlorine, chlorine trifluoride, fluorine, nitrous oxide, oxygen and about 10 other gaseous oxidizing materials that are not readily available.

• Liquid and Solid Oxidizing Materials. The NFPA Code for Storage of Liquid and Solid Oxidizing Materials, NFPA 43A, defines oxidizing material and four classes of oxidizer and establishes requirements based on quantities. "Oxidizing material" is defined as any solid or liquid that readily yields oxygen or any other oxidizing gas or that readily reacts to oxidize combustible materials. The four classes of oxidizer are Classes 1, 2, 3 and 4. The standard applies only if the quantities stored exceed the limits for the class.

If the quantities of oxidizers to be stored are regulated by the standard, the class of oxidizer may require that the storage area be segregated, cut off or detached, and the fire resistance required for cutoff storage will increase as the class increases.

Storage areas for Class 2 and Class 3 oxidizers in combustible containers must be provided with means of venting in a fire emergency. Class 3 oxidizers are permitted to be stored only on the ground floor of a building with no basement. Class 4 oxidizers in regulated quantities are permitted to be stored only in detached storage with means to vent fumes in an emergency.

Class 1 oxidizers increase the burning rate of combustible material with which they come in contact. Class 2 oxidizers moderately increase the burning rate or may cause spontaneous ignition in contact with combustible material. Class 3 oxidizers cause a severe increase in the burning rate of combustible material with which they come in contact or undergo vigorous, self-sustained decomposition when catalyzed or exposed to heat. Class 4 oxidizers can undergo an explosive reaction when catalyzed or exposed to heat, shock or friction.

Table 3.5-4 shows four classes of oxidizers, the minimum quantities for which the

Table 3.5-4. Classes of Liquid and Solid Oxidizing Materials

Class	Quantity (lb)	Limit (kg)	Examples of Material
1	4,000	1,816	Hydrogen peroxide solutions, 8 to 27.5% Magnesium perchlorate Nitric acid, 70% concentration or less Perchloric acid solutions, less than 60% Silver nitrate
2	1,000	454	Calcium hypochlorite, 50% or less by weight Chromic acid Hydrogen peroxide, 27.5 to 52% by weight Sodium peroxide
3	200	91	Ammonium dichromate Hydrogen peroxide, 52 to 91% by weight Perchloric acid solutions, 60 to 72.5% Sodium chlorate
4	10	4.5	Ammonium perchlorate, ammonium permanganate Hydrogen peroxide, more than 91% by weight Perchloric acid solutions, more than 72.5% Potassium superoxide

NFPA 43A standard establishes storage requirements, and examples.

Corrosive and Irritating Chemicals

Although until recently there have been no code requirements for storage of corrosive or irritating chemicals, such as alkaline materials and mineral acids, OSHA standards require that water be readily available for rapid flushing of chemicals from the eyes and body of employees who may be splashed. Ventilation is needed to remove corrosive vapors from volatile materials such as hydrochloric and nitric acids. Areas for storage of bulk quantities should be diked, trenched or otherwise designed to limit the spread of liquid spills to other buildings or community water supplies. Standards for flammable liquid storage rooms describe three different ways of limiting the spread of spills: sills, ramped dikes or trenches drained to a catchment area.

Toxic Chemicals

Until the Uniform Building Code and Uniform Fire Code were adopted in 1988, there were no code requirements for storage of toxic chemicals other than pesticides. Construction should limit the spread of liquid spills, ventilation should generally be provided to control vapors and odors, and emergency water should be provided in case of chemical splashes. The Uniform Fire Code sets standards for containment, ventilation, emergency response and other requirements for storage of chemicals with different health hazards.

Pesticide storage must be located or constructed so that runoff from fire-fighting operations will not contaminate streams, ponds, groundwater, land or buildings. Storage areas for pesticides and other highly toxic chemicals should be secured when these areas are not supervised.

Reactive and Incompatible Chemicals

Chemicals that are reactive if exposed to air or water are usually packaged in hermetically sealed containers. Such containers can be stored safely in sprinklered areas where they will be protected from rupture under fire conditions by the sprinkler discharge.

Temperature-controlled storage areas or refrigeration must be provided for chemicals that deteriorate or react if their temperatures exceed safe limits recommended by the manufacturer or the person synthesizing the chemical.

Acid-sensitive materials such as the cyanides and sulfides should be stored in a separate location from acids or protected from contact with acids.

Guidelines for segregation of incompatible chemicals may be found in NFPA 49, Hazardous Chemicals Data; NFPA 49 1M, Hazardous Chemical Reactions: and Coast Guard recommendations.

Compressed Gases

Compressed gas cylinders must be secured to prevent them from falling, because breakage of the valve or cylinder can release gas contents and cause catastrophic damage. Design of the storage facility should provide for securing each cylinder individually so that no group will fall when one is released to be moved into or out of storage. Figure 3.5-6 shows an example of an excellent design for securing cylinders effectively.

Combustible gases that are classified as fuel gases may be stored inside a building up to a total gas capacity of 2,500 cu ft of acetylene or nonliquefied flammable gas or about 309 lb of propane or 375 lb of butane. If there is more than one storage area within a building, each must be separated from the others by a distance of at least 100 ft. The quantity of acetylene or nonliquefied flammable gas in a storage area may be doubled if the storage area is protected with an automatic sprinkler system which will provide a density of at least 0.25 gallons per minute per square foot over an area of at least 3,000 sq ft. (NFPA 51 provides additional detail.)

NFPA 50A establishes requirements for gaseous hydrogen systems having containers with a total content of 400 cu ft or more.

Fig. 3.5-6. Secure, low-cost cylinder storage (Theodorus Ruys).

The standard also applies where single systems having a content of less than 400 cu ft of hydrogen are located less than 5 ft from each other.

Publications of the Compressed Gas Association give additional recommendations.

The Uniform Fire Code contains detailed requirements for storage of gases that are oxidizing, flammable, pyrophoric, reactive or toxic.

Hazardous Waste

Facilities should be designed to provide adequate space and protection for temporary storage of hazardous waste awaiting removal or treatment. Separate areas may be needed, depending on the classes of hazardous waste which are to be stored. Storage areas for hazardous waste should be separate from other storage areas for hazardous materials.

The number and size of storage areas for hazardous wastes will depend on information from the owner on the volume of wastes

to be stored and on the classifications which may need separation. As with new chemicals, separate storage areas are generally recommended for flammable liquid wastes and for oxidizing wastes.

Although the Environmental Protection Agency (EPA) does not have specific standards for the storage of hazardous waste within buildings, the same types of separation and protection should be provided as for hazardous new materials. Fire-protected storage should be provided if quantities of flammable and ignitable wastes are accumulated. Storage areas for waste materials which emit corrosive or toxic vapors should have ventilation, emergency water and spill limitations, as recommended for new materials with similar hazards.

Dispensing Facilities

Ventilation, spill-limiting construction and emergency water are usually required for safe dispensing of chemicals in volume or from shipping containers. If the chemicals are flammable liquids, bonding and grounding will need to be provided and explosion-proof electrical equipment will be required within the hazardous location, as defined by the National Electrical Code, NFPA 70. See Figure 3.5-7.

Provisions should generally be made to control spills and to limit their spread beyond the dispensing area. Leakage from dispensing containers or overfilled containers can cause damage or hazardous conditions in the dispensing area or in locations to which filled containers are taken.

General dilution ventilation is needed to prevent accumulation of vapors from leaking containers, and special local exhaust is needed at the points of dispensing to remove vapors which can cause corrosion, adverse health effects or accumulation of flammable concentrations of vapors.

Emergency equipment and an alarm station should generally be provided to be used in case of a spill, splash or fire. Additional provisions should be made for personnel protection if anyone is allowed to work

Fig. 3.5-7. Flammable liquids dispensing area (Lab Safety Supply).

Fig. 3.5-8. Preferred arrangement of drum storage in a dispensing area (Lab Safety Supply).

alone in a dispensing area; such measures might include monitoring the area for calls for help or monitoring it by television.

Flammable or combustible liquids should be dispensed within a separate room designed solely for dispensing, not in a room designed and used for storage of closed containers. Dispensing such liquids in flammable liquid storage areas larger than 1,000 sq ft is prohibited by NFPA 30. The author does not recommend dispensing in any storage area. Such liquids must not be dispensed in general storage areas unless the dispensing area is suitably cut off from ordinary combustibles and flammable liquid storage areas by fire-resistant construction.

See Article 80 of the 1988 Uniform Fire Code for detailed requirements for dispensing hazardous materials other than flammable liquids.

Drum Storage Configuration and Equipment

Rooms designed for dispensing from drums should be based on having the drums sit in a vertical position, if possible, rather than on their sides in cradles. See Figure 3.5-8. Gravity dispensing of flammable liquids is not allowed unless valves are self-closing.

Dispensing from drums in the vertical position will reduce the need for floor space and manual handling, minimize leakage from valves and bungs, and make it more convenient to provide adaptable local ventilation.

If dispensing is done frequently, compressed air can be provided for operating air-driven pumps. Air pressure must not be used directly on 55-gallon drums or other shipping containers because it presents a serious hazard and is prohibited by code. Although generally not recommended, transfer of flammable liquids by pressure of inert gas is permitted by NFPA 30 if controls and pressure relief devices are provided to limit the pressure so that it cannot exceed the design pressure of the vessel to which it is applied.

Ventilation for Dispensing Operations

Local exhaust ventilation should be provided within a few inches of every point at which hazardous liquids are transferred to prevent dispersal of vapors or aerosols that are corrosive, irritating, toxic or flammable. Effective capture ventilation is needed to prevent discomfort or adverse health effects, damage to the facility or equipment, or accumulation of flammable concentrations which could result in a flash fire or explosion.

The Uniform Fire Code also contains ventilation requirements.

NFPA 45 recommends that ventilation be provided for transfer operations to prevent overexposure of personnel transferring flammable liquids. Control of solvent vapors is most effective if local exhaust ventilation is provided at or close to the point of transfer to limit exposure in the breathing zone.

Movable "elephant trunks" or welding exhaust devices are preferred to fixed ductwork, since they are more effective in capturing vapors and the exhaust system can be sized for exhaust at only one or two points at a time.

NFPA 45 requires that the transfer of flammable liquids from containers of 5 gallons or larger capacity be carried out in a fire area separated from laboratory work areas by fire-resistant construction that meets NFPA 30 requirements or in an area outside the building.

Transfer of flammable liquids to smaller containers from bulk stock containers not exceeding 5 gallons in capacity is permitted inside a laboratory building or in a laboratory work area in a laboratory hood. Such transfer is also permitted in an area provided with ventilation adequate to prevent accumulations of flammable vapor/air mixtures exceeding 25% of the lower flammable limit, or in a separate inside storage area as described in NFPA 30.

NFPA 30 allows local or spot ventilation used for control of vapors released by dispensing operations to provide up to 75% of the ventilation required for the room. Ventilation required by NFPA 30 for storage areas is primarily for dilution to prevent accumulation of flammable vapors from leaking storage containers, not to protect dispensing operations.

A mechanical ventilation system for flammable liquid dispensing areas must, according to NFPA 30, be equipped with an airflow switch which will sound an audible alarm if the ventilation fails.

Explosion Venting for Storage and Dispensing Operations

Explosion venting is not required for separate inside storage areas for flammable liquids if containers are no greater than 60 gallons and if transfer from containers larger than 1 gallon is by means of approved pumps or other devices drawing through a top opening, according to NFPA 45.

If dispensing of flammable liquids with flash point temperatures below 73°F (Classes IA and IB) is done in a room with an exterior wall or roof, NFPA 30 requires that the room be provided with deflagration venting in accord with NFPA 68.

When deflagration explosion venting is provided for dispensing or storage operations, it is important to have a normally unoccupied area into which the explosion-relieving wall can fall without endangering anyone. The safety requirements for deflagration explosion venting are considerably less rigorous than those for detonation explosion venting, which may be required from pressure test cells such as those used for high-pressure hydrogenation.

The Uniform Fire Code contains detailed requirements for explosion venting and explosion suppression.

Preventing Ignition of Vapors

NFPA 30 requires that precautions be taken to prevent the ignition of flammable vapors, particularly where flammable or combustible liquids are dispensed. Such areas must not have any ignition sources within the hazardous areas, such as ordinary electrical equipment, open flames, hot surfaces, radiant heat, frictional heat, static electricity, electrical and mechanical sparks or heat-producing chemical reactions.

Static electricity is generated when liquids are dispensed and can build up enough voltage to ignite flammable vapors. Therefore, provision must be made for bonding, grounding, humidification or other measures to dissipate the static electricity. NFPA 30 requires bonding for dispensing of all flammable liquids and all combustible liquids at temperatures above their flash points.

Effective bonding between metal containers consists of an electrical connection between the containers with an electrical resistance not greater than 10 ohms. Bonding is not required when a container is filled through a closed system or when one of the containers is made of glass or another nonconductive material.

Electrical wiring and equipment located in inside rooms used for dispensing or storage of flammable liquids must be suitable for Class I, Division 2 classified locations. Within 3 ft of a dispensing nozzle or vent, wiring and equipmente must be suitable for Class I, Division I locations.

Equipment for hazardous locations is commonly called "explosion proof." However, equipment that is explosion proof for methane is not necessarily explosion proof for ethyl ether, acetylene or hydrogen. Equipment must be classified for the intended use. See Article 500 of NFPA 70 for requirements and consult manufacturers' catalogs.

Explosion-proof electrical equipment is not required in laboratory work areas and laboratory units under most circumstances, according to NFPA 45. Such areas are considered to be "unclassified electrically" or not hazardous locations with respect to Article 500 of NFPA 70. The exception would be if there were conditions of extraordinary hazard and it was necessary to classify a laboratory work area or part thereof as a hazardous location which would require classified or explosion-proof electrical equipment.

Emergency Alarms and Protection for Personnel in Dispensing Areas

Each dispensing area should be provided with an emergency alarm station outside of the dispensing area. The emergency alarm station could consist of a conventional fire alarm pull station, a special emergency pull station or an emergency telephone which rings automatically at an attended location.

Hazardous materials dispensing areas should be designed so that an accident or overexposure to a person working alone can be detected promptly and the person rescued. The dangers are greater if a person working in the dispensing area cannot be seen by someone outside of the area, if large quantities of material are stored or dispensed in the area, if the area is large and if the hazards of the materials are great.

Provision should be made for holding the door of a dispensing room open for deliveries and whenever anyone is inside the room, unless the interior of the room can be seen from outside the room. NFPA 30 allows doors to be held open during material-handling operations if they are provided with approved devices that will close the doors automatically in a fire emergency. This can be accomplished by connecting an electromagnetic hold-open so that it will release in case of power failure, or actuation of the fire alarm system, or operation of a smoke- or fire-detection device in the immediate vicinity.

An audible monitoring system may be needed if hazardous materials dispensing operations will take place without a second person being present. Such a system should allow another person to hear immediately any loud noise or call for help.

Emergency equipment should be provided in a safe and accessible location so that it can be reached and used in responding to chemical spills and splashes in the dispensing area. The location should be one that is not likely to be within the spill or splash area.

See the Uniform Fire Code for additional requirements for emergency prevention and response.

3.5.6 Fire Protection Needs and Requirements

A laboratory facility should be designed to be "fire worthy," so that the building and its contents will be protected from fire and so that any fire that occurs can be extinguished, with no injury to personnel and with minimum losses of building and contents. The owner should also be sure that a fire does not result in loss of productive use of the facility or loss of records, samples or business.

Fire Extinguishing Systems

Installation of an automatic extinguishing system is recommended to prevent or minimize fire and the resulting disruption. The added expense of such a system is likely to be offset by substantially reduced costs of fire and business interruption insurance.

Automatic fire detection and extinguishing systems are not generally required for laboratories unless they exceed a certain area, have limited fire resistance or contain a fire load greater than the fire resistance of the structure. NFPA 45 generally allows larger areas if they are sprinklered.

Many industrial laboratories are required by the insurance carrier to have an automatic extinguishing system such as sprinklers; in contrast, most educational laboratories have not been required to have such fire protection.

NFPA 45 does not require automatic fire protection unless areas or combustible loadings exceed the values specified in the standard. However, automatic fire extinguishing systems are desirable in a laboratory because they protect the building, equipment and records, particularly if the fire department's response is delayed or inadequate.

Automatic fire extinguishing and fire detection systems should be connected to the fire alarm system so that their operation will immediately sound an alarm within the facility. If possible, arrangements should be made to connect internal alarm systems to a central station that will summon the fire department whether the building is vacant or occupied.

Automatic fire extinguishing systems, other fire detection systems and alarm systems should be designed by an experienced fire protection engineer or firm. Based on its record of experience, the engineer or firm should be selected by the laboratory planner with the approval of the owner.

Fire Extinguishers

Laboratory facilities should be provided with fire extinguishers that can be used by laboratory employees to put out small fires effectively. Fire extinguishers should be selected for the types of fires that can occur and should be located so that they will be readily available. Guidance is included in NFPA 10, Standard for Portable Fire Extinguishers.

Fire Brigade

If a facility is located far from a fire department or if the hazards exceed the capabilities of the fire department, the laboratory planner should provide the extra fire extinguishing capacity and protective equipment necessary for a fire brigade. Protective equipment required for a fire brigade by OSHA standards is described in 29 CFR 1910.

Fire-Resistant Construction Requirements

Building codes in the United States do not seem to recognize laboratories as a unique type of occupancy and generally have not had a well-defined category for laboratories or laboratory buildings. They have often been built to meet construction requirements for office occupancies, which are less restrictive than those for high-hazard industrial occupancies. Recent editions of the Uniform Building Code and the Uniform Fire Code have established restrictions which may apply to laboratories.

In contrast, some specific requirements for construction and fire protection of laboratories are contained in a standard developed by the NFPA in 1975 and most recently revised in 1986. The standard, NFPA 45, is unique in relating the requirements for areas, fire hazards, and fire resistance. For example, a small laboratory with relatively little fire hazard has minimal requirements for fire-resistant separation from nonlaboratory areas. A laboratory with large amounts of flammable liquids is limited in size, and buildings with such laboratories have greater requirements for structural fire resistance and separation from other areas.

NFPA 45 sets limits on the sizes of laboratory units, based on their fire hazard, and establishes requirements for fire separation between units and nonlaboratory areas.

An enclosed space used for experiments or

tests is defined by NFPA 45 as a "laboratory unit." A laboratory unit may generally be considered as one fire area, and may contain any number of separate laboratory work areas or laboratories, as well as corridors, offices, lavatories and other contiguous rooms maintained for or used by laboratory personnel. See Section 7.3 for more about NFPA 45.

Laboratory units are classified by NFPA 45 into three categories according to the number of gallons of flammable and combustible liquids in the space per 100 sq ft of area. Class A laboratory units (high hazard) are those with the highest allowable quantities of flammable and combustible liquids. Class B units (intermediate hazard) have moderate limits, and Class C units the lowest limits.

NFPA 45 has different limits for flammable liquids and combinations of flammable and combustible liquids, for quantities in storage cabinets or in safety cans, and for unsprinklered and sprinklered laboratory units.

Table 3.5-5 from NFPA 45, Table 2-2, shows that a Class A laboratory unit is allowed to have up to 10 gallons of flammable liquids per 100 sq ft in ordinary containers on benches or open shelves, and that this quantity can be doubled to 20 gallons per 100 sq ft if the additional 10 gallons is in approved storage cabinets and safety cans. The maximum total quantity allowed in ordinary containers on open shelves in an unsprinklered Class A laboratory unit is 300 gallons, but up to 1,200 gallons is permitted in a Class A laboratory unit if half is in storage cabinets and safety cans and the unit is sprinklered.

There has been a question about whether the second major heading intended to exclude or include quantities that were both in safety cans and in safety cabinets at the same time. The NFPA has stated informally that the intent was to refer to quantities that were either in safety cans *or* in storage cabinets, but not at the same time.

The quantities allowed by NFPA 45 are not restrictive for petroleum research but are considered excessive for most laboratories. One federal agency has restricted quantities in its research laboratories to one-tenth of those specified in NFPA 45.

3.5.7 Emergency Equipment

Emergency equipment needed in a laboratory facility usually includes a fire alarm system, fire extinguishers, and equipment for responding to chemical splashes, and may include equipment for dealing with chemical spills. The basic requirements for alarms, extinguishers and spill response equipment are outlined in the first part of this section, and the requirements and considerations for emergency water in the last section.

In some large buildings or groups of buildings, there may be advantages in providing doors in corridors to prevent the spread of fire, smoke and vapor. The need for cross-corridor "smoke doors" becomes greater if two or more buildings are connected directly or by means of enclosed passageways, because of the increased possibility of air being drawn from one building into another. However, there are no guidelines for providing such barriers except in schools and health care facilities. If such smoke doors are installed, they can be kept in the open position, if air flows are balanced, by electromagnetic hold-opens which will release the doors in case of power failure, actuation of the alarm system, or by operation of a smoke- or fire-detection device in the vicinity.

Alarm Systems, Fire Extinguishers, Fire Blankets and Spill-Response Equipment

A fire alarm system is required in almost all laboratory facilities, and consideration should be given to installing a system which can be used for other emergency conditions to alert persons in the vicinity and summon emergency assistance. Selection of an alarm system that has multiple uses is recommended. If the alarm system is designed to signal fire evacuation, a spill response, or a weather emergency, different signals will be

Table 3.5-5. Maximum Quantities of Flammable and Combustible Liquids Allowed in Laboratory Units (Outside of Flammable Liquid Storage Rooms)

Laboratory Unit Class	Flammable or Combustible Liquid Class	*Excluding* Quantities in Storage Cabinets[7] and Safety Cans			*Including* Quantities in Storage Cabinets[7] and Safety Cans		
		Maximum Quantity[3] Per 100 Square Feet of Laboratory Unit	Maximum Quantity[3,4] Per Laboratory Unit		Maximum Quantity[3] Per 100 Square Feet of Laboratory Unit	Maximum Quantity[3,4] Per Laboratory Unit	
			Unsprinklered	Sprinklered[6]		Unsprinklered	Sprinklered[6]
A[1] (High hazard)	I	10 gallons	300 gallons	600 gallons	20 gallons	600 gallons	1200 gallons
	I, II and IIIA[5]	20 gallons	400 gallons	800 gallons	40 gallons	800 gallons	1600 gallons
B[2]	I	5 gallons	150 gallons	300 gallons	10 gallons	300 gallons	600 gallons
(Intermediate hazard)	I, II and IIIA[5]	10 gallons	200 gallons	400 gallons	20 gallons	400 gallons	800 gallons
C[2]	I	2 gallons	75 gallons	150 gallons	4 gallons	150 gallons	300 gallons
(Low hazard)	I, II and IIIA[5]	4 gallons	100 gallons	200 gallons	8 gallons	200 gallons	400 gallons

[1] Class A laboratory units shall not be used as instructional laboratory units.

[2] Maximum quantities of flammable and combustible liquids in Class B and Class C instructional laboratory units shall be 50% of those listed in the Table.

[3] For maximum container sizes, see Table 7-2.

[4] Regardless of the maximum allowable quantity, the maximum amount in a laboratory unit shall never exceed an amount calculated by using the maximum quantity per 100 square feet of laboratory unit. The area of offices, lavatories, and other contiguous areas of a laboratory unit are to be included when making this calculation.

[5] The maximum quantities of Class I liquids shall not exceed the quantities specified for Class I liquids alone.

[6] Where water may create a serious fire or personnel hazard, a nonwater extinguishing system may be used instead of sprinklers.

[7] See description of Flammable Liquid Storage Room in Section 4-4 of NFPA 30, *Flammable and Combustible Liquids Code*. See description of Storage Cabinet in Section 4-2 of NFPA 30.

For SI units: 1 gal = 3.785 L; 100 sq ft = 9.3 m².

Source: Reprinted with permission from NFPA 45, Standard on Fire Protection for Laboratories Using Chemicals, Table 2-2, Copyright, 1986, National Fire Protection Association, Quincy, Mass. 02269. This reprinted material is not the complete and official position of the NFPA on the referenced subject, which is represented only by the standard in its entirety.

needed. Signage should be provided to describe evacuation or other emergency procedures and to designate evacuation assembly points.

Fire Extinguishers

Portable fire extinguishers should be installed and located in accordance with NFPA 10, Standard for Portable Fire Extinguisher. Laboratory units which are designed as Class A shall have fire extinguishers as required for extra hazard occupancies.

Almost all laboratories require installation of extinguishers with ratings of 20B, 40B or more to provide adequate fire extinguishing capacity for gallon bottles of flammable solvents. No hand-held carbon dioxide fire extinguisher on the market has the capacity to put out a 1-gallon flammable liquid spill fire, so it is necessary to provide extinguishers which contain adequate quantities of dry chemical or special foam that have ratings of 20B or greater. Carbon dioxide fire extinguishers are suitable for small solvent fires and are often preferred because they leave no residue.

Multiple-purpose extinguishers are often recommended for areas where fires may involve different classes of materials. For example, an extinguisher with an ABC rating is the most effective type if solvent and paper are both burning and there is live electrical equipment in the same area.

Halogenated extinguishing agents may be preferred for electronic equipment, but extinguishers with such agents will not be rated to extinguish burning paper unless the extinguisher is large enough to have a Class A rating. Special extinguishers with a Class D rating are needed to extinguish fires in combustible metals such as magnesium and sodium.

Fire extinguishers should generally be located near the doors of laboratory work areas, either just inside or just outside. This location is preferred because an occupant who seeks the extinguisher in case of fire will be heading toward the exit. NFPA 10 specifies maximum travel distances to fire extinguishers.

NFPA 45 recommends that all laboratory buildings be provided with standpipes and 1.5-in. hose for use by occupants to supplement fire extinguishers, and that the hoses be equipped with special nozzles and a water flow alarm. The NFPA also requires that standpipes with 2.5-in. hose connections be provided in all unsprinklered laboratory buildings with two or more stories above or below the street floor.

Additional fire extinguishers, fire hoses and protective equipment will probably be required if a laboratory is going to have an emergency fire brigade because the laboratory has special hazards or is in a remote location.

Fire Blankets

There is no requirement for installation of fire blankets. If fire blankets are installed, they should *not* be the vertical type that directs the victim to use it in a standing position, but a type that can easily be taken to the victim. The recommended emergency response to a clothing fire is to stop, drop and roll. Standing will increase the amount of hot gases and smoke inhaled.

Spill Kits and Respiratory Protection

NFPA 43C, Standard for Storage of Gaseous Oxidizers, requires respiratory protective equipment and other appropriate protective equipment to be readily available outside of any storage area in which more than 100 lb of gaseous oxidizing material is stored. No specific travel distance is stated.

If spill control material is to be provided, it should be of a type and in a quantity adequate to provide safe control of potential spills. However, as little as 1 gallon of a volatile toxic material such as chloroform *cannot* safely be cleaned up without self-contained breathing apparatus.

If spill control stations are provided, they should be located in a corridor or other area away from those in which spills are likely to occur so that a spill does not prevent access to the emergency equipment.

The owner should decide whether spill control stations should be incorporated into the design of corridors and determine what space may be needed. If the owner elects to furnish spill control materials and possibly one or more spill control carts, the laboratory planner will have to base the space needs on the owner's decision.

The laboratory design should include one or more emergency spill stations containing a pair of self-contained breathing masks, protective clothing and spill control material if the laboratory must establish self-sufficiency for cleaning up spills of volatile hazardous chemicals. This decision will be based on the owner's determination of whether there is a need to provide emergency breathing equipment or whether the responding fire department will provide services in case of a nonflammable toxic spill. Figure 3.5-9

suggests a layout of an emergency spill station.

Emergency Water

Readily available supplies of water are needed for emergency flushing of chemicals from the eyes and body in every workplace in which irritating, corrosive or toxic chemicals are used. This section gives recommendations for the volume of water, drains, water temperature, long-term washing and decontamination, as well as the basic requirements of OSHA and ANSI standards. OSHA standards establish the general requirement for emergency water, and an ANSI standard defines different types of water delivery systems and sets standards for performance, location, installation, test procedures and maintenance.

A piped supply of water will be required except in very unusual situations. If shutoff

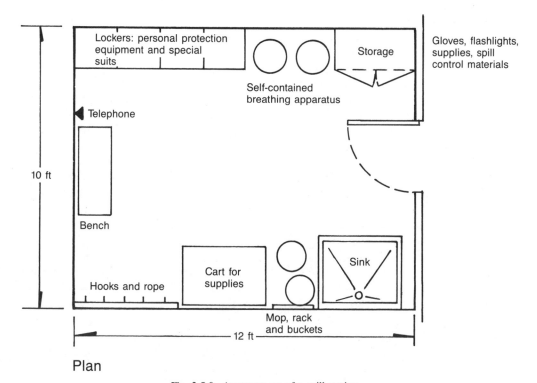

Fig. 3.5-9. Arrangement of a spill station.

valves are installed in the water line leading to safety drenching equipment, the valves must have an outside stem and yoke, and they must be sealed in the open position and labeled for identification. If for some unusual reason a piped water supply cannot be provided, the minimum required is a 15-minute supply of water.

Recommendations for Emergency Water Devices

- Water Supply. The minimum flow rate for plumbed eyewash equipment should be at least 3 gallons per minute and preferably 6 to 9 gallons per minute. The ANSI minimum flow rate is suitable only for portable eyewash units made for use in areas without a piped water supply. When deciding on the total volume of water that will be needed for flushing and that will have to be removed, consider that flushing may be required as medical treatment for periods ranging from 30 minutes to many hours, depending upon the severity of the burns.

   Hand-held drench hoses should generally be installed in combination with all emergency showers in order to facilitate effective flushing of chemicals from all parts of the body. Since emergency conditions often require *simultaneous* operation and use of a shower and a drench hose, or of a shower and an eyewash unit, the water supply and piping should be capable of providing for simultaneous operation of any combination installed.

- Location. Emergency eyewash devices should be located as close as possible to any area where chemicals may be handled. Locating such devices at a sink in the work area will take up less floor area, provide an economical and convenient water supply and drainage, and be easy to find in an emergency.

   Emergency showers should be located so that they will not be in the middle of the chemical splash or spill area. If the

laboratory space is subdivided into walled modules, emergency showers should be located in the corridors outside the modules. For locating emergency showers, we believe that the term "work area" in the OSHA standard should be construed to include the corridors.

- Actuation. Emergency shower valves should be installed so that they can be actuated by a person of any height and by someone in a wheelchair. One very effective way is to run a cord down a clear wall so that it can be found easily and pulled.

   The author recommends that safety showers not be installed as shown in manufacturers' catalogs, since these usually show the valve directly above the shower head and the actuating handle hanging next to the head. When a handle in such a location is pulled in an emergency, it will be in the way of the victim and the rescuers. Either the valve or the actuating handle should be offset so that it is out of the way in an emergency.

- Floor Drains. Floor drains should be installed close to each emergency shower to facilitate the removal of the great quantity of water that will be released at a rate of 30 gallons a minute for the minimum recommended flushing period of 15 minutes.

   It is necessary to prevent the traps in emergency shower floor drains from drying out and admitting sewer gases to the area. One recommended method is to provide a primed floor drain. Other possible methods are to fill the traps with a nonpolluting liquid (such as glycerine) that will not evaporate readily or to develop a method of sealing each floor drain with a quickly removable cap. Another possible preventive measure is to connect the waste lines so that the trap is kept full by the discharge from a drinking fountain.

- Water Temperature. Cold water is recommended for emergency flushing of chemicals from the eyes and body, as well as for emergency treatment of thermal burns. Cold water is generally best because it will slow the reaction rate of the chemical splashed, constrict blood vessels and minimize circulation of an absorbed chemical, slow cellular metabolism and enzyme reaction rates, and help reduce the pain of chemical contact.

Tepid water may be too warm to minimize the adverse effects of splashed chemicals, and hot water can increase the injury. However, prolonged washing with cold water can be painful and on large splashes may cause serious loss of body heat.

When prolonged washing is needed and medical judgment may require water temperatures above those coming from cold water lines, there are several ways in which the water temperature can be regulated. Eyewash devices attached to the outlet of the regular mixing faucets on a laboratory sink provide an economical and reasonably safe way to adjust water temperature for prolonged emergency washing.

Water temperatures for indoor showers can be raised above that delivered by a cold water line by automatic tempering valves, by in-line holding tanks and by manually-controlled valves. Automatic water tempering devices can be dangerous if they malfunction and yield hot water; they are not recommended except in unusual situations.

If in-line tanks are installed in a heated building to provide a volume of water at ambient building temperature, the water will probably need to be recirculated to prevent the growth of microorganisms that can seriously contaminate the water.

Safe, economical ways to furnish manually controlled temperatures to emergency showers are to provide showers with a normally closed connection to a hot water line or to provide special emergency shower rooms. The valve to

the hot water line should be accessible, sealed closed with a breakable seal, and provided with a sign which indicates that the valve may be opened in case of emergency to temper the water.

- Emergency Shower Rooms. One or two emergency shower rooms should be located in each laboratory building in which hazardous chemicals are used or stored. The floor of the room should be slip resistant, the room should be large enough to accommodate at least one victim and two or more members of the rescue team, and one or more wooden shower benches should be provided. Consideration should be given to accommodating two or more victims of one emergency. Figure 3.5-10 shows an emergency shower room which could serve as a prototype.

- Emergency Showers in Outdoor Locations. For emergency showers in outdoor locations, such as at a hazardous waste storage area, the water may need to be tempered to keep it from getting dangerously hot or from freezing. In areas where water lines are on or near the surface of the ground and subject to heating by the sun, it is important to provide water at temperatures which will not cause thermal burns or aggravate chemical burns. Water lines may need to be insulated and water circulated to prevent solar heating.

In areas where water lines may freeze, it is necessary to provide some means of heating the water supplied. Keeping water lines from freezing may require a carefully controlled system for heating the water directly or a heated building in which a large emergency water tank can be kept warm indirectly.

OSHA Standards for Emergency Water

The general OSHA requirement for emergency water is: "Where the eyes or body of any person may be exposed to injurious corrosive materials, suitable facilities for quick drenching or flushing of the eyes and body

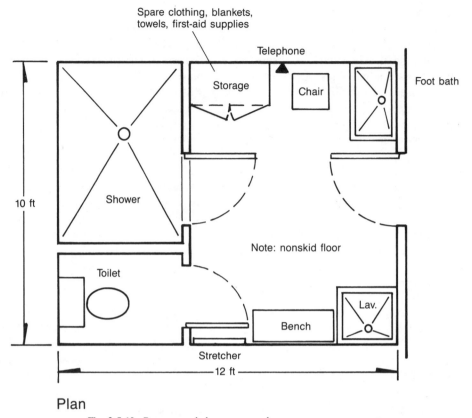

Plan

Fig. 3.5-10. Recommended emergency shower room arrangement.

shall be provided within the work area for immediate emergency use.'' Another section of the standards includes a guideline for providing emergency water for splashes of liquids which may burn, irritate or otherwise harm the skin. As a minimum, the OSHA standard calls for a piped supply of clean, cold water with a quickly-opening valve and at least 48 in. of hose not smaller than three-fourths of an inch. As an alternative, deluge showers and eye flushes are to be provided where harmful chemicals may be splashed on parts of the body.

ANSI Standard for Emergency Eyewash and Shower Equipment

The ANSI standard for emergency eyewash and shower equipment, ANSI Z 358.1, defines four different types of water delivery systems: emergency showers, plumbed and self-contained eyewash equipment, eye/face wash equipment and hand-held drench

hoses, and combinations of shower and eyewash equipment. Details of their installation are covered in Section 4.8.

The ANSI standard specifies that emergency eyewash units and emergency showers "shall be accessible within 10 seconds and should be within a travel distance no greater than 100 feet (30.5 m) from the hazard.''

The ANSI standard also specifies that if a shower enclosure is provided, there shall be a minimum unobstructed area of 34 in. (86.4 cm) in diameter. Such a small enclosure is definitely *not* recommended by this author because it will not provide space for the people who will have to assist a splash victim. A more suitable arrangement is shown in Figure 3.5-10.

3.5.8 Conclusion

The laboratory planner can provide many design solutions in new or remodeled facilities that will give the owner important means of managing laboratory hazards. The design of a safe working environment for laboratory users will depend on close cooperation with the owner and on the owner's identification of the hazards to be controlled and the importance of controlling them. If existing codes, regulations and standards do not provide sufficient guidance, the laboratory planner may need to encourage the owner to set higher standards.

Recent and pending regulations on laboratory safety and emergency procedures will increase the emphasis on providing safe and healthful working conditions in all types of research facilities.

REFERENCES
AND SUGGESTED READINGS

NFPA 10   Standard for Portable Fire Extinguishers
NFPA 13   Standard for the Installation of Sprinkler Systems
NFPA 14   Standard for the Installation of Standpipe and Hose Systems
NFPA 30   Flammable and Combustible Liquids Code
NFPA 43A   Code for Storage of Liquid and Solid Oxidizing Materials
NFPA 43C   Code for Storage of Gaseous Oxidizing Materials
NFPA 45   Standard on Fire Protection for Laboratories Using Chemicals
NFPA 49   Hazardous Chemicals Data
NFPA 68   Guide for Explosion Venting
NFPA 70   National Electrical Code
NFPA 80   Standard for Fire Doors and Windows
NFPA 99   Standard for Health Care Facilities
NFPA 101   Life Safety Code
NFPA 220   Standard Types of Building Construction
NFPA 325M   Fire Hazard Properties of Flammable Liquids, Gases, and Volatile Solids
NFPA 491M   Hazardous Chemical Reactions
NFPA 704   Standard System for Identification of the Fire Hazards of Materials
NFPA Standards for Fire Extinguishing Systems: 11, 11A, 12, 12A, 12B, 15, 17, 69
NFPA Standards for Fire Alarm and Detection Systems: 71, 72A, 72B, 72C, 72D, 72E
NFPA Standards for Ventilation Systems: 90A, 91
NFPA Standards for Compressed and Liquefied Gases: 50, 50A, 50B, 51, 54, 58
NFPA *Fire Protection Handbook*
NFPA *Industrial Fire Hazards Handook*
OSHA Safety and Health Standards 29CFR1900

American National Standards Institute 1981. Standard for Emergency Eyewash and Shower Equipment, ANSI Z 358.1. New York: ANSI.

Compressed Gas Association latest edition. Pamphlets: G-4 *Oxygen;* G-5 *Hydrogen;* P-1 *Safe Handling of Compressed Gases;* P-2 *Characteristics and Safe Handling of Medical Gases;* V-5 *Diameter-Index Safety System.* Arlington, VA: Compressed Gas Association.
Cottler, Stephen R., and Degraff, Alfred H., *Architectural Accessibility for the Disabled of College Campuses.* State University Construction Fund, 194 Washington Ave., Albany, NY 12210.
DiBerardinis, Louis, et al., 1987. *Guidelines for Laboratory Design—Health and Safety Considerations.* New York: Wiley.
International Conference of Building Officials (ICBO). *1988 Uniform Building Code.* Whittier, CA: ICBO.
ICBO and Western Fire Chiefs Association. *1988 Uniform Fire Code.* Whittier, CA: ICBO.
General Services Administration. *Design Criteria: New Public Buildings.* General Services Administration Business Service Center, 7th and D Streets SW, Washington, DC, 20407.
Mace, Ronald L., *Accessibility Modifications.* Special Office for the Handicapped, North Carolina Department of Insurance, P.O. Box 26387, Raleigh NC 27606.
Swanson, Anne Barrett, and Steere, Norman V., 1981. Safety Considerations for Physically Handicapped Individuals in the Chemistry Laboratory. *Journal of Chemical Education,* Vol. 58, p. 234.
Technical Committee on Chemistry Laboratories. *Standard for Fire Protection in Laboratories Using Chemicals,* NFPA 45-1986. Quincy, MA: National Fire Protection Association.
U.S. Department of Labor, Occupational Safety and Health Administration. *OSHA Safety and Health Standards for General Industry,* 29 CFR 1910 (latest edition). Washington, DC: U.S. Government Printing Office.

3.6 SITE SELECTION
AND EVALUATION   *T. Ruys*

There are a number of physical, regulatory and economic factors that must be considered in selecting a site for a laboratory facility. Aspects such as view, amenities, slope, soil conditions, demolition and cost are equally important but are not addressed in this discussion. Other issues dealing with public relations with the community and the neighborhood are covered in Section 2.10. If the site is in an existing building, read Section 2.7.

3.6.1 Zoning

The site under consideration must be appropriately zoned for the type of laboratory being planned. Even if it is, it may not allow enough flexibility. Check for the following:

- Permitted uses (labs, research, office, manufacturing)
- Lot coverage allowed, which affects the building's footprint
- Setback requirements
- Height limitations of the building *and* of mechanical stacks
- Parking requirements

An example of a site fact sheet is shown in Figure 3.6-1.

3.6.2 Expansion Potential

Laboratories have a way of growing. Because suitable laboratory space is much more difficult to find than, say, office space and because of the importance of sharing expensive equipment and common spaces such as chemical storage and pilot plants, it is extremely important to leave room for expansion. Moving laboratory facilities is very expensive indeed.

Expansion potential can take many forms besides owning the land outright: lease options, options to buy, etc.

In order to assess the adequacy of the site, it is important to know the size of the building being planned *in gross square feet* (GSF) and the number of stories anticipated, the size of the service yard and the number of parking stalls. Section 8.6 explains how GSF are derived from net assignable square feet (NASF).

3.6.3 Prevailing Winds

Many laboratory operations exhaust hazardous or potentially hazardous particles, gases and vapors. Even if these are removed from the exhausted air, there is always the potential for an accident.

Even nonhazardous materials may affect the operation if recirculated. The direction(s) of the prevailing winds will influence the location and height of building air intake and exhaust.

3.6.4 Access

Many things enter and leave a laboratory facility. Some of these should be combined and others must be separated. Ideally, public and service traffic are separated. The loading dock and service yard contain many items which are potentially hazardous and often not pleasing to look at: waste containers, gas cylinders, mechanical equipment, carts, trucks, etc.

In facilities with animal quarteres, the live-animal/receiving area must be separated from the waste disposal dock.

Does the site allow easy access and screening of the service yard? Is the access compatible with nearby uses?

3.6.5 Image and Security

Some laboratory facilities must be hidden from public view; others may require a high profile. The site selected will influence both potentials.

In either case, security is an issue, including its degree. Is the site intended to be fenced? Will a gate and guard house be provided?

3.6.6 Fire Safety

Assuming that local fire protection is available, is adequate access provided for fire department ladders and hose trucks? Is the turning radius of access roads and driveways adequate?

Local codes typically spell out required distances to adjacent structures.

3.6.7 Site Utilities

Laboratory facilities require a great deal of electrical power, water and, most often, natural gas, and generate large quantities of liquid waste. Ideally, two independent sources of electrical power are provided to secure backup for critical operations. Are these available and are the sources reliable?

3.6.8 Site Selection Process

If the selection is of any value, the process must be objective. Outside unbiased opinions are generally more acceptable to all par-

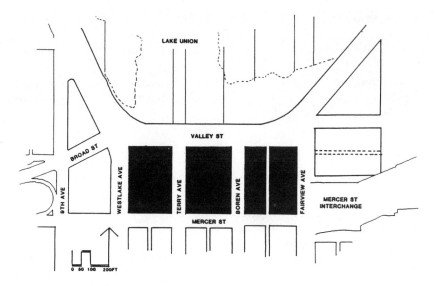

SITE AREA*	6.31 acres without ROWs/7.62 acres with ROWs
EXISTING ZONING	Manufacturing (M)
ASSUMED REZONE	Commercial-2 (C-2)
USE ALLOWED	Yes
DEVELOPMENT POTENTIAL (Existing Zoning)	687,100 square feet without ROWs 829,300 square feet with ROWs
DEVELOPMENT POTENTIAL (Proposed Rezone)	1,374,200 square feet without ROWs 1,658,000 square feet with ROWs
KEY DEVELOPMENT CONTROLS	Existing: FAR = 2.5, 65' height interim zoning ordinance Proposed: 65' height

ADVANTAGES

- Large parcels
- Regular shape
- Size
- City support

DISADVANTAGES

- Access uncertain
- Multiple owners

* City-owned land = 2.59 acres or 112,960 gsf

Fig. 3.6-1. Example of a site fact sheet (MPS).

ties. In addition, the process must be analytical, rigorous and defendable. It should include the following steps:

- Establish Goals and Objectives
  Expectations and priority values must be established.
  Issues of importance must be noted.

Interested parties and decision makers must be heard.

- Define Functions and Facilities Requirements
  Consider hazards that dictate distances and are affected by prevailing winds.
  Analyze public and service areas.

Anticipate expansion.

Consider image and security.

Investigate available utilities.

- Prepare Site Selection Criteria

Establish priorities and associated values.

Formulate threshold criteria for rejection.

- Identify and Evaluate Alternative Sites

Determine test facility fit.

Establish compatibility of the environment.

Test regulatory requirements.

Check availability of the infrastructure.

Estimate costs.

SITE ANALYSIS

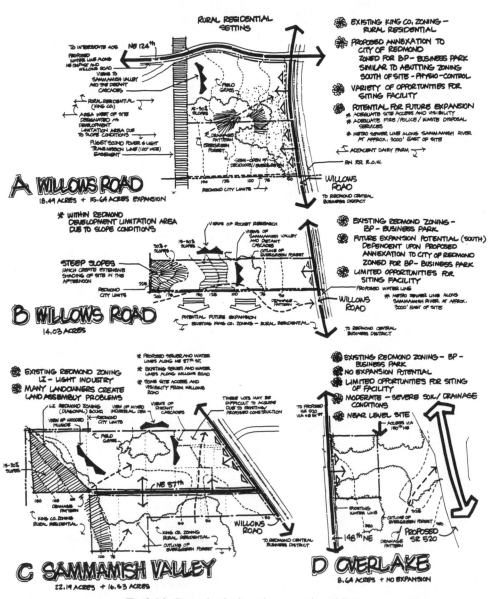

Fig. 3.6-2. Example of a four-site comparison (MPS).

SITE EVALUATION		SITE 1	SITE 2	SITE 3
PHYSICAL	**Location/Configuration**	NORTHWEST OF CITY - IN BOROUGH; IRREGULAR RECTANGLE; ± 190 ACRES — **+/+**	NORTH OF CENTRAL CITY - IN BOROUGH; SQUARE; ± 80 ACRES; ± 6 ACRES ACTUALLY AVAILABLE — **O/O**	WEST-CENTRAL - IN CITY; IRREGULAR; ±42 ACRES — **+/O**
	Soils	TANANA SILT LOAM - IMPERFECTLY DRAINED, HIGH WATER TABLE +, PERMAFROST — **—**	SOIL TESTS SHOW 5' TO 8' SILT OVER SAND + GRAVEL, NO PERMAFROST, + WATER TABLE AT 7.5' TO 12'	ROUGHLY 1/2 + 1/2 : TANANA SILT LOAM (SEE U. OF A. DESCRIPTION) + SALCHAKET SANDY LOAM (SEE GRAIDEN DESCRIPTION) — **O**
ACCESS	**Vehicular/Pedestrian**	PRIMARY ACCESS VIA GEIST RD + THE ALASKA HWY; NO CURRENT ... POTENTIAL CONNECTION WITH CAMPUS NETWORK — **—/O/+**	ACCESS AT COLLEGE ROAD ONLY - ARTERIAL NEAR ... CONNECTION — **+/+/O**	FRONTAGE ON AIRPORT WAY - MAJOR ARTERIAL; 1 BUS ...; RIVERFRONT PED/BIKE PATH NEARBY — **+/+**
	Parking	NEED TO DEVELOP ON SITE — **O**	SHARED WITH FAIRGROUND — **+**	SHARED WITH ALASKALAND SUPPLY OF 400 SPACES — **+**
CONTEXT	**Existing Use/Zoning/Amenities**	OLD AGRICULTURAL FIELDS; CURRENTLY 'NO STATE USE ZONE' - LIKELY ... REZ...; PASTORAL SETTING — **+/O/+**	FAIR, PLANNED 100% USE OF SITE; AGRICULTURE ...; WILDLIFE ... NEARBY, ON MIGRATORY FLYWAY — **+/O/+**	ALASKALAND PLANNING FOR USE OF TOTAL SITE; RE...; NEAR RECENT DEVELOPMENT ON AIRPORT WAY — **+/+**
	Adjacent Uses/Complementary Facilities	UNIVERSITY OF ALASKA TO NORTH, COMMERCIAL STRIP ALONG GEIST ROAD, RESIDENTIAL TO ... TWEG TO EAST; UNIVERSITY UTILITIES NEARBY: FOOD, LODGING + RETAIL DISTANT — **O/—**	COMMERCIAL ON COLLEGE ROAD, RESIDENTIAL TO SOUTH, OPEN SPACE TO NORTH; NO AQUATIC/COMPLEMENTARY FACILITIES — **O/—**	RESIDENTIAL TO EAST + WEST, CHENA RIVER TO NORTH + STRIP COMMERCIAL ON AIRPORT WAY — **—/O**
COST	**Ownership/Acquisition**	OWNED BY U. OF A., LEASE NECESSARY — **—/—**	OWNED BY STATE, LEASED TO FAIR; SUBLEASE NECESSARY — **O/—**	OWNED BY STATE OF ALASKA — **O/—**
	Extraordinary Site Development	OVER EXCAVATION OF SOIL MAY BE NECESSARY AS AT TVCC — **—**	SILT SOIL CONDITIONS - EXTRA SITE PREP + STRUCTURAL COSTS — **+**	RELOCATION OF EXISTING FACILITIES — **—**

Fig. 3.6-3. Example of an evaluation matrix (MPS).

CONCEPTS RANKING

	CONCEPT 1	CONCEPT 2	CONCEPT 3

CAMPUS FORM AND FUNCTION

	CONCEPT 1	CONCEPT 2	CONCEPT 3
Land Organization/Allocation	●	◑	◑
Circulation	●	○	◐
Scale	●	○	◐
Permanent Place	●	◑	◑
Symbolic Focus	◐	◑	●
Sense of Orientation	●	○	◑
Quality Pedestrain Movement	●	◑	◐
Enhanced Social Encounter	●	◑	○
Collegiate Atmosphere	◐	◑	●
Openness to Community	◐	◑	◐
Front Door Identity	○	◑	●
Minimum Distances	○	◑	●
Solar Response	◐	◑	●
Impact on Surrounding Circulation System	●	○	●
Buffer to Housing	●	◑	◐
Controllable Parking	●	●	◐
Security and Safety	●	◐	○
Academic Goals Responsiveness	◐	◐	◐
Consistency with Local Plans/Regulations	◐	◐	○

ECONOMICS

	CONCEPT 1	CONCEPT 2	CONCEPT 3
Costs/Revenues	●	◐	◐
Marketability of Commercial Space	◐	○	●
Conservation	◐	◐	◐

Fig. 3.6-4. Example of ranking (MPS).

CONCEPTS RANKING

	CONCEPT 1	CONCEPT 2	CONCEPT 3

IMPLEMENTATION

Building Phasing	●	○	○
Parking Phasing	●	◐	◐
Flexibility	●	○	◐

- Summarize Findings and Make Recommendations
  Weigh trade-offs.
  Rank sites.
  Prepare an action outline.

A sample comparison of four sites is shown in Figure 3.6-2. More complex multisite evaluations may take several pages and be recorded on a matrix for comparative evaluation. A matrix example is shown in Figure 3.6-3.

The relative value of the proposed options can be noted as negative, positive or neutral. It is also possible to assign a numerical value to those options and apply a multiplier to those issues deemed to have the highest priority. See Figure 3.6-4.

The advantage of this approach is that it is enables one to reach results efficiently with effective participation. It is objective and thorough, yet quick. The site selection analysis reduces risks by avoiding fatal flows in the development decision process.

3.7 ARCHITECTURAL FINISHES
T. Ruys

3.7.1 Introduction

Finishes in laboratory facilities are different in some respects from those in many other types of facilities because:

- They must be smooth for easy cleaning without joints.

- They must be impervious and nonabsorbent to avoid harboring contaminants and vermin.
- They must often be cleaned with disinfectants, live steam and high-temperature water.
- Ideally, they are chemical resistant (particularly floors) and in animal facilities withstand the corrosive effects of feces and urine.
- When wet, floors must be slip-proof.
- Walls and floors must be abrasion resistant.
- They should not add to the fuel in case of a fire.

Many choices are available which meet these requirements, and they will be discussed later. Finishes not appropriate for laboratory floors, although they have been used, are stone, wood, metal, paint and carpet.

One of the most important selection criteria, once the above criteria have been met, is the first cost. However, maintenance and replacement costs must also be considered. Chemical-resistant floor finishes have a higher first cost than resilient tile products, and tiles have the added advantage that they are easily replaced when stained by a spill or damaged. Resilient tile products are therefore the logical choice in many laboratories.

On the other hand, low-maintenance, more costly finishes are often desirable because laboratories are notoriously poorly maintained for several reasons (e.g., research laboratories are often off-limits to janitorial personnel or ongoing research does not allow equipment to be moved around).

In educational laboratories, maintenance can be accomplished between semesters but finishes must resist high wear and be vandal-proof.

Finishes must be coordinated with other building systems. For instance, the finish schedule and specifications must state clearly whether the floor finish is to be provided under the laboratory benches. When laboratory benches are fixed, the floor finish is typically installed after the benches. Based on traditional methods, the flooring subcontractor may dispute the need to finish the floor under movable or flexible benches. The same dispute may arise with wall finishes and base molding.

In containment facilities and in rooms where vermin must be controlled, the joints between mechanical and electrical devices and the room surfaces are sealed. Sealant and finishes must be compatible not just in appearance but chemically so that they will adhere to each other. The same applies to the joints between different materials that expand and contract at different rates, such as room surfaces and door frames. A critical joint is between concrete and concrete masonry walls; between gypsum wallboard partitions and masonry walls. The best way to deal with these cracks, which invariably occur, is to provide a joint which can be sealed with a suitable nonhardening product. See Figure 3.7-1. Some of the most difficult environments to accommodate are controlled-temperature rooms that have a large drop or a large fluctuation in temperature. The flooring material, if provided, moves independently of the metal insulated floor panels often provided with prefabricated rooms or applied over an insulated concrete slab.

Another difficult environment to accommodate is animal rooms, where high-temperature water (up to 180°F) is used to hose down and sanitize walls, floors and ceilings.

Finishes are often difficult to "spot" repair. It is important to protect the corners of surfaces subject to frequent abuse in order to avoid replacing the total surface more frequently than necessary. Corner guards, guard rails and kick plates on doors are the common devices used and are well worth the initial expense in laboratory facilities when frequent cart traffic occurs. These items are indispensable in animal facilities, where they must be nonabsorbent and designed to be vermin-proof, i.e., to prevent the harboring of vermin. Doors can be covered with polyvinyl chloride (PVC) sheeting, which can be heat welded at the seams to prevent moisture and vermin penetration.

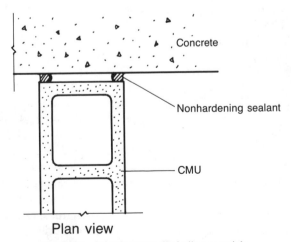

Plan view

Fig. 3.7-1. Joint between dissimilar materials.

Finishes are available whose chemical makeup will inhibit bacterial growth, but most are effective only for several months. These must be checked so that they will not affect research on the animals in animal facilities. At this time, these finishes are about 10% higher in cost than standard epoxy.

Floor finishes are important for another reason: to reduce the impact noise to the floor below. Impact noise is measured in impact insulation classes (IICs). For an apartment building, it is typically 50. The higher the value, the better, i.e., the less the impact noise below. There are no standards for laboratories, but it may be of interest to know that a 6-in. concrete slab has an IIC value of 34. A seamless floor or sheet product over this slab adds very little to this value.

The discussion of ceilings versus no ceilings is often a part of the laboratory planning process. Lack of ceilings provides ready access to utilities for maintenance and changes. See Figure 3.7-2. However, ceilings provide a cleaner work environment over

time; are generally more aesthetically pleasing to most people; and create a smaller space that must be cooled, heated and ventilated. These savings over the life of the building can be substantial, considering the large floor-to-floor heights required in most laboratory buildings. There is another good reason for having ceilings which is often overlooked: the reduction of transmitted noise from operations on the floor above. Sound transmission is measured in sound transmission classes (STCs). The higher the value, the better, i.e., the lower the noise transmission. A 6-in. concrete slab has an STC value of 46. What it should be for a laboratory depends on the type of work performed there. A vinyl asbestos tile floor increases the STC from only 46 to 48. Ceilings reduce both IIC and STC noise.

In many instances, the ceiling is deleted for cost reasons. In most cases that is the wrong assumption, since standard 2 × 4-ft lay-in acoustical ceilings are usually less expensive than no ceiling because, without ceilings:

Fig. 3.7-2. No ceiling in laboratories provides access to utilities (Theodorus Ruys).

- Every laboratory partition must be installed, spackeled and finished to the structure above and around many ducts, pipes and conduits.
- The installation of exposed ducts and utilities is more demanding.
- The ducts and utilities themselves are often finished.

As in most cases, there are some disadvantages. Therefore, when installing lay-in ceilings:

- Installation must be tight to avoid sound transmission to adjoining spaces if the partitions stop at the ceilings.
- Avoid sound transmission via air diffusers and light fixtures.
- Review security arrangements between adjoining laboratories. Many items have been removed from locked laboratories and offices by climbing over partitions that stopped at the ceiling.

The 2 × 4-ft lay-in tile ceiling is the most useful for laboratories because it provides easy access to utilities above the ceiling. Larger tiles are impossible to lift up and move out of the way; smaller tiles do not provide access. See Figure 3.7-3.

The color, pattern and reflectivity of finishes are important considerations. It may be desirable to spot contaminants or spills rather than hide them. Finishes have different light absorption characteristics and will affect the amount of light that must be provided in the space. In areas where ultraviolet (UV) light is used for decontamination, it is important to verify that the finishes will withstand the bleaching effect of UV light.

For areas with potentially explosive atmospheres, floor finishes are available that are nonsparking and/or provide conduct currents so that static charges will not build up. Careful consideration must be given to electrical resistance value and static decay.

The ease of cleaning is often a very important consideration. That may involve the finish itself (i.e., smooth, impervious and resistant to disinfectant solutions) but, more important, the interface between different surfaces such as floors, walls and ceilings. Corners may be coved, and edges and crevices avoided. Figures 3.7-4 through 3.7-6 provide a number of ways to facilitate cleaning and avoid dirt accumulation.

Comfort for individuals who move about or stand a great deal in the course of their work is another very important consideration. Concrete, terrazzo and tile floors are not desirable for that reason. Very often these types of floors are covered by vinyl or rubber matting, which makes maintaining sanitary conditions more difficult. Installed sheet products, particularly those made from vinyl or rubber, are more comfortable to stand on.

Architectural finishes can be applied to windows and doors as well. Window frame finishes and glazing have not been covered in this handbook. In our experience, door finishes in most laboratories are hardwood, laminate plastic faced or metal. Solid-core hardwood doors with an acid-resistant finish or faced with laminate plastic would be satisfactory for most types of laboratories. How-

Fig. 3.7-3. Lay-in ceiling for laboratories with 2 × 4 ft tiles (Theodorus Ruys).

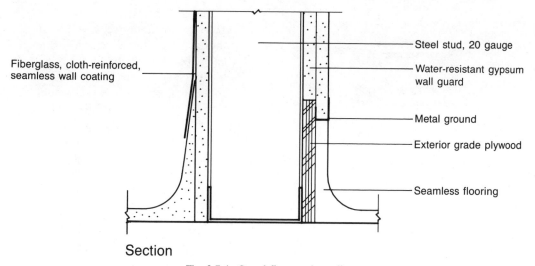

Fiberglass, cloth-reinforced, seamless wall coating

Steel stud, 20 gauge

Water-resistant gypsum wall guard

Metal ground

Exterior grade plywood

Seamless flooring

Section

Fig. 3.7-4. Coved floor at the wall.

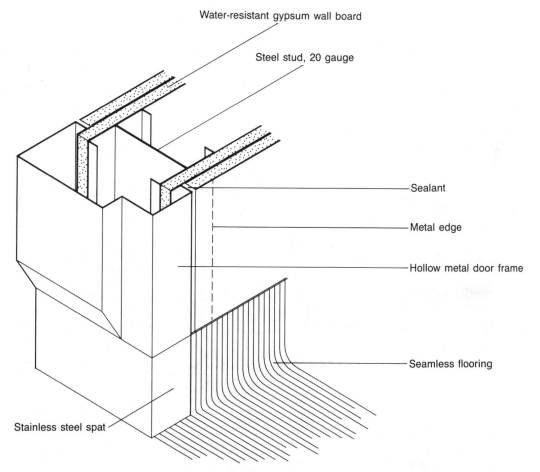

Water-resistant gypsum wall board

Steel stud, 20 gauge

Sealant

Metal edge

Hollow metal door frame

Seamless flooring

Stainless steel spat

Fig. 3.7-5. Door frame detail at the floor.

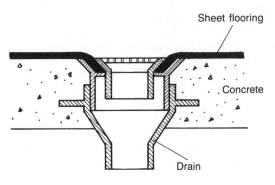

Section

Fig. 3.7-6. Joint at the floor drain in resilient flooring.

- Finishes and adhesives between the base material, the adhesive and the finish material must be compatible, but in some applications between the base coat and final coat as well. For instance, the base coat must not be water soluble in wet areas because the finish coat will delaminate from the base material.
- In high-moisture areas such as animal rooms, glasswash areas and cagewash areas, ceilings should be made of moisture-resistant materials such as cement plaster or water-resistant gypsum wallboard with an impervious finish.

ever, laminate plastic has a tendency to delaminate in high-moisture areas. Metal doors with an impervious, corrosion-resistant finish are most often used in animal facilities. PVC sheeting applied over these doors makes them resistant to damage by carts and animal racks as well.

Architectural finishes have proliferated over the years, providing some real improvements. The increase in choices, however, has created the need for increased knowledge and has produced some unusual and sometimes disastrous results. Besides the concerns expressed earlier, the following suggestions may be helpful:

- Do not accept substitutes unless you have investigated them carefully by requesting test results from an independent testing laboratory and by checking past installation with former customers. Request their names and telephone numbers from the supplier.
- Most often the product is not at fault in case of a failure, but rather the installation and the preparation of the base material. Therefore, the availability of local installers must be checked.
- Moisture, rather than the product itself, is often the cause of failure, particularly its effect on adhesives. Different finishes or vapor barriers often must be applied for concrete slabs on or below grade. Request a moisture test prior to installation.

Moisture causes adhesives and finish materials to deteriorate. It may also build up by capillary action under the finish coat and delaminate it from the base material.

Floods or water spills occur frequently in laboratory facilities when a drainline for a glasswasher or equipment which requires chilled water cooling is disconnected or breaks. In glasswash rooms the floor is usually designed for water conditions and commonly has a floor drain. That, however, is not the case in most laboratories. To avoid damage to lower floors, raised sleeves around floor penetration are often provided. See Figure 3.7-7. This, however, does little to prevent damage to floors and walls. In rooms where standing water is a frequent occurrence, a water barrier below the floor finish is highly recommended and well worth

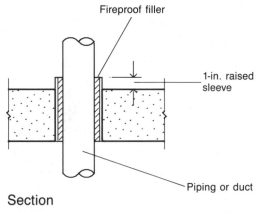

Section

Fig. 3.7-7. Mechanical floor penetration detail.

the extra cost. Concrete floors crack; sooner or later, even impervious finishes crack as well. When this happens, spills will create havoc with laboratory operation on lower floors.

So far, this section has pointed out some of the things to be concerned about but has not indicated which materials and applications are suitable for various laboratory spaces. The following sections will attempt to do this. However, it is not our intent to overlook any material or to promote one product over another. The difficulty is that many products are regional and not always available in other areas. Worse, reputable installers may not be available in certain areas. Finally, there is the fact that the architectural finishes industry is evolving. Therefore, the following suggestions are as generic as possible; further research on the part of the laboratory planner is in order. A good source is given in the references.

3.7-2 Floor Finishes (See Table 3.7-1)

Appropriate floor finishes for laboratory facilities are sealed concrete and other cementitious products; sheet products in roll or tile form made from vinyl, rubber or asphalt; and so-called seamless floors.

Cementitious Floors

These include standard concrete hardened and sealed; floors and terrazzo flooring. For reasons given in Table 3.7-1, these are suitable in laboratory facilities only for limited areas.

Resilient Floors

These consist of homogeneous and composition vinyls in sheets and tiles, as well as asphalt tile. Rubber tiles are suitable for certain areas. Cork and linoleum are not recommended. Vinyl asbesteos tiles (VAT) were once widely used but have been mostly replaced by vinyl composition tiles (VCT).

Resilient floors are most comfortable for stand-up work, which is frequent in labora-tories. This type of flooring is the most common material for laboratory facilities. It is resistant to alkalis but not to many chemicals. However, it can easily be replaced in case of damage.

Seamless Flooring

This consists of a resin matrix and fillers. The matrix is either thermosetting, which hardens permanently after curing, or thermoplastic, which can be reheated and remains plastic. Thermosetting matrices are epoxy resins, polyester, polysulfide, polyurethane, furan and neoprene. The substrate must be well prepared and dry in all cases. Glass fiber-reinforced polyester and polyurethane are more resilient than the other floorings and will better withstand cracking of the substrate.

All thermosetting matrices are available in one- and two-part compositions. The one-part applications harden by the evaporation of a solvent or cure by reaction with the moisture vapor in the air. The two-part application is mixed and cures by chemical reaction. Solvents present in both the one- and two-part applications are toxic and in some cases will continue to evaporate for some time; this may affect animals housed in animal facilities. Some isocyanates used in the manufacture of polyurethanes are also toxic; however, most polyurethane floor coatings are not toxic after the coating has cured.

Polyurethane floor coatings are usually applied like a coat of paint and cure overnight to accept light foot traffic such as might be required for a second coating on trowelled finishes. Ordinary pedestrian use would be acceptable in 1 to 2 days under standard temperature conditions. Five to 10 days might be necessary to develop higher levels of chemical and stain resistance. In this regard, polyurethane coatings are similar to epoxy or polyester chemically curing materials. Polyurethane floor coatings can be formulated to have hardness, toughness, and abrasion resistance higher than those of most other polymers.

The two-part applications are mixed and

Table 3.7-1. Suggested Laboratory Floor Finishes*

Material Type	Areas of Use	Material Composition	Limitations and Characteristics	Cost†/sq.ft (1989)	Remarks
Cementitious	Storage, receiving, machine and wood shops	Concrete, with or without hardeners and sealants	Shrinkage cracks, porous, stains, damaged by acids, poor appearance, uncomfortable, dust in high-traffic areas	$0.0-0.80	Not recommended for most laboratory facilities applications
	Public areas, corridors	Terrazzo, i.e., marble or granite chips and Portland cement	Expensive to install and change, uncomfortable	$9-$13	Attractive, long-lasting
Sheet products	Laboratories, instrument rooms	Vinyl tile	Areas of moderate wear; permanent dents after heavy loads, not acid resistant, not suitable for moist areas, fairly high flame spread rating (41)	$1.25-2.50	Easily cleaned; recommended for most laboratory areas because of moderate cost and comfort; below-grade acceptable for homogeneous types.
	Media preparation, containment, locker rooms, radioisotope labs	Sheet vinyl	Same as above	$2.50-$3.50	Typically used where coved base is desirable
	Laboratories, instrument rooms	Asphalt tile	Difficult to clean, not chemical resistant, for low-traffic areas; high flame spread rating (75)	$1.10-1.35	Lowest-cost finish; not recommended for laboratories
	Laboratories, instrument rooms	Rubber tile	Not chemical resistant; use vapor barrier below grade; high flame spread rating (75)	$2.25-$3.50	High-wear areas; good for below grade with a vapor barrier; electrical insulating
	Media preparation, containment, locker rooms, wet areas, radioisotope labs	PVC sheet	Requires a vapor barrier; low impact resistance; application by factory-trained individuals	$5-$6	Good chemical heat and abrasion resistance; hot-air welded seams; can be welded to same material applied to walls; flame spread rating 25 or less

Conductive floor areas	Vinyl and PVC tile, conductive type available		See above	$1.25–2.50	
Seamless	Epoxy resin	Wet areas, heavy-wear areas	Tempeature during installation at least 50°F; preparation of substrate critical; do not install over ceramic, vinyl, or asphalt tile; solvents in one part application toxic; stains; thermosetting	$4–$6	Too expensive for general use; good for high-impact, wet areas; high abrasion resistance; chemical resistance
	Polyester		Bond with substrate is affected by moisture; thermosetting	$2.75–$4	Properties very similar to those of epoxy resin; more resilient to cracking; one-part type for aesthetic areas, two-part type for industrial areas
	Neoprene		Not as hard as epoxy; primers recommended; thermosetting	$4.50–$5	Good resistance to water and chemicals; withstands thermal shock of 180°F water
	Polyurethane		For less aesthetic areas; may be toxic to animals until cured; thermosetting	$0.75–$1.00	Used as finish coats; excellent resistant to water, acids, oil, solvents, and staining
	Furan	Chemical areas	Primer required; brittle, thermosetting	Not available	Good chemical resistance
	Polysulfide	Wet areas	Low abrasion resistance; thermosetting	Not available	
	Silicone		Affected by chemicals and impact; primer required; thermosetting	Not available	Used for coating; flexible, abrasion and moisture resistant
	Acrylics		Not for permanently wet areas; two-coat application; requires a vapor barrier; thermoplastic	$2–$4	Nontoxic; short curing time at temperature of −10° to 104°F; chemical resistant; recoating easy; abrasion and impact resistant; chemical and mechanical bond to concrete

Table 3.7-1. (Continued)

Material Type	Areas of Use	Material Composition	Limitations and Characteristics	Cost[†]/sq.ft (1989)	Remarks
		Mastics	Low chemical resistance; softens at temperature over 125°F; not for heavy loads; needs primer, thermoplastic	$3–$5	Resurfacing material over concrete; low cost; built-up flooring to create slope to drain; flexible, resilient; good for wet areas
		Elastomeric	Low impact resistant; requires sound substrate; polyurethane product; thermoplastic	$1.75–2.25	Laboratories, animal quarters; resilient; thermal shock resistant
	Cold rooms and freezers	Polyacrylate	Not chemical resistant; thermosetting	$3.25–$3.75	Resistant to water and thermal shock; nontoxic, nonflammable
	Conductive floor areas	Epoxy thin-set terrazzo	Thermosetting	$8–$12	Excellent appearance
		Neoprene	Thermosetting		
		Epoxy	Thermosetting		Available with spark-proof and antistatic finishes

*Base material is assumed to be above-grade reinforced concrete unless otherwise noted.

[†]These prices are intended as guides only. Prices vary depending on the location, size of the project, and application. Verify local costs.

more difficult to apply, but in general are superior in quality.

Thermoplastic matrices include silicone, acrylics and mastics. Silicones are synthetic chemicals, acrylics are polymers and mastic is an asphalt emulsion product.

Self-leveling, seamless flooring is easiest to install and requires the least final surface work but will not hide cracks in the substrate. Trowel-finished flooring can be built up from 1/8 to 2 in. to create slopes to drains. Various coatings are applied over the troweled finish to arrive at the required anti-slip finish. See Figure 3.7-8.

All entries in Table 3.7-1 have chemical composition. Elastomeric is a property of a material. Elastomers can be formed from epoxies, polysulfides, polyurethanes, silicones, acrylics or other chemical types. In general, if the material is thermoplastic, it will have lower wear and resistance properties than a thermoset of the same chemical type. Polyurethanes are among the highest abrasion-resistant elastomeric materials and therefore are well suited for floorings. Modern polyurethane elastomers are also thermosetting materials. Some are moisture cured, and others are two-part chemical cured, using polyols or polyamines.

Seamless flooring in cold rooms and wet animal rooms is particularly difficult to deal with. Figures 3.7-9 and 3.7-10 show the suggested applications.

Seamless flooring materials generally have a lower flame-spread rating (25) than sheet products. They are typically in the Class A range, which is up to 25. Resilient flooring in the Class B range is up to 75 and in the Class C range is above 75.

Substrate Preparation

The substrate for all flooring must be clean; smooth; free of loose particles, oil, paints and grease; and permanently dry, i.e., containing no more than 16% moisture for seamless floors and 3% moisture for resilient floors on a fully cured slab. Any cracks must be filled and glazed surfaces etched or sandblasted. Concrete curing compounds must be removed because they may interfere with the bonding of adhesives. An effective vapor barrier is required beneath the substrate for slabs in contact with the ground or floors located above warm, damp areas such as laundries, baths, and cage and glasswash rooms.

Membrane waterproofing is recommended for wet areas where water damage may occur on lower floors. It has a neoprene latex composition with a fabric reinforce-

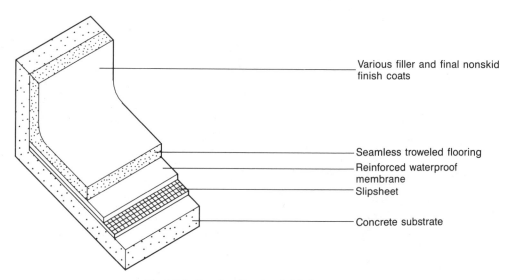

Various filler and final nonskid finish coats

Seamless troweled flooring
Reinforced waterproof membrane
Slipsheet

Concrete substrate

Fig. 3.7-8. Seamless flooring finish for wet areas.

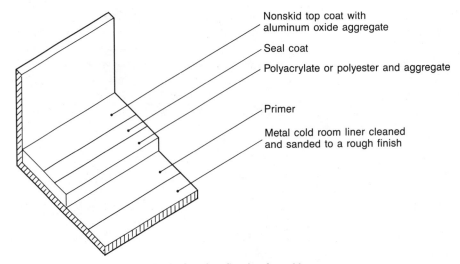

Nonskid top coat with
aluminum oxide aggregate

Seal coat

Polyacrylate or polyester and aggregate

Primer

Metal cold room liner cleaned
and sanded to a rough finish

Fig. 3.7-9. Seamless flooring for cold room.

ment, either a fiberglass matting or a rot-
and fungus-resistant jute fabric. Any cracks
must be filled before application. The rein-
forcement strengthens the membrane but
also makes it less elastic.

A membrane vapor barrier is recommended for slabs on grade to prevent soil

moisture from migrating up and below the
flooring finish. Damage may occur because
of the moisture affecting the flooring material or the adhesive or causing salts from the
earth to be deposited below and affect the
flooring material.

The membrane must be compatible with

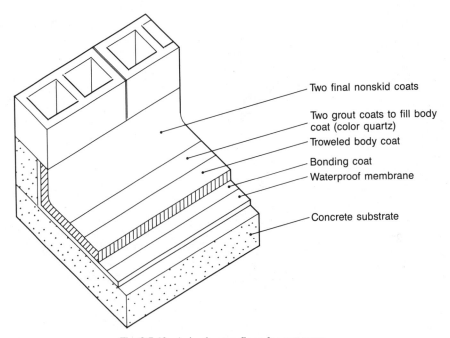

Two final nonskid coats

Two grout coats to fill body
coat (color quartz)

Troweled body coat

Bonding coat

Waterproof membrane

Concrete substrate

Fig. 3.7-10. Animal room floor for wet areas.

Table 3.7-2. Suggested Laboratory Interior Wall Finishes

Material Type	Conditions of Substrate	Conditions of Use	Primer	Top Coat	Remarks
Water based	Moist	Concrete masonry, gypsum wallboard	Acrylic	Acrylic	Water vapor permeable
			Polyvinyl acetate	Acrylic, two-part epoxy modified	Longer life and better stain resistance
			Polyvinyl acetate	Polyvinyl acetate	Water vapor permeable, excellent chemical resistance
	Dry	Wood doors	Styrene-butadiene	Polyvinyl acetate or acrylic	Over porous block
			Urethane, one-part moisture-cure	Same	Over stain; Seal doors to prevent moisture absorption
		Metal doors	Acrylic	Same	
			Acrylic, two-part epoxy modified	Same	
Solvent based	Dry	Masonry	Styrene-butadiene	Alkyd	Primer to fill porous surface; alkyd should not be used under alkaline conditions
		Gypsum wallboard	Alkyd	Alkyd	Poor permeability to moisture; solvent-based coat directly over gypsum wallboard will raise the nap of the paper
			Acrylic	Acrylic	Impermeable to water vapor
		Wet conditions	Chlorinated rubber	Same	Good resistance to microorganisms; damaged by solvents
		Wet areas	Epoxy	Same	Abrasion, water, alkali, chemical resistant; good adhesion to concrete
			Phenolic	Same	Good chemical resistance; use may be restricted (considered carcinogenic)
Chemical or moisture cure	Dry	Heavy-duty areas	Urethane	Same	Chemical, stain resistant; poor adhesion to concrete
		Wood and metal doors	Alkyd	Same	Clear, over-stain or opaque
Prefabricated PVC sheets	Dry	Wet areas	None	None	Impervious to water vapor, microorganisms; water and chemical resistant

Table 3.7-3. Suggested Laboratory Lay-in Ceiling Finishes

Areas of Use	Base Material	Finish	Remarks
Laboratories	Mineral wool		
	Fiberglass	Vinyl film	
	Fiberglass	Factory painted	Noncorrosive areas
High-humidity areas	Antibacteria-treated perlite	Aluminum clad with baked enamel	Perforated or unperforated
Clean areas	Mineral wool fiber	Plastic over-spray	

the flooring material and should be installed by the flooring contractor to avoid warranty problems.

3.7.3 Wall Finishes (See Table 3.7-2)

Wall finishes in laboratory facilities must usually be of a better grade than in office buildings because of the corrosive atmosphere and the cleaning with disinfectants. For special-purpose laboratories for containment, animal facilities and other high-humidity areas, wall finishes must be more specialized to withstand the demands put upon them.

The finish coat must be compatible with the primer, which in turn must be compatible with the substrate. The substrate for laboratory facilities is most often gypsum wallboard and concrete masonry units, but it may also be concrete at columns and other structural elements or existing finishes which must be refinished. Any substrate which includes Portland cement is alkaline and contains moisture. The coating on such materials must therefore withstand these. A water-based coating such as acrylic can be applied over masonry. Solvent-based coatings such as alkyl must be applied over a dry surface such as gypsum wallboard. A solvent-based finish coat must not be applied over a water-based primer because it will delaminate if moisture dissolves or loosens the primer.

Bond breaker compounds used on concrete forms must be removed before coatings are applied.

Table 3.7-2 covers interior finishes for different types of areas. Other factors dealing with color retention or appearance are not included.

3.7.4 Ceiling Finishes

Ceiling finishes for laboratory facilities are primarily on gypsum wallboard or of the lay-in tile type. The finishes on solid ceilings are basically the same as on walls. Lay-in tiles are noted on Table 3.7-3.

The discussion of ceilings versus no ceilings is covered in the introduction.

REFERENCES

Sweet's Selection Data. 1981. *Coatings.* New York: McGraw-Hill.

Sweet's Selection Data. 1981. *Flooring.* New York: McGraw-Hill, page 47.

3.8 NUISANCE FACTORS   *T. Ruys*

Section 2.9 dealt with risk assessment in regard to potential loss of life or property. This section assesses how much inconvenience in lost time and research data can be tolerated. These factors constitute a nuisance rather than a hazard, but they affect laboratory operations in significant ways.

The performance of many laboratory instruments is affected by building and utility constraints. The laboratory planner must minimize these constraints within the limitations of the client's budget.

The best procedure is to verify the user's equipment selection and to consult with the manufacturer about special requirements. Following are some of the more common nuisances and their limits that may serve as a guide.

3.8.1 Water Pressure Drop

Water pressure in the lines may fluctuate considerably if large volumes of water are drawn off downstream for fire fighting or similar high water use activity. This may cause problems for water-cooled equipment or, worse, back-siphoning into the water system. The latter can be prevented with a backflow preventer, but the water pressure should not be allowed to drop below 40 psig no matter what floor the outlet is on. The way to prevent this is to provide adequate pipe sizes, to alternate water sources for large users or to install booster pumps.

3.8.2 Drafts

Some laboratory operations are very temperature sensitive and should not be located where airflow will be aimed at them directly. For example, a balance table or microtome should not be located directly under an air diffuser. The makeup air from an auxiliary fumehood may also be a nuisance because it may cause a draft on the fumehood operator. To minimize the discomfort, the air temperature should be between 74° and 76°F at 50% relative humidity but no less than 65°F.

3.8.3 Dust

Many laboratory operations are adversely affected by dust. Although most laboratory buildings are under positive air pressure, or should be, dust is a problem because of the large air volumes moved through these buildings. Besides a good maintenance program for the air intake filters, it is helpful to locate the building air intake off the ground and away from the building air exhaust. For laboratory buildings, the air infiltration rate should be 80%. Table 3.8-1 specifies the environment desirable for critical laboratory instruments.

3.8.4 Noxious Odors

Many laboratory operations also produce odors. Ovens, furnaces, autoclaves, and glassware washers produce much heat, smoke, steam, vapors and fumes which are not necessarily hazardous but produce a load on the air conditioning system and are often unpleasant. Most of these are the result of operations which require heat, and heated gases rise. The most immediate solution, therefore, is to capture the gases through a hood located over the operation.

According to the *Industrial Ventilation Manual* (1986), the capture velocity at the hood rim, in order to be effective, must be at least 50–500 fpm for various conditions of release velocity and cross-drafts. The hood must also be large and deep enough to hold the heated gases until they can be exhausted. See Figure 3.8-1.

3.8.5 Temperature Variations

More and more laboratory equipment is affected by fluctuations in room temperature. At the same time, there is a greater concern to conserve energy. In order to keep temperatures within an acceptable range, it is important to know what those ranges are. Table 3.8-2 was provided by product manufacturers as a guide.

Many instruments are internally cooled by chilled water that is recirculated or disposed to the drain to prevent overheating. These are not affected by room temperature fluctuations.

3.8.6 Vibration

Many pieces of equipment do not perform at capacity when subjected to vibration. See

Table 3.8-1. Clean Environment Classification for Laboratory Equipment

Equipment	Clean Room Classification	Remarks
Stereo microscopes	Class 100	Used in PCB and industrial applications
Ultra microscopes, clinical and research microscopes	Class 1,000	Use usually dictates classification
N/A	Class 10,000	N/A

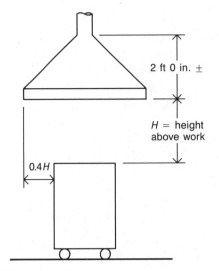

$Q = 1.4\ P \times H \times V,$
    Where:
    Q = air flow in cfm
    P = perimeter of the cart or tank below the hood
    V = capture velocity, (range, 50–500 fpm),
        depending on low-velocity release without
        cross-drafts to moderate-velocity release
        with cross-drafts.

Fig. 3.8-1. Canopy hood airflow requirements (AC-GIH, 1986).

Section 5.2. Vibration is measured in cycles per second (CPS). Vibration isolation pneumatic air tables should be considered for all sensitive equipment; some electronic balances use a digital filter to provide a stable display in the presence of external vibrations. A study by the National Institute of Health found that when the vibration level is in the range of 10^{-4} g, the performance of

many electron microscopes is impaired. That corresponds to an amplitude of 2 to 3 micro-in. at a frequency of 20 cps.

3.8.7 Magnetic Field

Electrical cables generate a magnetic field which affects some equipment. Table 3.8-3 gives the suggested distance from electrical panels, cable shafts, bus ducts and elevators. The nuclear magnetic resonance unit must be remote from ferrous metal including reinforcing bars, conduits, drains, etc. The distance depends on the ferrous object and the strength of the magnet. See Appendix G.

3.8.8 Electrical Interference

There are three types of electrical interference: voltage drop, spikes and interruptions. Table 3.8-4 lists some of the laboratory equipment affected by these problems. The remedies are as follows:

- Voltage drop can be minimized or eliminated by oversizing electrical cables or by eliminating other large, interruptible loads such as those of motors from the circuit. Equipment sensitive to voltage drop should have a direct line to the transformer switch gear.
- Spikes in electrical circuits are caused by transient voltage fluctuations. They are eliminated by installing proper voltage regulation.
- Interruptions can be in the power supply or due to a short circuit in the line.

Table 3.8-2. Acceptable Temperature Range for Laboratory Equipment

Equipment	Range (°F)	Remarks
Most instruments	59–100	Below 85% RH
Electron microscope	68–74	45% RH ± 10%; Rate change not to exceed 5.4°F per hour; no drafts.
Scintillation counter	54–86	Below 85% RH
Research microscope	70–76	50% RH optimum; no drafts
Microtome	—	Depends on use
Spectrophotometer	64–86	Rate change not to exceed 1.8°F per hour; 50% RH or less
Gas chromatograph/mass spectro meter (GC/MS)	50–85	20–90% RH

Table 3.8-3. Suggested Distance From Electrical Panels, Electrical Cable Shaft, Bus Ducts, Elevator Shafts and Rotating Machinery

Equipment	Distance	Remarks
Electron microscope	10	Including distance to other electron microscopes; check manufacturer's instructions
Nuclear magnetic resonance equipment	21–45 ft minimum in any direction from center of magnet for major ferrous objects	

Equipment that cannot be without power for long periods of time should be on emergency power. Equipment that cannot be without power at any time must have an uninterruptible power source.

3.8.9 Noise

Noise can be generated inside or outside a space. Sound is measured in decibels on three scales, A, B and C. The A, B, and C weighting describes three alternative frequency-response characteristics used for measuring sound levels. They are formally defined in the *American National Standard Specification for Sound Level Meters*. In practice, they are obtained by utilizing weighting networks usually built into sound level meters. Each network selectively discriminates against low and high frequencies, with A weighting providing the greatest reduction in the low frequencies and C weighting providing the least. The purpose of weighting sound pressure level measurements is to correlate apparent loudness, as perceived by humans, with the level measured by a sound level meter. All frequencies are not perceived equally by the ear; there is less sensitivity to low-frequency sound. The A, B and C weighting were developed in accordance with experimentally derived equal-loudness contours. The A weighting is by far the most commonly used of the three scales; it is common practice to assume that a sound level is A weighted if not otherwise specified. Table 3.8-5 shows acceptable limits for various spaces in a laboratory building. The noise criteria (NC) is a single numerical index commonly used to define design goals for the maximum allowable noise in a given space. They primarily apply to the noise produced by a ventilation system, but they may be applied to other noise sources. The NC criteria consist of a family of curves that define the maximum allowable octave-band sound pressure level corresponding to a chosen NC design goal. Although alternate contours have been proposed (most notably the room criterion or RC curves), the NC criteria remain the most widely accepted.

Table 3.8-4. Electrical Interference Precautions for Laboratory Equipment

Equipment	Separate Circuit	Spike Filter	Emergency Power	Uninterruptible Power*	Special Ground
Electron microscope	X	X			X
Computer	X	X		X	
EEG and EKG equipment	X				X
Liquid scintillation counter	X	X		X	X
Deep freezer			X		
Incubator			X		
GC/MS		X			

*May be included with equipment; check with the manufacturer.

Table 3.8-5. Acceptable Limits of Noise

| | Noise Limits in Decibels | | | Noise Criterion |
Space	A Scale	B Scale	C Scale	(NC)*
Lab office	43	53	60	35
Laboratory	52	61	67	45
Instrument room	48	57	64	40
Contr.-temp. room	52	61	67	45
Darkroom	43	53	60	35
Glasswash	52	61	67	45

*NC curves are the generally accepted method of specifying a background noise level in a given space.

Many laboratory operations generate noise, some of which can be minimized by:

- Moving noise-producing equipment (e.g., freezers, refrigerators, incubators and centrifuges) from the laboratory to an equipment room.
- Locating compressors for controlled-temperature rooms remotely.
- Providing acoustical treatment on ceilings and walls.
- Providing sound dampers, bends in the ducts or other means to reduce air noise in ventilation ducts or oversizing the ducts in order to reduce air speed.
- Locating fumehood fans remotely, if possible, and providing flexible connections between fans and ducts.

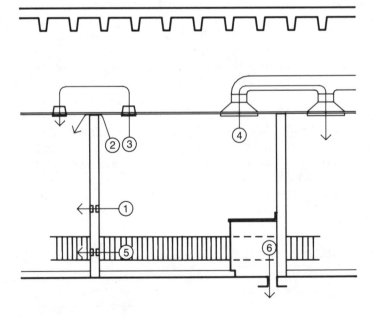

① through back-to-back electrical outlets
② between partition and ceiling
③ through light fixtures
④ through diffusers on a common duct
⑤ through perimeter heating cabinets
⑥ through piping sleeves in the floor

Fig. 3.8-2. Pathways of noise transmissions.

Sometimes the contrast in a very quiet space, such as the humming of fluorescent lights in a controlled-temperature room, is disturbing. Specifying a sound-rated ballast will overcome that problem.

When the noise is generated outside the space, there is another set of solutions:

- Eliminate all openings between the noise source and the receiver. Figure 3.8-2 shows some of these problems. If the noise is severe, sound insulation can be included in the partition, a double partition can be provided or a heavier material such as masonry can be specified.

REFERENCES

American Conference of Governmental Industrial Hygienists, 1986. *Industrial Ventilation Manual.* Cincinnati, OH: Committee on Industrial Ventilation.
American National Standard Specification for Sound Level Meters, 1971. *ANSI* S1.4.

3.9 DESIGN TO ENHANCE COMMUNICATION *T. Ruys*

3.9.1 Reasons for Poor Communication in Laboratory Facilities

Most laboratory facilities today do not enhance communication. Laboratory spaces are small, enclosed by walls and doors, and arranged in a linear fashion along a corridor so that there is also no visual contact.

The plan layout is most often arranged for the efficiency of the staff: offices next to labs; equipment rooms close to labs; administration in a separate wing or on a lower floor. That arrangement is equipment and facilities oriented rather than people oriented and results in spreading individuals apart.

There have been some attempts to delete walls so that staff members are aware of each other and can visually ascertain that an individual is present.

The reasons for the arrangement discussed above will now be presented.

Cost and Facilities Constraints

- A simple life cycle cost (LCC) analysis makes it immediately clear that over the life of a building, personnel costs far exceed the costs of maintaining, operating and even building a laboratory facility (see Figure 8.7-1). There is therefore the obvious desire to make the facility as staff efficient as possible, which results in spreading investigators apart.
- Laboratories are low-density/space-intensive facilities. It is not physically possible to place staff members in close proximity.

Institutional Resistance

- Many companies and institutions have a large investment in traditional laboratory facilities and are not able to add or renovate large enough areas to make a new arrangement possible. Renovations often are piecemeal as programs terminate or faculty members leave.
- Many academic institutions believe that, as a part of their recruitment effort, it is essential to have space enclosed with walls and a door and, most important, a key to turn over to the much-sought-after recruit. This becomes a highly symbolic act which denotes commitment and eliminates ambiguity: "The space behind that door is yours; you control it."

Investigators' Resistance

- Most laboratory users have been educated and trained in traditional facilities and are hesitant to accept unfamiliar layouts. There is a certain amount of traditional stagnation in the laboratory "culture."
- As a nation, we pride ourselves on the fact that we are individualistic people who distrust authority. This notion finds its greatest expression among "researchers" or "investigators." These labels themselves express this notion.

The extreme competition among investigators for honors, with the more recent development of commercial potential and associated riches, does not encourage cooperation. In fact, the opposite is often true: many do not trust their fellow investigators, maintenance staff or housekeeping personnel. This attitude is manifested not only in having enclosed and locked laboratories but also separate (duplicate) equipment, cold rooms, glasswash facilities, etc., close by and under one's control. This arrangement spreads people even farther apart.

- There seems to be a conflict: Many bright investigators seek out institutions which represent the skills and direction they are interested in, but communication with their peers is cumbersome at best. Besides, close contact may not be desirable because it may be perceived as working for a "mentor," which is hardly the path to a Nobel Prize.

Technicians' Resistance

- Technicians do not like visually open areas because they often feel that they are being watched or on display.

3.9.2 The Dynamics of Communications in Buildings

There is hope, however. Investigators have found ways to communicate during semiannual rituals or meetings. These gatherings are considered so important that the federal government has at times taken the initiative to organize them. The preceding sections explain why barriers are created, but these are by no means good reasons. Few individuals will argue with the notion that communication is good for a laboratory operation if for no other reason than to improve safety.

There is no doubt that when like-minded individuals talk to each other, great feats can be accomplished, especially combined with the right resources. The Manhattan Project and the project to place men on the moon are two well-known and impressive examples. Technology transfer is another aim of government policy today.

Industrial R&D laboratories, well aware of this potential, have for some time made attempts to encourage architectural innovations to enhance communication. It is a little easier for industry, as a condition of employment, to dictate how employees will work. Industry also has most to gain from new ideas, new patents and new technology.

Before mentioning what has been done or exploring what could be done, we should remind ourselves how physical facilities affect our behavior and inhibit communications. Winston Churchill has been quoted as saying: "We create our facilities and our facilities create us." Architects, by training, are good with pictures but poor with words. It is probably for that reason that nonarchitects have contributed most to our understanding of architecturally induced behavior. Sommers (1969) wrote about personal space, but it is T. J. Allen (1975) who made a career of doing research on communication in facilities.

Allen points out that communication drops off dramatically with distance, as shown in Figure 3.9-1. That by itself seems an obvious conclusion. What is surprising, however, is that communication by telephone replaces face-to-face communication only up to a point. This is particularly surprising given the prevailing notion among facilities designers that the telephone overcomes distance and remoteness. An often seen AT&T commercial suggests that to "touch someone you love" can overcome distance across a continent.

That may be acceptable between relatives, but it won't do in industry or academia, where the communication is nonverbal as well as verbal. A gesture, a gaze or a raised eyebrow are signals we want to observe for certain types of exchanges.

This means that the telephone is helpful for some exchanges, but if all communications must be made by phone because of distance, communication ceases. The surest proof of this fact is the volume of air traffic.

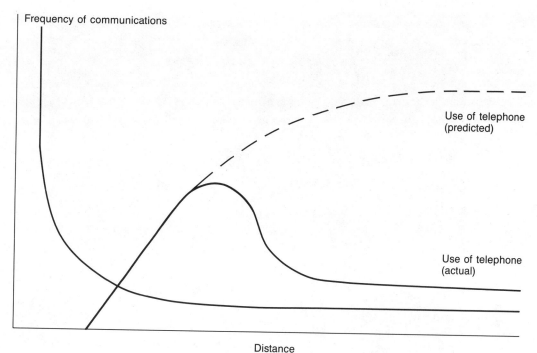

Frequency of communications

Use of telephone
(predicted)

Use of telephone
(actual)

Distance

Fig. 3.9-1. The effect of distance on communications (T. J. Allen)

People will go to great lengths and travel great distances in order to meet face to face.

Allen (1975) also points out that this perceived distance is both horizontal and vertical, as well as incremental in nature. It appears that after a floor area exceeds 9,800 sq m, additional floors will decrease the perceived distance. However, he also found that the increment is from one to four floors and that the distance between people on different floors is always greater in two- or three-story building than in four-story buildings with the same floor area. The next increment to five-story buildings does not occur until a total of 17,000 sq m of floor area is reached. This is an oversimplification, and the reader is encouraged to read the full text of this interesting article.

3.9.3 How to Improve Communication in Laboratory Facilities

If communication is important, the obvious conclusion seems to be to keep distances as short as possible and to force people to be-

come aware of each other. In laying out physical facilities that is not as easy as it seems, even when discounting the various code constraints and overcoming the resistance of individuals mentioned earlier.

The first step, however, is to find out who talks to whom and to analyze the various levels and types of communication. There seem to be three levels and types:

- Level A: between principal investigators relating ideas and practical experiences.
- Level B: between people as members of an organization, which encourages an esprit de corps.
- Level C: between individuals of the research team to facilitate cooperation, share facilities and keep costs down.

The most immediate and obvious need is for level C communication, and this is the type best accommodated in most facility layouts. Level B communication can be accommodated in lunch rooms, at Christmas parties, and at summer picnics. Level A

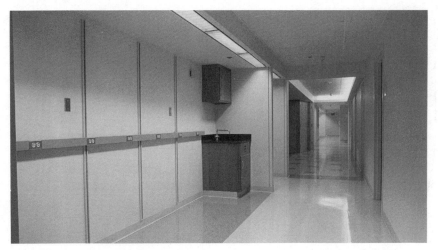

Fig. 3.9-2. Nook for informal standup impromptu meetings (Edwards Calderon).

communication is the most difficult to accommodate because it appears to be based on both subjective feelings and objective criteria, or design and planning. Nonarchitects can help with the planning; it is the architects who have to do the design: to create an environment where individuals feel comfortable and want to spend time. We all have our favorite bistro, coffee shop or terrace cafe. Even investigators are not immune to these feelings and, like all people, are affected by them, although as a group they are the first to deny the need. This is not because they believe it themselves but because of the fear that these "frills" will reduce their research space. To their credit, we must admit that there is no correlation between good research and good (architectural) space. Some of the best research has come out of the worst facilities. The Curies did their research in Paris, in what might be classified as a garage; the xerography process was developed in a space little larger than a closet at the Battelle Research Laboratories in Columbus, Ohio—and an ugly closet at that. Researchers will put up with almost any environment because their focus is primarily their work and secondarily the space they work in. This is not true of technicians, who spend more time in the laboratory, are not at liberty to move around and often do routine work all day long.

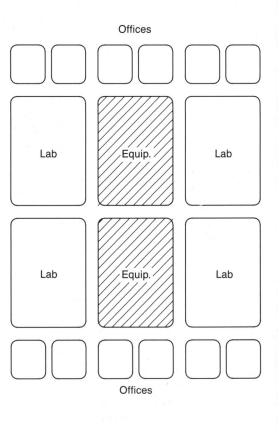

Fig. 3.9-3. Traditional laboratory plan. Crosshatched area: level C: shared equipment focus.

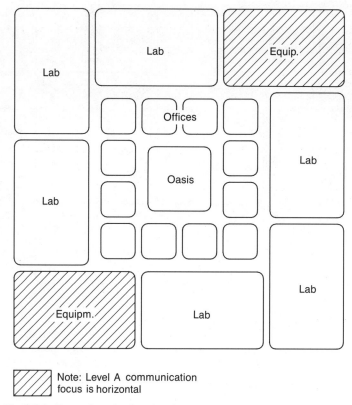

Note: Level A communication focus is horizontal

Fig. 3.9-4. Research oasis plan. Level A communication focus is horizontal.

What have we learned, and how can architectural design make a difference? We have learned that:

- Level A communication between principal investigators is the most difficult to accommodate.
- This type of communication must be provided at no cost or at reduced cost to the investigator in order to be acceptable.

Architectural design can make a difference:

- By questioning the reasons for partitions and providing lower-cost alternatives to satisfy those needs. Partitions provide security, keep contaminants in and noise out, and serve many other valid purposes. Many of these needs can be satisfied without creating barriers.

- By creating impromptu meeting nooks, informal gathering places with a white board and a coffee pot. See Figure 3.9-2. These nooks must be convenient to the laboratories or they will not be used.
- By creating laboratories with a feeling of openness with the aid of relites, natural light, an atrium and vistas. People are very reluctant to enter enclosed spaces perceived as belonging to others. Our territorial behavior is still very strong, but so is our need to belong to a group. If we can see individuals we are more likely to include them in our group. We are also more likely to express curiosity, offer assistance, share ideas or even borrow a test tube or two.
- By creating gathering spaces outside the laboratory. People have to take a break once in a while, and they must eat— which in most instances is not allowed

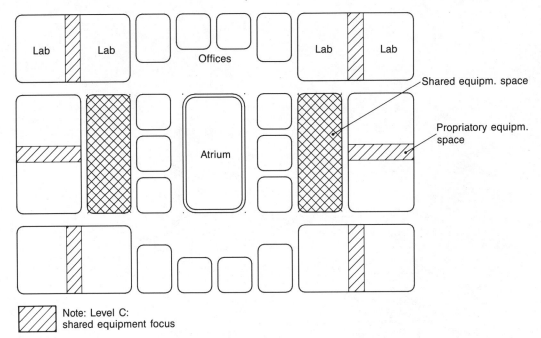

Fig. 3.9-5. Diagrammatic plan—Wexner Center for Pediatric Research (architect: BOHM/NBBJ). Levels A and C: communication focus and shared equipment focus—communication horizontal and vertical.

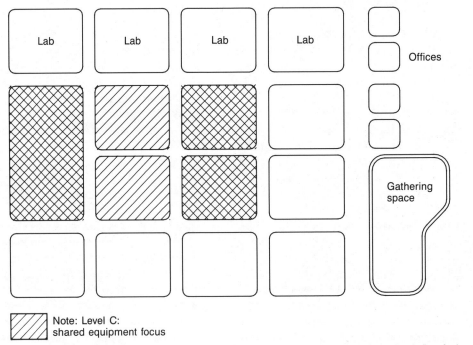

Fig. 3.9-6. Diagrammatic plan—Whitehead Institute (architects: Goody Clancy & Associates, Inc.). Levels A and C: communication focus and shared equipment focus.

Fig. 3.9-7. Atrium to enhance communications between floors. Exterior and interior views (BOHM/NBBJ)

in the laboratory. The design of these spaces can make all the difference in how they are used. See Section 3.4. All that has been said so far does not mean that planning cannot be helpful.

- By discussing and establishing the size of the research group and by concentrating on the desired interaction within the group which can consist of several investigators focusing on the same research area or interdisciplinary problem to be solved. This will establish and may be limited to the size of a floor or building footprint.

- By planning the equivalent of a "research oasis" around the watering hole or coffee pot, thus getting away from the traditional linear arrangement. See Figures 3.9-3 and 3.9-4. These plans create a communications focus on a horizontal level.

- By creating both a horizontal and a vertical or three-dimensional focus for communications. Figures 3.9-5 and 3.9-6 record, in a diagrammatic way, successful examples of how this was accomplished on two research laboratory

Fig. 3.9-8. Circulation space inside a laboratory suite. Sit-down spaces on the left are open to laboratories on the right (Theodorus Ruys).

projects. Figure 3.9-7 shows a photograph of the atrium space of the Wexner Center for Pediatric Research, Columbus, Ohio. By penetrating the building box vertically, the atrium creates a sense of place, community and participation because of the visual and auditory contact it provides. the laboratory suites on either side of the office area are also left as open as possible by removing the doors, which can be added if necessary, Level A communications in this facility are enhanced by locating investigators' offices around the atrium, while instruments and shared equipment are conveniently located next to the laboratories.

The Whitehead Institute, Cambridge, Mass., has the same concept in a somewhat different configuration. The investigators' offices are clustered around a two-story gathering space/lounge, which also includes an open stair that allows easy movement between two floors at the time. The laboratories are next to the offices, and the instrument rooms between laboratories located in the center. Shared equipment, cold rooms and glasswash areas are at the other end. Service elevators and public elevators are at opposite ends of the building, separating visitors and supplies.

3.9.4 The Effect of Space Flexibility on Communications

In corporate organizations, individuals are often moved in order to acquire skills and be exposed to new company environments, but also to become a part of the corporate culture. The same can be done in the corporate laboratory culture by moving individuals. A flexible laboratory design is necessary for such an approach (see Chapter 3) in order that new functions and group settings can be accommodated easily and at the least cost.

3.9.4 Conclusion

In planning and designing laboratory facilities where communication is considered important, the following must be kept in mind:

- Consider the level of communications and the individuals involved.

- Locate the center of gravity for these individuals on that level.
- Organize meeting places around this center of gravity.
- Make meeting places pleasant areas to use.

REFERENCES

Allen T. J., and Fustfeld, A. R., 1975. Research Laboratory Architecture and the Structuring of Communications. *R&D Management,* Vol. 5, No. 2, pp. 153–163.

Sommer, R., 1969. *Personal Space: The Behavioral Basis of Design.* Englewood Cliffs, NJ: Prentice-Hall.

3.10 SECURITY *T. Ruys*

3.10.1 Introduction

Security means many things. At times it is considered loss prevention, including fire detection and suppression and loss of life prevention through evacuation planning. In this section, the security of laboratory personnel and property is addressed. Laboratory facilities security problems are:

- Theft and destruction from the outside, including data.
- Destruction of evidence in forensic laboratories.
- Theft by insiders, i.e., drugs, expensive equipment, etc.
- Intruders can include spies, saboteurs, terrorists, burglars (forced entry), robbers (threat to individuals), vandals and rioters. Insiders can, of course, also commit crimes of this nature—most commonly theft, but also rape and assault.

Laboratory property includes chemicals, equipment and information that may lead to patents or products.

Security for laboratory facilities is generally grossly inadequate, particularly in public institutions, because of the conflict between the public's rights of access and the need for security. Many private companies also face a conflict between the need to maintain an image and the need to protect their interests.

A few words about the principles of security. Stormes (1979) points out that in order for an individual to commit a theft, three conditions must exist:

- The desire for the object.
- The ability to commit the crime.
- The opportunity to do so.

All of these conditions must occur at the same time. The obvious solution is to make the last one, the opportunity, very difficult, since desire and ability cannot be controlled.

The first step in planning for security is to analyze what type of security and what equipment are needed. The following sections deal with planning, types of security and available equipment.

3.10.2 Planning for Security

In planning for security, the objectives are to reduce risk and losses to an acceptable level.

The first way to accomplish this is to make an inventory of what needs to be secured. The second way is to determine what type of security and associated equipment are best suited to meet this need. The third way is to analyze the cost of the security provided against the potential loss and decide on the level of security to be implemented.

Walsh (1979) points out that there are several ways to prevent a loss:

- By preventing access to the secured object or at least making access very difficult and increasing the risk of detection.
- By removing the object which is in need of protection.
- By increasing the time needed for removal by creating multiple barriers and checkpoints.
- By stopping the loss after it has started before it has left the secured area.

Based on these principles, Walsh devised a risk logic tree, which has been modified by this author to apply to laboratory facilities. See Table 3.10-1.

Table 3.10-1. Risk Logic Tree

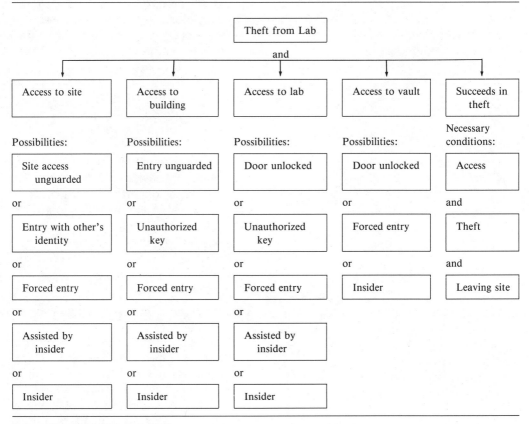

Source: Adapted after Timothy J. Walsh.

In order for a loss to occur, several events must take place (and) or other options must be available (or). By analyzing the events in a particular situation, it is more likely that all possibilities will be reviewed and all preventive measures taken. The logic tree allows for the potential loss from the inside, from the outside, or with the aid of insiders, and is a means to identify countermeasures and associated equipment.

An important aspect of security is to ensure the cooperation of the employees. Not only can they provide important suggestions on how to improve security, they become a part of the prevention by serving as checkpoints. However, the most important role of employees is in responding when security has been breached: checking the identity of strangers, responding to alarms, securing doors, reporting unusual occurrence and losses. Personnel have to be made security conscious and asked to cooperate.

Early on, the decision must be made on whether to have a high- or low-profile system. Perimeter systems may be very visible to deter intrusion or hidden. The best security against insiders it to make personnel aware of multiple security systems without revealing their details.

Another important aspect of planning is to match the system with the anticipated volume and flow of traffic. Frustrated employees will bypass systems or at times vandalize them.

Finally, the cost of potential losses must be estimated, including replacement, loss of

Table 3.10-2. Checklist for Planning a Security Access System

☐ Type of facility: R&D, quality control lab, clinical, teaching, academic research, other
☐ Authorized system access: how many individuals, grouping
☐ Visitors: how many individuals per day
☐ Objects or items needing protection: chemicals, equipment, data, etc.
☐ Cost of potential loss: inventory of potential loss and associated replacement cost
☐ Potential security threats: terrorists, activists, theft and burglary, vandals, etc.
☐ Operating vulnerability: public access, large areas, multiple access points, etc.
☐ Hours of system operation: 24-hour, after hours, days of week, holidays
☐ Reliability: fail-safe, vandal-proof, control check
☐ Backup system: emergency power, central monitor, guard
☐ Identity check intruder:* yes/no and type
☐ Printed record of intrusion:* yes/no and type
☐ Door groupings: by department, research group, number of doors
☐ Secondary system required: alarm, closed circuit television, intercom
☐ Coordination with other systems: vibration detection, motion detection, sound detection, etc.

*Intruder with the security system in place may be authorized or nonauthorized.

time, and loss of use of funds, and weighed against the cost of the security systems considered.

3.10.3 Types of Security

Combining the points discussed in the previous section, the security planning effort will be facilitated by thinking in terms of defense lines. The first line of defense from an intruder is the property line. This line can take the form of a barrier, fence or wall; illumination; guards; alarms; and closed circuit television. An important aspect of this first line of defense is the location of the site. The physical, social and political aspects of the neighborhood must be considered if a new location for the laboratory is planned.

The second line of defense is the building envelope and the protection of openings which penetrate this envelope.

The third line of defense is the laboratory space. Security typically takes the form of various locking devices.

The fourth line of defense is the protection of the asset itself through locked storage. The reverse, of course, is also true of an object leaving the premises; the last barrier becomes the first.

It is necessary to ask "What are we protecting?" in order to know which line or lines

of defense are most appropriate. Superimposed on these defense lines, which are physical in nature, is "procedural security":

- Checkpoints at each line by guards, receptionists, secretaries and lab technicians.
- Signing in and out, either physically or in a more reliable way through key access controls.

Two other issues must also be considered: reliability and redundancy. Reliability deals not only with functioning quality equipment and frequent checks but also with superimposing systems such as guards, locks, closed circuit television, etc., so that one system provides a check on another. The reliability of a system is a function of the rate of failure. An increase in the cost of a system is generally proportional to an increase in reliability. However, it is more cost effective to provide several lower-cost systems that are redundant than one very reliable and expensive system. Key card access control is a low-cost, low-reliability system, since the card may be unauthorized, but combined with a personal identification number (PIN) pad access code, the reliability has improved substantially. Combined with a fingerprint or signature reader, it is virtually tamper-proof for access control. Other means of entry are still possible, of course.

Redundancy is provided to make sure that each system continues to function, such as two power sources for the same system or an independent watch. Redundancy increases reliability.

3.10.4 Security Devices and Systems

There is a large selection of security equipment and devices. They are discussed in relation to the lines of defense against intrusion. It is important that these devices be convenient to use; otherwise, people will sabotage them, find ways to bypass them or vandalize them.

Many of these systems have alarms associated with them. These alarms may be local, with an immediate response; central—for instance, a silent alarm alerting a security control center; or outside the secured area, with an automatic dialing device alerting the police department or contract security force.

Property Line

Fences, gates and security guards are common for industrial complexes that include laboratories, but are not practical for freestanding R&D facilities and academic facilities.

Building Envelope

Electromechanical devices protect building openings with snap-action switches which, when shorted out or opened, activate an alarm. Other devices such as tape, foil, break-wire or pressure-sensitive mats can be used in lieu of switches. Pressure-sensitive devices can be hidden in entrance doormats and activate hidden cameras or a silent alarm. In conjunction with closed circuit television, they allow many entrances to be monitored after hours from a control center.

Surveillance cameras are used for deterrence and identification. They may be still cameras, activated by persons or as noted above; motion picture cameras, which are more expensive to install and operate but

provide more evidence; or television and video cameras for remote surveillance and recording.

Closed circuit television can be used with a manned command post, in conjunction with electromechanical devices, to verify the nature of the alarm. A door or gate control, during working hours, can be used along with closed circuit television and an intercom to admit authorized personnel at remote locations such as loading docks and receiving areas.

Keying systems of various types and levels of sophistication are available. The system that offers the greatest deterrent to insiders provides a computerized record of every use of a card key assigned to an individual.

A photoelectric light beam placed at the entrance to a facility can be deactivated by authorized personnel, by card, fingerprint or facial pattern recognition. This method can provide a friendly but secure atmosphere at a corporate R&D facility and ensure access in combination with a control desk.

Laboratory Space

Keyed access for laboratories can be the same as for building access but in addition can provide security after hours. There is a large selection of access control devices which will unlock secured areas with a wide price range and level of security. Besides the well-known card key system, there are devices based on computerized pattern recognition. The pattern may be an individual's fingerprint, hand geometry, retina or signature. These so-called biometric systems also include a device which will activate through voice verification. The advantages of these systems are that no card need be carried, identification cannot be transferred to others or stolen, and a high degree of reliability is provided.

Key cards themselves come in a variety of forms: magnetic dots or stripes and embedded tuned circuits. The latter is called a "proximity card" because it does not need to be passed through or in a slot and can be read by holding the card near a card reader.

Advantages are that the system is vandal- and weatherproof and cards can be read through cloth, leather, and plastic, which eliminates the need to remove them from a purse or billfold. See Figure 3.10-1, which shows the card reader built into a marble wall.

Not all key card systems can be integrated with other security systems. This may cause false alarms if key card entry does not deactivate other systems in place. To add an additional level of security, card keys can be provided with a secondary verification device such as a PIN pad or any of the biometric devices mentioned in this section. Key card systems can be provided with a "paper trail" documenting when and where certain cards were used. They can also be coded to allow access only to certain doors and restrict access to certain times.

An example of a possible scenario is shown in Figure 3.10-2 for a corporate R&D facility, showing examples of various types of protection and security systems.

Another system works on the principle of audio detection, which detects sound waves caused by breaking and entering or by a worker who stays after hours. This is not practical for academic facilities, where investigators may work any time during a 24-hour period or for high-noise level spaces.

Infrared motion detection devices are available for high-noise areas after hours. These devices are activated by a large heat-generating body such as a person. Other motion detectors use ultrasound waves or microwaves. The latter will detect motion through walls and other objects. This means that controlled areas must be shielded from the microwaves or false alarms will be caused by motions outside the secured area. That will raise the cost substantially.

Object Itself

The object that must be protected can be a chemical substance, an instrument or records. Locked drawers or files, with or without alarms, are, of course, the obvious solution. A common example is the narcotics drawer in clinical laboratories. A more sophisticated device is a trip wire, a snap-

Fig. 3.10-1. Proximity access control system standard (Schlage Electronics).

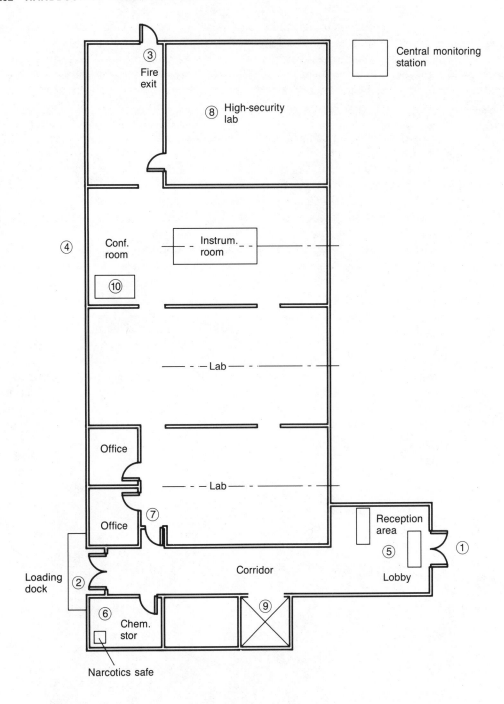

Building Perimeter
1. Card key access control with PIN pad and paper trail.
2. Telephone to reception area, closed circuit television and intercom, remote door release, key card access for working hours, no access after hours.
3. Alarm on fire exit, no access or exit at any time. Alarm monitored at central station.
4. Trip switches on operable windows, foil or vibration sensors on glazing. Activated after hours, coupled with intrusion alarm, monitored at central station.

Fig. 3.10-2. Hypothetical security system for a corporate R & D facility.

action switch electromechanical device, or a vibration detector which can be attached to expensive instruments after working hours.

Capacitance detection is also available. This system puts an electric charge on a metal object, which acts as an antenna. A capacitance coupling is formed between the antenna and an electrical ground. A person who approaches the protected object changes the capacitance, sounding an alarm.

Central Monitoring Station

Not every laboratory facility can justify a central monitoring station. At a minimum, every facility, including those of academic institutions, should have receptionist-controlled access and egress points during working hours; systems to monitor deliveries to the loading dock; and the ability to relay alarms to the appropriate security forces.

After hours, alarms can be monitored and responded to by a security contract agent who can be remotely located, even off site.

If a 24-hour occupied on-site central monitoring station is justified, it should:

- Monitor visitors' access and egress.
- Monitor personnel access and egress, including parking lot activities.
- Monitor loading dock and receiving areas.
- Monitor all incoming alarms and respond in an appropriate manner.

- Have two-way radio to communicate with patrolling security personnel.
- Have an intercom, closed circuit television, and remote access control to view access and egress points, communication with individuals, and allow entry.
- Have a paging system to instruct occupants in case of emergencies.
- A place to make keys, key cards, and ID cards.
- A toilet.
- For larger facilities, a security supervisor's office, which can be used to interrogate and to enter individual biometric data into the system.

In some emergencies, the ability to reach all the building's occupants quickly is crucial. This can be done through the standard existing telephone network with an automatic or manual dialing system. The alert may be a distinctive ring or a verbal recorded message. When the system is in operation, all normal telephone service is cut off. The alert can be routed to zones or designated areas. The monitoring panel shows which zones have been alerted and which phones have responded.

3.10.5 Conclusion

Only building owners and users can evaluate the value of their assets and the loss they are willing to sustain, but the selection of security systems should not be left to amateurs.

Laboratory Facility

5. Lobby: Pressure-sensitive mat which activates a still camera for identification.
6. Chemical storage: Key card access for authorized individuals during working hours only. Narcotics safe activated alarm located at secretary's desk during working hours and at central security after hours.
7. Laboratory suite: Key card access with paper trail after hours. Motion detector after hours, deactivated by authorized key card only. Silent alarm to central station. Closed circuit television if highly sensitive data are present. Intercom for identification of intruder.
8. High-security lab: Biometric access device; vibration detectors on walls, floor, and ceiling, activated at all times.
9. Elevator: Key controled.

Instruments

10. High-value instrument: Trip switch during working hours and vibration or capacitance detector after hours. Local alarm and monitored at central station.

The *Handbook of Building Security* edited by Peter S. Hopf (1979) contains a directory of security consultants. Verify if the consultant selected is a member of the American Society of Industrial Security and is a Certified Protection Professional.

This section has dealt only with security issues. Many security systems also monitor fire and smoke detectors, malfunctioning laboratory equipment, HVAC systems and the location of each alarm. It is highly recommended that the total facilities needs be considered and coordinated in the early stages of planning.

REFERENCES

Stormes, Hardy, Jr., 1979. Building Security Codes. *Handbook of Building Security,* Peter S. Hopf, ed. New York: McGraw-Hill.

Walsh, Timothy J., 1979. An Overview of Protection Systems. *Handbook of Building Security,* Peter S. Hopf, ed. New York: McGraw-Hill.

4

Laboratory Equipment
—Selection and Testing

4.1 INTRODUCTION *T. Ruys*

4.1.1 Equipment Planning

There is a great deal of confusion and misunderstanding among architects, planners and building owners or clients over who is responsible for equipment selection, budgeting and coordination. The following discussion may clarify these issues and assist in fee negotiations. See Table 4.1-1.

Group I Equipment—Fixed Equipment

This equipment is fixed or attached to the facilities by utilities and/or fasteners. Examples are laboratory casework, fumehoods, sterilizers, environmental rooms and Type II, Class B biological safety cabinets.

The laboratory planner typically selects and specifies this equipment after establishing the needs with the owner; the cost is included in the construction estimate. The planning fee is based on this estimate.

If the equipment is owner furnished or existing to be relocated, its value can be established. The planning fee is based on this estimate. However, the installation cost must be included in the construction cost estimate.

Group II Equipment—Major Movable Equipment and Furnishings

This equipment is not fixed and is typically depreciated over 5 years or more. Examples are refrigerators, centrifuges, ovens, furnaces and other floor-mounted equipment, including Type I, Class A biological safety cabinets.

The laboratory planner typically coordinates and provides space for this equipment and power requirements but does not select the items. Heat generated by this equipment must be accounted for in the HVAC design, and canopy hoods may need to be provided.

If the equipment occupies floor space, it is typically identified on the design development drawings with a dotted line. An equipment schedule may be helpful in coordinating power requirements.

The equipment owner is responsible for providing sizes, heat loads and utility requirements in a timely manner.

Coordination with several other consultants may be necessary. This may include an interior designer who selects furnishings such as desks, shelving, chairs and stools, and an equipment consultant who selects the laboratory equipment.

Table 4.1-1. Equipment Coordination

Phase	Task	Mechanical/Electrical/ Structural Coordination
Schematics	Equipment identification, cost estimate	
Design development	Equipment model selection	Utility connections, mechanical space
	Outline specification	requirements, access door location
	Check building and service access	and sizes
Contract documents	Detailed specifications	Utility and power sizes, mechanical/
	Installation details	electrical connection diagrams,
	Establish compressor sizes	canopy hood design
	Establish heat load	
	Establish exhaust requirements	
	Establish equipment insulation	
	Check UL labels	
	Establish water purity required	
	Update estimate	
Contract administration	Check shop drawings	Utility connections, coordination of
	Check warranties	trades, Rough-in drawings, Main-
	Change orders	tenance manuals
	Field inspection	
	Operators training	

Architects typically do not receive a fee for coordination, but laboratory planners do. For cost control purposes, the project's budget must include a line item for Group II equipment, since this may be a major component of the project cost. See Section 8.3.

Group III Equipment— Minor Movable Equipment

This type of equipment is not fixed and is typically depreciated over a period of less than 5 years. Examples are laboratory glassware, minor laboratory instruments, wastepaper baskets and fire extinguishers.

These items have no effect on the design, and the laboratory planner takes no responsibility for them. However, they may have a significant impact on the project's cost, and a line item must be included in the project budget. See Section 8.3. Ample storage should also be provided for these items.

As always, there are some situations where the equipment type can be both fixed and movable, depending on its size and function. Examples are sterilizers, ovens and biological safety cabinets. However, even laboratory benches, often referred to as "laboratory casework," can be movable and are then referred to as "laboratory furniture."

Fixed equipment is most often a part of the construction contract; movable equipment is most often bought and installed by the owner or user. Either type can be changed.

- FIO (furnished and installed by the owner) equipment typically does not show up on construction contract documents, but space and utility requirements must be provided for and checked. If laboratory casework is involved, shop drawings should be required from the supplier to minimize coordination problems. The owner's crew often is not allowed on the job site until beneficial occupancy to avoid disputes about damage, utility costs, insurance, etc. Only those with adequate and knowledgeable personnel should use this option.

- FIC (furnished and installed by the contractor) equipment typically increases costs but ensures better coordination. The installation cost is 15 to 20% of laboratory casework, depending on the system, and approximately 5% for washers and autoclaves. That does not include the mechanical or electrical connections. The general contractor charges an additional 5 to 10% for coordination. On the other hand, the contractor is solely responsible for delivery, uncrating, moving, installing, utility connections, testing, fixing during the warranty period and coordination between the various trades.

- FOIC (furnished by the owner but installed by the contractor) equipment typically is existing equipment that is moved or new equipment delivered to the job. The advantage is a lower cost through direct purchase by the building's owner. The disadvantage is the potential conflicts and coordination problems: for existing equipment, someone must disconnect, remove, catalog parts, and deliver to the job site. The general contractor typically requires 90 days for handling and installation of owner-furnished equipment before the project is turned over to the owner. This means that the equipment cannot be used during that time.

New equipment can be warehoused until contractor is ready to receive and install it. If equipment does not go through the door or does not fit in the space, there will be extra charges and delays, and possibly additional extra charges, attorney's fees, court costs, etc. because of these delays.

Making the equipment work, testing and warranties must be decided between the owner and the supplier; the latter is most often located in another state. The lead time for most equipment is 90 days. Holding up the general contractor will cost money.

Last but not least, it is very important to know who has a contract with whom: the manufacturer, the supplier, the general contractor. Even more important is to verify what is included in the contract: delivery, uncrating, setting in place, installing, safeguarding, testing, training and warranties. Maintenance contracts are usually separate.

4.1.2 Coordination

Some of the most common planning errors occur in the link between laboratory equipment and laboratory building, particularly in the utility service connections. This is where the multiple specialties of many individuals must be coordinated. The equipment supplier, user, architect, mechanical/electrical engineer, subcontractor and general contractor all have a part in the successful installation and operation of each piece of equipment. Coordination is the key to on-time, complete working laboratories and can best be accomplished under the guidance of the general contractor or construction manager. However, the architect or owner should be deeply involved in the buying decision. In Section 4.9, this coordination will be covered in greater detail.

4.1.3 Equipment Selection

The most common equipment in laboratory facilities consists of benches, commonly known as "laboratory casework." The selection of laboratory casework is not an easy task because it requires knowledge of what is available and what is desired or needed. A few years ago, the National Institutes of Health conducted a survey of preferences by casework users in order to standardize the casework for all future projects. This survey may serve as a model.

The objectives and reasons given for the standardization were cost control, better competition, compatibility of size and fit, consistency, timesaving improvements, quality control, stocking control and uniformity in appearance. A survey questionnaire was prepared (see Tables 4.1-2 and 4.1-3) based

on perceived objectives. One group of users gave rated preferences; another group evaluated how well these preferences were represented in submitted sample bench installations provided by selected manufacturers. A few open-ended questions gave respondents a chance to explain their responses.

The selection of equipment from among many suppliers is often very difficult. Equipment is an integral and very important part of a laboratory operation; the laboratory's purpose can be completely defeated if a crucial piece of equipment fails. For instance, the failure of a sterilizer in a biohazard facility, a glassware washer in a molecular biology laboratory, or a controlled-temperature room can paralyze the whole operation. It is also important to base the selection of reliable equipment on *both* performance *and* service:

- Performance can be verified by talking to past customers and observing the equipment in operation at the factory, but preferably in the field.
- Service can be verified by finding out where the nearest field service location is, by determining the turnaround time in case of breakdown, and by checking with other customers.

Equipment suppliers can and should be prequalified before they are allowed to bid.

4.1.4 Prequalifying Manufacturers

On federal and state projects, all manufacturers of products of comparable materials and quality must be allowed to bid under conditions fair to the manufacturer, the owner and the contractor. The judge is often the architect, but not always.

Manufacturers have long complained, and justifiably so, that fair bidding is often impossible because inferior products or installations are substituted for those specified. In effect, they question the judgment of the architect. However, fair judgment is not always possible and is always difficult.

Architects are expected not only to know about all products available to the building

Table 4.1-2. NIH Laboratory Furniture System Evaluation

Your Institute: _____   Your position (please circle one):
Your Laboratory: _____   Investigator (Permanent) (Temp)
Bldg. # _____   Technician
                                Other (specify): _____

I. Please rate the following issues with regard to whether these are (a) very important to you, (b) somewhat important to you, or (c) not important at all in your assessment of *any* laboratory furniture system (check appropriate column). Please consider your answers carefully so that we can get an accurate assessment of your needs.

	Very Important	Somewhat Important	Not Important	Check 3 most important items in Section A
A. Functionality				
1. Performance Issues				
a. Chemical resistance	___	___	___	___
b. Moisture resistance	___	___	___	___
c. Heat resistance	___	___	___	___
d. Vibration Resistance	___	___	___	___
e. Ability to support heavy weights	___	___	___	___
f. Ability to withstand impact	___	___	___	___
g. Ability to contain spills on bench top	___	___	___	___
h. Maximization of storage space	___	___	___	___
i. Sturdiness	___	___	___	___
2. Maintenance Issues				
a. Ease of repair	___	___	___	___
b. Ability of cabinets to stay clean	___	___	___	___
c. Ease of cleaning furniture components	___	___	___	___
d. Ease of access to utility lines for changes & repairs	___	___	___	___
e. Ease of cleaning below and behind furniture	___	___	___	___

	Very Important	Somewhat Important	Not Important	Check 3 most important items in Section B
B. Flexibility				
1. Adaptability				
a. Ability to easily modify:	___	___	___	___
1. Bench top height	___	___	___	___
2. Storage units: drawers vs. cabinets	___	___	___	___
3. Kneespace location	___	___	___	___
4. Bench top depth	___	___	___	___
5. Shelf height	___	___	___	___
b. Ability for system modification by lab worker	___	___	___	___
2. Versatility				
a. Choice of bench configuration (L- or U-shaped)	___	___	___	___
b. Ability to vary adjacent-bench top heights	___	___	___	___
c. Ability to adjust and level bench tops and/or cabinets	___	___	___	___
d. Availability of island bench option	___	___	___	___
e. Good range of choice regarding:	___	___	___	___
1. Bench top materials	___	___	___	___
2. Drawer units	___	___	___	___
3. Cabinet units	___	___	___	___
4. Overhead units	___	___	___	___
5. Drawer inserts, label holders, other accessories	___	___	___	___

Table 4.1-3. NIH Laboratory Furniture System Evaluation (Back Page)

	Very Important	Somewhat Important	Not Important	Check 3 most important items in Section B
3. Interchangeability				
a. Ability to easily change component parts	————	————	————	————
b. Ability to interchange components with existing system	————	————	————	————

	Very Important	Somewhat Important	Not Important	Check the most important item in *each* of Sections C & D
C. Appearance				
a. Choice of colors	————	————	————	————
2. Overall appearance and attention to detail	————	————	————	————
D. Cost				
1. Low initial cost	————	————	————	————
2. Durability	————	————	————	————
3. Ease of installation	————	————	————	————

II. Please rank the following issues according to the order of priority they would have for you if you were selecting a new laboratory furniture system ("1" being the highest priority)

	Priority
Functionality	————
Flexibility	————
Appearance	————
Cost	————
Other factors (list)	————
————————	————
————————	————

III. What do you like about your present bench and cabinet system?

IV. What problems do you have with your present bench and cabinet system?

trades, but also to be aware of new products being developed and the changed product standards of each manufacturer. Attempts have been made to control the situation by asking bidders to list in writing any products they intend to substitute for those specified and to submit this list to the architect during the bid period for approval.

However, it is impossible to request, install, review and test equipment samples during the normal 1- or 2-month bidding period, which is the only fair way to judge these products.

The obvious way to resolve this problem is to ask for prequalification samples before bidding. The objective is to ensure equality, not to disqualify bidders. The advantages are manifold:

- Only those manufacturers seriously considering bidding on a given project will participate.

- Ample time will be allowed for detailed evaluation.
- The project will not suffer as a result of changes in manufacturers' standards, since the products actual installation can be compared with the sample.
- Problems in laboratory furniture most often occur during installation, a situation often beyond the control of the manufacturer. Prequalification sample installations bring such deficiencies to light prior to actual installation on the job, when tight schedules make them difficult to correct.
- Unqualified bidders have the opportunity to bring their products up to specified standards.
- The samples, in effect, become part of the contract documents and can be used as a reference point in specifying changes prior to actual bidding.

It is important to spell out what the sample is intended to accomplish. It would be a mistake to expect manufacturers of metal, hardwood, plastic-faced or millwork cabinets to bid against each other. These clearly are not equal products and the result would be either that qualified manufacturers would not bid or that unqualified ones would be expected to upgrade their product beyond their capability.

It is equally important to check the legality of eliminating bidders who have not participated in the prequalifying process. It may be necessary to advertise for participation in the prequalification sample installation in an appropriate journal a prescribed number of times.

The prequalification process begins with the preparation of specifications. These should include:

- Correspondence and delivery addresses.
- A fixed schedule, giving required dates for shop drawing submittal, return of shop drawings to the fabricator, check of samples by architect prior to installation, completion of installation, check

of installation and return of samples (except those of successful bidders).

- Instructions for preparation of shop drawings, including the number of copies required, the scale and the details to be included.
- A requirement that manufacturers submit, with their shop drawings, an accurate record, in detail, of materials, hardware and finishes used; of the method of framing and other construction details; and of the results of tests of top and cabinet finishes.
- A statement that acceptance of future deliveries will be based on adherence to details of the accepted sample, along with any modifications required in bid specifications when issued.
- A clear statement that samples are furnished by the manufacturer at neither cost nor obligation to the client or the architect.
- A requirement that the sample installation be by a factory-qualified installation superintendent and that the sample be set up in the space assigned.
- Specification of construction features, including materials to be used. A drawing should be included to show the arrangement of the sample items and the basic dimensions.

This procedure may seem elaborate and unwarranted for small projects, but it can be used to prequalify several projects at one time.

4.1.5 Equipment Testing

Testing is a way to ensure that the product manufactured and installed meets the criteria established in performance specifications. (1) Some tests are required by code for a type or model of equipment, but not for every machine; (2) other tests are done to ensure performance at the job site and (3) to qualify a manufacturer for bidding on a job.

An example of the first type of test is the National Electrical Code requirements for

Underwriters Laboratory (UL) label or equivalent for electrical devices and equipment such as washers, dryers and sterilizers. The importance of compliance with this requirement for fixed equipment cannot be overemphasized; the electrical inspector has the authority and power to refuse occupancy of a multi-million-dollar facility because of one nonlabeled sterilizer. Not all manufacturers have labeled equipment, and even those that do may not have labeled each model, since it is an expensive and time-consuming procedure and since not all electrical inspectors enforce this provision in the code. Equivalent labels that are generally acceptable are those of the Electronics Testing Laboratory (ETL) and the Canadian Standards Institute, but the local authority having jurisdiction must be consulted to verify acceptable testing laboratories.

Tests can be used to prequalify manufacturers or products. They also discourage the unqualified from submitting bids if they cannot pass the tests.

Nothing said above, of course, guarantees that the equipment will work properly when it is delivered and installed. It is the test that proves that the equipment does what it is supposed to do. Because so many trades are involved in installing the product, it is sometimes difficult to establish who is responsible for fixing equipment that does not perform properly.

In our experience, the first step is to ascertain that the equipment performs properly. We hold the equipment supplier responsible because this person is most knowledgeable. There is an obvious bias built into this arrangement, and it is important to include in the equipment specifications the test that must be passed and who must be present during the test. Many trade organizations have published test standards, which have been reproduced in this chapter. At times, independent testers are available; this, of course, is preferable but will raise the cost.

The second step is to decide, as a result of the tests, which party is responsible for making corrections. It is conceivable that the problem is in the utilities to the equipment. The water may not be hot enough, the steam trap of the wrong type, the drain too small, the exhaust inadequate, etc. And the architect's contract documents may be in error.

4.1.6 Reliability, Validity, Redundancy

Reliability can be ascertained by selecting reliable equipment as outlined above. Validity is a function of selecting the right equipment to do the job. A home dishwasher will not wash chemical glassware adequately; a meat storage cold box is not adequate for a research controlled-temperature room. There are several types of sterilizers and biological safety cabinets. The laboratory user must ultimately be responsible for selecting the right equipment, because it is this individual who must know what the final product or result is.

Redundancy is another matter. Assuming that the right equipment was selected and is functioning reliably, there is still the possibility that it will stop working. The most common failure is the power source. Redundancy can be provided with an emergency generator for equipment that cannot be without power for long, such as freezers, refrigerators and incubators. Another form of redundancy is to provide two smaller units for one large one—for instance, two smaller sterilizers in lieu of one large one so that one acts as a standby for the other and the operation can continue.

4.1.7 Conclusion

Equipment selection, installation and testing are a cooperative effort and depend to a large degree on an individual's experience and preferences. This section has given the reader all the options available at this point in time, with their pros and cons, but the final decision is up to the individuals who need and pay for the equipment. This section covers only the most common fixed equipment found in laboratory facilities.

4.2 LABORATORY CASEWORK
T. Ruys

4.2.1 Introduction

Laboratory casework includes cabinets, tops, shelving, sinks and service fixtures. Each will be covered separately in this section. Laboratory casework has most of the same coordination problems as other laboratory equipment, but because there often is so much of it, there is the additional need for coordination of delivery, handling, and storage until it is ready for installation. There often is also a long time period between installation and acceptance by the owner, and the casework must be protected. The specifications must state clearly whose responsibility it is to protect the installed casework.

Traditionally, base cabinets supported the work surface and were built locally to suit a particular need. That type of installation is now classified as millwork. Laboratory casework cabinets are modular and factory produced, with a high degree of quality control. These cabinets are often shipped all over the country, including bench tops, but at times, tops are fabricated locally to save transportation costs. That is particularly true of laminate plastic and stainless steel tops. Service fixtures and sinks are usually supplied by other manufacturers but are included in one bid package by the cabinet supplier.

At times, an equipment supplier may buy cabinets from a casework manufacturer, and fixtures, tops and sinks from other manufacturers or fabricators, and package the bid along with sterilizers, washers, etc. It is often very attractive for the general contractor to deal with one responsible party instead of many.

An important requirement of laboratory casework is that it be flexible. That can mean several things:

- Adaptable. The ability to raise or lower the work surface, modify storage units and delete bench sections.
- Expandable. The ability to add utility services and lengthen the bench.
- Interchangeable. Modular components that can be reused over and over again with little or no modification.

Another important aspect is that the casework be designed for the intended purpose without being rigid. For instance, bench setups for chemical laboratories and analytical instrumentation (see Figure 4.2-1) are quite different, and for good reasons.

The following discussions cover the various components of laboratory casework, the advantages and disadvantages, the standard tests that apply and some of the things to watch out for in selecting them.

It should be kept in mind that laboratory casework fails most often and most drastically in the installation under field conditions. Therefore, even if manufacturers are prequalified, selected, and checked there is no assurance that all is well. Casework must be checked, including the installation, which is often done by a third-party bidding to the manufacturer, supplier or contractor. Select, identify, and specify the responsibility for each component of the contract.

4.2.2 The Laboratory Casework System

The casework system consists of a work surface with storage cabinets and knee spaces below and shelving or storage cabinets above. The system includes a way to support the top, service fixtures, sinks, electrical devices, and the associated piping, drainlines and electrical conduit.

There are two basic types of casework systems:

- Those that use the building partitions for support.
- Those that are self-supporting.

The first type has two different configurations for a wall or center bench condition, since there is no partition at the center bench. The second type may be identical along the partition or as a center bench. Each system has a number of variations.

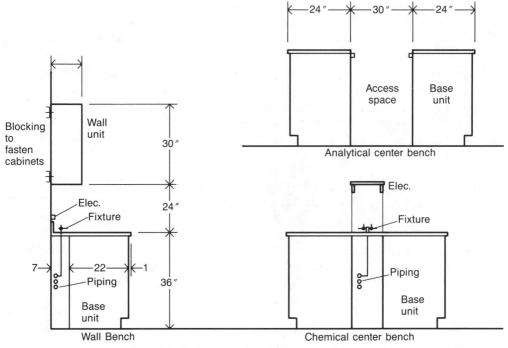

Fig. 4.2-1. Traditional casework system—wall supported.

Partition-Supported Casework Systems

In the *traditional (conventional) system,* which is still the most common, the work surface is supported by the base cabinets and the wall cabinets are mounted on the wall. Base cabinets are typically 22 in. deep and bench tops are 30 in. deep. The difference, assuming a 1-in. overhang, is the 7-in. space used for utility piping. Figure 4.2-1 shows both the wall and center bench conditions.

- Advantage

    Least costly, assuming that the base units which support the top are required and used, because the system is uncomplicated and can be fabricated locally with the fewest number of components.
- Disadvantage

    Very inflexible, since the utilities are part of the bench, which makes the bench very costly to change.

The *service ledge system* is almost identical to the previous system except that a joint is provided parallel to the wall, separating the cabinet part of the bench top from the utility chase component. See Figures 4.2-2, 4.2-3 and 4.2-4. This system was developed to provide a measure of flexibility to the previous system. The service ledge frame supports the piping and utility fixtures and forms a horizontal chase which is fastened to the walls and floors. Panels mounted on the chase hide the piping from view when cabinets and their portion of the top are not present. Lower cabinets are required to lower the top.

- Advantage

    A portion of the top can be removed, raised or lowered without touching the utilities.
- Disadvantages

    There is a cost for the service ledge and top joint and a higher cost for installation of the casework, which, however, is probably offset by the lower cost of piping installation. There is a much higher cost if a service ledge is provided to support every service fixture required without the associated bench.

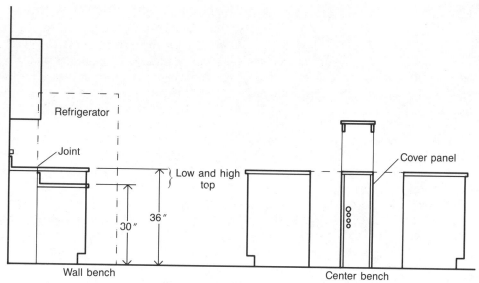

Fig. 4.2-2. Service ledge system—section.

Removing a 24-in.-deep portion of bench to locate a 30- in.-deep refrigerator leaves the service ledge in place and narrows the aisle width by at least 1 ft. If that is a common occurrence, each laboratory module should be wider, which enlarges the building footprint and, of course, raises the cost.

Horizontal piping along the wall makes it very difficult to expand the

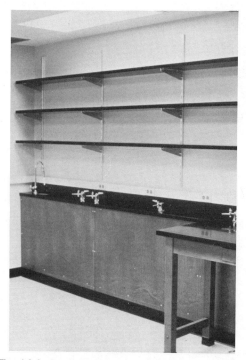

Fig. 4.2-3. Service ledge system—wall condition without cabinets (Theodorus Ruys).

Fig. 4.2-4. Service ledge system—wall condition with cabinets in place (Theodorus Ruys).

laboratory operation to the next module.

The top lowered to 30 in., without a corresponding lowering of the service ledge, is only 24 in. deep, which is inadequate for many laboratory instruments.

The rail hung system was developed to incorporate the advantages of the service ledge system without the disadvantages; see Figures 4.2-5 and 4.2-6. The wall cabinets and work surface are clipped to a rail so that individual units can be removed without affecting adjacent units. The base cabinets are provided with leveling feet which can lower the cabinet in order to remove each cabinet independently if desired. The piping comes down in the wall to service fixtures mounted on the wall above the bench top. The casework is treated as furniture, and can be moved and removed easily (for wall benches). The center benches are like those of the traditional system except that the base cabinets can be removed and relocated. Lowering the wall bench work surface requires lower cabinets, but the depth of the top is the standard 30 in.

- Advantages

The system is very flexible, particularly for the wall benches. The bench is independent of the utilities and power connections, making it easy to remove and rearrange.

The cost is slightly higher than that of the traditional system but much lower than that of the service ledge system. The installation cost is 5 to 10% lower than that of the previous systems because the ease of installation offsets most of the cost of the rails.

This system utilizes the partition, which is already provided, as a pipechase and does not provide an additional cover for piping.

Except where the piping comes down in the wall, penetration is possible anywhere to the next laboratory module.

Any qualified casework manufacturer can provide this system with standard components, with an investment in a couple of extrusion dies to get rail and clip sections extruded. However, the wall construction must provide for the rail to be fastened.

- Disadvantages.

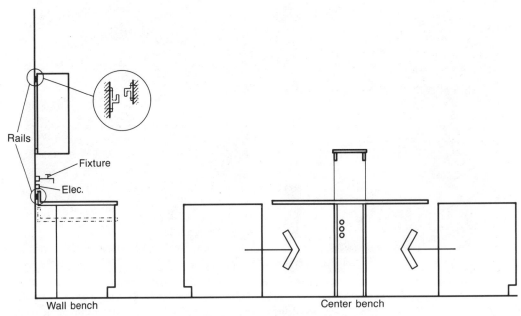

Fig. 4.2-5. Rail hung system—section.

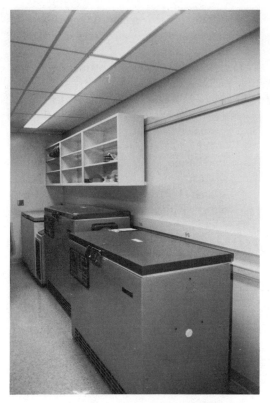

Fig. 4.2-6. Rail-hung system (BOHM/NBBJ).

If not installed or reinstalled properly, the bench may not be as stable as required for instruments sensitive to vibration.

The vertical mounting slot system was developed for multidisciplinary teaching laboratories, which allowed the casework to be removed very quickly in order to use the same space for classrooms, thus increasing the utilization rate. See Figures 4.2-7 and 4.2-8. Instead of the horizontal rail, a vertical slot is provided, much like those commonly used in department stores to mount displays. Brackets mount wall cabinets, shelving, utility mounting units and leg frames into this slot. Leg frames support the tops, and base units slide underneath. Separate leg frames are required for lower bench conditions.

- Advantages

    These are the same as for the rail system but the base units are even easier to rearrange or remove, since they are totally independent of the bench tops.

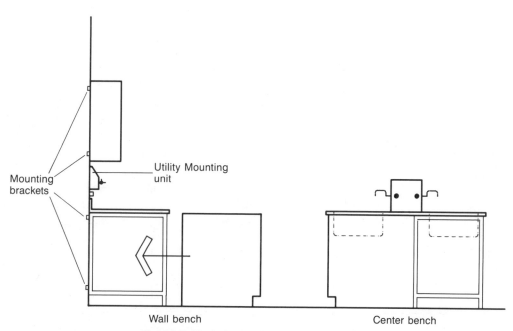

Mounting brackets

Utility Mounting unit

Wall bench

Center bench

Fig. 4.2-7. Vertical mounting slot system—section.

Fig. 4.2-8. Vertical mounting slot system—wall condition (Eduardo Calderon).

The center bench is removable as well, leaving only a covered utility panel in the wall.

More vertical adjustment to wall units is provided.

- Disadvantage

It is higher in cost than the rail system.

Without special provisions, the slot stud cannot be used in 1-hour rated partitions.

Less horizontal adjustment is provided. All cabinets must be a certain width, generally 48 in.

Self-Supporting Casework Systems

All the systems discussed so far use the partition to mount system components, and the wall bench condition is different from the center bench condition; there are, in fact, two systems. The self-supporting systems all try to unify these and to become independent of a partition. In doing so, the piping and electrical systems again become an integral part of the system, as in the traditional and service ledge systems. See Figures 4.2-9, 4.2-10 and 4.2-11.

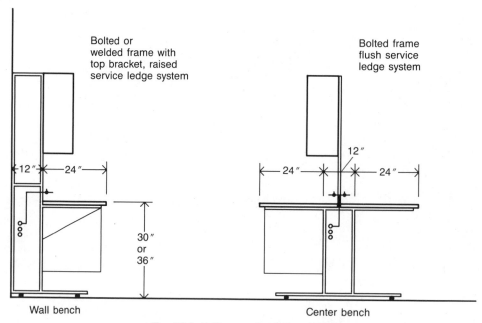

Fig. 4.2-9. Self-supporting frame system.

Fig. 4.2-10. Self-supporting frame system—wall condition (Theodorus Ruys).

The support frame may be welded for greater rigidity or bolted for greater flexibility. It may have a raised or a flush service ledge.

There are a multitude of options from the manufacturers, each with its own trade name. They come with metal, hardwood, and plastic-faced casework. Most of these options were designed in response to the health care market, mounting base cabinets off the floor so that there is space for cleaning below. Some manufacturers have gone one step further, incorporating the storage components into a materials handling system. Most systems incorporate mobile units on wheels or heavy-duty tables for heavy or sensitive equipment. In choosing a system, one should:

- Select a system that has a minimum number of parts. Avoid left-handed and right-handed brackets, caps, closure panels, etc.
- Select a system with the largest choice of storage unit sizes and accessories.
- Select the most stable frames.
- Try to install fixtures independent of the bench, as shown in Figure 4.2-10, so that benches can be moved easily.
- Select the flexibility that is desired.
- Inquire about available top materials and about the type and frequency of joints.
- Select a system that will be available at competitive prices for years to come or is compatible with other systems.
- Select a system that provides access to

Fig. 4.2-11. Self-supporting frame system—center bench condition. (Miyamoto).

piping and traps for installation and service.

- Select a "nonproprietary" system for future additions by other fabricators.
- Advantages

    Systems and components, like furniture, can be used over and over again; components are interchangeable.

    Many have flexible features built into the system.

    No partition are required to support casework.

- Disadvantages

    The cost is generally 20 to 30% higher than that of the traditional system.

    It is a very expensive way to mount plumbing.

    Components require a large amount of storage space when benches are not in use.

    Because of the extra depth of the bench along the wall due to the service ledge, a larger building footprint is required. It may be as much as 1 ft width for every 500 sq ft of module.

    Storage space is reduced by as much as 30% in each base unit mounted off the floor.

Installation

In installing laboratory casework, the following must be considered:

- Trades involved. The casework system used determines not only which trades are affected, but the order in which they are used and the number of times they are needed. Some systems make it possible to have all or most of the piping and fixtures in place before the cabinet and tops are installed. Others require a great deal of coordination between trades for delivery and installation.
- Flexibility of removing and relocating requires that laboratory floor and wall finishes be provided under and behind the benches.
- The partitions on which casework is mounted must be designed to support it

and make provisions to mount cabinets. See Figure 4.2-1.

Moving Casework Components

Several vehicles have been designed to move cabinets for the various flexible systems. The one shown in Figure 4.2-12 is a hand-operated forklift which slides under the base cabinet by removing the cabinet base. It can also be used for the wall cabinets. The large back wheels can be turned 90 degrees so that the card with a cabinet 4 ft wide can go through a 3-ft door sideways.

Testing Laboratory Casework Systems

There are no official tests for casework systems, although there are tests and performance standards for several system components such as cabinets, tops, finishes and fixtures. There are, however, some suggested performance criteria which are noted here.

- The front edge of the bench top should not deflect more than 1/4th in. (0.64

Fig. 4.2-12. Portable forklift to move base and wall cabinets (Theodorus Ruys).

cm) when a load of 600 lb (272 kg) is applied, including the weight of a fully loaded base cabinet.

- The top supported by a 4-ft-wide base cabinet on four levelers should hold a 2,000-lb (907-kg) load without affecting door or drawer operations. The permanent set, after removal of the load, should not be greater than 1/16th-in. (0.16 cm).

4.2.3 Cabinets

Cabinets come in a number of shapes, designs and materials of construction. The selection is sometimes tied to the selection of the casework system, but more often it is a matter of tradition and, of course, cost. The health care industry has traditionally used metal cabinets and, more recently, laminate plastic-faced cabinets; academic research laboratories seem to prefer hardwood; industrial research laboratories prefer metal; and teaching laboratories often use laminate plastic-faced casework. There are no good reasons for these traditions, but we have listed some of the advantages and disadvantages of each so that readers can determine their own preferences. See Table 4.2-1. It is assumed that all cabinets are modular and factory produced. All systems come with glass sliding or hinged doors on their wall cabinets.

Hardwood Cabinets (See Figure 4.2-8)

Hardwood cabinets come in red or white oak and northern hard maple, although white or yellow birch is also available. Because of the reduced availability of quality lumber, the quality and appearance of hardwood cabinets have declined. In order to compete with laminate plastic-faced casework, further cost reduction changes have been made over the years, reducing the quality even further. This still leaves plenty of structural strength to hold the anticipated loads but may compromise the appearance as follows:

- Hardwood plywood instead of solid hardwood door and drawer fronts.
- Rotary-cut instead of sliced-cut veneer plywood.
- Fir plywood instead of hardwood plywood in cabinet interiors.

Hardwood cabinets have some features which one should be aware of so that specifications can be modified, if necessary, to ensure the desired results:

- Solid lumber drawer fronts.
- Overlap door and drawer construction with rounded edges.
- Wood glides instead of the steel tracks and nylon rollers common in other types of cabinets.

Table 4.2-1. Summary of Cabinet Choices

Material	Advantages	Disadvantages
Hardwood	Quiet Easy to repair Corrosion resistant	Adds fuel to fire Stains Limited sizes Fire hazard with oxidizers
Metal	Large selection of manufacturers Easily incorporated with bench support systems	Corrosion Limited sizes
Laminate plastic	Lower cost: 30% below that of plastic, metal/hardwood Available in sizes within 1-in. increments	Delaminates Heavy Generates toxic gases in a fire
Plastic	Machine washable Part of materials handling system Modular components	Expensive Not readily available Manufacturer specific Limited sizes Damaged by certain chemicals

- Unfinished sides and back where concealed during installation, which makes relocating difficult.
- No leveling feet.

The following features are provided by some manufacturers and should be specified to make sure that they are included:

- Removable base cabinet backs if access to plumbing lines and traps is desirable.
- Security panels between drawers, so that with individually secured drawers, entry cannot be gained by removing the drawer above it.
- Advantages
  Natural finish, pleasant appearance.
  Less noisy than metal and noise absorbent.
  Does not corrode.
  Easy to repair in place if damaged.
  Special-size cabinets easily made without special tools.
- Disadvantages
  Adds to fuel in the laboratory in case of fire.
  Vermin control difficult with cracks, holes and joints.
  May warp and swell due to moisture absorption.
  Drawers on wood slides cannot be fully opened.
  Odd sizes in width, limited sizes in depth for some but not all hardwood cabinet manufacturers.
  Drawers may absorb moisture and become difficult to open.
  May absorb chemical spills and radioactive materials.
  May ignite in contact with strong oxidizers such as nitric acid.

Metal Cabinets (See Figure 4.2-16)

Metal cabinets are generally made from painted steel to resist corrosion and finished with an acid-resistant finish. Sometimes cabinets are made from stainless steel.

The cost of metal cabinets is approximately 10 to 15% higher than that of hardwood, and the cabinets are 30 to 40% of the casework cost. That means a 3 to 6% higher cost for the casework package. However, there is a wider choice of suppliers than for hardwood, which makes the selection of the supplier of choice crucial. Unlike wood cabinets, metal cabinets have flush construction door and drawer fronts and come with levelers and drawer glides.

Metal cabinets designed to allow drawers and doors to be interchanged within the cabinet carcass are available. The carcass is fixed, but the drawer/cupboard configuration can change with snap connections. The demand is often not great enough to warrant the extra cost. Instead, complete cabinets are most often interchanged.

- Advantages
  They come in several colors.
  All sides are finished so that they can be relocated.
  Drawers on glides open fully if so specified.
  Easier to clean.
- Disadvantages
  Dent easily.
  Noisier in operation.
  Corrosion, particularly on the inside, is often a problem.
  Repair and refinishing are more difficult than with hardwood.
  Special sizes or configurations are generally not available.

It is in the finish where metal cabinets fail. Several procedures and finishes are used in the industry.

Kewaunee used an exclusive electro-deposition paint system. Casework components are completely submerged in an electro-deposition paint tank. Positively charged paint is bonded to negatively charged metal. To ensure maximum adhesion, the following prepaint treatment precedes the painting process:

- Alkaline cleaner washing is done to remove physical and chemical traces.
- A metallic phosphate solution spray

treatment provides a bonding surface for the paint coat and protection against corrosion.

- The components are oven dried.
- Electro-deposition is performed.
- Curing is done by baking at high temperatures.

Hamilton uses an electrostatically applied epoxy powder coating. To ensure maximum adhesion, the following pretreatment and final coat are applied:

- All metal is spray cleaned with a heated cleaner/phosphate solution and pretreated with an iron phosphate spray, followed by a water rinse. This is followed by a passivating sealant spray. All parts are dried by heating in an oven and allowed to cool gradually before application of the finish.
- The finish coat is baked in a controlled high-temperature oven.
- The finish coat is at least 1.5 mil. thick.
- Surfaces not exposed to view have at least 1.0 mil. thickness.
- The hardness is equivalent to that of a 4H or 5H pencil lead.

Laboratory Furniture uses a sprayed thermo-setting, acrylic-baked enamel coating. All metal parts are chemically cleaned and coated with a uniform, fine-grained, crystalline phosphate surface before the final finish is applied. The finish is baked at high temperatures to complete polymerization.

Laminate Plastic-Faced Cabinets

PLAM cabinets, as these are commonly known, are generally a laminated particleboard box with doors and drawers. The laminate material varies, depending on the part of the cabinet (see Figure 4.2-13):

- Cabinet fronts—high-pressure laminate, 0.028 in.
- Cabinet interior—high-pressure melamine laminate 0.028 in.
- Backs and drawer bottoms—acrylic paint.
- Shelving, bottoms, ends—PVC laminate 50-lb pressure paper, melamine laminate low-pressure paper.

Drawers come with metal glides. Exterior-grade plywood may be substituted for parti-

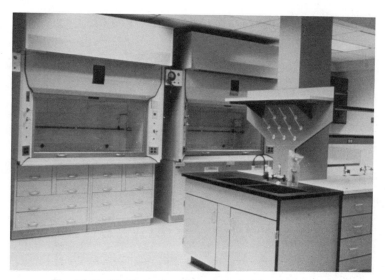

Fig. 4.2-13. Plastic-faced cabinet casework (Theodorus Ruys).

cleboard in locations where moisture may affect the lamination, such as base cabinet toe boards or sink cabinets; however, the plywood grain may show through. The edge detail must be evaluated for impact resistance and the ability to keep moisture out.

Cabinets are available in both overlap and flush construction, and can be fabricated to be used with self-supporting casework frame systems. If floor mounted, each cabinet must have its own base and levelers so that it can be moved easily.

The cost of PLAM cabinets is 10 to 20% lower than that of hardwood or metal cabinets because of lower tooling, labor and material costs and often lower shipping costs because manufacturers are distributed around the country. That translates into a PLAM casework cost 3 to 7% below that of hardwood.

At times, PLAM fronts have been applied to metal cabinets or combined with plastic drawers.

- Advantages
  High-impact resistance except for edges.
  Lower cost.
  Available in many colors.
  Modular to any dimension
  Odd sizes or configurations readily provided. See Figure 4.2-14.
  Does not corrode.
  Easy to clean.
- Disadvantages
  Does not stand up as well as other types for some fabricators.
  Easily damaged in water.
  Surface damage cannot be repaired.
  Some manufacturers may not have access to certain top materials.

Plastic Cabinets

A fairly recent addition to laboratory casework choices is plastic cabinets. These were originally developed for health care facilities—patient rooms, nurses' stations and central supply areas. The emphasis was on cleanliness and materials handling. The cabi-

Fig. 4.2-14. Media pouring bench with multiple hinged tops (Theodorus Ruys).

nets and drawers can be sanitized in a utensil washer and mounted on carts to make them mobile. They are very light in weight and can be moved easily.

These cabinets were later adapted for laboratory casework use by being mounted on frames much like those of the self-supporting system described earlier. See Figure 4.2-15. The first applications were in clinical laboratories, where materials handling was a need.

- Advantages
  Light in weight.
  Easy to assemble.
  Easy to clean; vermin control simple.
  Very tough material; damage unlikely.
  Part of a materials handling system.
  Available in many colors.
  Interchangeable with patient room

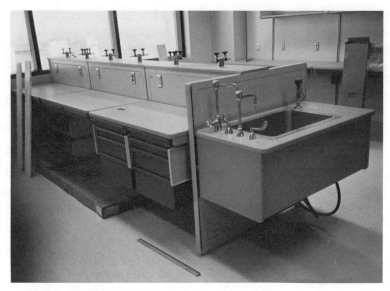

Fig. 4.2-15. Plastic cabinet casework system.

and office systems by the same manufacturer.

- Disadvantages

    High cost.

    Low storage capacity.

    Limited sizes.

    Products of combustion when exposed to fire.

    Toxic gases generated in a fire.

    Affected by some chemicals.

Testing Cabinets

A number of standards institutes have standards for cabinet strengths, which will be noted. In addition, manufacturers have established a list of chemicals to test cabinet finishes. The MASTERSPEC published by the American Institute of Architects gives chemical resistance tests for cabinet finishes. They carefully point out that these are guide specifications and not standards. The Scientific Apparatus Makers Association (SAMA) no longer publishes test standards, but they have graciously allowed the use of those in the public domain. These standards have been included in their entirety in Appendix G.

Cabinet strength (wood—metal very similar).

- Door Test: An open door with a 200-lb (90.7 kg/load) applied 12 in. (30.5 cm) from the hinge should not affect the door operation or loosen hinges. The door should operate for 15,000 cycles without loss of function. Appendix G provides procedures and evaluation.
- Door Impact Test: A closed door should withstand a 240-in.-lb (27.12 J) impact without affecting the operation, door structure or finish. Appendix G provides procedures and evaluation.
- Drawer Test: An unloaded open drawer at 13 in. (33 cm) should support a point load of 150 lb (68 kg) applied at the center of the drawer front for at least 5 minutes. An open drawer should support a 20-lb (9.07-kg) shot bag dropped from 12 in. (30.5 cm) without affecting its function. The drawer should operate for 15,000 cycles with a load of 50 lb (22.68 kg). Appendix G provides procedures and evaluation.
- Shelf Test: A shelf should support a uni-

form load of 200 lb (90.7 kg) without permanent deformation.

- Drawer and Door Pull Test: Pulls should, when subjected to a 50-lb (22.68-kg) pull or suspended weight, not show any signs of changed performance.
- Wall Cabinet Load Test: A 48 × 30 × 12-in. cabinet should support 100 lb (45.36 kg) on the shelves and cabinet bottom for a total of 300 lb (136.1 kg) without permanent change.

Cabinet Finish

- Chemical Resistance: Former SAMA Standards LF 8, 11, and 13 (1976, 1980, and 1982, respectively) gives about 20 different chemicals to which the finish on wood and metal cabinets must be resistant for 1 hour without blistering, dissolving or discoloring. The AIA MASTERSPEC lists 38 chemicals.
- Adhesion: ASTM D2197-68, "Standard Method of Test for Adhesion of Organic Coatings" for metal cabinets. Two sets of 11 parallel lines 1/16th in. apart should be cut with a razor blade to intersect at right angles, thus forming a grid of 100 squares. The cuts should be made deep enough to go through the coating but not into the substrate. They should be brushed lightly with a soft brush and examined under 100 fc illumination. Ninety or more squares should remain coated after the scratch adhesion test.
- Bending: There should be no cracking or peeling of an 18-gauge metal strip when bent 180 degrees over a 1/4-in.-diameter mandrel.
- Hardness: Standard pencils of various hardness are sharpened on emery paper to resemble chisel points and chiseled across the cabinet finish. The finish hardness designation is the same as that of the hardest pencil that does not scratch the surface. Pencils are available in increasing hardnesses as follows: 5-B, 4-B, 3-B, 2-B, B, HB, F, 2-H, 3-H, 4-H, 5-H, 6-H, 7-H.

- Heat Resistance: The cabinet should withstand 190° to 205°F water dripping on a 45-degree surface for 5 minutes.
- Moisture Resistance: The cabinet should withstand a soaked 2 × 3 × 1-in. cellulose sponge for 100 hours on horizontal surfaces.
- Impact Resistance: The cabinet should withstand a 1-lb, 2-in. diameter ball dropped 12 in.
- Cold Crack: The cabinet should withstand 10 cycles of temperature change from 20°F for 1 hour to 125°F for 1 hour.

4.2.4 Tops

Work surfaces are generally known as "laboratory bench tops." Many choices are available (see Table 4.2-2). The primary reason for selecting one top over another is the appearance, both initially and over time, i.e., how well the finish resists the chemicals used without blistering, bleaching, staining or absorbing. Tops come in three basic types:

- Natural and artificial stones.
- Laminate plastics.
- Others.

Tops are most often 1 in. thick but are available in other sizes.

The purpose of bench tops is to provide a work surface. That is the primary consideration, but the following must also be kept in mind:

- Reflectivity: Does the surface create glare and eyestrain?
- Light absorption: Does it appear dark?
- Contrast: White paper on a black top creates eyestrain.
- Cleanliness: Dark surfaces show dirt and stains more than light surfaces.
- Chemical absorption: Porous surfaces are impossible to clean up, difficult to decontaminate, and with solvent spills can, in fact, become flammable.
- Hardness: Abrasion resistance may be important, but glass breakage tends to be higher with stone tops than with most other types.

Table 4.2-2. Chemical Resistance Standards for Laboratory Tops

| Chemical | MASTERSPEC* | | | Former SAMA Test† | | |
	Impregnated Stone	Composition Stone	Glazed Comp. Stone	Case Epoxy Resin	Class 1	Class 2
Acetone	X	X	X	X	X	X
Acetic acid		X				
Alcohol					X	X
Ammonia hydroxide	X	X	X	X		
Aqua regia				X		
Benzene	X			X	X	X
Butyl alcohol				X		
Calcium hydroxide	X			X		
Carbol fuchsin					X	
Carbon tetrachloride	X	X	X			
Chromic acid	X		X	X		
Chloroform	X			X	X	X
Creosol	X					
Ether	X	X	X			
Ethyl acetate				X	X	X
Ethyl alcohol	X	X	X	X		
Ethyl ether				X		
Ferric chloride			X			
Formaldehyde	X			X		
Formic acid	X					
Gasoline	X	X				
Glacial acetic acid	X		X	X		
Hydrochloric acid	X	X	X	X	X	X
Hydrofluoric acid	X					
Hydrogen peroxide				X		
HN03					X	X
Kerosene				X		
Methyl alcohol	X	X		X		
Methylene blue					X	
Methyl ethyl ketone			X	X		
Mineral oil	X	X	X			
Nitric acid		X	X	X		
NAOH					X	X
Phenol	X			X	X	X
Phosphoric acid	X	X	X	X		
Potassium permanganate			X			
Silver nitrate				X		
Sodium hydroxide		X	X	X		
Sodium hypochloride			X			
Sulfuric acid	X	X	X	X	X	X
Toluene	X	X				
Trichloroethylene	X			X		
Xylene	X	X		X		
Xylol			X			
Zinc chloride	X		X	X		

*Standard laboratory concentrations, spot tests for 24 hours. No effect or slight strain or etching.

†Former SAMA test: Apply 5 drops (± 1/4 cc) and cover with watch glass, convex side down. Solvents are kept in a liquid state with a 1-in. cotton ball covered by a glass jar. Test for 24 hours and wash with soap and water, rinse and dry before examination. No effect or slight softening, etching, or discoloration. The following concentrations are assumed:

HCL—37%   NaOH—10%
HN0₃—70%   Phenol—85%
H₂S0₄—96%

Class 1 top: soapstone, impregnated natural stone, coated composition stone.

Class 2 top: coated welded fiber, plywood, composition wood or solid wood.

Source: MASTERSPEC and former SAMA test.

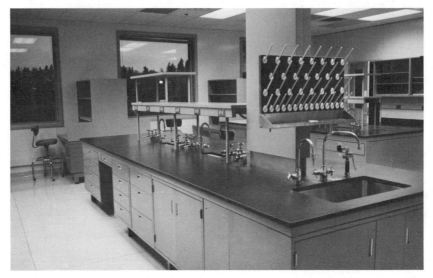

Fig. 4.2-16. Artificial stone tops (Miyamoto).

- Breakage: Stone tops are subject to breaking, particularly where sink cut-outs occur and by thermal shock.
- Chemical resistance: How great is it?
- Absorption: How impervious is the surface to radioactive materials and chemicals?
- Repair: Can the surface be repaired and refinished in place?
- Reuse: Can the surface be removed, relocated, and cut to fit? Are joints tight, waterproof and chemical resistant?
- Availability: Are the tops manufactured or fabricated locally? Are there competitive or comparable products?
- Compatibility: How are tops fastened to frames, each other or sinks?
- Cost: High, low or medium in range?

Installation is where good tops are separated from average or poor ones.

- Tops must be level, with flush and tight joints.
- Tops must be supported properly to minimize deflection and vibration.
- Kneespace rails are not required for -1/4-in.- thick tops, aiding access for persons in wheelchairs.
- Sealing to walls and floors is not desir-

able for benches that are intended and designed to be moved frequently.
- Fastening cabinets to each other and to the bench top may or may not be desirable, depending on the casework system desired.
- Top joint fasteners that do not destroy the top edges should be used.

Natural Or Artificial Stone Tops

For years, soapstone was the material of choice because of its chemical resistance. It was available only from a few suppliers; labor costs increased, and the quality went down. A resin-impregnated sandstone with a baked-on finish replaced soapstone until other choices became available. See Figure 4.2-16.

Substitutes were made of a phenolic resin-impregnated cast cement asbestos product and coated with the same baked-on finish. Because of the asbestos scare, cement asbestos products such as Colorlith and Colorceran tops are no longer available, but very similar products made of cement without the asbestos fibers have replaced it. These are called Colorlith II and Colorceran II.

About the same time, cast and epoxy resin tops became available.

The advantages and disadvantages are listed for each, except for natural stone, which is rarely used.

Artificial Stone—cast cement, coated and natural

- Advantages
  Good chemical resistance.
  Can be repaired in place.
  Available in several colors.
  Readily available.
- Disadvantages
  Medium-range cost.
  Difficult to tool, cut, drill.
  Finish coat fairly thin, subject to mechanical or chemical damage.
  Uncoated product very porous.
  Breakable.

Cast Epoxy Resin

- Advantages
  Homogeneous material.
  Available in black and off-white.
  Readily available.
- Disadvantage
  High-range cost.

Laminated Plastics (PLAM)

Not all plastics are acid resistant. Several acid-resistant-sheet PLAM products exist, and the acid-resistant grade comes in many colors.

Epoxy resin sheets are also laminated to plywood to lower the cost of solid tops while retaining the benefits of the epoxy resin.

- Advantages
  Low-range cost.
  Readily available.
  Easily tooled, cut, drilled, fastened to the frame.
  Good chemical resistance.
  Available in many colors.
  Resilient, lower glass breakage.
- Disadvantages
  Not very abrasive resistant.
  Cannot be repaired.

Subject to water damage of substrate at sinks.
Warps.

Other Top Choices

There are a number of other choices: stainless steel, glass, ceramic tile, laminated hardboard and hardwood.

Stainless steel comes in many types. The types used for laboratory tops are type 316, which is resistant to most chemicals, and type 304, which is not.

Tempered glass tops are very resistant to chemicals but very expensive, and the edging leaves much to be desired in terms of appearance and protection. When the edge is damaged, tempered glass will shatter.

Ceramic tile, common in kitchens, is still used in European labs but rarely found in U.S. labs because of the many joints.

Laminated hardboard tops coated with an acid-resistant finish were popular, because of their lower cost compared with stone tops, until plastic laminates became available.

Hardwood tops were common in the past when other options were limited. Laminated maple tops are still available and are commonly used for electronics, mechanical and wood shops.

Only the advantages and disadvantages of the top materials still regularly used today will be noted.

Stainless Steel Tops

- Advantages
  Can be fabricated to any length and shape without joints with a marine edge (dipped) and sloped to a drain.
  Sinks can be integral with the top, i.e., no joints.
- Disadvantages
  High-range cost.
  Not even type 316 is resistant to all chemicals.
  High maintenance; stains very noticeable; corrodes in contact with iron objects or steel wool.

Laminated Hardwood Tops

- Advantages
  Easily refinished.
  Easily tooled.
- Disadvantages
  High-range cost
  Limited to dry conditions of use.
  Will warp if not properly constructed.

Testing Laboratory Tops

There are a number of performance standards for tops that are often included in project specifications by reference, although rarely is the product tested or proof of compliance requested. These standards establish a level of quality to be obtained before bidders can participate and may establish compliance in case of disputes.

The most obvious and frequent failure is in the finish. Therefore, it is in this area that proof of performance by an independent laboratory is highly recommended if the purchasers do not have the means to test a sample themselves.

- Chemical Resistance: Table 4.2-2 lists the chemicals to which the various tops must be resistant under the test conditions noted, as suggested by the AIA MASTERSPEC and SAMA.
- Strength and Hardness: Table 4.2-3 gives the strength and hardness standards for various natural and composition stone tops, as suggested by AIA MASTERSPEC. Table 4.2-4 gives the strength, hardness and water absorption

for cast epoxy resin tops per the AIA MASTERSPEC.

- Heat Resistance: Former SAMA tests distinguished two classes of tops.
  Class 1: Coated natural and composition stone. These tops should pass the following heat test: A high form porcelain crucible size 0, 15-ml capacity, should be heated over a Bunsen burner until the bottom turns dull red. Immediately the hot crucible should be transferred to the top surface and allowed to cool. Upon removal of the cooled crucible, there should be no blistering, cracking or breakdown of the top surface. Slight superficial marking, such as a slight change of gloss, is acceptable.
  Class 2: Coated welded fiber, plywood, composition wood or solid wood. The final finished intermediate-duty tops should be resistant to heat, to a degree described by the following test: A polished steel washer 2 in. in diameter, 7/64ths in. thick and with a 13/16th-in. hole should be heated to 400°F in a mechanical convection oven operating at 400°F for 30 minutes. The heated washer should then be placed immediately in contact with the test surface and allowed to cool to room temperature. After cooling, the washer should slide from the surface when the surface is inclined at a 45 degree angle, with no tendency to stick to the surface. Upon further examination, there should be no blistering, cracking or breakdown of the surface. A slight surface haze, which is readily removed by rubbing with the finger, is acceptable.

Table 4.2-3. Performance Standards for Laboratory Tops

Top Material	Modulus Density (pcf)	Compressive of Rupture (psi)	Brinnell Strength (psi)	Screw Hardness	Holding (lbs)*
Soapstone	Not listed				
Impregnated sandstone	140	3,200	15,900	84	
Composition stone	100	4,000	15,000	20	1,600
Glazed composition stone	100	4,000	15,000	20	1,600

*7/8-in. penetration.

Source: MASTERSPEC.

Table 4.2-4. Performance Standards for Epoxy Resin Top

Top Material	Water Absorption (24 hour)	Flexural Strength	Heat Distortion Point	Rockwell M Hardness
Cast epoxy resin	0.05%	4,000 psi	400° F	197

Note:
  Flexural strength use ASTM D790.
  Compressive strength use ASTM D695–14,000 psi.
  Hardness, Rockwell M use ASTM D785.
Source: MASTERSPEC.

- Moisture Resistance: A cellulose sponge (2 × 3 × 1 in.) should be soaked with water and placed on the surface of the finish for 100 hours. The sponge should be kept wet throughout the test. At the end of the test, the surface should be dried and, upon examination, should show no visible effect on the finish. Further, resistance to boiling water shall be tested by trickling boiling water for 5 minutes over the surface inclined at 45 degrees. After the test, the surface should be wiped dry and should show no visible effect.
- Abrasion Test: A new one-cent coin held at right angles to the surface scraped across the finish, using 10 reciprocal strokes and under a load of 10 lb, should show no effect other than a slight brightening of the gloss.

4.2.5 Sinks And Drainage Fittings

A surprising number of things can be said about sinks, how they drain, and about other types of drainage devices in the laboratory. The following is a checklist for easy reference.

Types And Materials

- Standard Sink (Figure 4.2-17): Most often made of type 316 acid-resistant stainless steel, but also common in 304 stainless steel for low-chemical applications and polypropylene, polyethylene, molded resin, epoxy resin, and even porcelain and soapstone for high-chemical applications. Polyethylene sinks are not recommended because of their poor resistance to solvents and heat.
- Scullery Sink (Figure 4.2-18): All stainless steel counters, including large sinks used in glasswash and animal cagewash areas. Fabricated in type 316 and type 304 stainless steel.
- Cupsinks: Used in conjunction with cold water gooseneck faucets in the bench or with water-cooled equipment mounted on the wall. Available in glass, epoxy resin, polypropylene, lead and stainless steel.
- Drain Troughs: In the past, commonly found in center benches. Not recommended because of the difficulty of cleaning and the space they take up.
- All concealed surfaces of stainless steel sinks and drainboards must be sound deadened to minimize noise generation in using them.

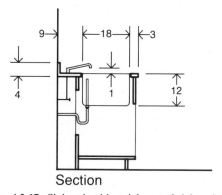

Section

Fig. 4.2-17. Sink unit with stainless steel sink and top. Open cabinet back for plumbing: location of standing overflow, distance from front of counter to edge of sink; distance from faucet spout to sink bottom.

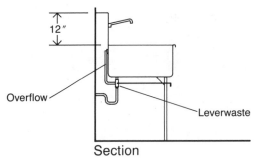

Fig. 4.2-18. Scullery sink with leverwaste and overflow.

Drainage Fittings

- Standing Overflow (Figure 4.2-17): When the sink is used for a continuous flow of water or to prevent it from plugging up and causing floods. Located off center so that the maximum sink area can be used.
- Crumcup Strainer: To close and strain for standard operations.
- Leverwaste. Used with scullery sinks that are filled with hot or harmful solutions. The drain can be opened without reaching into the sink. See Figure 4.2-18.
- All drainage fittings must be provided with tail pieces to connect the fittings to the laboratory waste piping.

Installation

- Sink installation may create disputes between the carpenters union and the plumbers union, depending on the type of sink. The responsibility for the sink cutout and fixture location, however, must be the casework supplier's. Sinks are sometimes specified by the mechanical engineer in the plumbing specifications but should be specified in the Laboratory Casework section of the specifications for better coordination.
- Sinks must be coordinated with the cabinet unit below so that the sink bowl and trap will fit inside the cabinet frame. See Figure 4.2-17. A sink greater than 18 in.

from front to back will not fit in a standard 30-in. bench with a standard 22-in. base unit and a hot/cold water faucet deck mounted. An alternate design is shown in Figure 4.2-19 for applications where a larger cabinet-supported sink is required.

- Epoxy resin sinks need an adjustable cradle to support them if they are not integral with the top. The joint between sink and top is the cause of frequent leaks and must be sealed and checked. See Figure 4.2-20.
- Stainless steel sinks can be integral with stainless steel tops or self-rim types with laminated tops. Loose-rim-type sinks, often found in kitchens, are not recommended because cleanliness is more difficult to maintain. The joint between sink and countertop must be sealed carefully to prevent moisture from penetrating the top core.
- Drainage fixtures come with tail pieces and cupsinks with threaded or flanged connections. Connections to traps and drainlines are taken care of by the mechanical contractor, but coordination is crucial. Sediment traps must be planned for.
- Laboratory casework must be designed to provide access for installing and maintaining traps or sinks and cupsinks.

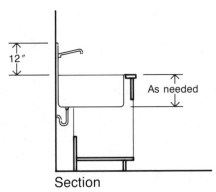

Fig. 4.2-19. Sink unit modified for large stainless steel sink. Back top rail of cabinet removed. HCW fixture with integral control valve.

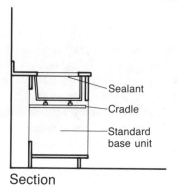

Section

Fig. 4.2-20. Cast resin sink with support cradle.

Ergonomics

- A sink deeper than 12 in. (Figure 4.2-17) is discouraged because it is non-standard and because washing glassware at a deeper sink is backbreaking for most people. One deeper sink can be shared by several labs to accommodate larger items.
- Locate the sink as close to the front as possible because bending over to reach the sink bottom is also backbreaking.

Testing

Stainless steel sinks are not recommended for slide staining operations or hydrochloric acid use.

Epoxy resin sinks should possess high resistance to mechanical and thermal shock, and should meet the following mechanical and physical strength requirements:

Tensile strength	9,500 psi
Compressive strength (ASTM method D695-77)	35,000 psi
Flexural strength (ASTM method D790-71)	19,000 psi
Hardness, Rockwell M (ASTM method D785-65)	115
Specific gravity	1.93
Water absorption (ASTM method D570-77)	
Percent by weight, 24 hours	0.02
Percent by weight, 7 days	0.04
Percent by weight, 2-hour boil	0.04

4.2.6 Utility Service Fixtures

Utility service fixtures are not located in as many places on laboratory benches as they once were in order to reduce the cost and because there is less need for piped services with the increase in automated equipment. Some laboratory facilities opt for gas and compressed air from cylinders and local vacuum pumps for greater flexibility, reduced installation and lower maintenance costs.

All laboratory casework manufacturers buy their service fixtures from fixture manufacturers. The selection of the casework manufacturer should include the fixture manufacturer if:

- Existing fixtures must be matched.
- Inventory of parts by different suppliers is undesirable.
- Cost and delivery schedules are critical issues.

Vandal-proofing fixtures is highly recommended for teaching laboratories. It adds very little to the cost. That means:

- Adding a pin which prevents a fixture from being twisted off the pipe from above the bench top.
- Removing aerators and spout ends with special tools only.

Corrosion-resistant, powder-coated epoxy coatings are available from a number of manufacturers in various colors or in clear phenolic over chrome. See Figure 4.2-21. These are recommended inside fumehoods and other highly corrosive environments. In teaching laboratories, black polypropylene handles on standard chrome fixtures will resist corrosion from frequent handling of fixture valves.

Water fixtures are the most common type in laboratories. A number of issues must be considered:

- There are hot/cold water swingspouts, cold water goosenecks, treated water fixtures and eyewash fixtures.

Fig. 4.2-21. Coated corrosion-resistant fixture (Paul Warchol).

- All come deck mounted or panel mounted. Some come with internal shutoffs so that a leaky gasket can be replaced without the need to search for a remote shutoff valve. See Figure 4.2-22.
- Water fixtures should be specified with a replaceable stainless steel seat for long-lasting service and a water-saving device to control the water flow.
- All water fixtures which allow the attachment of a hose should have a backflow preventer (vacuum breaker) to prevent contamination of the laboratory water system in case of negative pressure in the piping system. A nonremovable antihose ring can be applied to the spout in lieu of a vacuum breaker.

  Vacuum breakers come in two types: "atmospheric," which are integral with the spout and cannot be removed, or "inline," which are attached to the end of the spout. The advantage of the integral type is that it cannot be removed. The disadvantage is that it may leak and is not centered over a cupsink. The attached vacuum breaker can be vandalized but, if leaking, is centered over the drainage fitting. Plumbing inspectors may not accept the inline type.

- A hot/cold water fixture typically comes with a four-arm control handle but is available with wrist control, knee control or foot control when the hands are either dirty, contaminated or must be kept clean. Unfortunately, knee controls are often in the way and foot controls make cleaning around them difficult. In addition, the cost is substantially higher than that of standard fixtures.

- Deionized water systems typically use a PVC or polypropylene fixture which is available with warning lights which are activated if the purity drops below the desired point. A nearby electrical outlet is required. Because of the material of which they are made, these systems break easily.

- Distilled water fixtures are available in stainless steel, tin-coated brass and solid tin-lined brass. The choice depends on the water quality that must be maintained.

- Cold water goosenecks should be specified with a gasket and fastener so that they can swivel or be fixed in place and installed in tight places. See Figure 4.2-23. The goosenecks must be high enough to apply an aspirator for vacuum, but not so high that it will not fit under the reagent shelf on center benches. The gooseneck must be over a drainage device in case it leaks and must have an anti-splash device attached to prevent spraying the bench top. See Figure 4.2-24.

- Eyewash fixtures are covered in Chapter 4.

Other fixtures commonly found in laboratories to control the flow of various gases are as follows:

- Natural gas or propane gas fixtures are typically of a ground key type and are tested at 100 psi air underwater. They are the least expensive. See Figure 4.2-25.

- Specialty gases under high pressure or where the flow is critical are controlled with needle valves. See Figure 4.2-26.

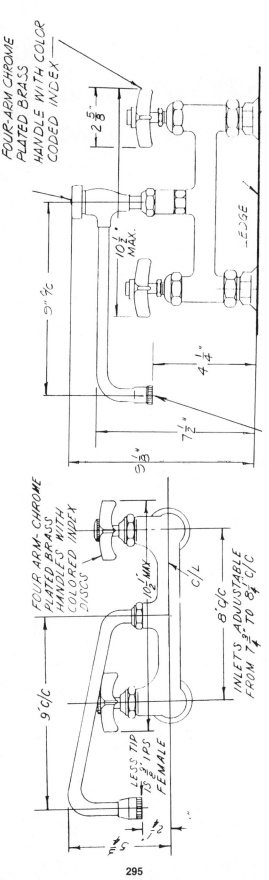

Fig. 4.2-22. Hot/cold-water fixtures mounting (T&S Brass and Bronze Works, Inc.).

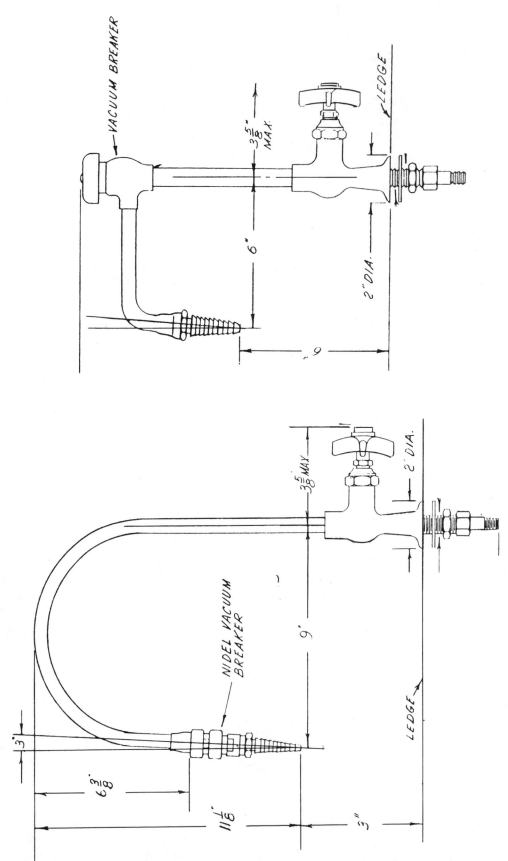

Fig. 4.2-23. Vacuum breaker types (T&S Brass and Bronze Works, Inc.).

296

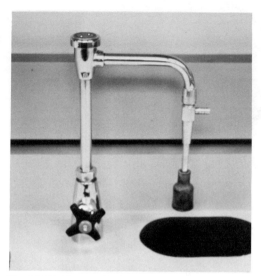

Fig. 4.2-24. Gooseneck with vacuum breaker, aspirator and splash arrestor (Theodorus Ruys).

The same fixtures are used for compressed air and lab vacuums. No grease or oil should be used in fixtures which control flammable gases.

• Remote-controlled valves are available for fumehoods, which can also be used for handicapped stations. See Figures 4.2-27 and 7.5-12. Fumehood valves are typically serviced through access panels inside the hood. If that is undesirable, such as in stainless steel-lined radioisotope or perchloric hoods, fixtures are available that can be serviced from the hood front. See Figure 4.2-28.

• Fixtures must be color-coded for various uses and so designated. The serrated outlet inside the fumehood must have the same color as the fixture index button outside the fumehood.

Standard colors accepted by the industry are:

Hot water—red
Cold water—green

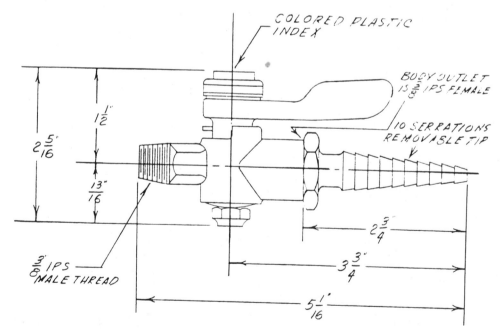

NOTE: THIS VALVE IS TESTED AT 100 P.S.I. AIR PRESSURE UNDER WATER. IT IS RECOMMENDED FOR USE WITH GAS, AIR OR VACUUM UP TO 30 P.S.I. MAXIMUM WORKING PRESSURE. IT SHOULD _NOT_ BE USED FOR WATER OR STEAM.

Fig. 4.2-25. Ground-key gas fixture (T&S Brass and Bronze Works, Inc.).

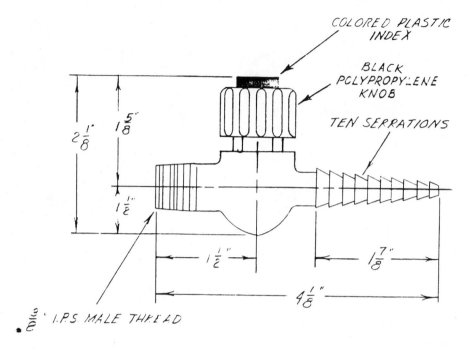

NEEDLE POINT IS STAINLESS STEEL AND FLOATING

COLORED PLASTIC
INDEX

BLACK
POLYPROPYLENE
KNOB

TEN SERRATIONS

$2\frac{1}{8}$" $1\frac{5}{8}$"

$1\frac{1}{2}$"

$1\frac{1}{2}$" $1\frac{7}{8}$"

$4\frac{1}{8}$"

$\frac{3}{8}$" I.P.S. MALE THREAD

THIS VALVE IS RECOMMENDED FOR USE WITH GASES AND AT
PRESSURES HIGHER THAN THOSE USED WITH B1-4000-1 GROUND
KEY HOSE COCK. WHEN FURNISHED FOR OXYGEN, HYDROGEN,
OR SPECIAL GASES, A SPECIAL NON-FLAMMABLE LUBRICANT WILL BE USED.
IT SHOULD NOT BE USED FOR WATER OR STEAM.

Fig. 4.2-26. Needle valve gas fixture (T&S Brass and Bronze Works, Inc.).

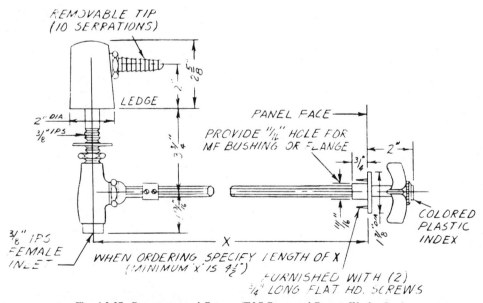

REMOVABLE TIP
(10 SERRATIONS)

LEDGE

PANEL FACE

PROVIDE "$\frac{11}{16}$" HOLE FOR
MF BUSHING OR FLANGE

2" DIA
$\frac{3}{8}$" IPS

2"

$\frac{3}{4}$"

COLORED
PLASTIC
INDEX

$\frac{3}{8}$" IPS
FEMALE
INLET

X

WHEN ORDERING SPECIFY LENGTH OF X
(MINIMUM X IS $4\frac{1}{2}$")

FURNISHED WITH (2)
$\frac{3}{4}$" LONG FLAT HD. SCREWS

Fig. 4.2-27. Remote control fixtures (T&S Brass and Bronze Works, Inc.).

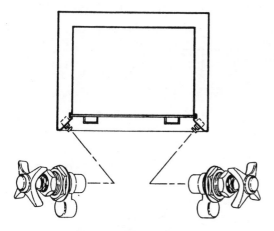

Fig. 4.2-28. Fumehood valve with front access for service (T&S Brass and Bronze Works, Inc.).

Chilled water—brown
High-purity water—white
Natural gas—blue
Compressed air—orange
Lab vacuum—yellow
Other—white
Steam—black

- Gas fixtures can be mounted on the wall, a service ledge or, if several outlets are required, on one-, two-, or four-way turrets. See Figure 4.2-29. Combination fixtures for water and gases for teaching workstations are also available.
- Steam fixtures must be provided with insulated handles.

Electrical raceways detached from laboratory benches are most often not a part of the laboratory casework. Electrical raceways attached to reagent shelves over a center bench may or may not be a part of the casework, but electric outlets on the bench tops are part of the casework most of the time. These receptacles are mounted in turrets and:

- May be single or two-gang for two or four outlets. See Figure 4.2-30.
- Single-faced or double-faced for access from one or both sides.
- Must meet the requirements of the National Electric Code and be UL labeled.
- Rated for the electrical current characteristics connected.

Installation

Fixtures are made up of components that are most often shipped to the job site in separate containers. Under multiple bid contracts where the fixture contract is separate from the mechanical contract, it is critical to know who is responsible, that is, who receives, assembles and coordinates installation.

Laboratory casework must be designed to provide access to install fixtures during construction and for service in the future.

Access panels and holes in bench tops and cabinets should be provided by the casework supplier or installer—not by mechanics and electricians in the field, who are not knowledgeable enough about casework systems.

4.2.7 Cabinet Hardware

Hardware is an integral part of cabinets, but not all cabinets have the same hardware. Typically, hardwood cabinets do not have any metal roller glides, and locks are not standard equipment unless specified. The important considerations are given below for each type.

Hinges

- Hinges for plastic laminate cabinets with particleboard cores require more screws because the holding power is less

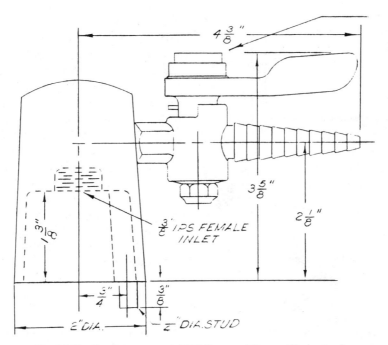

Fig. 4.2-29. Gas fixtures turret (T&S Brass and Bronze Works, Inc.).

per screw, and are of the wrap-around type because cabinet doors are typically flush with the cabinet face. See Figure 4.2-31.

- Hinges should be of the tight-knuckle type so that the pin cannot be removed

to gain entry into the cabinet should it be locked. See Figure 4.2-32.

- Hinges should be of stainless steel in corrosive atmospheres.
- Hinges should allow the cabinet door to open 270 degrees.

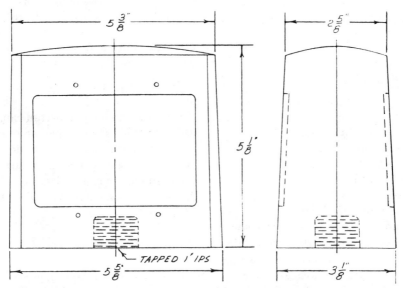

Fig. 4.2-30. Electrical service turret, single-face/two gang (T&S Brass and Bronze Works, Inc.).

Fig. 4.2-31. Wraparound hinge for PLAM cabinets. (Theodorus Ruys).

- Spring-loaded, surface-mounted hinges are not used for laboratory casework because they defeat the points brought up above.
- Avoid hinges welded to metal cabinets because the door cannot be adjusted or removed.
- See cabinet section tests for hinge holding power.

Catches

- There are magnetic catches and friction catches. Magnetic catches last longer but corrode.

Pulls

- There are many types of pulls. The most appropriate types for chemical laboratories are those that are acid resistant, such as stainless steel, nylon or powder epoxy coated.
- However, recessed plastic types are available for high cart traffic areas or for teaching laboratories where protruding pulls interfere with standup work stations.
- The location and direction of pulls must be noted. Drawer and door pulls do not always point in the same direction.

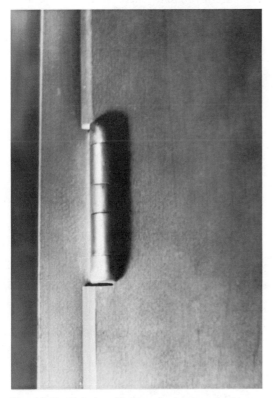

Fig. 4.2-32. Tight knuckle hinge for hardwood cabinets (Theodorus Ruys).

Drawer Glides

- Glides must be specified on hardwood cabinets if desired.
- The quality varies greatly; heavy-duty types are desirable and available.
- Specify the full extension type so that the back of the drawer can be seen when fully open.
- Epoxy-coated glides are available.

Levelers

- There are several types of levelers, both light-duty and heavy-duty. If the cabinets support the bench top, then the levelers must be able to support both the cabinet and the top, plus the load in and on the bench. See Figure 4.2-33.

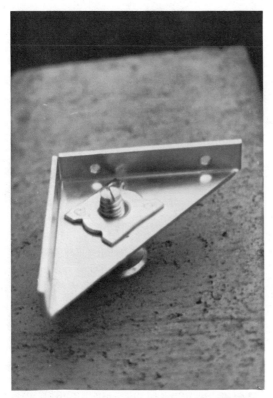

Fig. 4.2-33. Cabinet levelers (Theodorus Ruys).

Locks

- Security is becoming increasingly important with the increase in crime, the reduction in supervision and the increase in laboratory room sizes, particularly in academic institutions.
- Locks should be no less than a five-pin tumbler cylinder type.
- Keeping track of keys and master keys is a time-consuming task. Some academic institutions have provided for their teaching laboratories the hardware for a padlock to be supplied by the students. It is not very pretty, but it is effective.

4.2.8 Equipment Built Into Casework

Some equipment is typically built into the bench and must be coordinated to avoid cutting and patching later.

- Undercounter refrigerators and freezers are available; there is a considerable price range. Explosion-proof types require more space. All need clearance for air circulation to cool the compressor unit for proper operation and for removal in case of repairs. Don't forget to provide an electrical outlet below the bench.
- Undercounter glassware washer and dryer. The requirements are the same as for undercounter refrigerators and freezers.
- Disposal units for laboratory applications are typically of the heavy-duty type and may be larger than a kitchen type. A removable sink cabinet bottom may be required. Provide power and a switch at a convenient location.
- Stills and other water-purifying units are typically mounted over the bench on mounting boards which include the required utilities. See Appendix J.
- Foot valves for water fixtures require special modifications to cabinets, including a possibly removable bottom for access to the plumbing.

REFERENCES

Scientific Apparatus Makers Association (SAMA)
1101 16th Street N.W.
Washington, DC 20036.
Telephone: (202) 223-1360
American Institute of Architects
Professional Systems Division
1735 New York Avenue N.W.
Washington, DC 20006
Telephone: (800) 424-5080

4.3 BIOLOGICAL SAFETY CABINETS
D. Eagleson

4.3.1 Introduction

As research and related work in the life science field have increased during the past decades, the importance of protective equipment in the workplace has similarly increased. The need to prevent accidental infection of personnel and to protect the environment and the product have resulted in the development of a wide variety of biological safety cabinets. In addition, a diverse array of new procedures and scientific applications have made biological safety cabinets (BSC) increasingly desirable.

It is important to recognize that all cabinets are designed to meet specific needs in the workplace. Before selecting a cabinet, potential users must assess their program and match specific requirements to the appropriate equipment. Further, they must be able to recognize the limitations as well as the capabilities of each type of cabinet. It is also important to remember that the equipment is designed to supplement, rather than substitute for, accepted contamination control and/or safety procedures. To minimize hazards and maximize protection, an assessment of risk is essential prior to the selection of a cabinet (Miller, 1986; Richardson and Barkley, 1988).

The following information is offered to help you better understand the purpose and functions of safety cabinets. It is important that the adequacy of any biological safety cabinet for a particular use be confirmed by an industrial hygienist or qualified safety professional.

Cabinet Purpose

Laminar flow biological safety cabinets are designed and manufactured for (see also Table 4.3-1):

- Personnel protection: To protect personnel from harmful agents inside the cabinet.
- Product protection: to protect the work, product, experiment or procedure performed inside the cabinet from contaminants in the laboratory environment or from cross-contamination inside the cabinet
- Environmental protection: to protect the environment from contaminants in the cabinet.

Table 4.3-1. Purposes of Biological Safety Cabinets

	Cabinet Classification		
Purpose	Class I	Class II	Class III
Containment (operator protection)	Yes—partial air barrier	Yes—partial air barrier	Yes—absolute physical barrier
Containment (environment protection)	Yes—partial HEPA-filtered exhaust air	Yes—partial HEPA-filtered exhaust air	Yes—absolute double HEPA-filtered exhaust air
Cleanliness (product protection)	No—room air drawn across work area	Yes—HEPA-filtered supply air (laminar flow), class 100 or better	Yes—partial HEPA-filtered supply air (may not be laminar flow)

The High-Efficiency Particulate Air (HEPA) Filter

The HEPA filter is present in all classes of biological safety cabinets. This is a device which removes particulates, including micro-organisms, from the air. A HEPA filter removes only particulates—not vapors or gases. Airborne particulates are generally called "aerosols."

The media of HEPA filters are made of boron silicate microfibers formed into a flat sheet by a process similar to that of paper-making. The flat sheets are pleated to increase the overall surface area of the filter. Pleats are separated by aluminum baffles which direct the air flow in the filter. Depending on its quality, a HEPA filter is able to trap at least 9,997 of every 10,000 particles with a diameter of 0.3 um. For most applications in biological safety cabinets, this minimum efficiency level of 99.97% is acceptable if the filters are routinely tested and found to be free of leaks.

Because of the physical mechanisms of filtration from an air stream, the HEPA filter is least efficient in filtering out particles in the 0.3-μm size range. It is more efficient on both larger and smaller particles. See Figure 4.3-1.

4.3.2 Types Of Biological Safety Cabinets

Biological safety cabinets are divided into three classifications—Class I, Class II, and Class III. Class I and Class II cabinets are used for work involving low-risk and moderate-risk biological agents. Class III cabinets are used for work with agents of high risk. See Table 4.3-2.

Class I Cabinets

The Class I biological safety cabinet is a partial containment device suitable for work involving low- to moderate-risk agents where there is a need for containment but not for product protection. It protects personnel using the cabinet and protects the environment

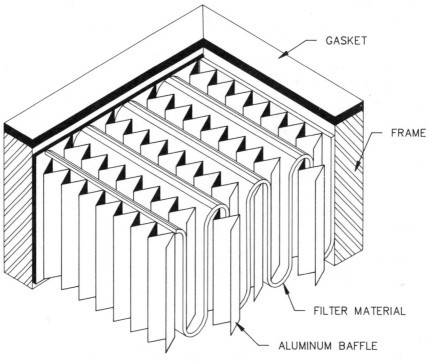

Fig. 4.3-1. HEPA filter cross section.

**Table 4.3-2. Classification of Biological
Safety Cabinets**

Classification	Microorganism Risk Level	Type of Protection Offered
Class I	Low–moderate	Personnel
Class II	Low–moderate	Personnel and product
Class III	High	Personnel and product

from contaminants within the cabinet. A Class I cabinet does not protect the product from contamination from dirty room air.

The HEPA filter in the Class I cabinet constitutes the major difference between this equipment and a typical chemical fumehood. Environmental protection is made possible by the presence of the HEPA filter in the cabinet's exhaust system, which keeps aerosol contaminants from escaping into the atmosphere. Personnel protection is provided by a constant flow of unfiltered air through the front opening.

As shown in Figure 4.3-2, a controlled airflow into the work area prevents the escape of airborne contaminants through the front opening, providing personnel protection.

The inward airflow is induced by a fan which exhausts cabinet air through the HEPA filter, resulting in negative pressure within the cabinet. Air passes through the HEPA filter before exiting the cabinet to the outside, providing environmental protection. The exhaust fan should be located on the roof, following good practice associated with fumehood ventilation systems.

Minimum specification. The specifications presented are minimum performance specifications. End users should add to these any additional specifications which will help to clarify their particular needs. Additional specifications for materials, dimensions, features, cost of ownership or benefits will be

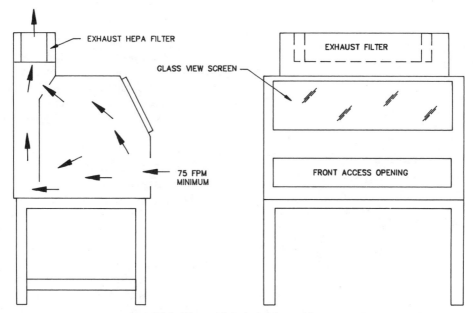

Fig. 4.3-2. Class I biological safety cabinet.

necessary in order to define for suppliers those aspects of the equipment which are important to each situation.

Class I minimum specifications

- Operational Airflow: Minimum airflow should be 75 fpm intake velocity, to be used at up to 150 fpm intake velocity.
- Filtration: The integral HEPA exhaust filter should be DOP tested to be at least 99.97% efficient in filtering 0.3-μm particles and should be scan tested by the manufacturer to be leak free.
- Performance: The cabinet model type should have been tested with biological aerosols to document minimal performance of containment. Test results should be submitted for acceptance.
- Cabinet Leak Tightness: The cabinet should be tested to demonstrate carcass integrity to the soap bubble test.
- Testing Documentation: Full documentation of all tests should be required for submittal and acceptance.

Applications. The Class I biological safety cabinet is appropriate for work involving low- and moderate-risk biological agents. It protects only the user and the environment. In those applications which require protection of the work (or samples) from contaminants in the laboratory air, the Class II cabinet is more appropriate.

Class I cabinets may be useful in certain clinical laboratory manipulations where exposure to potentially infectious samples is expected (Miller, 1986; Richardson and Barkley, 1988) and for research with recombinant DNA molecules at Biosafety Levels (BLs) 1–3 (*Federal Register,* 1976, 1980, 1986).

Class II Cabinets

Unlike Class I cabinets, Class II cabinets meet the requirements for protection of the product, the personnel, and the environment. As such, this cabinet is widely used in laboratory, hospital and pharmaceutical fa-

cilities where particulate-free work areas are necessary, as well as for containment of the agents involved in the work.

In general, the Class II biological safety cabinet features a front-access opening with carefully maintained inward airflow, HEPA-filtered vertical airflow within the work area, and HEPA-filtered exhaust air. The vertical airflow and the front-access opening are common to all Class II cabinets. See Figure 4.3-3.

However, airflow patterns and velocities, HEPA filter positions, ventilation rates and exhausting methods vary in different Class II cabinet designs.

Types of class II cabinets. Since the development of the very first Class II cabinet, modifications in cabinet designs have led to the designation of various types of Class II cabinets. The designation of these types has, in turn, led to some confusion. The most practical and easiest-to-understand discussion of Class II cabinetry uses just three type designations within the class: Type A, Type B and Type B2 100% Total Exhaust. All other type designations within Class II are derived from these three classic designs.

The major differences between Type A, Type B and B2 100% Exhaust cabinets are the percentage of air that is exhausted or recirculated and in the manner in which exhaust air is removed from the work area. Table 4.3-3 provides an explanation. In the classic Type A cabinet, two-thirds of the cabinet air is constantly recirculated, and one-third is exhausted out of the cabinet via a common plenum. In the classic Type B cabinet, one-third of the air is recirculated, and two-thirds is exhausted directly off the work surface through a dedicated duct to the outside. Finally, in the 100% Exhaust cabinet, there is no recirculation. All air is continuously exhausted directly from the work area and out of the cabinet.

A recent classification scheme is currently in use by many institutions or individuals. This scheme is the one devised by the National Sanitation Foundation for use in their

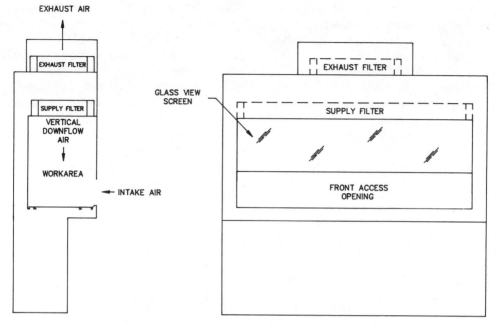

Fig. 4.3-3. Class II biological safety cabinet.

Standard 49 (National Sanitation Foundation, 1987).

NSF classification. The National Sanitation Foundation (NSF) is a nonofficial, noncommercial agency devoted to research, education and service. It conducts tests on biological safety cabinets to ensure that the products meet minimum standards for cabinet classifications devised by the NSF. Prod-

ucts which meet minimum standards are listed by the NSF. The tests are conducted on cabinets submitted to the NSF by the manufacturer. Tests are done on each model and size of cabinet once every 5 years. The NSF standard is reviewed every 5 years.

The NSF restructured its Class II cabinet classification system to reflect modifications in cabinet designs (National Sanitation Foundation, 1987). The new system differs

Table 4.3-3. Basic Designs of Biological Safety Cabinets

Classic Type	Minimum Intake Velocity (fpm)	Particulate-Contaminated Plenums	Origin of Exhaust Air	HEPA Filter Location
Class II, Type A	75	May be under positive pressure	From common plenum	Last place before air enters work area or room
Class II, Type B	100	Under negative pressure	Directly from work area	Directly under work area and just before leaving cabinet to exhaust
Class II, 100% Exhaust	100	Under negative pressure	Directly from work area	Just before air enters work area and just before leaving cabinet to exhaust

from the classic system described earlier. The differences are shown in Table 4.3-4. For easy reference, Table 4.3-5 lists the design characteristics a cabinet must have to meet the NSF Standard 49 definitions for the various classes.

It is important to note that the Class II, Type B3 cabinet is identical in airflow design to the classic Type A cabinet; one-third of the air is exhausted and two-thirds is recirculated. There are three major differences between the Type A and Type B3 cabinets:

1. The Type B3 cabinet requires a minimum intake velocity of 100 fpm, while the Type A cabinet requires 75 fpm.
2. The Type A cabinet allows contaminated, positive-pressure areas to be adjacent to the room environment. In the Type B3 cabinet, all biologically contaminated areas are required to be under negative pressure or, if under positive pressure, to be surrounded by negative pressure.
3. Type B3 cabinets must be exhausted to the outside of the building.

Since two-thirds of the air in the Type A or Type B3 cabinet is recirculated, this is an important consideration in terms of the removal of vapors. In tests with toluene vapor (Stuart et al., 1983), all three cabinet types were vented to the outdoors. The Type A and Type B3 cabinets held the highest concentration of vapor during the test.

Table 4.3-4. Comparison of Classic Type and NSF Cabinet

Classic Type	NSF Classifications
Class II, Type A	Class II, Type A
Class II, Type B	Class II, Type B
Class II, 100% Exhaust	Class II, Type B2
Class II, Type A (with 100 fpm intake velocity, exhaust to the outdoors, and negative-pressure or positive-pressure plenums surrounded by negative pressure)	Class II, Type B3

Since the airflow characteristic is the same in both the Type A and Type B3 cabinets (whether or not it is vented to the outside), these cabinets are not suited for work involving hazardous vapors. Refer to the section "Characteristics of Handling Vapors by Class II Cabinets" for more information on the vapor-handling capabilities of these types of cabinets.

Type A And Type B3 Cabinets

In Type A and Type B3 cabinets, approximately one-third of the air is exhausted through an exhaust HEPA filter from a common plenum, while the remaining two-thirds is recirculated through the supply HEPA filter back into the work area.

Figure 4.3-4 shows the airflow in a typical Class II, Type A biological safety cabinet. HEPA-filtered air descends through the work zone in a vertical flow. At the approximate center of the work surface, the air splits. A portion of the air exits to the base of the cabinet through the front perforated grille, and the remainder exits to the base through the rear perforated grille. Escape of potentially harmful agents is prevented in part by an air barrier of inward-flowing room air at the front-access opening. Room air is drawn into the front perforated grille and does not enter the work area. In the base of the cabinet, the total volume of air is pushed by the motor/blower through a rear airflow duct. Upon reaching the top of the cabinet, approximately one-third of this air is pushed through the exhaust HEPA filter and reenters the room or is vented to the outside. The remaining two-thirds of the air is pushed through the supply HEPA filter and enters the work area as clean, vertically flowing air.

Class II, type A minimum specifications

- Operational Airflow: Minimum intake air velocity should be 75 fpm. Approximately one-third of the total air delivered is exhausted from the cabinet, while two-thirds is recirculated within the cabinet.

Table 4.3-5. Design Requirements of Biological Safety Cabinets (using NSF Standard 49 definitions)

Cabinet Type	Proportion of Air Recirculated	Proportion of Air Exhausted	Minimum Intake Velocity (fpm)	Origin of Downflow (Supply) Air	Origin of Exhaust Air	Air Exhausted To	Contaminated Ducts and Plenums
Class I	None	All	75	None	Direct exhaust from work area	Vented to outside	All under negative pressure
Class II, Type A	Two-thirds	One-third	75	From common plenum	From common plenum	Room	May be under positive pressure
Class II, Type B1	One-third	Two-thirds	100	30% from work area, 70% from room	Dedicated exhaust duct from work area	Vented to outside	All under negative pressure or surrounded by negative-pressure plenums or ducts
Class II, Type B2	All	None	100	From room	Dedicated exhaust duct from work area	Vented to outside	All under negative pressure or surrounded by directly exhausted negative-pressure plenums or ducts
Class II, Type B3	Two-thirds	One-third	100	From common plenum	From common plenum	Vented to outside	All under negative pressure or surrounded by negative-pressure plenums or ducts
Class III	None	All	100% through one armport when glove removed (0.50-in. negative pressure)	From room	From work area	Vented to outside through double filters	All sealed and under negative pressure

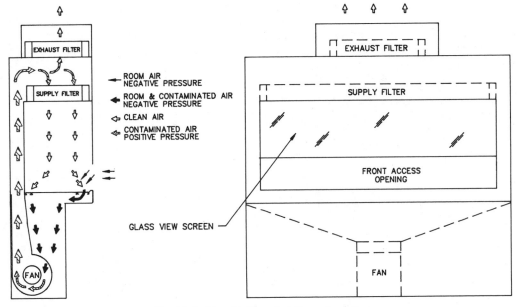

Fig. 4.3-4. Class II, Type A airflow schematic.

- Design Configuration: Supply and exhaust air should emanate from a common plenum. Both should be HEPA filtered.
- Filtration: The integral HEPA supply and exhaust filters should be DOP tested to be at least 99.97% efficient in filtering 0.3-μm particles and should be scan tested by the manufacturer to be leak free.
- Performance: The cabinet model type should be listed by the NSF for Standard 49. As an alternative, documentation should be produced to verify that all microbiological tests as specified in NSF Standard 49 or another acceptable international standard for Class II cabinets have been met by the model submitted.
- Electrical Integrity: The cabinet must be listed by the Underwriters Laboratory (UL) or certified by the Canadian Standards Association (CSA) for electrical safety. Current leakage should be no greater than 500 μamps to ground. Ground circuit resistance should not exceed 0.15 ohm.
- Testing Documentation: Each cabinet

should undergo a complete series of tests to ensure that it meets the requirements. A copy of the documentation must by provided with the cabinet.

Applications. The Type A cabinet is appropriate for work involving low- and moderate-risk biological agents. It protects the user and the environment from aerosols. In addition, it protects the work from exposure to contamination in the laboratory environment. Type A cabinets are useful for manipulations of recombinant DNA molecules at BL 1–3 (*Federal Register,* 1976, 1980, 1986) and infectious agents at BL 1–3 (Richardson and Barkley, 1988) and low- to moderate-risk biological agents treated with minute quantities of nonvolatile, toxic chemicals and trace quantities of radionuclides (National Sanitation Foundation, 1987).

Type A cabinets do not require an exhaust fan to work properly when the exhaust air is dumped into the laboratory environment.

In certain instances, the user may determine that it is desirable to vent this air to the outside through an air exhaust system. Reasons for doing this may include compliance with a particular city or state code, conformance with a regulatory or advisory authority or increased confidence in the dilution factor of an outside environment in the event of an undetected filter leak.

When connected to an exhaust system, Type B3 cabinets may also be used for preparation of cytotoxic drugs (ASHP, 1985, 1986; National Study Commission, 1987; U.S. Department of Labor, 1986; U.S. Department of Health and Human Services, 1983), in addition to the above.

Class II, Type B1 Cabinets

The classic Class II, Type B cabinet was developed to meet the requirements of the National Cancer Institute specification "General Purpose Clean Air Biological Safety Cabinet" (U.S. Department of Health, Education and Welfare, 1976).

As indicated previously, the classic Type B cabinet exhausts approximately two-thirds of its air and recirculates one-third. In addition, the Type B cabinet includes the following design elements which make it unique:

- All of the exhaust air is taken directly from the work area (direct exhaust) and

pulled through a dedicated exhaust duct into the facility's separate exhaust system to a fan on the roof. The one-third recirculated air is HEPA filtered immediately below the work surface before it is recirculated.

- All unfiltered air in the cabinet flows under negative pressure in dedicated ducts. All positive-pressure areas are essentially free of particulate contamination because of the location of the supply HEPA filter.
- All of the air volume handled flows down through the work area.

To clarify these design elements, the airflow schematic presented in Figure 4.3-5 shows the classic Type B design.

Directly above the work surface, the descending vertical airflow separates. Approximately two-thirds of this air is pulled directly off the rear portion of the work area—the cabinet's direct exhaust feature. This air flows through a dedicated negative-pressure plenum and passes through an exhaust HEPA filter. Once filtered, the air continues through the facility's own exhaust system to

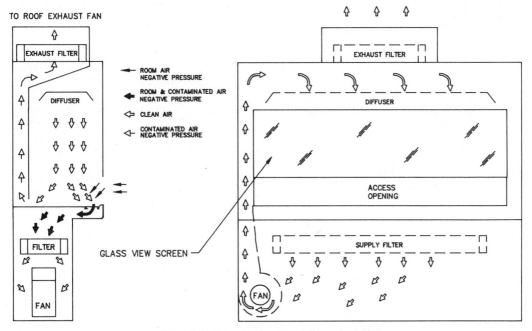

Fig. 4.3-5. Class II, Type B1 airflow schematic.

an appropriate treatment center or to the outdoors via a rooftop fan.

The remaining one-third of the descending air is pulled forward and into the front perforated grille. At the same time, room air enters the front perforated grille through the cabinet's front access opening. Together, this total volume (100%) immediately passes through the supply HEPA filter located directly below the work surface. Once it is HEPA filtered and has passed through the motor/blower, the air flows under positive pressure through a dedicated duct to the top of the cabinet. It then descends as the vertical airflow.

Additional advantages of the classic Type B cabinet are discussed in the section "Characteristics of Handling Vapors by Class II Cabinets."

Class II, type B1, minimum specifications

- Operational Airflow: Minimum intake air velocity should be 100 fpm. Approximately two-thirds of the total air delivered should be exhausted, and the one-third is recirculated through the cabinet.
- Design Configuration: Exhaust air should be pulled directly from the work area by a dedicated duct or plenum which relies on the building's exhaust system. The air supply consists of the air recirculated from the work area plus the intake air. All air is HEPA filtered before entering the blower and being delivered to the work area. All biologically contaminated areas of the cabinet should be maintained under negative pressure.
- Filtration: The integral HEPA supply and exhaust filters should be DOP tested to be at least 99.97% efficient in filtering 0.3-μm particles and should be scan tested by the manufacturer to be leak free.
- Performance: The cabinet model type should be listed by the NSF for Standard 49. As an alternative, documentation should be produced to verify that all microbiological tests as specified in NSF Standard 49 or another acceptable

international standard for Class II cabinets have been met by the model submitted.
- Electrical Integrity: The cabinet must be listed by the UL or certified by the CSA for electrical safety. Current leakage should be no greater than 500 μamps to ground. Ground circuit resistance should not exceed 0.15 ohm.
- Testing Documentation: Each cabinet should undergo a complete series of tests to ensure that it meets Class II requirements. A copy of the documentation must be provided with the cabinet.

Applications. The Class II, Type B1 cabinet is appropriate for work involving low- and moderate-risk biological agents and the handling of cytotoxic drugs, as well as certain chemicals in small quantities in an experimental research environment. It protects the user and the environment from aerosols. In addition, it protects the work from exposure to contamination in the laboratory environment.

Type B1 cabinets are useful for manipulations of DNA molecules at BL's 1–3 (*Federal Register,* 1976, 1980, 1986) infectious agents BL 1–3 (Richardson and Barkley, 1988) preparation of cytotoxic drugs, (ASHP, 1985, 1986; National Study Commission, 1987; U.S. Department of Health and Human Services, 1983; U.S. Department of Labor 1986), biological agents treated with minute quantities of toxic chemicals and trace amounts of radionuclides required as an adjunct to microbiological studies if work is done in the direct exhaust portion of the cabinet (National Sanitation Foundation, 1987) and low- to moderate-risk work involving chemical carcinogens (U.S. Department of Health, Education and Welfare, 1976).

Class II, Type B2 Cabinets (100% Total Exhaust)

The third type of Class II cabinet is the 100% Total Exhaust cabinet. This cabinet type is widely used in toxicology laboratories and similar applications in which chemical effluent is present but clean air conditions must be maintained.

As its name indicates, 100% of the cabinet air volume is exhausted to the outside or to a separate treatment facility which renders the effluent harmless. There is no recirculation of air within the cabinet.

Figure 4.3-6 provides a view of the airflow within the 100% Exhaust cabinet. Air enters through a motor/blower in the top of the cabinet and passes through a supply HEPA filter into the work area as the vertical airflow. Descending air is pulled into the base of the cabinet through the front and rear perforated grilles, where it is exhausted to the facility's separate exhaust system for proper treatment. Simultaneously, air entering through the cabinet's front opening is immediately pulled into the front intake grille, combined with the downflow air and immediately exhausted into the facility's exhaust system.

Class II 100% exhaust (type B2) minimum specifications

- Operational Airflow: Minimum intake air velocity should be 100 fpm. All of the air delivered by the supply air fan should be totally exhausted from the cabinet, along with all of the total intake air.
- Design Configuration: Both intake air and supply air should be pulled directly from the work area by a dedicated duct or plenum which relies on the building's exhaust system. Supply air shall consist of air taken from the laboratory air and HEPA filtered before being delivered to the work area. Exhaust air should be HEPA filtered before being discharged to the environment. All contaminated areas of the cabinet should be maintained under negative pressure or completely surrounded by directly exhausted negative-pressure areas.
- Filtration: The HEPA supply and exhaust filters should be DOP tested to be at least 99.97% efficient in filtering 0.3-μm particles and should be scan tested by the manufacturer to be leak free.
- Performance: The cabinet model type should be listed by the NSF for Standard 49. As an alternative, documentation should be produced to verify that

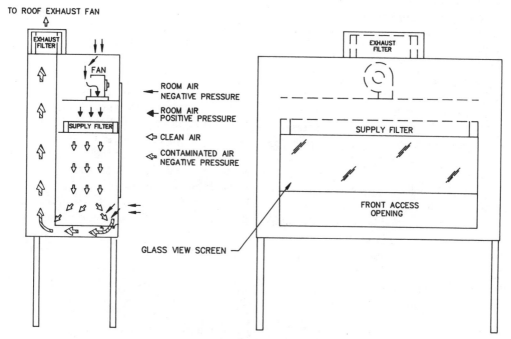

Fig. 4.3-6. Class II 100% exhaust airflow schematic.

all microbiological tests as specified in NSF Standard 49 or another acceptable international standard for Class II cabinets have been met by the model submitted.

- Electrical Integrity: The cabinet must be listed by the UL or certified by the CSA for electrical safety. Current leakage should be no greater than 500 μ amps to ground. Ground circuit resistance should not exceed 0.15 ohm.
- Testing Documentation: Each cabinet should undergo a complete series of tests to ensure that it meets Class II requirements. A copy of the documentation must be provided with the cabinet.

Applications. The Class II, Type B2 cabinet is appropriate for work involving low- and moderate-risk biological agents, as well as certain biological agents treated with toxic chemicals and radionuclides (National Sanitation Foundation, 1987). It protects the user and the environment from aerosols. In addition, it protects the work from exposure to contamination in the laboratory environment.

Class II, Type B2 cabinets are useful for the same work as are the B1 cabinets. In addition, they are more appropriate for a wider variety of chemicals and somewhat larger quantities.

Depending on the design, some may be viewed as clean-air, chemical fumehoods as opposed to biological safety cabinets with no recirculation of airflow. Design constraints on this type of equipment do not necessarily allow its use for all chemical applications, so the user must carefully consider its safety for each application.

Chemicals which can attack the HEPA filter medium will cause corrosion of work surfaces. Existing flammable or explosive conditions must be carefully evaluated for their suitability with this design.

Characteristics of Handling Vapors by Class II Cabinets

All types of Class II cabinets are required to provide containment and product protection

from particulate contaminants. The distinctions between Type A, Type B, and 100% Total Exhaust cabinets are most dramatic when the three types are subjected to tests for the handling of chemical vapors.

There has been increasing attention given to personnel and environmental protection from agents which are not microbial and which are volatile. Regardless of the cabinet's class or type, it is essential to remember that the HEPA filter traps particulates only. It is porous to gases and vapors. Therefore, it is important to know as precisely as possible what happens to volatile chemicals inside the different types of Class II cabinets.

Tests have been conducted to demonstrate the differences in performance among the three Class II cabinet types (Stuart et al., 1983). Toluene was evaporated by a generator whose location on the work surface was moved from the front to the rear. Air samples were taken at a single location in the center of the work area.

The results showed distinctly different patterns of vapor returns for each of the three cabinet types. See Figure 4.3-7.

In the Type A cabinet, vapor concentrations in the downflow air reached a constant value, which did not significantly change as the vapor source was moved from the front to the rear of the work surface.

In the Type B (B1) cabinet, dramatic changes took place as the vapor source was moved from the front to the rear of the work surface. When the source was placed in the front, the amount of vapor returned in the downflow air equaled that of the Type A cabinet. When the source was placed in the rear of the cabinet, the amount of vapor returned equaled that of the 100% Total Exhaust cabinet. This is due to the direct exhaust from the work area found in the Type B cabinet. The downward curve from front to rear shows that the vapor concentration in the Type B cabinet varied as a function of the location of the vapor source.

In the 100% Total Exhaust cabinet, with no recirculation of air, all vapor was removed. By the very nature of its design, the cabinet allowed no return of vapor in the downflow air.

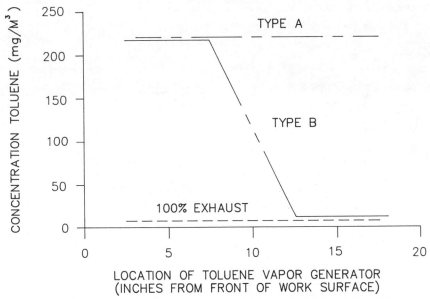

Fig. 4.3-7. Comparison of vapor handling characteristics of biological safety cabinets.

The results of this challenge affirmed that the performances of different types of Class II cabinets are distinctly different in terms of filtration, ventilation and airflow. The airflow in a Type A cabinet is not suited for work with hazardous vapors. When minute amounts of hazardous vapors are present, the 100% Total Exhaust or Type B cabinets should be considered. If vessels containing hazardous materials that might vaporize are placed in a Type B cabinet, they should be placed on the rear third of the work surface without blocking the flow of air into the exhaust plenum. That is, they should be placed in the "direct exhaust" portion of the cabinet.

This reference can be useful in predicting the amount of vapor that would be recirculated for a particular experimental protocol. If it is possible to quantify this value, it has great use for the safety professional in determining which (if any) cabinet design is suitable.

Class III Biological Safety Cabinet System

The Class III cabinet is a gas-tight enclosure for use with high-risk biological agents.

(*Federal Register,* 1976, 1980, 1986; Richardson and Barkley, 1988). Because this system provides the highest level of protection, it is used when absolute containment of highly infectious or hazardous experimental materials is required. Because of the sensitive nature of many procedures performed in a Class III cabinet system, equipment is built to the exact specifications of the user.

These physical-barrier cabinets are used to control airborne particulate contaminants generated during various procedures, including weighing and diluting chemical carcinogens, working with high-risk biological agents, working with high concentrations of low- or moderate-risk agents, or when using equipment which can generate a high volume of aerosols.

This class of safety cabinets provides the means to control airborne particulate contaminants, including microorganisms determined to be potentially harmful to personnel, the product and the environment. The system's gas-tight design protects personnel from contaminants within the enclosure, protects the product from contaminants in the ambient environment and protects the environment from exposure to potentially hazardous materials. See Figure 4.3-8.

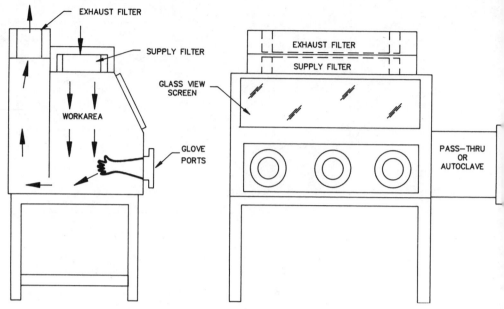

TO ADDITIONAL FILTRATION & ROOF EXHAUST FAN

EXHAUST FILTER

SUPPLY FILTER

GLASS VIEW
SCREEN

WORKAREA

GLOVE
PORTS

EXHAUST FILTER

SUPPLY FILTER

PASS—THRU
OR
AUTOCLAVE

Fig. 4.3-8. Class III cabinet schematic.

4.3.3 Testing And Servicing of Class II Biological Safety Cabinets

It may not be readily apparent that a Class II cabinet is operating properly. Air movement caused by an internal fan is no assurance of correct operation. A series of physical tests on the equipment must be conducted to assess its performance. These tests must be done by qualified individuals using proper instrumentation to be valid. Some institutions have people who test this type of equipment in-house, often connected with the Environmental Health and Safety or Facilities Engineering and Maintenance Departments or their counterpart. In the absence of in-house capability, there are a number of independent companies that perform this work, often called "certifiers." Testing should be monitored by the owner of the equipment for proper technique and evaluation of applicability. It is prudent to ensure that the persons performing these tests are independent of the supplier and installer so that no conflict of interest exists.

There are no requirements for the certification testing of Class II cabinets. There are

documents that may be used by the individual in charge of monitoring the testing. (Canadian Standards Association, 1987; U.S. Department of Health, Education and Welfare, 1975). Each institution must determine what constitutes a full test program for this type of equipment, including the test equipment to be used, qualifications of the test personnel and company, procedures to be followed and frequency of tests.

A complete series of operational tests should be done upon installation of a cabinet (before use) and at regular intervals thereafter, no longer apart than 1 year. If equipment is moved to a different location or damage is suspected, the tests should be repeated at that time. More frequent testing should be done if the risk assessment or other laboratory conditions indicate the necessity.

Each cabinet should be tested in accordance with the manufacturer's instructions or recommendations and certified by qualified people to meet the manufacturer's criteria for that product. The objective of these tests is to ensure that the cabinet is operating as intended by the manufacturer, as these tests are not a direct measure of its safety. In this context, "safety" is defined as the ability of a cabinet to contain a microbiological aerosol/tracer text which challenges the front access opening. This test was developed and used by the U.S. Army, National Institutes of Health, National Cancer Institute and others, and is generally considered to be a worldwide test for evaluation of cabinets. Unfortunately, it is not suitable for use as an in-site laboratory test because of the extra microbiological burden it would add to the lab environment.

Guidelines for passing the physical tests may be obtained from the manufacturer. In addition, the NSF has a list of all cabinets tested and listed under Standard 49; the list's data may be helpful in monitoring a test program.

Table 4.3-6 lists tests that are generally required to be run on a routine basis. Brief descriptions of the tests, equipment used and significance are included. For the individual who will be monitoring this function, a more complete set of requirements will be necessary and is available (Baker Company, 1988; Harvard University, 1988).

The user of the cabinet should perform routine tests to ensure proper operation and sterile conditions. Specific procedures will be determined by the laboratory supervisor to suit the work's needs. Maintenance responsibilities of the laboratory user are:

- Keep the equipment neat and clean and the cabinet components intact and in place.
- Provide surface disinfection of the work areas. Disinfectant and contact time will be determined by the agents used in the cabinet (Miller, 1986).
- Provide for gaseous decontamination of the entire cabinet. This may be done routinely—once or twice per year with the usual test program or as needed. That is, if access to the contaminated areas of the cabinet is required because of filter changes, maintenance or service, then gaseous decontamination may be needed. The decontaminant and

the procedures used will depend upon the agent(s) which have been used in the cabinet since its previous decontamination process (Fink et al., 1988; U.S. Department of Health, Education and Welfare, n.d. [b]).

Other routine maintenance of the cabinet will be desirable and can be done at the same time as testing. It should be done only by personnel with appropriate training for this task. Routine maintenance procedures include:

- A series of operational tests should be run to test the proper functioning of the cabinet. These tests well described previously and are listed in Table 4.3-7.
- HEPA filters should not be changed prematurely in order to minimize costs and hazards to maintenance personnel. As long as they pass the leak test and allow enough airflow to meet the cabinet's operating parameters, they should remain in the cabinet. If damage to a filter has occurred or the flow through the filter has dropped off so that it cannot remain within the operating parameters of the set point (usually 5% or more below the set point), the filter should be replaced. Obviously, a filter's structural life is limited, so judgment on filter replacement must be exercised in maintaining very old cabinets.
- Any monitoring equipment for the cabinet should be checked for proper operation and recalibrated and/or cleaned. This includes airflow measuring devices and pressure indicators. The method used will vary depending on the device.
- Germicidal lamps, if present, should be checked for intensity and replaced if below the acceptable limit of 40 microwatts per square centimeter. As the hours of use increase, the lamps lose intensity and effectiveness. This will mean fairly frequent bulb replacements. Germicidal lamps present a hazard to lab personnel, and their benefits probably do not outweigh their cost and risk.

Table 4.3-6. Tests for Class II Biological Safety Cabinets (To Be Conducted by Someone Other Than the Supplier and Installer)

Electrical safety tests

Objective: To verify the absence of electrical shock hazard

Description: Plug cabinet into test instrument and allow it to operate. Record electrical current leakage rate. Reverse polarity and repeat. Turn off cabinet, calibrate resistance test portion of tester, connect test lead to work surface. Record resistance.

Equipment: Electrical Safety Tester with 1K input impedance.

Cabinet integrity test

Objective: These tests are done to ensure that the cabinet is free of leaks. Leakage is defined according to the cabinet's classification and method of detection.

Description: Cabinet is pressurized either with air or with freon R12 gas. All seams are probed with the appropriate method and equipment. If leaks are located, they are repaired.

Equipment: (1) Soap bubble method: a soap solution is applied while the cabinet is held under pressure. Formation of bubbles indicates a leak. (2) Gas tightness (R12 freon) method: a halogen leak detector (capable of detecting 1×10^{-8} cc/sec) is used to locate leaks when the cabinet is held under 2"wg pressure with 100% R12 freon.

HEPA filter leak test

Objective: To verify leak tightness and integrity of the HEPA filters and their installation.

Description: A particulate challenge consisting of DOP (di-octyl-phthalate) or an acceptable nontoxic alternative is injected into the airstream of the cabinet. The clean side of the HEPA filters is probed by a light-scattering photometer which identifies leaks for repair or replacement of the filter.

Equipment: DOP generator calibrated to proper specification (Echols and Young, 1963). Aerosol photometer is capable of detecting an aerosol of 1×10^{-3} μg/liter of polydispersed DOP particles.

Airflow velocity measurements test

Objective: To verify that the airflows are set in accordance with the manufacturer's recommendations for the model of cabinet.

Description: Measuring airflow velocity in order to arrive at a direct or calculated measure of intake air velocity (average speed of the air entering the front access opening) and downflow air within the work area.

Equipment: A thermoanemometer mounted on a ring stand is most widely used. Depending on the difficulty of the particular installation (configuration of the exhaust vents), pitot tubes or a microprocessor-controlled micromanometer using multiple sampling points with back pressure compensating damper with an adapter to fit the front intake opening may be desirable, if not necessary.

Airflow direction test

Objective: To verify that the direction of flow within the cabinet is correct. Air should be entering through the front access opening, there should be no outflow of air from the cabinet to the room, and air should descend vertically within the work area.

Description: Use a smoke generator to trace along the front access opening and within the work area, and observe airflow direction.

Equipment: Any smoke source that delivers a continuous supply of smoke in moderate amounts (smoke pencil, smoke ventilation tubes, incense stick, cigarette).

Calibration of airflow monitors test

Objective: To ensure that the flow monitors and alarms are in working order and have been properly calibrated.

Description: The procedure will vary depending on the type of device and its intended purpose. Some of these are exhaust failure devices such as static pressure sensors and sail switches. Others are thermal sensing mass airflow monitors. Follow the directions of the manufacturer for the particular device.

Equipment: As required by the service.

4.3.4 Decontamination

Several methods are used in the laboratory for decontamination of biological safety cabinets. The reason for disinfection or decontamination is to protect personnel and the environment from hazardous organisms being used, as well as to prevent contamination of the experiment by other microorganisms in the laboratory environment. These reasons should be taken into consideration before the laboratory manager determines

Table 4.3-7. Certification Tests for Class II Biological Safety Cabinets—a Checklist

Test	Result*	
Electrical safety	Pass	Fail
Cabinet integrity		
Soap bubble	Pass	Fail (N/A)
Gas tightness	Pass	Fail (N/A)
HEPA filter leak		
Supply filter	Pass	Fail
Exhaust filter	Pass	Fail
Airflow velocity		
Supply	Pass	Fail
Exhaust	Pass	Fail
Airflow direction	Pass	Fail
Airflow monitor calibration	Pass	Fail (N/A)

*N/A = not applicable

the methods, substances and frequency of use to achieve these ends. The following methods are generally used in combination:

- Surface Decontamination: The method most widely used in laboratories to perform disinfection of cabinet surfaces is to apply liquid disinfectant and wipe the cabinet clean after the appropriate contact time (Miller, 1986). The disinfectant should be selected by the laboratory manager.
- Germicidal Light: While many cabinets are equipped with germicidal (or ultraviolet) lamps, their effectiveness is questionable and it is not worth the additional potential hazard of exposing the operator to the damaging light (Illuminating Engineering Society, 1972). Germicidal lamps are not necessary in a laminar flow biological safety cabinet. If proper sterile technique is used in the cabinet and surface disinfectant procedures are rigidly adhered to, a germicidal lamp in the work area is unnecessary and needlessly costly.
- Gaseous Decontamination: Whenever maintenance, service or repair is needed in a contaminated area of the cabinet, the unit should first be decontaminated by an appropriate agent. The National

Institutes of Health, the National Cancer Institute and the Center for Disease Control have recommended the use of formaldehyde gas for most microbiological agents. Its application requires individuals who are experienced in the decontamination of cabinets, since the gas itself is toxic. Procedures for decontamination are available (Fink et al., 1988; U.S. Department of Health, Education and Welfare, n.d. [b]).

The proper safety equipment (gas masks, protective clothing, etc.) should be used. Also, one must be sure that the gas being used will be effective against all of the biological agents in the cabinets.

Decontamination of chemical agents (as opposed to biological agents) used in biological safety cabinets requires specific procedures, depending on the chemical agent, the hazardous waste disposal policy of the institution and the availability of neutralizing agents for the chemical (ITT Research Institute, 1978; Kusick, 1981). It is possible to wet all areas within the cabinet with water or the neutralizing agent, thereby accomplishing decontamination to some extent. This involves a carefully planned and accomplished procedure in order to reach all areas of the cabinet.

4.3.5 Mechanical Considerations of Biological Safety Cabinets

Ventilation Requirements for Biological Safety Cabinets

Type A. This type of cabinet does not require a separate exhaust system for proper operation. The exhaust air from the cabinet is HEPA filtered, and the internal fan causes exhaust air to be pushed out of the cabinet. The air can be exhausted directly to the laboratory if the user and local codes permit that practice after a risk assessment is done.

Some users desire to vent the exhaust effluent to the outside, either as added insurance against the exhaust filter's developing leaks or to get rid of chemical odors from the work being performed. When the Type A cabinet is used as a Type B3 cabinet, exhaust must be vented to the outside.

When air is exhausted to the outside, there are two methods of exhaust ducting design available to the facilities designer: (1) direct exhaust connection and (2) thimble connection.

Direct exhaust connection is a sealed duct from the cabinet exhaust filter connection to the fan located on the roof. See Figure 4.3-9. When properly designed and installed, this method allows all of the cabinet's exhaust air to be removed from the laboratory. It also provides easy decontamination of the cabi-

net without disconnecting the exhaust system if an airtight damper is installed in the line.

Thimble connection to an exhaust system is used so that unexpected changes in the exhaust air volumes of the system will have minimal effects on the exhaust air volume of the cabinet. (National Sanitation Foundation, 1987; U.S. Department of Health, Education and Welfare, n.d. [b]. See Figure 4.3-10. In order for the thimble to work properly, it must be sized so that an open perimeter or gap is created around the perimeter of the exhaust filter in the cabinet. The exhaust air volume for the roof fan must be set to pull the volume of air necessary to make the cabinet operate properly plus the

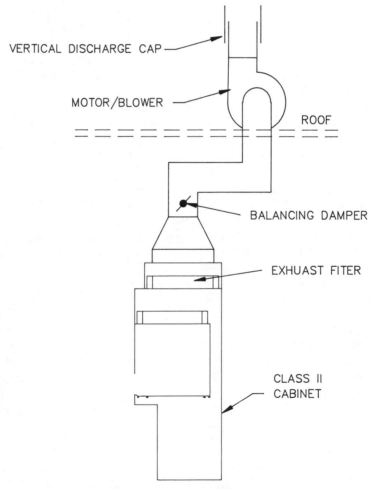

Fig. 4.3-9. Direct connected exhaust system.

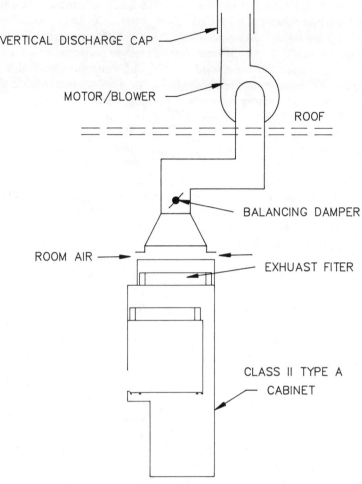

Fig. 4.3-10. Thimble connected exhaust system.

volume necessary to provide approximately 200 fpm velocity of room air through the gap. The gap and the extra air volume should be adequate to prevent outward air leakage to the room.

Connections to a duct system from a biohazard hood should be made through a cone-shaped transition (from a rectangular to a round duct) in order to minimize resistance. An access panel is desirable to allow testing of the exhaust filter without removal of the transition.

Types B1 and B2. These types of cabinets require a separate exhaust fan for proper functioning. They are incapable of exhausting air without the independent suction created by the roof-located fan. The exhaust system must be of the sealed, directly connected duct-type system. More suction (static pressure) will be required in these cabinets than in the other types.

Exhaust for these cabinets may be singly vented (one cabinet—one exhaust duct and fan) or ganged with other biological safety cabinets. The designer will find it simpler to achieve an adequately performing exhaust system with the single-cabinet, single-fan approach because it eliminates some variables.

If a ganged exhaust duct approach is to be used, the following guidelines should be followed:

1. Connect only biological safety cabinets of the same type together. Do not try to connect a Type B1 or B2 cabinet on the same system as a Type A or B3 cabinet or one with a chemical fumehood.
2. Install balancing dampers in the room near the cabinet, one damper for each cabinet.
3. Provide some form of accurate automatic volume sensing and control. If one cabinet is shut down and another continues to operate, the exhaust system must ensure that the proper volume from the operational cabinet remains constant. Acceptable operating parameters of biological safety cabinets are ± 5% of the exhaust air volume (National Sanitation Foundation, 1987).

Additional Exhaust Air Treatment. Most biological safety cabinets include a HEPA filter in their exhaust systems. If not, one must be included in the installation for the cabinet to be a biological safety cabinet. A clean-air fumehood may operate without an exhaust HEPA filter under some circumstances. In addition, further air treatment may be necessary or desirable, depending on the particular laboratory work. This should be determined by a risk assessment of the particular laboratory application and the implications of the effects of dumping effluent into the surrounding environment.

- Double HEPA filtration: This method is attractive if extra precautions against microbiological or particulate chemical escape to the environment are necessary. It will add a large static pressure requirement to the system. If the risk is severe enough to warrant double HEPA filtration, the use of a Class II cabinet may be questionable. The added risk may demand absolute containment equipment (Class III).
- Incineration: This may seem to be a good idea but will most likely not be cost effective initially or operationally. A true biological incinerator is ex-

tremely expensive to install and run correctly. Correct exposure time as well as correct temperature is necessary for effective incineration of microorganisms. There are no reasonable small-volume incinerators that will do an appropriate job when all biological safety cabinet exhaust air is passed through them. In addition, selection of an incinerator for a number of cabinets in a facility will require sophisticated research on that equipment.

- Chemical Removal and Treatment: This may seem desirable, but much study is needed before a proper selection of the system can be made. There are a variety of filters made for a broad range of chemical compounds. The selection of each filter must match the conditions of use in order for it to remove a specific gas or vapor from the airstream. In order to make a wise choice of chemical filter, the supplier must be aware of a number of conditions, such as the chemical to be filtered and its amount, other chemicals present in the airstream and their amounts and the speed of the airflow through the filter. It is difficult to determine the loading (or poisoning) of a chemical filter so as to change it at the correct time. If the filter is not changed in time, it can out-gas (interject back into the air) the filtered substances. Concentrating the laboratory chemicals in a filter may be a less desirable method of disposing of a large volume of concentrated hazardous waste than slow dilution to the atmosphere.
- Chemical Removal by a Water Wash System: This method of removing vapors and odors presents similar problems, is maintenance intensive and expensive, and has not been a desirable approach to the treatment of biological safety cabinet effluent.

Location of Exhaust Filter. In most biological safety cabinets the exhaust filters are an integral part of the cabinet. In certain types of design (B1 and B2) and with certain manufacturers, the user can choose the location of the exhaust filter. The facilities designer must decide if the filter should be located in the same laboratory as the cabinet, in a service penthouse or on the roof of the facility.

A comparison of the advantages and disadvantages of each location is presented in Table 4.3-8.

When deciding on the exhaust filter location, the designer should keep in mind that in Types A, B1 and B3 cabinets, supply filters will be contaminated with the same types of particles as exhaust filters. This awareness can be used to determine the procedures for changing both sets of filters.

Careful planning should be done when changing contaminated filters if they have not or cannot be decontaminated first. If the filters are located in the lab, changing may result in loss of contaminated particles into the lab. If they are located above the ceiling or on the roof, there may be difficulty in gaining proper access.

Exhaust Air Requirements. The following data are presented as general information to be used as a guide in sizing ventilation systems. Data vary by manufacturer, model and size. This initial information should be obtained before final calculations are made. See Table 4.3-9.

Exhaust systems must be designed and built to operate within strict tolerance of the air volume set point ($\pm$ 5%) (National Sanitation Foundation, 1987). In order to be certified, the supply and exhaust air volumes should be within $\pm$ 5 fpm of the manufac-

turer's recommended operational set point. The following must be kept in mind:

- In designing the exhaust system, the static pressure of the cabinet exhaust must be added to all other static pressure losses of the duct system in order to select the proper fan.
- These values are given to provide for a reasonable life of the HEPA filter. Reasonable life is assumed to be twice the initial pressure drop of the new (unloaded) HEPA filters. The longer the life of the filter, the less downtime involved and the lower the risk of changing contaminated filters. The designer may want to increase these minimum values if it is felt that a longer filter life is desirable from a cost and/or safety standpoint. It is usually good practice to arrive at the precise air volume.
- If a thimble-type connection is used for Type A or B3 cabinets, the volume used in calculating makeup air from the room through the thimble must be added to the volume of exhaust air from the cabinet.

Components and Characteristics of a Biological Safety Cabinet Exhaust System. The following list describes some of the components necessary for and unique to the exhaust system for biological safety cabinets. Also see Figure 4.3-11 for a schematic treatment.

- Transition from cabinet exhaust connection to duct. Whether directly con-

Table 4.3-8. Advantages and Disadvantages of Alternative Exhaust HEPA Filter Locations

Exhaust HEPA Filter Location	Advantages	Disadvantages
In laboratory	Confines contaminants to a single area Under control of lab space user	More difficult to change filter (on step-ladder) Possible contamination of lab during filter change
On roof	Easy access for safe changing All exhaust filters located in same area Usually accessible only to service personnel	Total duct work upstream of filter will be contaminated Accessible to all service personnel

Table 4.3-9. Exhaust Air Requirements for Various Types of Biological Safety Cabinets

Cabinet Type	Model Size (ft)	Exhaust Air Volume* (cfm)	Initial Static Pressure Required†	Suggested Lifetime Static Pressure Required†
A, B3	4	275	0.0 to −0.05	0.0 to −0.05
	6	400	0.0 to −0.05	0.0 to −0.05
B1	4	260	−0.40	−0.60
	6	375	−0.40	−0.60
B2	4	600	−0.75	−1.125
	6	1,000	−0.75	−1.125

*Expressed in cubic feet per minute.

†Expressed in inches of a water column (suction or negative values given).

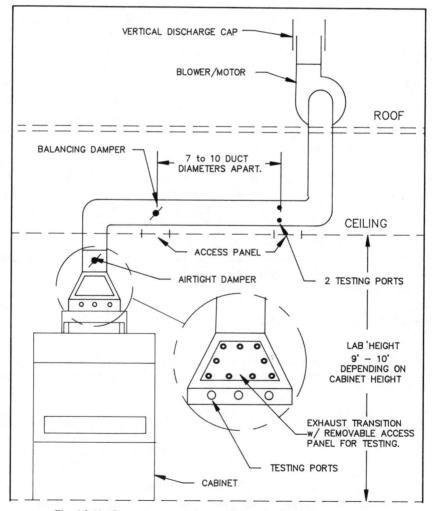

Fig. 4.3-11. Components and characteristics of a BSC exhaust system.

nected or thimble connected, the transition should be of gradual, smooth conical design to minimize static pressure. Room height must be taken into account, as some biological safety cabinets are quite high. Refer to drawings of a specific cabinet's dimensions to determine the required ceiling height.

- Removable access plate in transition or removable transition. Access to the top of the exhaust HEPA filter must be gained in order to allow proper scanning of the filter face to detect leaks.
- Airtight damper. This will enable easy gaseous decontamination of the cabinet system.
- Air-balancing damper. This should be located in the laboratory with the cabinet for easy access when testing.
- Ports in the duct to allow duct traversal with a pitot tube and/or thermoanemometer. The ideal location is 7 to 10 duct diameters away from any source of turbulence.
- Duct completely under negative pressure. No section of the duct system should be operated under positive pressure.
- Airtight joints in ductwork.
- Electrical interlock of the exhaust blower with the biological safety cabinet switch. This will prevent the user from turning on the cabinet if the exhaust fan is not operating. This is appropriate for cabinets with individual exhaust fans but may not be suitable for a ganged system.
- Exhaust air alarm monitor compatible with the owner's philosophy of system design and other control components.
- When calculating static pressure losses, include all duct components that add static pressure. An overestimate of losses can be adjusted for by dampering down to the desired level. An underestimate can be compensated for only by changing the fan and its components.
- Follow good design and installation practice for duct design (ASHRAE, 1975; Carrier, 1965).

Utilities and Connections

For some applications, biological safety cabinets do require services. Usually this is known at the time of purchase, and the service fixtures are installed in the cabinet for external connection. Some of these services will require special treatment because of their use. Examples are:

- Vacuum lines from a biological safety cabinet must be equipped with an appropriate filter or trap to prevent contamination of the vacuum pump or system by the infectious or hazardous materials in the cabinet.
- Air and other gas lines may require high purity or filtration.
- Flammable gas in a biological safety cabinet can be dangerous, since in most cabinet designs the air is recirculated back through the cabinet. This results in a buildup of gas which could be ignited. Flammable gas is often employed in laboratories to flame-sterilize equipment used in sterile manipulations. There should be no need for flaming in a Class II biological safety cabinet if materials are presterilized, the cabinet is working correctly and good procedures are used. Electrical devices are available for this purpose as an alternative to gas flames. In some cases, laboratories are allowed to use open flames in the cabinets with the consent of a safety professional. If this is the case, an easily accessible shut-off gas valve should be installed on the exterior of the cabinet, the petcock and piping should be properly labeled, a gas burner with a low flame and pilot light should be used and a shielded hose should be installed to prevent leaks. Tygon tubing should not be acceptable. Class II biohazard cabinets are not designed to be explosion or vapor proof.

Space and Weight Requirements

Dimensions and weights of biological safety cabinets vary, depending on the manufacturer, model, size and accessory equipment.

Model sizes are nominal; actual dimensions will generally be greater than the values in the chart expressed in feet. See Table 4.3-10.

Designers should allow for 12-in. access on all sides and at the top of the cabinet to enable complete testing of the cabinet with ease.

Heat Load

It is necessary to consider the heat load of a biological safety cabinet when designing air conditioning systems. See Table 4.3-11.

Effects of Building Ventilation Systems on the Performance of Biological Safety Cabinets

It is critical to maintain the airflow balance of biological safety cabinets if they are to continue to perform properly in the laboratory. The building's ventilation system is critical to this end, since small changes to exhaust and supply systems can easily cause imbalance to the cabinet's airflow. Since the desirable airflow parameters are ± 5 fpm of the original set point, there is only a small margin for change to the airflow volume.

If a Class II, Type A or B3 cabinet is used and its exhaust air is not ducted from the laboratory, there will be no effect on the cabinet's air balance due to varying laboratory ventilation conditions. However, if any type of cabinet is vented, a change in room conditions will affect the cabinet's airflow balance to some extent. The extent to which this occurs will determine whether or not the change to the cabinet's airflow balance re-

sults in diminished safety, sterile conditions or both. Using an appropriate design for the systems and controls can minimize or eliminate these effects so that the biological safety cabinet continues to function properly.

In a constant air volume (CAV) building design, it will be much easier to eliminate variable conditions that have an effect on the cabinet's air balance. With a variable air volume (VAV) design, there are more changing conditions to consider. The building's owner must be prepared to make some concessions based on the importance of all factors. Safety, room differential pressure, temperature and humidity control and energy conservation concerns may be mutually exclusive and may require a compromise on performance requirements (Takahaski and Okada, 1988)

Table 4.3-12 specifies the causal relationships between exhaust airflow volume from biological safety cabinets and room pressure or other room ventilation characteristics.

A VAV building design should compensate for these changes and should be able to keep a biological safety cabinet operating within its parameters when running. However, the response time of these control systems may not be adequate to adjust quickly to a change and may momentarily upset the cabinet's air balance. This fluctuation in exhaust air volume may result in the cabinet's operating in an imbalanced condition, which is unsafe. The alarms installed must indicate changes to these conditions. The building's owner should be prepared to respond to these alarms by correcting building ventila-

Table 4.3-10. Space and Weight Requirements of Biological Safety Cabinets

Cabinet Type	Model Size (ft)	Depth (in.)	Height (in.)	Weight Range (lbs.)
A, B3	4	34	80–96	500–1,000
	6	34	80–96	700–1,200
B1	4	34	91	900–1,100
	6	34	91	1,000–1,200
B2	4	34	90	700–1,000
	6	34	90	800–1,200

Table 4.3-11. Heat Load of Biological Safety Cabinets

Cabinet Type	Model Size (ft)	Sensible Heat Load (BTU/Hr)*
A, B3	4	1,700
	6	2,300
B1	4	1,800
	6	2,000
B2	4	1,200
	6	2,000

*This estimate of heat load will vary by manufacturer and model. The value is only for the biological safety cabinet (motor, light, electrical components). Any equipment used inside the cabinet which generates heat is not included here. This may be considerable in some cases.

tion systems. Personnel who have been trained in troubleshooting of laboratory HVAC systems must be readily available to respond to alarm conditions.

In any ventilation system used, the volume of air exhausted from the cabinet must remain reasonably constant for proper operation. Certification procedures generally use ± 5 fpm variance to airflow velocity set

points for compliance with the manufacturer's NSF values. In general, a building ventilation system is acceptable if it can be held within a ± 5% range of the volume required for the biological safety cabinet. National Sanitation Foundation, 1987. This is particularly critical if the performance envelope is unknown or is not very broad. That is, as the cabinet's airflow operating set point changes, the cabinet's performance will at some point degrade. The range of airflow settings within which a cabinet passes the performance tests of containment and product protection defines its performance envelope (Stuart, 1983).

Containment labs with exhaust ventilation should be kept under slight negative pressure at all times. The exhaust system for a biological safety cabinet should not be the sole source of negative room pressure. If it is, minor disturbances of the room pressure or air supply will have larger effects on the exhaust air volume. At times, a facility may have a small lab where a biological safety cabinet must be located. Adding room exhaust to a very small room may create air turbulence in

Table 4.3-12. Effects of Variables on the Exhaust Volume of a Biological Safety Cabinet

Given the following set of constant laboratory conditions, a change in one of these variables will affect the cabinet's exhaust air volume as indicated. Refer to Figure 4.3-12 for an illustration of the laboratory model.

Change to This Variable	Resultant Change to Cabinet Exhaust Air Volume (All Other Conditions Remaining Constant)
+ Room supply air volume	+
− Room supply air volume	−
+ Room exhaust air volume	−
− Room exhaust air volume	+
+ Room ΔP	+
− Room ΔP	−

Key: + = positive change
    − = negative change
    ΔP = differential pressure (if expressed in the negative, a positive change to the pressure will result in a value closer to 0.)

Note: A change to one of the variables listed will also change some of the other variables, as well as the cabinet's exhaust air volume. For example, condition 1 above will tend to increase the room air exhaust volume as well as the cabinet's exhaust air volume. Consequently, a direct relationship between two variables cannot be expected.

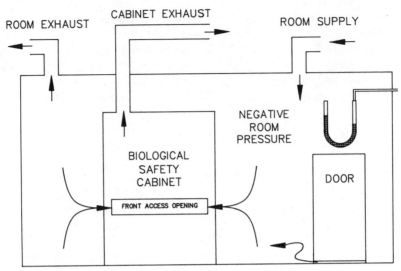

Fig. 4.3-12. Model for Table 4.3-12. Arrows indicate airflow direction.

the room, which causes disruption to the cabinet's air patterns, especially if the makeup air is of high velocity. This may be worse than allowing the cabinet exhaust to be the lone exhaust from the room. Once the installation is approved for use, procedures for lab personnel should be enforced to ensure that lab conditions do not change during cabinet operations. Some of the conditions that can be controlled are the door (open or closed), movement of people within the room and room air supply.

Monitoring of Exhaust Systems for Biological Safety Cabinets

Several methods are used to monitor the exhaust from biological safety cabinets when vented. The designer must first determine what must be monitored and why before selecting the monitor. Table 4.3-13 gives various monitoring options for exhaust air.

Keep in mind that if a monitor is chosen to sense the exhaust air volume, its sensitivity must match the range in which the cabinet

Table 4.3-13. Devices for Monitoring the Exhaust Air

Devices	Advantages	Disadvantages
For sensing the presence/absence of exhaust air:		
Manometer	Useful for go, no-go situations	No direct relationship to velocity (can become plugged to affect the results)
Sail switch	Useful for go, no-go situations	Can be easily bent or damaged; frequent maintenance required
For sensing the velocity or volume of airflow:		
Averaging pitot tube	Accurate if duct velocity is in appropriate range	Turbulence in duct affects accuracy
Thermoanemometer	Very accurate if installed and calibrated properly	Expensive; turbulence in duct affects accuracy; easily fouled and damaged
Mass airflow monitor	Direct indication of volume	

will operate. For example, if it is desirable to keep the cabinet within an operating range of ± 5% of the set point, the alarm must be reasonably sensitive at the cabinet exhaust airflow values to respond to that magnitude of change.

4.3.6 Electrical Services for Biological Safety Cabinets

The electrical services required for almost all biological safety cabinets is 120 volts, 60 cycles and 20 amps. The circuit should be dedicated to the cabinet. Ground fault protection on the circuit should be provided.

Many biological safety cabinets are listed by the UL or the CSA for electrical integrity, and this should be a requirement. In some cabinets, such as when process equipment requiring power is installed or in cabinet design modifications, the electrical listings may not be available. In those cases, it is important to verify that the cabinet has been manufactured to National Electrical Code specifications and to inspect and test the cabinet for electrical safety.

Fluctuation to line voltage will definitely have an effect on the performance of a biological safety cabinet (Jones et al., 1988). A heavily loaded electrical circuit will result in decreased voltage, affecting the airflow of the cabinet. In order to prevent this, the facility's circuit loads must be balanced and overloading prevented. In geographic areas where brownouts or power outages are not uncommon, a backup power system or voltage booster may be desirable or necessary.

If a biological safety cabinet is connected to an exhaust system, it may be wise to interlock the cabinet with the exhaust fan. Care must be taken to interlock in such a way that the design will prevent the operator from switching on the cabinet if the exhaust fan is not on. On the other hand, if the exhaust fan is inadvertently turned off, the unit can be interlocked to shut down as well. This is appropriate for a 100% Total Exhaust cabinet (Type B2), since the work area would become pressurized immediately, but may not be the best practice for a Type A, B3 or B1 cabinet, because these designs would continue to recirculate a significant portion of the air through HEPA filters, thereby providing some operator protection.

Electrical interlocks are not a substitute for good exhaust volume monitoring. As a go or no-go safeguard, however, they are worthwhile. Air volume monitoring is still necessary for alerting the user to unacceptable conditions as opposed to warning of a total failure of exhaust.

GLOSSARY

Aerosol—A colloid of liquid or solid particles suspended in a gas, usually air.

Agent—Any biological, chemical or physical substance capable of acting on a subject organism, usually to its detriment.

Biological safety cabinet—A work area that provides primary containment of aerosols.

Certification—A procedure to ensure that biological safety cabinets meet the criteria of physical testing; usually includes air balancing, filter integrity, cabinet integrity, electrical grounding, etc.

Concentration—The relative content of a component.

Cytotoxic drug—A drug poisonous to cells.

Decontamination—The destruction or reduction of hazardous entities to safe levels.

Disinfectant—A chemical agent which kills or inactivates microorganisms.

Duct—A tube or channel that conveys a substance, usually air.

DOP (dioctylphthalate)— Oil used to generate an aerosol of particles to challenge HEPA filters (Other substances which may be less toxic dioctyl sebecate [DOS] can be used as acceptable substitutes.)

Flammable—Capable of being easily ignited and of burning quickly.

fpm (feet per minute)— A unit measure of velocity.

Gas—A formless fluid which tends to occupy an entire space uniformly at ordinary temperatures and pressures.

HEPA filter—A high-efficiency particulate arrestance filter, technically capable of retaining 99.97% of all 0.3-μm particles.

Incineration—Burning a substance to ashes in order to effect sterilization.

Laminar Airflow (better called "unidirectional airflow" in biological safety cabinets)— Air flowing in a single pass in a single direction through a clean room or a clean zone with generally parallel streamlines (Federal Standard 209D).

Micrometer—A unit of length equal to 10^{-6} m.

Operational set point—The intake and supply air flow balance values at which a Class II biological safety cabinet is set to or is found to be operating at when in use.

Particulate—Minute separate portions of a substance.

Performance envelope—The range of intake and supply airflow balance set points within which a Class II biological safety cabinet will pass the standard microbiological aerosol tracer tests.

Plenum—An enclosed space in which the pressure of air is greater or less than that of the atmosphere outside. In Class II cabinets, it is also a chamber for conveying or containing air.

Radionuclide—A radioactive atom characterized by the constitution of its nucleus.

Nominal set point—The intake and supply airflow balance values at which the manufacturer of a Class II biological safety cabinet determines the cabinet to be operated (NSF Standard 49).

Static pressure—The potential pressure exerted in all directions by a fluid at rest. For a fluid in motion, it is measured in a direction normal to the direction of flow. Usually expressed in inches on a water gauge.

Sterile—An environment or material free of viable microbes.

Suction—The result of exerting negative pressure within a duct or plenum.

Thermoanemometer—A nondirectional air velocity measuring instrument.

Thimble (canopy hood)—An exhaust connection which allows air from the room to make up for variations in the exhaust system without unbalancing the cabinet.

Vapor—The gaseous form of substances which are normally in the solid or liquid state.

Velocity—The rate of linear motion in a given direction.

Vent—An opening for the escape of a gas or liquid for the release of pressure.

Volatile—A chemical that vaporizes or evaporates quickly. Likely to be unstable or explosive.

Volume—The amount of space occupied by a three-dimensional figure, as measured in cubic units.

REFERENCES

American Society for Hospital Pharmacy, 1985. ASHP Technical Assistance Bulletin on Handling Cytotoxic Drugs in Hospitals. *American Journal of Hospital Pharmacy*, Vol. 42, 131–137.

American Society for Hospital Pharmacy, 1986. OSHA Work Practice Guidelines for Personnel Dealing with Cytotoxic (Antineoplastic) Drugs. *American Journal of Hospital Pharmacy*, Vol. 43, 1193–1204.

ASHRAE, 1975. *Laboratory Methods of Testing Fans for Rating*. ASHRAE Standard 51–75 and AMCA Standard 210–74. Atlanta, GA: American Society of Heating, Refrigerating and Air Conditioning Engineers.

Baker Company, Inc., 1988. *Seminar—Safety Cabinet Technology*. Sanford, ME: Baker Company, Inc.

Canadian Standards Association, 1987. *Biological Containment Cabinets: Installation and Field Testing*. CAN/CSA-Z316.3-M87. Rexdale (Toronto), Ontario: Canadian Standards Association.

Carrier Air Conditioning Company, 1965. *Handbook of Air Conditioning System Design*. New York: McGraw-Hill.

Echols, W. H., and Young, J. H., 1963. *Studies of Portable Air Operated Aerosol Generators*. Washington, DC: Protective Chemistry Branch, Chemistry Division, U.S. Naval Research Laboratory.

Federal Register, 1976. *Recombinant DNA Research Guidelines*, Vol. 41, No. 131. Part II. Washington, DC: U.S. Government Printing Office.

Federal Register, 1980. *Guidelines for Research Involving Recombinant DNA Molecules*, Vol. 45, No. 20. Washington, DC: U.S. Government Printing Office.

Federal Register, 1986. *Guidelines for Research Involving Recombinant DNA Molecules*, Vol. 51, No. 88. Washington, DC: U.S. Government Printing Office.

Fink, R., Liberman, D. F., Murphy, K., Lupo, D., and Israeli, E., 1988. Biological Safety Cabinets, Decontamination or Sterilization with Paraformaldehyde. *American Industrial Hygiene Association Journal*, Vol. 49, No. 6, 277–279.

Harvard University, School of Public Health, Department of Environmental Health Engineering, 1979. *Certification of Biological Safety Cabinets*. Manual for Harvard Workshop. Boston: Harvard University School of Public Health.

IIT Research Institute, 1978. *The Safe Handling of Chemical Carcinogens in the Research Laboratory: An NCI Training Course*. Washington, DC: National Cancer Institute, Office of Research Safety.

Illuminating Engineering Society, 1972. *IES Lighting Handbook—The Standard Lighting Guide*. Baltimore: Committee on Hazardous Substances in the Laboratory, Illuminating Engineering Society.

Jones, R. L., Greenier, T. J., Stuart, D. G. and Eagleson, D., 1988. Potential Solution to Voltage Fluctuation in Biological Safety Cabinets. Paper read at the 31st Biological Safety Conference, October 9–12, Bethesda, MD.

Kusick, Blaine C. 1981. Prudent Practices for Handling Hazardous Chemicals in Laboratories. Science Vol. 211; p. 777–780.

Miller, Brinton, ed., 1986. *Laboratory Safety: Principles and Practices*. Washington, DC: American Society for Microbiology.

National Research Council, Assembly of Mathematical and Physical Sciences, 1981. *Prudent Practices for Handling Hazardous Chemicals in Laboratories*. Washington, DC: National Academy Press.

National Sanitation Foundation, 1987. *Standard Number 49: Class II (Laminar Flow) Biohazard Cabinetry*. Ann Arbor, MI: National Sanitation Foundation.

National Study Commission on Cytotoxic Exposure, 1987. *Recommendations for Handling Cytotoxic Agents*. Boston: National Study Commission on Cytotoxic Exposure.

Rake, B., 1983. Definition of the Performance Envelope of a Class II Biological Safety Cabinet. Paper read at the 25th Biological Safety Conference, October 17–19, Houston, TX.

Richardson, John, and Barkley W. Emmett, eds., 1988. *Biosafety in Microbiological and Biomedical Laboratories*. U.S. Department of Health and Human Services Publication No. (NIH) 88–8395. Washington, DC: U.S. Government Printing Office.

Rockville Bio-Engineering Services, Dow Chemical USA, 1975. *A Workshop for Certification of Biological Safety Cabinets*. Workshop Manual. Rockville, MD: Dow Chemical USA.

Stuart, D., 1983. A Performance Envelope Concept for Biological Safety Cabinets. Paper read at the 25th Biological Safety Conference, October 17–19, Houston, TX.

Stuart, D. G., First, M. W., Jones, R. L., and Eagleson, J. M., Jr., 1983. Comparison of Chemical Vapor Handling by Three Types of Class II Biological Safety Cabinets. Particulate *and Microbial Control,* Vol. 2, 18–24.

Takahashi, A., and Okada, T., 1988. Study of Constant Airflow Rate and Constant Room Pressure Control Systems for Physical Containment Laboratories. *Journal of Environmental Science,* Vol. 31, 56–61.

U.S. Department of Health, Education and Welfare, n.d. (a). *Design and Construction Standard. Subject: Installation of Canopy Hoods for Class II Type A Biological Safety Cabinets*. Bethesda, MD: National Institutes of Health, Division of Engineering Services.

U.S. Department of Health, Education and Welfare, n.d. (b). *Formaldehyde Decontamination of Laminar Flow Biological Safety Cabinets*. Slide program and pamphlet. Bethesda, MD: National Institutes of Health, Office of Biohazard and Environmental Control.

U.S. Department of Health, Education and Welfare, 1975. *Certification of Class II (Laminar Flow) Biological Safety Cabinets*. Slide program and pamphlet. Bethesda, MD: National Institutes of Health, Office of Biohazards and Environmental Control.

U.S. Department of Health, Education and Welfare, 1976. *National Cancer Institute Safety Standards for Research Involving Chemical Carcinogens*. DHEW Publication No. (NIH) 76–900. Washington, DC: U.S. Government Printing Office.

U.S. Department of Health, Education and Welfare, 1976. *NCI Specification: General Purpose Clean Air Biological Safety Cabinet (Class II Type 2 Safety Cabinet)*. Bethesda, MD: National Cancer Institute.

U.S. Department of Health and Human Services, 1983. *Recommendations for the Safe Handling of Parenteral Antineoplastic Drugs*. NIH Publication No. 83–2621. Washington, DC: U.S. Government Printing Office.

U.S. Department of Labor, 1986. *Work Practice Guidelines for Personal Dealing with Cytotoxic (Antineoplastic) Drugs*. OSHA Instruction Pub. 8–1.1. Washington, DC: Office of Occupational Medicine, Occupational Safety and Health Administration.

4.4 FUMEHOODS *T. Ruys*

4.4.1 Introduction

Much has been written about laboratory fumehoods. It is not the intent to cover the ins and outs of hood design, construction and installation, but rather to provide a guide for their selection from among a number of types, the options available, and the reason for their selection, the regulations, standards, and codes that apply to laboratory fumehoods and safety issues.

The primary purpose of a fumehood is to contain and dispose of the effluents generated by the work performed inside the hood, with or without the operator's presence. The following points should be noted:

- The need for a fumehood should primarily be decided by the individual responsible for the operation. This section will address the selection of the type of fumehood, not the reason.

- A fumehood is a safety device, so the selection of the manufacturer is crucial. Those listed in Appendix B have been found to make a good product. Others may be acceptable, but the performance of their product should be verified under the test conditions outlined in this section.
- Much research and testing have gone into the production of available fumehoods, and it can be assumed that those from reputable manufacturers perform well. However, other forces influence the performance of the fumehood, such as the mechanical system, airflow, presence and work practices of the operator, location in the laboratory, and location and velocity of the makeup air. These forces will be discussed, but not the design of the hood itself.
- The trend is toward more fumehoods as more chemicals are classified as hazardous.

Misconceptions

There are several misconceptions in the literature (Reinhart, 1977):

- The reason often given for the adjustable slots inside the fumehood is that it exhausts heavier- or lighter-than-air gases or fumes. So much air is exhausted through a standard fumehood that the fumes take on the characteristics of air. The adjustable slots are designed to direct the air for best performance and should be fixed after testing in place is done or the final location of the fumehood is established. The slots should be changed only by air-balancing personnel.
- The reason given for not combining fumehood exhaust ducts into a common system is that incompatible chemicals may react violently. Vapors are diluted by the air drawn through the hood to such low levels that chemical reactions yielding significant energy levels are highly unlikely. For example, vaporiz-

ing a quart of liquid per minute in a hood exhausting 1,000 cfm will produce less than a 1% concentration of vapor.
- In order to decontaminate a hood, it may be necessary to close a control damper in the duct. This is often given as a reason why fan motors are overloaded and burn out. The opposite is true. Fans are overloaded if more air is exhausted than the rated design calls for.

Noise Control

High noise levels are a common complaint with fumehood systems. These may be caused by the fumehood design, the fan and the ducts. Noise is caused by moving air and fan vibration transmitted to the duct. The goal of hood design is to minimize static pressure levels. The following will minimize noise:

- Baffle plenum velocity should be approximately half the slot velocity, and slot velocity should not exceed 1,200 fpm.
- The hood collar must have a 1-in. radius between the chamber and the duct, and the air velocity must not exceed 1,400 fpm at this point. Provide a 12-in. diameter sleeve for a 6-ft hood and two 10.5-in. sleeves for an 8-ft hood or larger.
- Air velocity in the duct must not exceed 1,600 fpm, unless dust and other solid particles must be exhausted.
- Locate the fan as remotely as practical; fan rotation should not exceed 1,800 rpm.
- A squirrel cage fan produces less air noise than a backward-inclined airfoil fan. Forward-curved fan blades move more air with less velocity and may even be less noisy.
- A vibration isolator must be installed between the fan and the duct, such as a flexible, neoprene-coated glass fiber cloth.

- The fan must be mounted on vibration isolators.
- Locate volume control dampers away from the fumehood.
- Specify sound rated ballast on light fixtures.

Noise in a laboratory should not exceed 50 dB on the NC curve, but 63–65 dB is more realistic. OSHA allows 90 dB average for 8 hours on the A scale, but this is intolerable for fumehood operations.

4.4.2 Fumehood Types*

There are many types of hoods, such as canopy hoods, equipment exhaust hoods, biological safety cabinets and chemical fumehoods. This section covers the last type. Other hoods are discussed elsewhere in this handbook. See Table 4.4-1.

Fumehoods come in various types and sizes, depending on their function. This section describes the various options commercially available; it makes no attempt to describe the design features. That information is readily available from the manufacturers and the extensive literature on the subject.

Fumehoods are designed to contain var-

---

*See the glossary of terms at the end of this section.

ious levels of hazardous materials or to enclose certain apparatus. Examples of the former are the standard balanced bypass air hood, the radioisotope hood and the perchloric acid hood. Examples of the latter are the walk-in hood and the distillation hood. In addition, the auxiliary air feature has been introduced that can be applied to all hoods. Most fumehood types come in 4 ft 0 in., 5 ft 0 in., 6 ft 0 in. and 8 ft 0 in. lengths.

Standard Fumehoods (or Bench-Type Hood)

The most common type (see Figure 4.4-1) is an extension of the chemistry bench with the superior protection of directional airflow. A number of design modifications over the years have improved its ability to capture and contain contaminants by reducing turbulence, primarily by introducing airfoils at the jambs and sill of the fumehood opening.

"Balanced bypass air" refers to the feature whereby the makeup air enters the hood through a grille or opening above the sash when the sash is lowered so that the air exhausted is "balanced," or approximately the same, at all times. The bypass also limits the maximum velocity of the air. This is important, considering the fact that high air veloc-

Table 4.4-1. Examples of Hoods That Are Not Chemical Fumehoods

Type	Covered	Comments
Canopy hood	Figure 3.8	Used over equipment to capture heat, moisture, noxious odors.
Conventional hood		Should not be used for chemical fumehood because of poor aerodynamics.
California hood		Distillation hood with access from front and back. Should not be used for chemical fumehood.
Laminar flow cabinet		Directional airflow cabinet to protect the work and/or operator from airborne particles. This is not a chemical fumehood.
Biological safety cabinet	Chapter 4.3	Directional airflow cabinet to protect the operator. This is not a chemical fumehood.
Glove box	Chapter 4.3	Air enclosure; sealed from its surrounding and operable through gloves. This is not a chemical fumehood.
Local exhaust		Point exhaust on fixed or flexible duct. Slot velocity must be 2,000 fpm or greater. This is not a chemical hood.

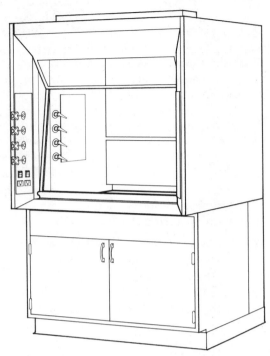

Fig. 4.4-1. Standard fumehood (Kewaunee Scientific Corp).

ities inside the hood are undesirable for several reasons.

This fumehood comes with a vertical sliding sash, a horizontal sliding sash or a combination of both. Horizontal sliding sashes with the proper glass may be used as safety shields, and are advocated to reduce the face opening and thus conserve energy because of lower exhaust air needs. However, horizontal sliding sashes are often not acceptable to users and building owners because they limit access to the hood, are frequently removed and create more turbulence in the hood. A combination of horizontal sliding panels inside a vertical sliding sash may be the best compromise but is also the most costly.

A fumehood without airfoils, air bypass or sashes should not be considered a chemical fumehood, but it can still be useful for exhausting of noxious odors, heat and steam. See Table 4.4-1.

Fumehoods may be delivered to the job site prewired and preplumbed, depending on local labor union conditions and specifications. It must be clear who is responsible for internal wiring and plumbing on the job site to avoid disputes.

All electrical devices, i.e., receptacles, switches and lighting fixtures, must have a UL label or equivalent.

Radioisotope Hood

This fumehood, as the name implies, is used for work with radioisotopes. It is identical to the standard hood except that the material of the liner and top is designed for easy cleaning and is typically made of stainless steel, seamless and with coved corners and joints. Various filters may be part of the exhaust system. The work top must be able to support 200 lb/sq ft.

Perchloric Acid Hood

This fumehood is used for perchloric acid digestion. It is identical to the standard hood in design and is similar to the radioisotope hood, with a stainless steel interior and coved corners and joints. However, there are certain features that are included in this type of hood because the perchloric acid residue reacts with organics, is explosive and condenses in the exhaust system:

- Nonorganic liner, ducts, coating or sealants in contact with the exhaust air. Material is typically 316 stainless steel.
- A washdown system which flushes the fan housing, duct and plenum behind the baffles. A shutoff valve is provided at the hood because the washdown system should be used daily or after every use.
- A trough below the plenum to catch the flushing water, with a drain large enough to handle the volume of water generated.
- In order to flush the duct properly, it is advisable to flush it along the full length of the duct and to install the exhaust duct in a vertical direction.

Walk-in Fumehood

This fumehood is not intended to be walked into, but it is designed to accommodate tall equipment and therefore has a work surface at floor level. See Figure 4.4-2. At times, a hinged work surface is provided at a normal bench height so that the hood can be used for normal operations when not in use for tall equipment. This type of hood comes with a vertical or horizontal sliding sash.

Distillation Fumehood

This fumehood is specifically designed for distillation. It is like any distillation bench except that it is enclosed with a fumehood. See Figure 4.4-3.

Auxiliary Air Fumehoods

In addition to the fact that fumehoods are designed to accommodate equipment and chemicals, another feature has been introduced to minimize the use of conditioned air and possibly lower the cost of operation.

The makeup air is drawn from the outside or another part of the building instead of from the laboratory itself, and is supplied above and outside the hood face. See Figures 4.4-4 and 4.4-5.

Typically, auxiliary air hoods make sense under the following conditions:

• When there are many fumehoods in the laboratory, i.e., when the makeup air for the hood exceeds the air volume needed to ventilate the laboratory. Assume two 6-ft fumehoods in a 500-NASF laboratory.
 The makeup air needs are:
 2 hoods × 12 sq ft face opening × 100 fpm face velocity =
 2,400 cfm

The ventilation air needs are:

Room volume × changes per hour divided by 60 minutes

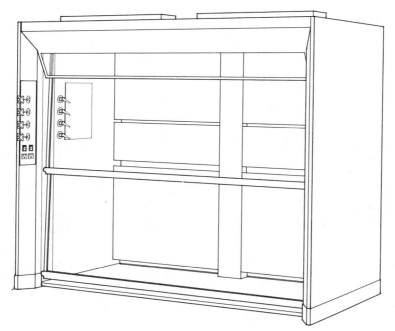

Fig. 4.4-2. Walk-in fumehood (Kewaunee Scientific Corp).

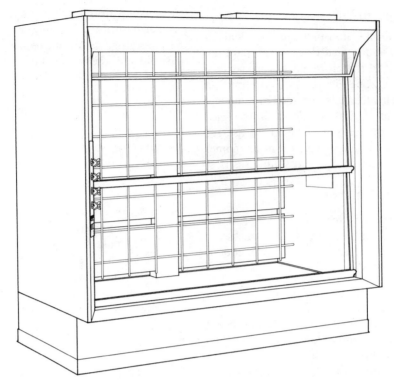

Fig. 4.4-3. Distillation fumehood (Kewaunee Scientific Corp).

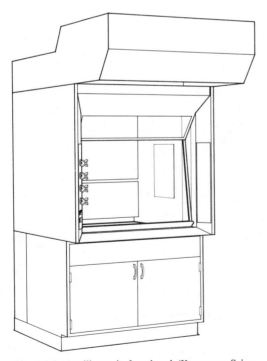

Fig. 4.4-4. Auxiliary air fumehood (Kewaunee Scientific Corp).

$$\frac{\begin{array}{c}500 \text{ square feet} \times 8 \text{ ft } 6 \text{ in.} \\ \text{ceiling height} \\ \times\ 10 \text{ changes/hour}\end{array}}{60 \text{ minutes}} = 708 \text{ cfm}$$

There is a large discrepancy between the exhaust air needed and used. If we put stops on the sash at 18 in. (previously at 30 in.), the calculation for makeup air is:

2 hoods × 7.5 sq ft face opening × 100 fpm face velocity = 1,500 cfm and provide auxiliary air at 50% = 750 cfm

The exhausted air through the fume-hoods is about what is needed to venti-late the laboratory. Ventilation rates, needed face velocities, percentage of makeup air from the lab, number of hoods, square feet of lab area and ceil-

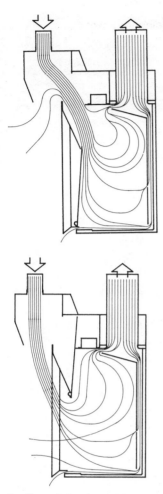

Fig. 4.4-5. Auxiliary air hood operation. Auxiliary air is filtered air obtained from outside the building or from nonlaboratory areas within the building. The air need not be cooled for warm weather operation, but it should be tempered to near room temperature for cold weather operation. (Kewaunee Scientific Corp).

ing heights are, of course, variables, and some hood users will not accept the limitations of the sash stop at 18 in.

- Auxiliary air hoods are also safer, if properly designed and maintained, because they overcome the low-pressure area in front of the operator standing in front of the hood and create an air curtain forcing air away from the operator's breathing zone. The air curtain must be evenly distributed along the hood face opening and of low velocity (200 fpm); otherwise, it will draw con-

taminants from the hood by the Venturi effect into the laboratory.

- Auxiliary air does not need to be conditioned because it is exhausted immediately, but it is often cooled to within 5°F of room temperature. However, it must be heated if lower than 70° to 72°F, because of discomfort to the operator, in order to maximize capture and to minimize the effects on temperature-sensitive equipment and procedures. Auxiliary air hoods are therefore more economical in temperate climates or where exhaust air from office areas or corridors can be used. However, the impact of humidity on the activities inside the hood must also be considered when selecting this type of hood.

Fumehood Selection

Fumehoods are selected, first, for safety reasons and, second, for their energy-saving design. The exhaust system design is selected for safety, trouble-free operation and the degree of energy recovery. See Table 4.4-2. Construction costs should not be an issue in selecting and installing a fumehood because of the reasons for this device. However, operating cost considerations definitely are a part of the selection process.

4.4.3 Factors That Affect Fumehood Performance

Hood Performance

Many of the problems with fumehood performance can be explained with a simple experiment. A person can make a candle flame flicker from a considerable distance by blowing at it, but cannot do so by inhaling the same amount of air at the same velocity even from a very short distance. This phenomenon accounts for the following:

- It is much more difficult to capture and pull contaminants into the fumehood than it is to disrupt the air at the hood face and blow contaminants out of the hood.

Table 4.4-2. Sample Form for Fumehood Selection

Project:	Date:	By:
Type of Fumehood	Size:	Quantity:

Function
Description of Use:

Chemicals and Quantities:
(Threshold limit Values)

Sash Operation
Vertical ( )   Horizontal ( )   Stop at 18 inches ( )

Materials
Top: Liner:

Base Units
Standard ( )   Acid Storage ( )   Flammable Storage ( )   None ( )
Material: Steel ( )   Hardwood ( )   PLAM ( )

Utilities (list quantities)

Cold Water	( )	Gas	( )	120 V Receptacle ( )
Cup sink	( )	Air	( )	208 V Receptacle ( )
Sink	( )	Vacuum	( )	
CW Flush	( )	Other	( )	_____

Mechanical
Face Velocity: fpm (average)
Duct Material:
Fan Location:
System: Single Hood/Fan ( )   Multiple Hood/Fan ( )   Auxiliary Air ( )
Fan Control: Automatic ( )   Switch at Hood ( )

Performance
ASHREA 110 Rating: _____ AM _____
(See recommendations in *ACGIH Ventilation Manual*)

- A person walking at 3 mph hour will generate a 264-fpm air velocity. A 100 fpm face velocity represents only 1.13 mph.
- Room air supply grilles must not blow directly at the hood face unless they have a throw velocity of only one-half to two-thirds of the face velocity (Caplan & Knutson, 1978; ACGIH, latest ed.). Even lower velocities are advisable to maximize hood performance.
- Items within the hood must be placed at least 6 in. back from the sash; otherwise, incoming air will bounce back and blow contaminants into the laboratory.

This bounced air force will easily overcome the pulled air entering.
- Any leaks in the fumehood system will drastically reduce the face velocity.

The best performance provides maximum protection with the least amount of air. The purpose of a fumehood is to contain contaminants. The factors affecting its performance will now be discussed.

Mechanical System

- The performance of the airflow through a fumehood depends on a delicate balance. Even if the exhaust and makeup air systems are designed properly, which unfortunately is not always the case, the system must be balanced. Improperly balanced systems are the leading cause of poor hood performance. Time also has an effect: Fan belts start slipping, fan blades may be corroded and leaks may develop in the duct. When first installed, the fan may be connected in reverse at only 20% of the exhaust capacity or the wrong voltage may be provided, resulting in lower fan efficiency.

- Over time, additional fumehoods may be added, which will disturb the air balance of the systems. A common problem in hood performance is inadequate room makeup air.

Airflow Characteristics and Quantity

- The quantity and velocity of air affect performance. Too much as well as too little air will effect fumehood performance.
- The face velocity of air required at the hood face is a function of the hazards anticipated. Table 4.4-3 gives the hazards and associated airflows recommended. Airflows higher than 125 fpm may cause more turbulence inside the hood and create backflow into the laboratory. More is not better in this case.
- The air velocity inside the exhaust duct should be in the range of 1,400 to 1,700 fpm but no higher, because it will increase air noise. About 1,800 fpm is required in order to move particulate matter.

- The makeup air for an auxiliary air hood should be balanced, like that of any other hood, but at low velocity and in a laminar airflow fashion above the hood face. The air velocity leaving the auxiliary air grille must not exceed 200 fpm and must be directional so that it can be captured by the hood.
- Air velocity should not exceed 20 fpm at the hood face from any source: ceiling diffusers, open doors or windows, etc. measured with the exhaust fan turned off.
- The presence of the operator produces a low-pressure zone in front of the operator, which may create backflow from the fumehood into the breathing zone of the operator. Auxiliary fumehoods, designed and maintained properly, minimize this negative pressure and therefore may be safer. They also direct airflow away from the breathing zone toward the hood opening.
- A person walking by the fumehood may create enough backdraft temporarily to reverse the airflow into the hood. To minimize this problem, locate hoods away from traffic paths wherever possible.

Location and Velocity of Makeup Air

- The location of the makeup air must not create the problems mentioned earlier in the discussion of airflow. The makeup air grille should be located on the side wall or on a remote ceiling diffuser, not opposite the fumehood face, and the air must be discharged at low velocity and adequate volume. This arrangement has

Table 4.3-3. Face Velocities

Classification	Average Face Velocity (fpm)	Lowest (fpm)	Comments
Low hazard	80	60	Noxious odors, vapors, duct fumes, low toxicity
Medium hazard	100	80	Most operations
High hazard	150*	125	Low-level radioisotopes, perchloric acid; consider glove box for higher levels

*Note: May be too high for safest hood performance, but may still be required by local standards and codes.

the added advantage of sweeping the complete laboratory with fresh air. Introduce makeup air as far away from hoods as possible. Let it purge the laboratory and exit through the hood system.

Location of the Fumehood in the Laboratory

- Fumehoods should not be located by the primary exit door for two reasons: (1) the traffic past the hood may create a backdraft from the hood into the laboratory and (2) fumehoods may be the location of an explosion or fire and may block the path of exit. If traffic is minimal and a second exit exists, locating the fumehood by the primary exit may be acceptable.
- Fumehoods should be away from sources of drafts such as open doors, windows and air supply grilles to prevent backdraft, as mentioned earlier.
- Fumehoods should not face each other within a short distance because the air may be sucked from one to provide the

makeup air for the other, particularly if each is exhausted by a separate fan.

4.4.4 Fumehood Materials and Accessories

Materials

As Table 4.4-2 shows, there are a number of options available for the selection of materials and accessories. Most fumehood exteriors are made from painted steel, although a few are made from fiberglass.

Interior liners are composed of reinforced cement products, epoxy resin, reinforced plastics and stainless steel. Limitations are noted in Table 4.4-4.

Sometimes, for the analysis of trace metals, the fumehood must be nonmetallic. Fiberglass hoods are available with all metal parts coated.

Work surfaces or tops can be made of any one of the above products but may be in different combinations with the liner. For instance, a coated, reinforced cement liner with an epoxy resin top is economical and effective for most applications.

Table 4.4-4. Fumehood Interior Materials and Finishes

Material	Heat and Flame Resistance	Comments
Liner		
Cement composition	Excellent	Reinforced cement with glazed finish has good chemical resistance. Select white finish for reflectivity.
Fiberglass	Good to 600°F	Seamless interior with coved corners, good chemical resistance. Available in many colors.
Poly resin	Excellent	Polyester reinforced with glass fiber. Excellent chemical resistance.
Epoxy resin	Very good	Excellent chemical resistance. Available in black and off-white.
Stainless steel	Excellent	Seamless with coved corners. Type 304 has low chemical resistance. Type 316 resistant to most chemical except concentrated chloride compounds and sulfuric acid.
Polypropylene	Poor above 250°F	Excellent chemical resistance.
Polyvinylchloride	Poor above 160°F	Excellent for acids, less good for some solvents.
Top		
Coated cement	Excellent	Coating peels off over time.
Fiberglass	Good to 600°F	See above.
Epoxy resin	Very good	See above.
Stainless steel	Excellent	See above.

Accessories

Fumehoods have a number of optional accessories which must be specified, primarily utility fixtures and base cabinets.

For most fumehoods, utility fixtures are remote controlled, with the handles mounted on the airfoil on both sides of the face opening. For stainless steel-lined hoods where an access panel to the valves may be undesirable, a special fixture is available that can be serviced from the front. See Figure 4.4-6.

Electrical receptacles and a light switch are also located in the sidepost, as well as a fan switch if the exhaust system design requires it.

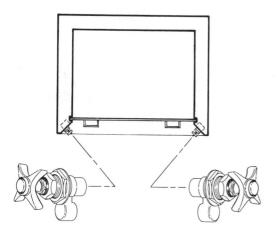

Fig. 4.4-6 Utility fixture control valve for stainless steel fumehoods (T&S Brass and Bronze Works, Inc.).

There are several options available in base cabinets in terms of both materials and type. Hardwood, plastic laminate and metal are available to match adjacent benches. An acid storage cabinet is lined and vented. A flammable liquids cabinet must conform to standards and is described in detail in Chapter 7.

4.4.5 Fumehood Safety

The fumehood is probably the location where the most hazardous work is performed, so the selection of this piece of equipment is crucial. In spite of this, there is much ignorance about fumehood selection, operation and maintenance.

Fumehoods must be selected with the usage in mind. When installed, they must be tested and retested at regular intervals. They must be maintained, and they must be used properly.

Safety includes the incorporation of certain safety features in the hood design, as well as maintenance and inspection.

Safety Features (see Figure 4.4-7)

- Utility fixtures color coded to match the outside handle and inside outlet to avoid mistakes in mixing services.
- A low-airflow alarm (both visible and audible) to warn when a dangerously low face velocity is present, lockable to prevent tampering.
- Automatic fire extinguishing system that will function with the exhaust air operating. Halon 1301 system with discharge nozzles directed toward the rear and up (Mosbacher, 1976). However, Halon systems are expensive and admit hydrocarbons to the atmosphere. Dry powder systems adequate to extinguish hood fires may be considered.
- Adjustable slots at the top and bottom in the back baffle to control airflow for best performance. Operable only by a special tool so that only authorized personnel can adjust them.
- Dipped top and cupsink to catch spills. Dipped top starts at 6 in. behind the

Static Pressure
Gauge

Automatic Fire
Extinguishing
System

Explosion-proof
Light

Fire Alarm

Remote
Handles

Single Baffle
Control

Elec. Receptacle
Outside
The Hood

Raised Edge

Cupsink

Coved Corners, Seamless
Construction

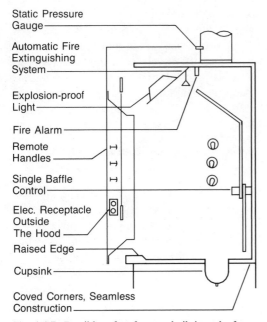

Fig. 4.4-7. Possible safety features built into the fume-hood.

sash to force users to keep items away from the hood face and avoid backflow of incoming air into the laboratory.

- Opening to allow electrical cords and piping from electrical receptacles and gas cylinders located outside the hood to service instruments located inside the hood.

- No spark-producing devices inside the hood. Electrical receptacles and switches are outside the hood chamber; light fixtures are sealed, and lamp replacement is done from the outside.

- Sash stops if a sash is required to be lower than normal. Stops should be self-activated but can be bypassed to place large items inside the hood. Stops connected to visible and audible alarms to warm of hazardous conditions when the sash is up.

- Signs: Instructions for proper use and warnings. Labeling of required face velocity and last date of inspection and testing. See Figure 4.4-8.

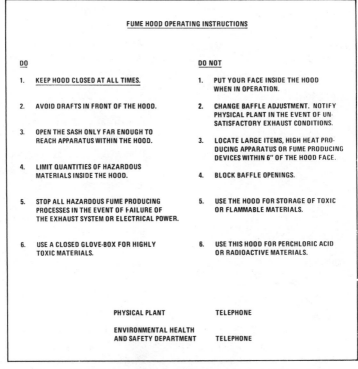

Figure 4.4-8. Example of fumehood operating instructions sign.

- Auxiliary air must be shut off automatically should the exhaust fan fail to prevent pressurizing of the fumehood's interior.
- Airflow dampers must fail open so that the exhaust system always exhausts.
- Good lighting inside the hood. At least 60 foot-candles at the work surface.
- Sash with safety glass or Lucite which will serve as a blast shield.

Inspection and Maintenance

Inspection on a regular interval is required by NFPA No. 45, OSHA, and many other standards and regulations, but it is not covered in this handbook except for after installation.

Maintenance may be routine or it may be the result of needed replacement discovered during inspection.

Several things will reduce hood performance initially and over time:

- Not enough makeup air is provided for the hood to work.
- Adjustable baffles may be closed.
- The fan belt will slip over time and exhaust less.
- Fan blades will corrode over time and exhaust less, or sucked-up paper or tissue may clog fans.
- Ducts will corrode, leak over time and exhaust less.

Radioisotope and HEPA filters should be installed as close to the hood as practical in order to avoid contaminating the duct. Ideally, the filter is replaced within the isotope and biohazard lab.

For high-level radioisotopes with a remote filter location, the ducts should be flanged with neoprene gaskets for removal and decontamination.

4.4.6 Fumehood Testing

Two types of tests are performed: those at the factory to test the design performance of the hood itself under known conditions and those in the field to test the performance of the hood under field conditions. Factory conditions can be controlled; performance and tests are the responsibility of the fumehood manufacturer.

Field conditions are, of course, never the same for any two hoods and, as explained earlier, many factors can influence the performance of the fumehood.

The Society of Apparatus Makers Association (SAMA) previously published test procedures for both factory and field conditions. They no longer perform this service, but they have generously consented to have the field test procedures incorporated in this handbook.

The field tests should be performed by the manufacturer of the fumehood, rather than by the mechanical contractor or engineer, because the manufacturer is most knowledgeable about the product. These tests, of course, should be performed after the building's mechanical system is balanced, since this system has a direct effect on the hood's performance. The tester must report deficiencies, explain why these occurred, and suggest remedial action.

If the right manufacturer has been selected, the fumehood should not be at fault.

Table 4.4-5 is an example of a fumehood deficiency checklist. After measurements are made, the design cfm and actual cfm for exhaust air and makeup should be compared. A certain amount of exhaust air will leak past the sash and not enter through the hood face, so that the entering cfm is slightly less than the exhausted cfm through the exhaust duct. Leakage in a standard hood is about 5%.

The cfm values from the auxiliary air supply and the room must also be compared to make sure that they are within the design parameters.

After corrections and adjustments have been made, the hoods must be rechecked and the results recorded on the same form for the record, dated and initialed.

Fumehood Evaluation in the Field

It is recommended that the user make provisions to have the following tests performed on all laboratory fumehoods. These tests

Table 4.4-5. Example Fumehood Deficiency Checklist

Manufacturer:

Room Number:	Date Inspected:	By:	Phone:
	Date Rechecked:	By:	Phone:

Hood Number: Hood Type:

Fan Number: Fan Location:

 1. Appearance
 2. Sash: Operation _____ Stops _____ Warning Light _____
 3. Operational and Maintenance Signs:
 4. Baffles: Top slot adjusted at
          Bottom slot adjusted at
 5. Top:
 6. Light Fixture _____ FC at Working Surface: _____
 7. Fire Extinguisher:
 8. Fixtures and Receptacles:
 9. Sound Level (measure at 12 inches above work surface, 12 inches in front of hood):
    A Scale _____ db B Scale _____ db C Scale _____ db
10. Field Test:
    Cross-draft (not to exceed 20 percent of face velocity with auxiliary air off)
         _____ fpm

Face Velocity Readings: (with auxiliary air off, not to exceed 300 fpm with sash down)

Average face velocity: _____ fpm

Exhaust air = area _____ × avg. velocity _____ = _____ cfm (design cfm _____)

Auxiliary air downdraft (not to exceed 200 fpm at bottom of sash with sash full open): _____ fpm

Auxiliary Air Readings:
(at three inches from grill) Average Velocity _____ fpm
Auxiliary air = _____ cfm (design cfm _____)
Ratio auxiliary air to exhaust air = _____ to _____ percent
Titanium tetrachloride test:
11. Corrective Action Recommended:

should be performed by qualified personnel to verify proper operation of the fumehoods before they are used. The tests of the fumehoods should be performed after the installation is complete, the building ventilation system has been balanced and all connections have been made. Any unsafe conditions disclosed by these tests should be corrected before the hood is used.

Test Conditions

Verify that the building's makeup air system is in operation, the doors and windows are in normal operating position, and all other hoods and exhaust devices are operating under design conditions.

Test Procedures

1. *Equipment List.*
   a. A properly calibrated hot-wire thermal anemometer similar or equal to Alnor Model #8500.
   b. A supply of half-minute smoke candles.
   c. A bottle of titanium tetrachloride and a supply of cotton swabs or another recognized device for producing smoke.

2. *Room Conditions.* Check room conditions in front of the fumehood, using a thermal anemometer and a smoke source to verify that the velocity of cross-drafts does not exceed 20% of the specified average fumehood face velocity. Any cross-drafts that exceed these values must be eliminated before proceeding with the fumehood test. Caution: Titanium tetrachloride fumes are toxic and corrosive. Use this compound sparingly, and avoid inhalation and exposure to the body, clothing and equipment, which might be affected by corrosive fumes.

Note: It must be recognized that no fumehood can operate properly if excessive cross-drafts are present.

3. *Face Velocity.* Determine the specified average face velocity for the fumehood being tested. Perform the following test to determine if fumehood velocities conform to specifications or to the designated fumehood class in accordance with Table 4.4-3. The face velocity with the exhaust blower on, must be determined by averaging readings taken at the fumehood face. Readings shall be taken at the center of a grid made up of sections of equal area, as shown in Figure 4.4-9.

- Bench-mounted hoods with vertical rising sash(es) shall be rated and tested with all sashes in the full open-design working position.
- Walk-in or distillation hoods with vertical rising sash(es) must be rated and tested with one sash in the full open position.
- Fumehoods with horizontal sliding sash(es) must be rated and tested with sash(es) in the maximum open position.

The face velocity must be determined by averaging the velocity readings taken at the open fumehood face.

Note: If the face velocity is not in accordance with the specified face velocity, correct the problems, but if the face velocity cannot be corrected to that specified, reclassify the fumehood to conform to the actual face velocity.

4. *Sash Operation.* Check the operation by moving the sash through its full travel. Sash operation should be smooth and easy. Vertical rising sashes must hold at any height without creeping up or down.

5. *Verification of Proper Airflow and Patterns for Fumehoods without Auxiliary Air.*
   a. Turn the fumehood exhaust blower on.
   b. With sash(es) in the full open position, check the airflow into the fumehood using a cotton swab dipped in titanium tetrachloride or another smoke source.

   Note: On fumehoods with horizontal sliding sash(es), check the airflow with sash(es) at various full open positions. A complete traverse of the fumehood face should verify that airflow is into the fumehood over the entire face area. A reverse flow of smoke indicates unsafe fumehood operation.
   c. Move a lighted smoke candle throughout the fumehood work area, directing smoke across the work surface and against the side walls and baffle. Smoke should be contained within the fumehood and be rapidly exhausted. (Fumehoods with horizontal sliding sash(es) will show reverse flow and turbulence behind the sash panel, but no outflow of smoke must be evident.)

6. *Verification of Proper Airflow and Pattern for Fumehoods with Auxiliary Air.*
   a. Turn the exhaust blower on and determine the face velocity of airflow in accordance with step 3.

   Note: Face velocity and exhaust

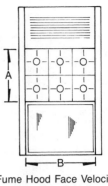

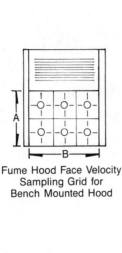

Fume Hood Face Velocity
Sampling Grid for
Bench Mounted Hood

Fume Hood Face Velocity
Sampling Grid for
Walk-In Hood

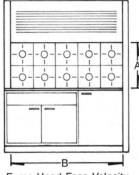

Fume Hood Face Velocity
Sampling Grid for
a Combination Hood

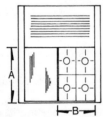

Fume Hood Face Velocity
Sampling Grid for Bench
Mounted Fume Hood with
Horizontal Sliding Sash(es)

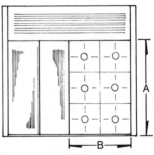

Fume Hood Velocity
Sampling Grid for
Walk-In Hood with
Horizontal Sliding Sash(es)

Fig. 4.4-9. Face velocity readings for various types of fumehoods.

volumes must be determined with the auxiliary air blower off.

b. Calculate exhaust volume from face velocity data.

c. Turn on auxiliary air and verify that the auxiliary air volume is as specified. Locate a straight sec-

tion of the supply air duct and drill two holes of a size appropriate for the pitot tubes to be used, 90 degrees apart, on a plane through the duct at the downstream end of the straight section. Measure the air velocity and calculate the air volume. Compare the volumes determined with the specified volume of auxiliary air and with the exhaust volume to determine if a proper ratio exists. Deviations of ± 5% are acceptable. If deviations of more than 5% are noted, corrective measures should be taken. Seal holes in the duct with duct tape or a suitable sealant.

d. With sash(es) in the open position, check airflow into the fumehood using a cotton swab dipped in titanium tetrachloride or another smoke source. A complete traverse of the fumehood face should verify that airflow is into the fumehood over the entire face area. A reverse flow of air indicates unsafe fumehood operation.

e. Move a lighted smoke candle throughout the fumehood work area, directing smoke across the work surface and against the side walls and baffle. Smoke should be contained within the fumehood and be rapidly exhausted. Fumehoods with horizontal sliding sash(es) will show reverse flow and turbulence behind the sash panel, but no outflow of smoke must be evident.

7. *Evaluation of Low Airflow Monitor.* On fumehoods with low flow warning devices, verify that the monitor functions properly and indicates unsafe conditions.

8. *Other Sources.* ASHRAE has also published test procedures: ASHRAE 110—*Method of Testing Performance of Laboratory Fumehoods*

4.4.7 Regulations Dealing with Fumehoods*

Several standards cover fumehoods. They are summarized here.

1. NFPA No. 45. Fire Protection for Laboratories Using Chemicals, 1986 edition: Extensive coverage of fumehood design, construction, operation, location, inspection, testing and maintenance, and associated mechanical systems. Paragraphs from the standard are noted in parenthesis.

   Perchloric acid fumehoods and exhaust systems are also covered in some detail.

   Some of the salient points are:
   - Air exhausted from fumehoods shall not be recirculated (6–5.1). This means that ductless hoods are

*Reference is made to sections in those standards.

Table 4.4-6. Rules of Thumb: Summary

Face velocities should never be less than 60 fpm any location.
Face velocity should never be less than 80 fpm average.
Face velocity should never be more than 150 fpm average with sash up.
Face velocity should never be more than 300 fpm any location with sash down.
Face velocity may increase when sash is lowered but should not exceed three times the full open face velocity.
Face velocity of 100 fpm average is good for most hoods.
Downdraft at hood face should never exceed 20 fpm or 20% of the face velocity from any source.
The cost of the hood exhaust system approximately equals the cost of the hood itself.
Auxiliary air capture efficiency should be 95% with the sash up and 100% with the sash down.
Auxiliary air is 50 to 70% of required exhaust air at temperatures of 70° to 90°F.
One ton of air conditioning is needed for every 250 to 400 cfm of exhaust air. Requirement varies with design conditions at the site.
Room air supply grille terminal throw velocity should not exceed one-half to two-thirds the face velocity, preferably 20%.
To keep noise down to acceptable levels, slot velocity should not exceed 1,500 fpm; hood collar air velocity 1,600 fpm; duct air velocity 1,600 fpm, more if there are moving particles. Fan rotation should not exceed 1,800 rpm.

not acceptable for flammable or hazardous chemicals.

- Energy conservation devices shall not be a type that could reintroduce contaminants into the laboratory (6–5.2).
- Fumehood exhaust ducts shall be under negative pressure when they pass through occupied areas (6–5.4).
- Fumehood exhaust ducts shall be ducted separately for each laboratory unit (6–5.9; for an explanation of a laboratory unit, see Appendix D). Ducts may be combined outside the building and inside the mechanical room or when they reach a mechanical shaft.
- The exhaust system must continue in case of a fire within the fumehood (6–11.3) This means that no fire dampers shall be installed in the exhaust duct, that the fan must not shut down when the alarm system is activated and that control dampers fail open (6–6.7).

2. NFPA No. 99. *Healthcare Facilities,* 1987 edition: Generally the same requirements as NFPA No. 45 but much shorter (5–4.4).

3. CFR Title 29, Labor, Chapter XVII part 1910. Occupational Safety and Health Act, 1987 edition. Requirements are very vague. Reference is made to a document by the National Research Council which suggest 2.5 ft of fumehood per person for every two workers who work most of the time with chemicals. Hood application and performance (containment)-related recommendations are tied to threshold limit values.

GLOSSARY

Airfoil—Curved jambs and sill at the fumehood entrance to reduce air turbulence.

Air volume—Quantity of air needed to exhaust the fumehood, normally expressed in cubic feet per minute (cfm).

Auxiliary air—Air supplied to the outside face of a laboratory fumehood to reduce room air consumption and improve hood safety.

Baffle—A false back across the fumehood's interior back. Baffles control the pattern of air moving into and through the fumehood. Typically, three horizontal slots at the top, bottom, and middle direct the airflow.

Bypass—An opening above the sash which maintains a relatively constant volume exhaust through a fumehood, regardless of sash position, and limits the increase in face velocity as the sash is lowered.

Capture velocity—The air velocity at the hood face necessary to overcome opposing air currents and to contain contaminated air within the laboratory fumehood.

Deflector vane or airfoil sill—An airfoil-shaped vane along the bottom of the hood face which directs incoming air across the work surface to the lower baffle opening. The opening between the work surface and the deflector vane is open even with the sash fully closed.

Duct velocity—Speed of air moving through a duct, expressed in feet per minute (fpm).

Exhaust collar—Point of connection between the fumehood chamber and the exhaust duct.

Face opening—Front opening of the laboratory fumehood in the same plane as the sash.

Face velocity—Speed of air moving into the fumehood at the face opening, expressed in feet per minute (fpm).

Fan—The device which is turned by a motor and moves the air through the fumehood and duct. Sometimes called a "blower."

Fume removal system—The laboratory fumehood and the exhaust system. Supply air system, fans, filters and scrubbers are an integral part of the system.

Imbalance—Condition in which the ratio of auxiliary air to room air is greater than the design maximum.

Laboratory fumehood—A ventilated, enclosed work space intended to capture, contain and exhaust fumes, vapors and particulate matter generated inside the enclosure. It consists basically of side, back, and top enclosure panels, a work surface or countertop, an access opening called the "face," a sash and an exhaust plenum equipped with a baffle system for the regulation of airflow distribution.

Liner—Interior lining used for side, back, and

top enclosure panels, exhaust plenum and baffle system of a laboratory fumehood.

Manometer—Device used to measure air pressure differential, usually calibrated in inches of water.

Makeup air—Air needed to replace the air taken from the room by laboratory fumehood(s) and other air-exhausting devices.

Negative air pressure—Air pressure lower than ambient pressure.

Pitot tube—Device used for measuring air velocity.

Plenum or plenum chamber—Chamber used to equalize airflow and pressure.

Positive air pressure—Air pressure higher than ambient pressure.

Room air—That portion of the exhaust air taken from the room.

Sash—Movable panel set in the fumehood entrance to adjust the opening size and protect the operator.

Service fitting—Item of laboratory plumbing mounted on or fastened to the laboratory furniture or fumehood and intended to control the supply of piped gases and liquids for laboratory use.

Static pressure (P_S)—Air pressure in laboratory fumehood or duct, expressed in inches of water. *See* Total pressure.

Static pressure loss—Measurement of resistance created when air moves through a duct or hood, expressed in inches of water.

Superstructure—The portion of a laboratory fumehood that is supported by the work surface or countertop.

Threshold limit value (TLV)—Established maximum concentration of hazardous materials to which most individuals may be exposed over a specific period of time such as a normal 8-hour work day or 40-hour work week.

Titanium tetrachloride—Chemical that generates white fumes used in testing laboratory fumehoods. These fumes are toxic and corrosive.

Total pressure (P_T)—Sum of velocity pressure and static pressure. $P_T = P_V + P_S$

Transport velocity—Minimum speed of air required to suspend and carry materials in an air stream.

Velocity pressure (P_V)—Pressure caused by moving air in a laboratory fumehood or duct, expressed in inches of water.

Work area—That part of the fumehood interior where apparatus is set up and fumes are generated. It is normally confined to an area 6 in. behind the plane of the sash to the face of the baffle.

REFERENCES

ANSI/ASME, 1980. *Testing of Nuclear Air-Cleaning Systems,* N510. New York.

ASHRAE, 1971. *Guide and Data Book.* Atlanta.

ASHRAE, HVAC, lastest ed. *Systems and Applications.* Chapter 30, "Laboratories"; Chapter 32, "Clean Spaces," Atlanta.

ASHRAE, *Handbook of Fundamentals* latest ed., Atlanta.

ASHRAE, 1985. *Method of Testing Performance of Laboratory Fume Hoods.* ANSI/ASHRAE, 110. Atlanta: ASHRAE.

American Conference of Governmental Industrial Hygienists (ACGIH), latest ed. *Ventilation Manual: A Manual of Recommended Practice,* Cincinnati.

Caplan, Knowlton J., and Knutson, Gerhard W., 1978. Laboratory Fumehoods: Influence of Room Air Supply. ASHRAE Transactions Vol. 84, Part 1, Atlanta, GA.

Mosbacher, C. J., 1976. Fire, *Research and Development,* October. pp. 19–21.

NIOSH, *Recommended Industrial Ventilation Guidelines.* HEW Publication NIOSH 76-162.

NFPA 45—Standard on Fire Protection for Laboratories Using Chemicals, 1986. Quincy, MA.

Reinhart, Robert H., 1977. Unpublished comments. Stanford, CA: Stanford Research Institute.

Scientific Apparatus Manufacturers Association (SAMA), Laboratory Fume Hoods Standard LF10-1980. Washington, DC: SAMA.

U.S. Department of Energy 6430.1A - General Design Criteria 1550 Heating, Ventilating, and Air-Conditioning Systems, 1589–99 Special Facilities

4.5 GLASSWARE WASHERS AND DRYERS   *T. Ruys*

4.5.1 Introduction

It should be kept in mind that washers and dryers wash, dry and sanitize; they do not sterilize.

These types of equipment come in several sizes and with many options. They do not all wash glassware to the same degree of cleanliness. This section does not recommend any manufacturers (although several have been noted in appendix B), because companies come and go and quality changes over time.

This section does, however, suggest ways to select the appropriate equipment to fulfill a need and tests to ensure that this equipment meets the specifications. Manufacturers do not agree on what is important, so their equipment varies. Some have patented parts; therefore others, in order to be competitive, must provide similar devices.

This equipment can be heated by steam or electrical power. Steam heating generally has a lower operating cost.

Some manufacturers use the same glassware-holding devices for washing and drying, so the glassware can be transferred directly from one to the other without being manually touched between operations. The washer and dryer chambers are approximately the same size. Other manufacturers claim that drying is faster than washing, so the dryer is much larger. However, transferring glassware between operations becomes necessary.

Washers come with various options; these must be specified:

- Booster heater to raise the water temperature to 180°F
- Acid rinse to clean glassware
- Automatic detergent wash dispenser to clean, decontaminate and wash
- Deionized water rinse, as the last cycle, to clean off the last traces of contaminants. This deionized water should be heated so that glassware flash dries when removed from the washer. A holding tank with enough capacity for the rinse water cycle is necessary. The piping, pump and tank should be stainless steel.

The following should be kept in mind:

- At the end of washing and the rinse cycle, large quantities of water are disposed of in a short time. Drains must be large enough to accommodate this volume.
- Washing machines generate a lot of va-

pors. These can be vented to the atmosphere or a vapor-condensing system can be provided, with the residue eliminated to the drain.

- Washers are quite noisy in operation. The partitions between the machine service space and adjoining rooms should be acoustically treated.
- Glassware dryers do not dry small-mouth containers or pipettes very well; a hot air oven is recommended for that type of glassware.
- As with all equipment, long-lasting, trouble-free operation is important, as is the quality of the service and availability of parts. Ask the manufacturer for a list of past customers, with the names of persons to contact and telephone numbers. Check the equipment's reliability, performance and service.

4.5.2 Washers

Washers consist of a machine, accessories and carts. Machines come in various sizes for undercounter installation or free-standing cabinet and recessed models. A typical chamber size is 26 in. wide × 28 in. deep × 27 in. high, but wider models are available. The limiting factor is the need to reach and wash the inside and outside of each piece of glassware. Some models use spindles, rotating spray units or oscillating spray units. A great deal of pressure is required to wash glassware properly, so the pump size and horsepower plays an important role. A 5-hp motor system is standard but a 7.5-hp motor system is available.

Washers go through a number of cycles, which vary with the manufacturer. It is important to verify which cycles are standard, which ones are optional and which ones are required to do the job.

Standard cycles are (options noted):

1. Prewash: 140°F water from the last cycle of the previous wash or cold tap water (optional) to remove blood and protein.
2. Wash: 140°F water; 180°F water (op-

tional); detergent injection (optional); acid injection (optional)

3. First rinse: 140°F water; 180°F (optional)
4. Second rinse: 140°F water; 180°F (optional)
5. Third rinse: 140°F water (optional); 180°F (optional)
6. Deionized rinse: cold or preheated (both optional)

Controls are now mostly electronic, which makes changes much quicker and easier. Controls should be both automatic, for most glassware operations, and manual so that special requirements can be accommodated.

Doors can be of the guillotine type, which is handy for tight places, or of the hinge drop type, which becomes the track to remove the spindle header holding the glassware. See Figure 4.5-1.

Various accessories are available, such as spindles for different sizes, shapes and quantities of glassware. Other special devices can hold many petri dishes in racks, test tubes in baskets and pipettes in stainless steel tubes. For the most common glassware, order two holding devices each so that one can be filled with glassware while the other is in the washer. Spindles should have plastic tips to prevent glassware breakage.

Carts are used to hold and transport spindles and wire baskets from counter to washer and, if the equipment is designed for it, from washer to dryer. Two carts should be available for each washer to allow loading one while the other is available for unloading the washer.

4.5.3 Tests and Standards

The equipment shall meet UL standards or equivalent. Equivalents are the Electronics Testing Laboratories (ETL) or the Canadian Standards Institute (CSI). Labeling equipment is very expensive, and these laboratories require retesting for every modification. That means that only the standard cataloged equipment is labeled; customization is not labeled unless the customer pays for it—in the range of $30,000 to $40,000 more. Unfortunately, the National Electrical Code requires it, and the local electrical inspector may refuse to approve the installation; in fact, may prohibit occupancy of the whole facility because of the one noncomplying piece of

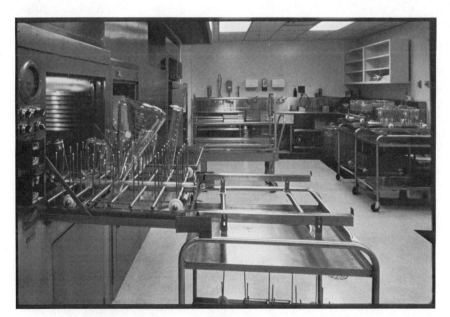

Fig. 4.5-1. Washer with drop door and cart (BOHM/NBBJ).

equipment. Two possible ways to avoid paying the extra cost for testing are:

- Pay to have the UL, ETL or CSI inspector field inspect and test the equipment.
- Get a variance from the National Electrical Code from the authority having jurisdiction, usually the local building department, i.e., a one-of-a-kind waiver.

In the present climate of accountability and litigation, the latter is not likely to happen or may not be advisable from an insurance standpoint. The message is: Stick with standard equipment; find a manufacturer that makes what is needed or pay the price.

None of the washer features or compliance with safety standards, no matter how well designed and executed, is helpful if the washer does not wash glassware. Many things can go wrong:

- The washer is not designed properly.
- It is not built per specification.
- It is not installed properly.
- It is not field tested.

Besides the standard tests of controls and cycles, it is very important to test the washer as specified next.

Veterans Administration Soils Test

Performance requirements: The glassware washer should be capable of removing standard soil from glassware during a standard cycle.

Standard soil: Standard soil should consist of a homogeneous mixture of the following ingredients, applied to interior and exterior surfaces allowed to drain for 10 minutes, and placed in a preheated oven at 105°C for 5 minutes in an upright position.

Peanut butter	100 g
Butter	100 g
Flour	100 g
Lard	100 g
Dehydrated egg yolk	100 g
Evaporated milk	150 ml

Distilled water	500 ml
India ink	40 ml
Printing ink diluted 1:1 with boiled linseed oil	100 drops
Blood agar base (dehydrated)	10 g
NaOH	30 ml

4.5.4 Dryers

Dryers are available steam-heated, with a temperature range from 180° to 325°F, or electrically heated to 325°F. The typical chamber size is 26 in. wide × 26 in. deep × 55 in. high, which is twice as much volume as for washers, since it takes less time to dry than to wash. Wider models are available.

Doors and chambers must be insulated for better operations, for energy conservation and to avoid radiant heat in the wash area. Controls should allow for various settings so that plastics that are affected by heat can be dried at a lower temperature.

4.5.5 Installation

Washers and dryers should be recessed into the wall and the space behind the wall well ventilated; otherwise, they generate a lot of heat in the glasswash area. See Appendix J.

The space behind the recessed equipment should also have a dropped floor to a floor drain. Washers handle large quantities of water, and leaks do occur with potentially disastrous results.

Equipment comes preplumbed and prewired. Appendix J shows typical minimal rough-in requirements, which should be verified for the equipment selected.

An exhaust hood is commonly installed over the chamber opening for both washers and dryers in order to vent steam vapors and heat when the equipment is opened.

Washers are typically connected to the building's hot water system, which is 120° to 140°F. A booster heater should be provided to generate 180°F water.

It is very important that adequate space be provided next to the equipment for installation, service and maintenance.

Some types of washers have mechanical exhaust systems. The exhaust duct should be welded stainless steel up to the point where condensation may be expected, and a drain must be provided to drain the condensation to the waste line.

Large quantities of waste water are disposed of in a short time. The drain may be a closed system or an open drain, depending on local code requirements. A floor sink and a 4-in. drain should be provided for open drain connections to avoid floods.

Low-pressure steam (LPS) is generally preferred to high-pressure steam (HPS) because in some locations a licensed boiler attendant is required for the HPS system. LPS, however, requires larger coils and more space.

Steam to heat the wash water is in a closed system with a condensate return which needs to pitch back to the steam generator. This may pose some problems for the washer on the ground floor without a crawl space.

4.6 AUTOCLAVES AND STERILIZERS
T. Ruys

4.6.1 Introduction

Autoclaves are sterilizers, but sterilizers are not necessarily autoclaves. Autoclaves, which are self-closing, are pressure vessels that use saturated steam at elevated pressures to kill microorganisms. Dry-heat sterilizers use heated air to do this; gas sterilizers use gas.

The most effective way to destroy living matter, which contains protein and nucleic acids, is by heat in the presence of moisture. Proteins that contain an abundance of water coagulate by heat at lower temperatures. Some microorganisms, particularly spores which contain little or no moisture, however, are very resistant and will survive even boiling water at 100°C.

It has been discovered that only a film of moisture is needed on dry goods such as cloth, glassware, and instruments at the right temperatures to kill microbes. The film of moisture is the result of steam condensing on the material of a lower temperature than the steam in the autoclave.

Steam at standard atmospheric pressure at sea level or 0 lb gage (14.7 pounds/sq in. absolute, psia) is 212°F (100°C). Most living matter is rapidly destroyed at 122°F (50°C) to 194°F (90°C), but saturated steam at 250°F (121°C) at 15 lb gage pressure is considered the minimum temperature to ensure destruction of all microorganisms. Most autoclaves, however, can reach two ranges:

- A low range of 250°–254°F (121°–123°C)
- A high range of 270°–274°F (132°–134°C)

Saturated steam is the point at which steam is formed from boiling water. In order to increase the temperature, the pressure must be raised, hence the pressure vessel. The temperature of steam can be raised by heating it, but it is no longer saturated and loses its ability to kill to the same degree. Dry-heat sterilizers kill by oxidation and require a much higher temperature.

In order for autoclaves to be effective, it is therefore necessary that every corner and every part of the contents be reached by saturated steam. That is not as easy as it seems because air is a very good insulator. It is, therefore, essential that every bit of air be replaced by saturated steam at 250°F (121°C). Air and steam do not readily mix, which is both good and bad. It is good because steam entering the chamber is lighter than air and will force the air out, but it is bad because air trapped in vessels, glassware, and surgical packs will not mix with steam and may reach the required temperature but not the necessary saturated moisture levels essential for destroying microbes.

There are two types of autoclaves, based on the way they replace air in the chamber with saturated steam:

- The gravity displacement autoclave
- The prevacuum autoclave

As the names imply, the first type is based on the fact that steam will replace air and force it out at the bottom. The second one operates by removing all the air from the chamber with a vacuum pump or water ejector and replacing it with steam.

The water ejector is less noisy and less expensive than a pump but takes more time.

Gravity displacement autoclaves are lower in cost but much slower and, as pointed out, may trap air in the load and therefore not sterilize some of the load. The water ejector and gravity displacement systems have about the same cost.

The exposure times given in Table 4.6-1 give an indication of the difference in operating time for gravity displacement and prevacuum autoclaves. For effective sterilization:

- Contents must be loaded properly for the steam to reach all parts.
- Glassware must be laid on its side or upside down to allow air displacement with steam. Pippettes and other small-opening vessels should be sterilized in dry-heat sterilizers.
- Steam will not penetrate oils, which

must be sterilized by other means. Surgical instruments covered with fat or grease may not sterilize.

- Liquid must sterilize by absorbing heat from the surrounding steam until it reaches the required temperature. In the autoclave, the liquid can reach higher temperatures without boiling than is possible in dry-heat sterilizers or on a heating element.

The quality of the steam is important. Building steam boilers contain additives such as amines to control corrosion. These substances are toxic and should not be used for sterilization of glassware for tissue culture or for feed products, but they are acceptable for surgical instruments, packs, and decontamination of waste products or disposables before disposal. Clean steam systems are available as part of the autoclaves to generate acceptable-quality steam. This steam generator may be steam or electrically heated to produce the steam.

Besides saturated steam and dry-heat sterilization, there are two other methods: chemical disinfection and sterilization with gas. These methods are rarely used in laborator-

Table 4.6-1. Cycle Times for Gravity Displacement and Prevacuum Autoclaves Standard Type (20 × 36 × 36 Chamber, in Minutes)

	Approximate Time in Minutes for Various Cycles*		
Cycle Phase	P1 Wrapped Goods (HiVac or Ejector) 275°F (135°C)	P2 Hard Goods (Gravity Displacement) 250°F (121°C)	P3 Liquids (Gravity Displacement) 270°F (121°C)
Air removal by vacuum	5–10	N/A	N/A
Air removal by gravity displacement	N/A	5	5
Charge to temperature and sterilizing exposure	5	15	Heat-up[†] (5–45) +15
Exhaust of steam to atmospheric pressure	1	1	15–30
Drying vacuum	5–15	5–15	N/A
Filtered air to chamber ready to unload	4	4	N/A
Typical total cycle time	20–45	30–45	40–110

*Range varies with load and type of material.
[†]Glassware at the low side, solutions at the high side of the range.
Source: Gettinge International, Inc.

ies except to remove valuable instruments that cannot be autoclaved or heated from a containment facility. An additional problem with gas sterilization is that it will leave a film of toxic residue on the object if the object is not properly aerated.

4.6.2 Autoclaves

All autoclaves have the following features (see Figure 4.6-1):

- A door with a safety closure device activated when the chamber is pressurized, hence the name "autoclave."
- A steam inlet with a thermometer.
- A steam trap which automatically removes air, condensate and lower-temperature steam.
- A temperature sensing device (i.e., a thermistor or resistive thermal device) at the discharge which senses the required steam temperature and activates the

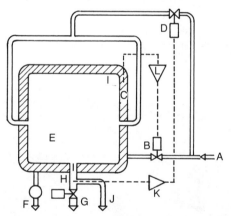

Fig. 4.6-1. Principal parts of an autoclave. A, steam supply; B, jacket valve; C, jacket; D, camber valve; E, camber; F, steam trap; G, drain valve; H, temperature transducer, chamber; I, temperature transducer, jacket; J, steam supply restrictor; K, temperature control, chamber; L, temperature control, jacket. Chamber and jacket: Steam enters the chamber (E) and jacket (C) from the steam supply (A). The temperature in the chamber and the jacket is sensed by the temperature transducers H and I. The temperature is reported to the cotnrol unit, which, via temperature regulators K and L, actuates chamber valve D and jacket valve B, respectively. These then release the steam required to achieve process requirements. Air and steam are evacuated from the system via G and F by a vacuum pump (Getinge International, Inc.)

sterilizing cycle when the temperature of the released vapors reach the temperature of the saturated pressurized steam.

- A pressure relief valve vented outside the laboratory.

Most autoclaves are jacketed, which means that they have a double wall. The steam enters the jacket, heats the chamber wall and then enters the chamber. This arrangement ensures that the interior surface of the chamber has the same temperature as the saturated steam so that the steam will not condense on the interior chamber wall. Condensation on the walls would reduce the saturation of the steam and make it less effective as a sterilizing agent. The jacket is kept at high temperatures throughout the work day, which ensures quick startup and helps to dry the load at the end of each cycle.

The steam trap is calibrated for the temperature and pressure required, and is activated by a temperature-sensitive bimetal element which opens the valve when the temperature at the bottom of the chamber is lower than required to release the remaining air, which is heavier than steam, by gravity.

When the temperature at the trap reaches the required level, the sterilizer cycle starts. The assumption is that all air has been replaced and that the temperature inside the chamber is uniform throughout. As pointed out earlier, that may not necessarily be the case.

Prevacuum autoclaves were developed to overcome even the slightest possibility that parts of the contents would not be sterilized. A vacuum pump or water ejector removes most of the air from the chamber and contents before replacing it with saturated steam. Prevacuum pulsing admits steam and creates a vacuum in alternate cycles until all the air is removed, which makes better penetration possible.

Prevacuum autoclaves are:

- Much faster (see Table 4.6-1), and can therefore use smaller models to handle the same daily load.

- So fast that the chamber size has a negligible effect on the sterilizing time.
- More energy efficient.
- Lower in initial or purchase cost and operating cost because the unit can be smaller and operates more quickly.

4.6.3 Selecting an Autoclave

Autoclaves come in many sizes and types. Some of the smaller models fit on a laboratory bench and require no plumbing. There are cabinet freestanding types and floor-loading wheel-in types. Most models can be recessed into the wall and are available with double doors for installation between the soiled and clean sides of a barrier. Sealing flanges and gaskets are available to make the barrier around the autoclave airtight, and electric interlocks prevent both doors from being open at one time or the door from being opened on the clean side until the cycle is completed. The space in front of the autoclave must allow for room to open the door and maneuver the cart to empty the autoclave. See Figure 4.6-2.

An autoclave is typically designated by the size of the interior space; however, an autoclave of twice the chamber volume does not necessarily sterilize twice the volume of goods. In order for saturated steam to reach all parts of the load, there must be space between items. A three-shelf autoclave chamber of the same size typically sterilizes more goods than a two-shelf one.

The types of items and the way they are wrapped also have an effect on the selection of the size of the autoclave.

The selection of the size depends on:

- The size(s) of item(s) to be sterilized
- The load anticipated per day or per week
- The work day in hours
- The types of loads and numbers of each
- The cycle times for the various loads
- The need for a standby autoclave
- The available sizes. There are many sizes available, but there are slight differences among manufacturers.

For help in making a selection, call one of the manufacturers listed in Appendix B. To

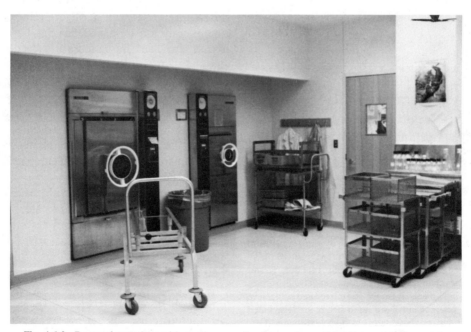

Fig. 4.6-2. Recessed autoclave with ample space for door swing and loading cart (Miyamoto).

establish load productivity, use the example at the end of this section.

Autoclaves are often used for decontamination of biologically contaminated items or products prior to cleaning, such as glassware and instruments, or prior to disposal. The same autoclaves should not be used for both decontamination and sterilization because of the possibility that the equipment will not operate properly and may cause cross-contamination.

If an autoclave or sterilizer is important to an operation, a standby unit should be provided so that the operation does not come to a halt in case the primary unit is out of commission.

The following cautions pertain to decontamination autoclaves:

- The air displaced by gravity or a prevacuum may be contaminated because it has not yet been sterilized and must be filtered or treated before release to the drain or atmosphere. A special system to decontaminate waste water and air can be provided but must be specified.
- The condensate removed from the autoclave may also be contaminated until programmed temperatures are reached.
- In time, autoclaves will leak at the door gasket and will not reach the pressure and vacuum required to reach the temperatures necessary everywhere inside the chamber. Testing is required more often than at construction time. Consult the manufacturer.

Laboratory autoclaves have special features that allow sterilization at low and high temperatures in the range 212°F (110°C) to 273°F (134°C). Isothermal autoclaves, through a process of cooling the incoming steam, can operate in the range 140°F (60°C) to 273°F (134°C).

This capability makes the laboratory autoclave very flexible for research purposes, and it can be used to sterilize heat-sensitive materials such as media. A "flowing steam" condition can be programmed where steam

at atmosphere pressure of 212°F (100°C) flows through the chamber.

Pure steam from distilled or deionized water must be used for media sterilization for mammalian cell cultures, although the heat source to the jacket may be boiler steam. The pure steam is generated by an electrically or steam-heated generator attached to the autoclave.

Liquid solutions are heated to 250°F (121°C) by absorbing heat from the autoclave chamber. The additional time it takes for the liquid to reach 250°F after the chamber has reached the "exposure" cycle varies, depending on the load. This time can be measured by means of a thermocouple. The liquids will not boil so long as the chamber is under pressure; however, during the cool-down period, the pressure must be lowered slowly to allow an equilibrium of pressure over the surface of the liquid in the bottle to the pressure in the chamber and to prevent violent boiling and loss of liquids.

4.6.4 Dry-Heat Sterilizers

There are two types of dry-heat sterilizers: the gravity convection type and the mechanical convection type. The source of heat is typically electricity, but gas or steam can be used. Temperature regulation should be variable. Glassware can be sterilized at high temperatures, as high as 400°F (204°C), while materials that are affected by heat must be sterilized at lower temperatures over longer periods of time. Temperature variations are more difficult to control with gas.

The gravity convection dry-heat sterilizer operates on the principle that hot air rises and cold air falls down over the heating element for recirculation. The mechanical convection sterilizer uses a motor and fan to force air across a heating element and to recirculate until the desired temperature is reached.

The following must be kept in mind:

- Gravity convection is slower than mechanical convection.
- Dry heat has serious limitations for ster-

ilization and should be used only if autoclaving is impractical or impossible; however, depyrogenation can be accomplished only by dry heat, not by steam sterilization.

- The process is slow because hot air must replace cold air. High temperatures affects materials that are sterilized and may destroy them.
- Dry-heat sterilizers are preferred for small-opening devices where steam may not penetrate, such as pipettes, stoppered glassware and needles or instruments, where steam may have a corrosive effect.
- Dry-heat sterilizers are preferred for substances that do not contain moisture or where moisture will not penetrate, such as grease and oil.
- Dry-heat sterilizers take longer and require higher temperatures, and are therefore more expensive to operate in terms of personnel and energy use.
- In dry heat, microorganisms are destroyed by oxidation, dehydration or burning.
- Dry heat of 320°F for 60 minutes is the equivalent of 250°F for 15 minutes for moist heat, according to Perkins (1970).

4.6.5 Testing of Autoclaves

Autoclaves must meet a number of manufacturing standards:

- Federal Specifications GG-S-1340A (gravity units) or GG-S-1343A (prevacuum units)
- The Unfired Pressure Vessels Code, Section VIII, Division 1, published by the American Society of Mechanical Engineers
- The Boiler Makers Association standard or ASME Code, Section VIII, Division 1 for unfired pressure vessels
- UL standard or the equivalent
- *Guide for Industrial Moist Heat Sterilization of Medical Products,* ANSI/AAMI, ST 25-1987
- Eastern Testing Laboratories (ETL)

- ASTM Specification A240 for stainless steel
- ASTM B88, B43, or B135 for copper and brass tubing
- ASTM Code Section 1, Part PMB for steam generators

None of the above safety standards ensures that the autoclave will sterilized properly. Tests must be performed in the field by a qualified individual. The Association for the Advance of Medical Instrumentation (AAMI) has published test procedures and set criteria for biological indicators used for testing.

Example: Evaluating sterilizer productivity* The following is an example of computing the existing total *daily* workload of a hospital and comparing this workload in terms of processing time, utilizing various size sterilizers. In this example, the hospital is using *three* sterilizers for terminal *steam* sterilization.

Existing Sterilizer 1

A. Sterilizer make and type: Amsco Medallion Vacamatic A
B. Sterilizer chamber size: 24 × 36 × 48 in.
C. Type of loading equipment: Medallion loading car with carriage
D. Number of cycles processed daily: 8
E. Number of shelves utilized each cycle: 2
F. Loading equipment *shelf size:*

$$(47 \text{ in. L} \times 22 \text{ in. W}) \div 144$$
$$= 7.18 \text{ sq ft/shelf}^\dagger$$

G. Daily workload:

$$7.18 \text{ sq ft/shelf} \times 2 \text{ no of shelves/cycle} \times 8 \text{ no. of cycles/day}$$
$$= 114.88 \text{ sq ft/day}$$

---

†From Table 4.6-2. (If shelf size information for a particular sterilizer is *not* included on Chart A, you will need to measure the shelf.)

*Source: American Sterilizer Co.

Table 4.6-2. Clear Space Per Shelf Available To Place Material To Be Processed, Using Various Types of Sterilizer-Loading Equipment

Sterilizer-Loading Equipment	Shelf Size (In.) L × W	Sq Ft per Shelf
AMSCO Small Sterilizers		
16 × 16 × 26 with rack and shelves	21½ × 13¼	1.98
20 × 20 × 38 with rack and shelves	33¼ × 17¼	3.94
20 × 20 × 38 with loading car	30½ × 18¼	3.88
AMSCO Medium Sterilizers (Medallion loading equipment)		
24 × 36 × 36 with loading car	35 × 22	5.35
24 × 36 × 48 with loading car	48 × 22	7.18
24 × 36 × 60 with loading car	29 ×22	4.41
(Eagle loading equipment)		
24 × 36 × 36 with loading car	36 × 22	5.5
24 × 36 × 48 with loading car	48 × 22	7.33
24 × 36 × 60 with loading car	30 ×22	4.56
AMSCO Floor Loaders (Medallion)		
24 × 56 × 51 with loading car	48¾ × 22–¾	7.68
24 × 46 × 51 with loading car	48¾ × 22–¾	7.68
24 × 56 × 36 with loading car	33¾ × 22–¾	5.32
24 × 46 × 36 with loading car	33¾ × 22–¾	5.32
AMSCO Floor Loaders (Eagle)		
26 × 62 × 42 with loading car	35⅜ × 20¼	4.97
26 × 62 × 76 with loading car	35⅜ × 21¼	4.97
CASTLE FLOOR LOADERS		
26 × 62 × 42 with loading car	35⅜ × 20¼	4.97
26 × 62 × 76 with loading car	35⅜ × 20¼	4.97

Source: AMSCO.

Daily workload sterilizer 1 = 114.88 sq ft

Existing Sterilizer 2

A. Sterilizer make and type: Amsco Eagle Vacamatic
B. Sterilizer chamber size: 24 × 36 × 36 in.
C. Type of loading equipment: Eagle loading car with carriage
D. Number of cycles processed daily: 4
E. Number of shelves utilized each cycle: 2
F. Loading equipment *shelf size:*

(36 in. L × 22 in. W) ÷ 144
= 5.5 sq ft/shelf[†]

†From Table 4.6-2.

G. Daily workload:

5.5 sq ft/shelf × 2 no. of shelves/cycle × 8 no. of cycles/day
= 44.0 sq ft/day

Daily workload sterilizer 2 = 44.0 sq ft

Existing Sterilizer 3

A. Sterilizer make and type: Amsco Eagle Vacamatic
B. Sterilizer chamber size: 24 × 36 × 48 in.
C. Type of loading equipment: Eagle loading car with carriage
D. Number of cycles processed daily: 3
E. Number of shelves utilized each cycle: 3

F. Loading equipment *shelf size:*

$$(48 \text{ in. L} \times 22 \text{ in. W}) \div 144$$
$$= 7.33 \text{ sq ft/shelf}^\dagger$$

G. Daily workload:

7.33 sq ft/shelf $\times$ 3 no. of shelves/cycle $\times$ 3 no. of cycles/day
$$= 65.97 \text{ sq ft/day}$$

Daily workload sterilizer 3 = 65.97 sq ft

H. Compute the total workload to be processed each day:

Daily workload sterilizer 1
$$= 114.88 \text{ sq ft}$$

Daily workload sterilizer 2
$$= 44.0 \text{ sq ft}$$

Daily workload sterilizer 3
$$= 65.97 \text{ sq ft}$$

Total existing daily workload
$$= 224.85 \text{ sq ft}$$

Since the daily workload has been computed to be 224.85 sq ft, we can compare the productivity of various sterilizers in processing this identical workload utilizing the document titled *"Terminal 'Steam' Sterilizer Productivity"*

TERMINAL "STEAM" STERILIZER PRODUCTIVITY

Small Rectangular

Sterilizer 20 $\times$ 20 $\times$ 38 Pre-Vac; utilizing *2 shelves* or 7.76 sq ft per cycle; Cycle time* 37 minutes or 0.617 hours:

224.85 total sq ft/day $\div$ 7.76 sq ft/cycle
$$= 28.97^\dagger \text{ or } 29 \text{ cycles/day}$$

1 unit: [29 cycles $\div$ 1 unit] = 29 cycles† $\times$ 0.617 hrs/cycle = 17.89 hours/day

2 units: [29 cycles $\div$ 2 units] = 15 cycles† $\times$ 0.617 hrs/cycle = 9.25 hours/day

---

†From Table 4.6-2.
†Round "UP" to next higher whole number.
*See Table 4.6-3 for cycle times.

3 units: [29 cycles $\div$ 3 units] = 10 cycles† $\times$ 0.617 hrs/cycle = 6.17 hours/day

Medium Rectangular

Sterilizer 24 $\times$ 36 $\times$ 48 Pre-Vac; utilizing *2 shelves* or 14.67 sq ft per cycle; Cycle time* 43½ minutes or 0.725 hours:

224.85 Total sq ft/day $\div$ 14.67 sq ft/cycle
$$= 15.3^\dagger \text{ or } 16 \text{ cycles/day}$$

1 unit: [16 cycles $\div$ 1 unit] = 16 cycle† $\times$ 0.725 hrs/cycle = 11.6 hours/day

2 units: [16 cycles $\div$ 2 units] = 8 cycles† $\times$ 0.725 hrs/cycle = 5.8 hours/day

3 units: [16 cycles $\div$ 3 units] = 6 cycles† $\times$ 0.725 hrs/cycle = 4.35 hours/day

Medium Rectangular

Sterilizer 24 $\times$ 36 $\times$ 48 Pre-Vac; utilizing *3 shelves* or 22.0 sq ft per cycle; Cycle time* 43½ minutes or 0.725 hours:

224.85 total sq ft/day $\div$ 22.0 sq ft/cycle
$$= 10.2^\dagger \text{ or } 11 \text{ cycles/day}$$

1 unit: [11 cycles $\div$ 1 unit] = 11 cycles† $\times$ 0.725 hrs/cycle = 7.97 hours/day

2 units: [11 cycles $\div$ 2 units] = 6 cycles† $\times$ 0.725 hrs/cycle = 4.35 hours/day

3 units: [11 cycles $\div$ 3 units] = 4 cycles† $\times$ 0.725 hrs/cycle = 2.9 hours/day

---

Floor Loader:

Sterilizer 26 $\times$ 62 $\times$ 42 Pre-Vac; Utilizing *3 shelves* or 14.91 sq ft per cycle; Cycle time* 43¾ minutes or 0.729 hours:

224.85 total sq ft/day $\div$ 14.91 sq ft/cycle
$$= 15.08^\dagger \text{ or } 16 \text{ cycles/day}$$

1 unit: [16 cycles = 1 unit] = 16 cycles† $\times$ 0.729 hrs/cycle = 11.66 hours/day

2 units: [16 cycles $\div$ 2 units] = 8 cycles† $\times$ 0.729 hrs/cycle = 5.83 hours/day

3 units: [16 cycles $\div$ 3 units] = 6 cycles† $\times$ 0.729 hrs/cycle = 4.38 hours/day

Table 4.6-3. Cycle Times for Three Sizes of Autoclaves

Pre-Vac Sterilizer Size (In.)	Cycle Time (Minutes)	Load/ Unload Time (Minutes)	Total Cycle Time (Minutes)
20 × 20 × 38	36	1.00	37.00
24 × 36 × 48	42	1.50	43.50
26 × 62 × 42	42	1.75	43.75

Note: Cycle times are based on processing mixed loads of material at 270° to 274°F with 4-minute exposure time and 20-minute dry time. The cycle time also includes loading and unloading of the sterilizer chamber.
Source: AMSCO.

Floor Loader:

Sterilizer 26 × 62 × 42 Pre-Vac; Utilizing *4 shelves* or 19.88 sq ft per cycle; Cycle time* 43¾ minutes or 0.729 hours:

224.85 total sq ft/day ÷ 19.88 sq ft/cycle
= 11.3[†] or 12 cycles/day

1 unit: [12 cycles ÷ 1 unit] = 12 cycles[†] × 0.729 hrs/cycle = 8.75 hours/day

2 units: [12 cycles ÷ 2 units] = 6 cycles[†] × 0.729 hrs/cycle = 4.37 hours/day

3 units: [12 cycles ÷ 3 units] = 4 cycles[†] × 0.729 hrs/cycle = 2.92 hours/day

GLOSSARY

Decontamination—Physical/chemical process by which an object is made safe for handling. Decontamination includes sanitation, disinfection and sterilization. It involves physical cleaning and a biocidal process of sterilizing biological agents.

Depyrogenation—A pyrogen is a fever-producing substance; depyrogenation removes the ability to cause a fever.

Disinfection—The process of destroying disease-causing microorganisms, but not bacterial spores; it may not be adequate for destroying some viruses. Walls, floors, ceilings, lab furniture and objects can be sprayed and wiped clean with disinfectants available on the market.

Sanitization—The process of reducing the number of microbial contaminants on an inanimate object's surface to a relatively safe level. Glassware and cage washers at 140°–203°F (60°–95°C) sanitize. The process primarily removes dirt or soil.

Sterilization—The process of destroying all forms of microbial life on inanimate surfaces. This process can be controlled and the results monitored. Steam at 250°–285°F (121°–141°C) sterilizes.

REFERENCES

Association for the Advancement of Medical Instrumentation, 1986. *American National Standard for Biological Indicators for Saturated Steam Sterilization Processes in Health Care Facilities.* Arlington, VA: AAMI.

Association for the Advancement of Medical Instrumentation, 1988. *Good Hospital Practice: Steam Sterilization and Sterility Assurance.* Arlington, VA: AAMI.

Block, S.S., ed., 1983. *Disinfection, Sterilization, and Preservation.* Philadelphia: Lea & Febiger.

Perkins, John J., 1983. *Principles and Methods of Sterilization in Health Sciences,* 2nd ed. Springfield, IL: Charles C. Thomas.

4.7 ENVIRONMENTAL ROOMS
T. Ruys

4.7.1 Introduction

Environmental rooms include cold rooms, warm rooms, incubator rooms and growth chambers dealing with temperature and humidity controls. They do not include clean rooms. This section deals with factors in the selection and testing of environmental rooms. It does not cover reach-in (as opposed to walk-in) equipment available for the same purpose because the laboratory user rather than the laboratory planner selects that type of equipment.

Prefabricated environmental rooms are

far superior in quality to built-in rooms and far more flexible in use because they can be moved.

Environmental rooms generally do not follow codes and standards for rooms but rather for equipment. They are rarely ventilated and are not fire rated, so they cannot be a part of a fire-rated enclosure. See Figure 4.7-1. Flammable liquids and gases must not be used inside these rooms.

Compressors require service and generate heat and noise. For these reasons, it is not a good idea to locate them on top of the chamber within the laboratory space. Air-cooled compressors must be located in well-ventilated spaces or outside with easy access for service. Rough-in requirements are shown in Appendix J.

Because of the high cost of water in many locations, water-cooled compressors are often cooled with a recirculated chilled-water system.

In laboratories, environmental rooms are used to store samples or chemicals, grow plants or carry out critical operations. A failure of the system is often disastrous. The following precautions should be taken:

- Provide a separate system for each chamber instead of one system for many chambers.

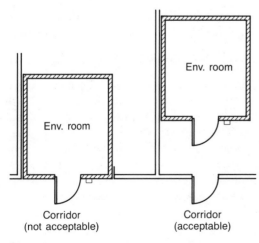

Plan

Fig. 4.7-1. Environmental rooms and fire enclosures.

- Provide several smaller chambers instead of one large one.
- Provide standard and emergency power.

For freeezers, vapor-proof electrical conduit and junction boxes must be used because water vapor may condense inside these boxes, freeze and eventually burst the conduit or junction box because of the ice buildup.

As with any equipment, the quality and price will vary, so the selection of environmental rooms requires some knowledge. The following sections will cover these options.

Coordination between trades is critical. Appendix J provides a diagram of the typical installations by the various trades. Adequate space must be provided to service all components of the environmental rooms system.

4.7.2 Environmental Room Selection

Chamber

Modular panels are available in 4-, 5-, and 6-in. urethane, which is formed in place between two sheets of metal skin under tightly controlled conditions.

The metal skin can be galvanized, aluminum or stainless steel. The galvanized steel is available with a polyester finish for easy cleaning and good reflectivity.

The modular panels have a tongue-and-groove edge for accurate fit and a fastening device for attaching panels to each other. The better manufacturers provide three fastening points on each panel side and two at the top and bottom, with metal straps through the urethane connecting the fasteners. See Figure 4.7-2. Environmental rooms may or may not need a prefabricated floor. A freezer should have a floor, but cold rooms, incubators and growth chambers frequently are installed without one. However the cold room floor must be insulated to prevent condensation of the moisture in the air on the cold surface.

The insulation of urethane foam should be poured, not frothed in place, for better uniformity and skin adhesion and is heat cured. The insulation value affects the cost of en-

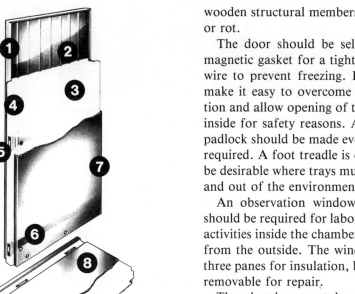

1. **Outside metal pan.** Your choice of patterned aluminum, bright galvanized, or stainless steel, die-formed to exact size.
2. **Rigid urethane,** 4″ thick (optional 5″ thick), "foamed-in-place". Its great strength, reinforced by metal skins eliminates the need for wood framing. Panel is 100% insulation.
3. **Tongues and grooves** on opposite edges, formed during foaming assures tight seal.
4. **Bally cam-action Speed-Lok,** precisely positioned for tight, accurate joining of panels.
5. **Steel straps** connect locking arms with locking pins on opposite sides of panel. This means that an assembled Bally Walk-In has continuous steel perimeters within the insulation to hold panels tightly in place.
6. **Inside metal pan.** Your choice of patterned aluminum, bright galvanized, or stainless steel, die-formed to exact size.
7. **Floor panel.** Includes extra heavy interior pan of 14 gauge galvanized steel as standard.

Fig. 4.7-2. Environmental room construction. (courtesy Bally Engineered Structures, Inc.).

ergy, so a comparison is important. Table 4.7-1 explains the insulating values. Four inches of urethane equals 8.5 in. of fiberglass, and the closed-cell structure of urethane does not absorb moisture.

The better-quality panels contain no

wooden structural members which can warp or rot.

The door should be self-closing, with a magnetic gasket for a tight seal and heating wire to prevent freezing. Hardware should make it easy to overcome the magnetic action and allow opening of the door from the inside for safety reasons. A provision for a padlock should be made even if a lock is not required. A foot treadle is optional but may be desirable where trays must be carried into and out of the environmental room.

An observation window is optional but should be required for laboratory use so that activities inside the chamber can be observed from the outside. The window should have three panes for insulation, be heated, and be removable for repair.

The chamber must be provided with a thermometer and a light.

Ramps are often required for handicapped access or cart traffic. Ramps are available internally or externally. See Figure 4.7-3.

Light fixtures should be sound rated because of the noise that the transformer generates in a small space with hard surfaces. Fixtures for cold rooms and freezers should also be vapor tight to keep condensation out and should have cold temperature-rated lamps for freezers and cold rooms.

Refrigeration System

The refrigeration system consists of five essential components: the compressor, the condenser, an expansion device, an evaporator or fan coil unit and the controls.

The condensing unit, which includes the compressor, is a heat exchanger. It rejects the heat absorbed from the cold room through the evaporator to the air or to water. Condensing units are either air or water cooled, depending on the geographic location and the cost and availability of water.

The 1988 ASHRAE handbook is an excellent reference for greater detail.

The condensing unit should have the following components (see Figure 4.7-4):

- Compressor: Self-contained or "hermetic" units are available at a lower

Table 4.7-1. Insulation Comparison

The insulating value of any material may be stated as its thermal conductivity, or "K" factor. The K rating applies to a 12-inch square of insulation material, one inch thick. The lower the rating, the more efficient the insulation.

The K factor of the foamed-in-place urethane used by Bally is .118. Compare it to the K factors of fiberglass (.26) and polystyrene (.23).

When we adjust for the actual thickness of insulation, we get a truer picture of its insulating value. The figure derived this way is called U factor. For Bally's four-inch panel, the U factor is 0.29, for a five-inch panel, U is .024. A four-inch layer of fiberglass, in contrast, rates a U factor of only 0.65.

Note that K and U factors are like golf scores—the lower the better. Most of us are a little uncomfortable with this "less is more" thinking. That's why R values are now widely used. The R value is a direct measure of insulating capacity. The higher the R value, the better an insulator is at slowing the transfer of heat.

Foamed in place urethane has an R value of 34 for four inches, 42 for five inches. In contrast, the R value for a four inch thickness of fiberglass insulation is only 16. This makes a big difference in operating costs. So it's very important to make the comparison among insulations.

This chart shows the difference in K factors and R values for four-inch thicknesses of urethane and polystyrene insulation.

	Bally Urethane	Polystyrene
Thickness	4″	4″
"K" Factor	.118	.230
"R" Factor	34	17

A panel insulated with polystyrene would have to be eight inches thick to provide the equivalent insulating value of the four-inch Bally panel.

Source: Bally Engineered Structures, Inc.

cost. Custom made or "semihermetic" compressors are more flexible and can be made to operate more efficiently. They are also accessible and can be serviced in the field.

- Suction accumulator: A device to prevent liquid refrigerant or oil from returning to the compressor.
- Oil separator: A device placed in the discharge line, which will remove 50 to 90% of the oil from the refrigerant and returns it to the compressor crankcase.
- Sight glass: A device which provides a visible indication of the refrigerant charge.
- Vibration eliminator: A flexible device in the line to prevent breaking of the pipe.
- Crankcase heater and winter control: A heating device to keep the oil in the crankcase viscous and prevent migration of liquid refrigerant to the crankcase.
- Dual pressure control: Pressure-sensi-

tive device. The low point turns it on and off; the high point is a safety device to cut off if the pressure is too high.

The fan coil or evaporator unit should have the following components (see Figure 4.7-5):

- Heat exchanger: A device which exchanges heat between the suction and liquid lines in order to lower the temperature in the liquid line and increase the temperature in the suction line.
- Thermostatic expansion valve: Refrigerant flow device.
- Solenoid valve: Electrically operated shutoff valve.
- Defrost terminating thermostat: A device which senses the temperature at the set point in order to terminate the defrost cycle.
- Fan delay thermostat: A device which delays the startup of the evaporator fan until the coil unit is cold enough.

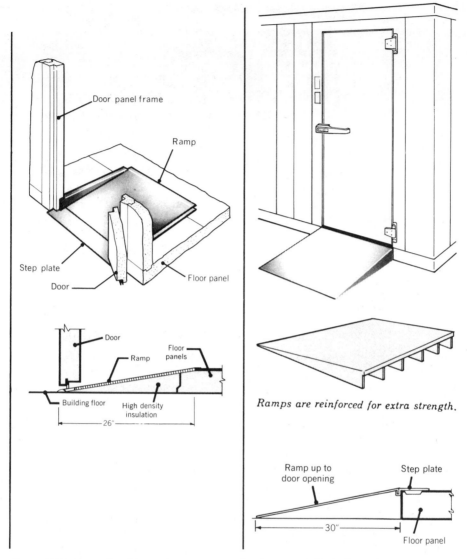

Ramps are reinforced for extra strength.

Figure 4.7-3. External and internal ramp construction (courtesy Bally Engineered Structures, Inc.).

- Temperature control: Room thermostat which controls the cold box temperature at the set point.
- Filter/drier: Filters impurities from the refrigerant. The drier absorbs water in the line to keep it from freezing and prevents other problems.

The refrigeration system must be designed for the temperature range and tolerance required. Some systems require only one temperature, with a range of ±2°F. Others require a variable temperature range with a closer tolerance of ±0.5°F.

The controls for a storage cold room are fairly simple, but those for a plant growth chamber can be quite complicated. The following decisions must be made:

- What is the acceptable or required range of temperature and humidity? The high point and low point?
- Are air temperature and humidity recorders desirable? They may be re-

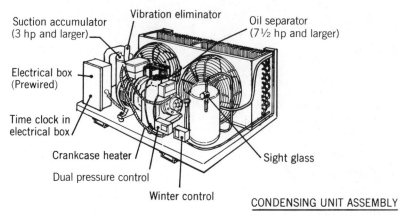

Suction accumulator
(3 hp and larger)

Vibration eliminator

Oil separator
(7½ hp and larger)

Electrical box
(Prewired)

Time clock in
electrical box

Crankcase heater

Dual pressure control

Winter control

Sight glass

CONDENSING UNIT ASSEMBLY

Fig. 4.7-4. Condensing unit components (Courtesy Bally Engineered Structures, Inc.).

quired for work governed by the Good Laboratory Practice (GLP) Act.

- What types of alarms must be provided—audible, visible, local or remote?

The manufacturers listed in Appendix B can be very helpful, but the needs must first be established with the user. Table 4.7-2 provides a framework for collecting and documenting these requirements.

A preliminary power requirement can be established with the calculation from Table 4.7-3 and the data from the 1985 ASHRAE handbook.

Coordination between the mechanical contractor and the controlled environment room supplier is critical. It must be clear which components are provided by each party. Appendix J shows typical rough-in re-

quirements for a small research walk-in cold room.

4.7.3 Environmental Room Testing

A number of tests establish the quality of the components or systems that make up the environmental room or varies its performance after installation.

National Sanitation Foundation (NSF) label establishes a standard of cleanability which may be more appropriate to the food service industry.

Underwriters Laboratories (UL) provides many test for various reasons. The ones of importance to environmental rooms are those provided for electrical devices or assemblies. Devices include the control panel, light fixtures, evaporator

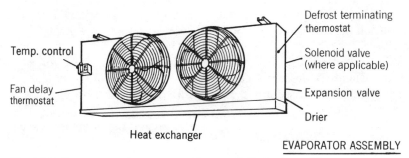

Temp. control

Fan delay
thermostat

Heat exchanger

Defrost terminating
thermostat

Solenoid valve
(where applicable)

Expansion valve

Drier

EVAPORATOR ASSEMBLY

Fig. 4.7-5. Evaporator unit component (Courtesy Bally Engineered Structures, Inc.).

Table 4.7-2. Environmental Room Requirements Form

Job:	Room No:	By:	Date:

Dimensions   W   D   H   (Note: locate on plan, outdoor or indoor.)
  Outside   _____   _____   _____
  Inside   _____   _____   _____

Floor   Required _____   Not required _____

Door   Width _____   (Note: locate on plan including door swing)

Material   White Enamel Steel _____   Galvanized Steel _____
   Aluminum   _____   Stainless Steel   _____

Refrigeration   Self-contained   _____   Remote _____ (Note: locate on plan)
   Air-cooled   _____   Water-cooled _____

Temperature Range _____ to _____°F tolerance: plus or minus _____°F
            _____ to _____°C tolerance: plus or minus _____°C
            (Note: for diurnal cycles note cycle temperature, ranges and times)

Humidity Range   Not required   _____
   Humidified   _____% RH at _____°F (plus or minus 5%)
   Dehumidified   _____% RH at _____°F (plus or minus 5%)

Air-Handling System   Standard fan coil unit   _____
            Laminate air floor perforated ceiling   _____

Lighting   Vapor-proof   _____   Light level at 36 in.   _____ FC
   Incandescent   _____   Fluorescent   _____
   Standard switch   _____   24-hour diurnal cycling   _____
            switch

Control Panel   (Note: locate on plan)
     Recording thermometer   _____   Indicating thermometer   _____
     Hunmidity recorder   _____
     Local alarm   _____   Remote alarm   _____
     Location of remote alarm   _____

Accessories   View window   _____   Light tight cover   _____
   Foot treadle   _____
   Plugged cable access ports   _____   Number _____ (Note: on location plan)
   Shelving _____ Wx _____ Lx _____ H, Material: _____

Electrical   Breaker for condensing unit _____V _____ A _____ HP _____ Ø
(available)   Breaker for evaporator, lights, controls _____V _____ A _____ Ø

Product Loads   Number of persons _____   Hours per 24 hours: _____
   Frequency of entry per hour: _____
   Products to be cooled: _____
   Weight in lbs.: _____
   Temperature of entering products: _____
   Time to reach room temperature: _____

and compressor. Assemblies include the heating wire in the door panel.

Chamber panels shall have a flame spread rating of 25 or lower and a smoke generation rating of 450 or lower when tested according to ASTM Standard E-84-76.

Factory Mutual (FM). FM conducts many tests based on the nature of the product and its application. Some tests are similar to those performed by UL; others are unique FM designs. Of importance to environmental rooms is the rating that FM assigns. A minimum Class I rating is essential for most applications.

System Tests. Multipoint stripcharts are used to record data on various conditions as a function of time. Typical conditions monitored include temperature and humidity. The nature of a continuous stripchart makes it possible to keep a permanent record of the recorded characteristic for any given time.

Table 4.7-3. Power Calculation for a Cold Room*

1. Surface Heat Gains:

Walls	_____ square feet	× .0295 × 24 hr.	× _____ T.D.†	= _____
Ceiling	_____ square feet	× .0295 × 24 hr.	× _____ T.D.	= _____
Floor	_____ square feet	× _____	× _____ T.D.	= _____

2. Air Change Load

Volume	_____ cubic feet	× _____	= _____

3. Product Loads

Respiration	_____ lbs.	× _____	BTU/lb./day	= _____
Cool Product	_____ lbs.	× _____	Specific Heat	
Above Freezing		× _____	Temp. Reduction	= _____
Freeze Product	_____ lbs.	× _____	Latent Heat	= _____
Cool Frozen Product	_____ lbs.	× _____	Specific Heat	
Below Freezing	_____ lbs.	× _____	Temp. Reduction	= _____

4. Miscellaneous Heat Gains

People	_____ × _____ BTU/person/hr. × _____ hr.		= _____
Lights	_____ watts × 3.42 BTU/hr./wt.x _____ hr.		= _____
Other			= _____
Evaporator Fan Motors			= _____
		BTU/24 hr.	= _____
		BTU/hr.	= _____
		+ 10%	= _____
		Total BTU/hr.	= _____

5. Recommended Condensing Unit: _____
6. Recommended Evaporator: _____
7. Capacity _____ BTU/hr. _____ HP

*4-in. urethane.
†T.D., temperature differentials available from ASHRAE (1985).
Source: Bally Engineered Structures, Inc.

REFERENCES

ASHRAE, 1985. *Fundamentals,* Chapter 29. Atlanta, GA: ASHRAE.
ASHRAE, 1988. *Equipment.* Atlanta, GA: ASHRAE.

4.8 EMERGENCY SHOWERS AND EYEWASH FOUNTAINS
T. Ruys

Emergency showers and eyewash fountains are standard features in a laboratory. This section summarizes the standards and practices for laboratory facilities planning. In 1981, the American National Standards Institute published standard ANSI Z-358.1–1981 for Emergency Showers and Eyewashes. This standard has not been adopted yet by OSHA but very likely will be.

4.8.1 Emergency Showers

Time is of the essence in emergencies. The location of and distance to an emergency shower are critical. A standardized location for every laboratory, clearly marked and labeled, will be remembered in an emergency. A 3-ft-diameter green circle on the floor under the shower head is often used, in addition to a clearly visible sign and posted procedural instructions. The ANSI standard calls for a brightly colored surface behind the unit. Emergency showers are primarily for chemical spills, but may be used for individuals on fire if available in the immediate vicinity. However, personnel could be trained to drop to the floor and roll to extinguish the flames first.

OSHA 29CRF 1910 requires an emergency shower for hazardous areas. That is generally interpreted to mean one shower for every laboratory using acids and caustic chemicals and where fires and explosions may be expected, at the loading dock and in the chemical storage areas. There should be no door in the path of travel between the spill area and the shower. Showers should be located where they cannot be obstructed by carts or other laboratory equipment.

Because the laboratory may be on fire, emergency showers must also be located in corridors in strategic locations: however, they may be subject to vandalism in those locations. It is advisable to provide audible and visible alarms in a central location activated by the emergency shower to minimize water damage in case of vandalism or to assist a victim in case of an emergency.

The first few seconds are critical to preserve life and avoid major injury. The distance should therefore be no greater than can be traversed in 10 seconds per the ANSI standard. That is assumed to be no more than 100 ft from any location in the laboratory to the nearest shower. That is the maximum distance. Shorter distances may be advisable and have been used in past standards.

The emergency shower is just that: for emergencies only. A standard shower with hot and cold water where the victim can undress and rinse for an extended period of time is essential in every laboratory facility. Blankets must be available nearby.

In order to be effective, showers need to release a large volume of water at low velocity. ANSI requires 30 gallons/minute; however, 20 gallons/minute may be acceptable if the spray pattern meets the standards. The spray pattern must have a minimum diameter of 20 in. at 60 in. above the floor (see Figure 4.8-1), and the center of the spray must be at least 16 in. from any obstructions and a greater distance from electrical devices. The shower head itself must be at least 82 in. from the floor but not higher than 96 in.

Because of the large volume of water, many installations have floor drains below the shower, although this is by no means standard practice. Floor drains are expensive and dry out because of infrequent use, al-

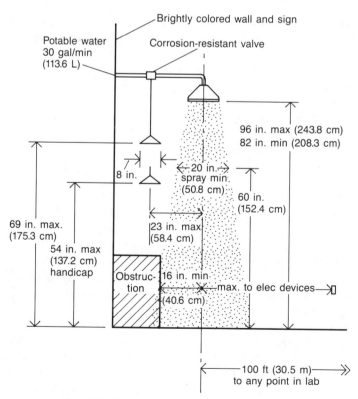

Fig. 4.8-1. Emergency shower—critical dimensions.

lowing sewer gases to enter the laboratory. A primed floor drain should be provided if floor drains are desired.

Most installations provide cold water only to the shower head, which makes the prescribed 15-minute rinse of acid spills on exposed skin very unlikely. Ideally, the water temperature should be somewhere between 60° and 95°F (15° to 35°C). At times, a recirculated tempered water source is provided, which can also be used at outside locations such as loading docks subject to freezing temperatures. In all cases, the source has to be potable water.

The shower handle must be reachable to be effective, i.e., not higher than 67 in. from the bottom of the ring or triangle. In locations where persons in wheelchairs are stationed, that distance must not exceed 54 in. The handle must be a ring at least 8 in. in diameter or a triangle 8 in. on each side.

Flow control valves come in many styles. The self-closing types are not recommended because they require repeated efforts to keep the flow of water going or, worse, fail to shut at times because debris in the line may settle in the low points in the line—the valves—lodge there, and keep the valves from closing during tests. A positive-action valve which stays open or shut with a bar handle in lieu of a set of two chains is recommended. This arrangement makes the flow easier to control and prevents tampering with handles. The reach from the center of the shower head spray to the handle must not exceed 23 in.

The shutoff valve to the water source should not be accessible to laboratory personnel and should be clearly marked to guard against accidental shutoff. Any shutoff valve should be equipped with "lock-open" capability.

Many spills involve the face, eyes and other body parts. It is therefore common practice to combine the eyewash and the emergency shower. See Figure 4.8-2.

For laboratories dealing with highly toxic or radioactive materials, a deluge shower and a central overhead spray combination

Fig. 4.8-2. Emergency shower/eye/face wash combination (Speakman Company).

unit close by should be considered. See Figure 4.8-3.

4.8.2 Eyewash Fountains

OSHA 29 CFR 1910.151C requires suitable eyewash facilities where the eyes may be exposed to corrosive materials. That is a minimum requirement; the University of Washington has interpreted this to mean that an eyewash facility must be provided nearby if the following conditions exist:

- A chemical fumehood used for acids, bases or organic solvents (corrosive, caustic or volatile materials) which may be irritating; fumes or aerosols with toxic or irritating properties.

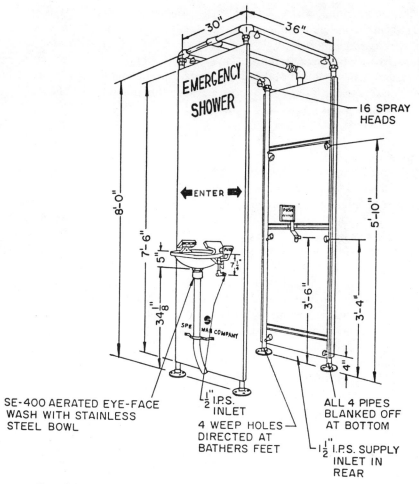

Fig. 4.8-3. Deluge shower—whole body irrigation (Speakman Company).

Table 4.8-1. Summary of ANSI Emergency Shower Standards (Z-358.1-1981)

The following should be noted as quoted from the standard: "The . . . standard does not in any respect preclude anyone, whether he has approved the standard or not, from . . . purchasing, or using products, processes, or procedures not conforming to the standard. American National Standards are subject to periodic review and users are cautioned to obtain the latest editions."

- Shower head—clear distance 82 in. minimum, 96 in. maximum.
- Spray pattern—20-in. diameter at 60 in.
- Clearance—center line of spray 16 in. minimum from any obstruction.
- Volume—30 gallons per minute, minimum iron pipe size of 1 in.
- Control valve—stay-open type, full open position in 1 second or less. Resistant to corrosion from potable water.
- Valve actuator—easy to locate, readily accessible.
- Shower enclosure—unobstructed area 34-in. diameter minimum.
- Distance to shower—can be reached in 10 seconds or within less than 100 ft (30.5 m) travel distance.
- Notation—identify with highly visible sign, brightly colored wall or enclosure, well lighted.

Note: Combination shower/eyewash units should conform to the requirements of each unit.

- Dishwashing rooms where chromic or nitric acid baths, ammonia or caustic cleaning agents are used.
- Shops where grinding, sanding or soldering processes could be abrasive to the eyes.
- Other areas where procedures could produce hazards to the eyes.

"Suitable eyewash facility" has not been defined. Standards do exist, but there are also so-called standard practices. Standards and standard practices are not necessarily in conflict; in fact, they are often complementary. This section deals with the ANSI Z-358.1–1981 standard, which has not yet been adopted by OSHA, and with some common practices in various institutions.

The ANSI standard requires both an eyewash and an eye/face wash unit no greater than 100 ft away. Providing a combination eye/face wash facility in all cases is the most economical method.

Eyewash fountains, of course, are used to rinse the eyes (and face) in case of a chemical spill. Some spills may be caused by an explo-

sion; some result in fires. Common sense tells us that close proximity is essential. Also, an individual must be able to find the eyewash blinded, unaided and possibly in shock. In extreme cases, a victim must be aided by others while unable to stand. After the first critical seconds of an emergency wash, continuous flushing for 15 minutes becomes important. It may be difficult for some people to bend over a fixed eyewash fountain for 15 minutes under any conditions.

ANSI standards encourage the use of hand-held eyewash hoses in addition to fixed eyewash units. Hopefully, that suggestion will not encourage institutions to remove devices that do not meet ANSI standards but are now available over and above the standards. One should be reminded that ANSI standards are minimum standards. Some of the practices that should be encouraged are:

- Provide a hand-held eyewash hose at each sink. Weaver et al. (1977) recommend an eyewash within 25 ft. Figures 4.8-4 and 4.8-5 give two available types.

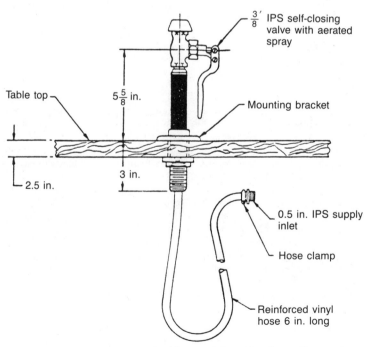

Fig. 4.8-4. Deck-mounted, hand-held eyewash hose (Speakman Company).

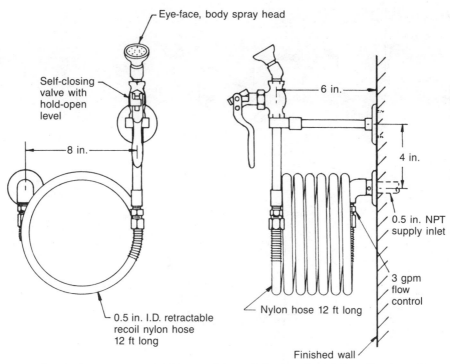

Eye-face, body spray head

Self-closing valve with hold-open level

6 in.

8 in.

4 in.

0.5 in. NPT supply inlet

3 gpm flow control

0.5 in. I.D. retractable recoil nylon hose 12 ft long

Nylon hose 12 ft long

Finished wall

Fig. 4.8-5. Wall-mounted, hand-held eyewash hose. Nylon hose is 12 ft long (Speakman Company).

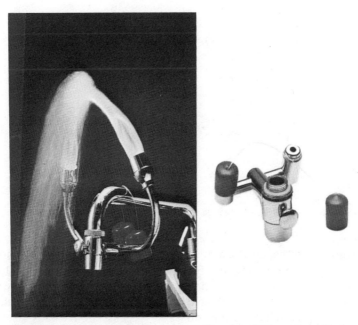

Fig. 4.8-6. Eyewash retrofit to sink faucet (Quardran Equipment and Markson Science, Inc.).

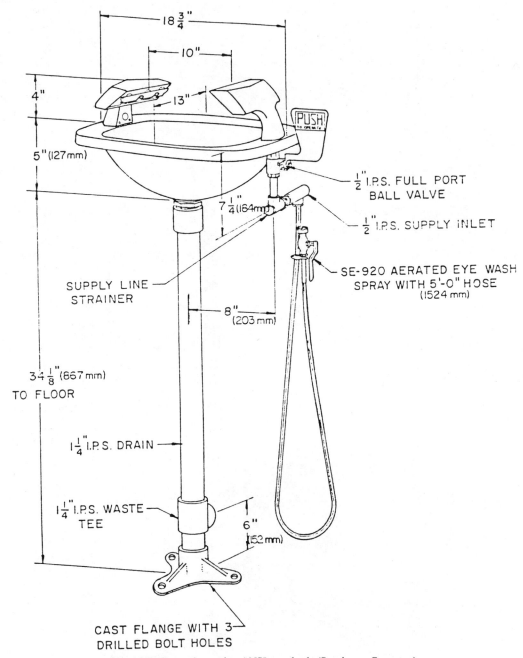

Fig. 4.8-7. Eyewash meeting ANSI standards (Speakman Company).

These valves, at nominal cost, can also be used as useful laboratory tools for rinsing glassware, putting out small fires, and acting as handy eyewash acid spill rinse units. Although these units do not meet ANSI standards in some important respects, they have four impor-tant advantages over those standards: (1) they are in close proximity to the site of the accident, simply because there are more sinks than eyewash facilities; (2) because of its daily use, the victim is very familiar with the location of this device; (3) these units take less space;

Table 4.8-2. Summary of ANSI Eye/Facewash Standards (Z-358.1-1981)

The following should be noted as quoted from the standard: "The . . . standard does not in any respect preclude anyone, whether he has approved the standard or not, from . . . purchasing, or using products, processes, or procedures not conforming to the standard. American National Standards are subject to periodic review and users are cautioned to obtain the latest editions."

- Controlled flow—potable water to both eyes and face simultaneously at velocity which does not cause injury.
- Operating area—no sharp projections.
- Nozzles—protected from airborn contaminants, but removal should not require a separate motion.
- Volume—minimum of 0.4 gallons (1.5 liters) per minute for eyes and 3.0 gallons (11.4 liters) per minute for eyes and face for 15 minutes.
- Clearance—enough room to hold eyelids open with hands in the water stream.
- Control valve—stay-open position, without the use of hands, until intentionally shut off. From on to off position in 1 second or less. Resistant to corrosion by potable water. Activator simple to operate and large enough to locate easily.
- Supply—0.5-in. pipe at minimum 30 lbs/sq in. Potable water.
- Height—nozzles to floor 33 in. minimum, 45 in. maximum
- Distance to eyewash—can be reached in 10 seconds or within less than 100 ft (30.5 m) travel distance.
- Notation—identify with highly visible sign, brightly colored surface, well lighted.

Note: Hand-held drench hoses support shower and eyewash units but do not replace them. They have the same requirements as eye/facewash units except that:
- They are hand held, and the valve must be kept open during use. Only one eye can be flushed at a time.
- No height limitations are provided.

and (4) a unit at the end of a hose can be used to aid victims in shock who are lying on the floor.

- If the hand-held spray nozzle hose is impractical or difficult to install in existing labs, another device is available that can be mounted at the end of any hot or cold water fixture. See Figure 4.8-6. As noted above, it is close by and at a known location, but it has the added advantages that it is far less expensive, easy to install, and leaves the hands of the victim free to flush under the eyelids. A potential disadvantage is that hot water may inadvertently be turned on to the eyewash. Weaver and Britt (1977) reported that 112°F water is considered the upper limit for comfort, but a lower temperature is recommended. Cold or even ice water does no harm but is not well tolerated by the eye.

It is expected that the ANSI standard will be adopted by reference in the OSHA regulations. The requirements are summarized in Table 4.8-2 and the critical dimensions are illustrated in Figure 4.8.-7.

4.8.3 Conclusion

Standards for emergency showers and eyewash fountains are still in a state of flux and have not been adopted by OSHA. This section only covers facilities-related items; it does not cover eye protection, protection against injuries by other than chemical spills, portable equipment, training, posting of hazardous areas or testing of these safety devices. The complete standards and other references should be consulted for those issues.

It should be remembered that irrigation of the eyes must occur within seconds of the spill to have the greatest benefit.

The U.S. Department of Energy (1986) reports that water systems may be contaminated with Acanthamoebae, which causes serious eye infections. Water sources must be potable, and a weekly flushing of 3 minutes is recommended.

REFERENCES

ANSI. ANSI Standard Z 358.1–1981 for Emergency Eyewash and Shower Equipment. NY: ANSI.

U.S. Department of Energy, 1986. Environments,

Safety and Health Bulletin DOE/EH-0010, Issue No. 15. Wash. D.C.

Weaver, Albert, and Britt, Karen A., 1977. Criteria for Effective Eyewashes and Safety Showers. *Professional Safety,* June, 38–45, 53–54.

Weaver, Albert, Britt, Karen A., and Pierce, David, 1977. *Eyewash and Safety Shower Criteria Document.* Raleigh: Occupational Safety and Health Administration, North Carolina Department of Labor, p. 11.

4.9 FLAMMABLE LIQUIDS STORAGE CABINETS   *T. Ruys*

4.9.1 Introduction

Flammable Liquid Storage Cabinets are an integral part of most chemistry laboratories. This chapter deals with the construction and location of this safety equipment, but not with the quantities in storage, handling or disposal of flammable liquids. Storage rooms are covered under codes (see Section 7.2) in this Handbook.

4.9.2 Definitions

The following definitions are quoted from NFPA Standard 30:

Fire Area. An area of a building separated from the remainder of the building by construction having a fire resistance of at least one hour and having all communicating openings properly protected by an assembly having a fire resistance rating of at least one hour.

Labeled. Equipment or materials to which has been attached a label, symbol or other identifying mark of an organization acceptable to the "authority having jurisdiction" and concerned with product evaluation, that maintains periodic inspection of production of labeled equipment or materials and by whose labeling the manufacturer indicates compliance with appropriate standards or performance in a specified manner.

Liquids. For the purpose of this code, any material which has a fluidity greater than that of 300 penetration asphalt when tested in accordance with ASTM D-5-78, *Test for Penetration for Bituminous Materials. When not otherwise identified, the term liquid shall mean both flammable and combustible liquids.*

Combustible Liquid. A liquid having a flash point at or above 100 degree F (37.8 degree C).

Combustible Liquids shall be subdivided as follows:

Class II liquids shall include those having flash points at or above 100 degree F (37.8 degree C) and below 140 degree F (60 degree C).

Class IIIA liquids shall include those having flash points at or above 140 degree F (60 degree C) and below 200 degree F (93 degree C).

Class IIIB liquids shall include those having flash points at or above 200 degree F (93 degree C).

Flammable Liquid. A liquid having a flash point below 100 degree F (37.8 degree C) and having a vapor pressure not exceeding 40 pounds per square inch (absolute) (2,068 MM Hg) at 100 degree F (37.8 degree C) shall be known as a Class I liquid.

Class I liquids shall be subdivided as follows:

Class IA shall include those having flash points below 73 degree F (22.8 degree C) and having a boiling point below 100 degree (37.8 degree C).

Class IB shall include those having a flash points below 73 degree F (22.8 degree C) and having a boiling point at or above 100 degree F (37.8 degree C).

Class IC shall include those having flash point at or above 73 degree F (22.8 degree C) and below 100 degree F (37.8 degree C).

Listed. Equipment or materials included in a list published by an organization acceptable to the "authority having jurisdiction" and concerned with product evaluation, that maintains periodic inspection of production of listed equipment or materials and whose listing states either that the equipment or material meets appropriate standards or has been tested and found suitable for use in a specified manner.

Note: This means that listed equipment may vary for each organization concerned with product evaluation, some of which do not recognize equipment as listed unless it is also labeled. The "authority having jurisdiction" should utilize the system employed by the listing organization to identify a listed product.

Ventilation. As specified in this code, ventilation is for the prevention of fire and explosion. It is considered adequate if it is sufficient to prevent accumulation of significant quantities of vapor-air mixtures in concentration over one-fourth of the lower flammable limit.

4.9.3 Regulations and Standards

OSHA 29 CRF 1910.106 requires:

(3) Design, construction, and capacity of storage cabinets—(i) Maximum capacity. Not more than 60 gallons of Class I or Class II liquids, nor more than 120 gallons of Class III liquids may be stored in a storage cabinet.

(ii) Fire resistance. Storage cabinets shall be designed and constructed to limit the internal temperature to not more than 325 degrees F. when subjected to a ten-minute fire test using the standard time-temperature curve as set forth in Standard Methods of Fire Tests of Building Construction and Materials, NFPA No. 251–1969. All joints and seams shall remain securely closed during the fire test. Cabinets shall be labeled in conspicuous lettering, "Flammable—Keep Fire Away."

(a) Metal cabinets constructed in the following manner shall be deemed to be in compliance. The bottom, top, door, and sides of cabinet shall be at least No. 18 gauge sheet iron and double walled with 1-1/2-inch air space. Joints shall be riveted, welded or made tight by some equally effective means. The door shall be provided with a three-point lock, and the door sill shall be raised at least two inches above the bottom of the cabinet.

(b) Wooden cabinets constructed in the following manner shall be deemed in compliance. The bottom, sides, and top shall be constructed of an approved grade of plywood at least one inch in thickness, which shall not break down or delaminate under fire conditions. All joint shall be rabbetted and shall be fastened in two directions with flathead woodscrews. When more than one door is used, there shall be a rabbetted overlap of not less than one inch. Hinges shall be mounted in such a manner as not be lose their holding capacity due to loosening or burning out of the screws when subjected to the fire test.

Nowhere do the standards call for ventilated cabinets or exhausts from these cabinets. The purpose of these cabinets is to separate flammables from fire in the laboratory in order to reduce the fuel in the laboratory in case of a fire. The author has seen flammable liquid cabinets vented into fumehood chambers. This may be a dangerous practice with the potential to cause a flashback into the cabinet.

However, ventilated cabinets provided with flame arrest vents have been manufactured and tested successfully.

Fresina (1980) reports that according to FM, only Philadelphia's fire code requires mechanical venting. Both FM and NFPA state that the vents are worthless and that the ASTM fire endurance test is done with the vent caps in place. If mechanical venting is necessary, FM recommends 2 in. schedule 20 iron pipe, taking suction from the bottom vent. FM prefers no mechanical venting and use of the top vent for insertion of a pipe for a sprinker. Figure 4.9-1 shows a recommended exhaust system installation if the system is required.

The NFPA Standard No. 30 has been approved for incorporation by reference in the OSHA standard.

NFPA Standard 30 (1984) Section 4–3, deals with the "Design, Construction, and Capacity of Storage Cabinets," which is summarized as follows:

- Quantities: No more than 120 gallons (454 liters) of Class I, Class II and Class IIIA liquids may be stored in a cabinet. Of the 120 gallons, not more than 60 gallons (227 liters) may be of Class I and Class II liquids.
- Numbers: No more than three such cabinets may be located in a single fire area. Exception: In industrial occupancies, three additional cabinets in a group are allowed if separated by at least 100 ft (30 m).
- Construction Acceptable (in Metal): 18 gauge steel double walls with 1.5-in (3.8-cm) air space. Joints tight, riveted, welded or by some other means. Door with three-point latch. Door sill 2 in. (5 cm) to retain spills.

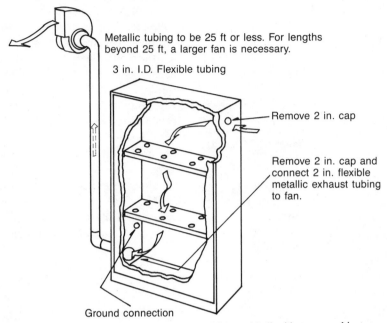

Explosion-proof motor, 220 cfm

Metallic tubing to be 25 ft or less. For lengths beyond 25 ft, a larger fan is necessary.

3 in. I.D. Flexible tubing

Remove 2 in. cap

Remove 2 in. cap and connect 2 in. flexible metallic exhaust tubing to fan.

Ground connection

Fig. 4.9-1. Recommended installation of flammable liquid storage cabinet.

- Construction Acceptable (in Wood): 1-in. (2.5-cm) exterior grade plywood. Joints rabbetted and fastened in two directions with wood screws. Rabbetted overlap of 1 in. (2.5 cm) for two-door construction. Latching and hinges must withstand test conditions. Door sill 2 in. (5 cm) to retain spills.
- Labeling: Conspicuous label reading "Flammable—Keep Fire Away."
- Testing: 10-minute fire test per ASTM Standard E152-81a. The temperature must not exceed 325°F (162.8°C) at the internal center 1 in. (2.5 cm) from the top of the cabinet. The joints must remain tight and door securely closed.
- Venting: The cabinet is not required to be vented.
- Self-closing doors: These are not required but are highly recommended and available.

4.9.4 Testing

Flammable liquid storage cabinets should be tested for conformance with standards and labeled accordingly. UL and FM conduct such tests. The following is a summary of FM's approval standard.

FM has tested flammable liquids cabinets manufactured by various suppliers for compliance with OSHA and NFPA No. 30 standards. They publish submittal specifications for testing or so-called approval standards. The following was summarized from their Standard Class Number 6050, Revised Standard December 12, 1975:

- Basic requirements: Identical to those of NFPA No. 30 except as follows.
- Quality control: Not only is a cabinet sample tested, but the fabrication and quality control are reviewed and inspected in order to ensure uniform quality. FM approval is based on tests *and* examination of production facilities.
- Venting: FM assumes that cabinets may be vented but requires an approved flame arrester. The vents, when not in use, must be plugged both from the inside and from the outside. Upper and lower vents must be located in opposite corners.

- Grounding: A device allowing a wire to be attached for metal cabinets to be grounded must be provided.

Examination and Tests

- Tests are performed per NFPA Standard No. 30. The cabinet is subjected to a loading test which is maintained for 72 hours after the fire tests. Deformation of the cabinet and doors is checked.
- Flame arresters, not mentioned in NFPA No. 30, "shall be subjected to 15 minute fire exposure test by passing a combustible hydrocarbon gas-air mixture through the arrester and allowing it to burn on the surface of the arrester. At 5 minute intervals, the flow will be cut off abruptly and no evidence shall be found of the flame passing through the flame arrester."
- The FM approval label must be removed if any changes are made to the cabinet outside the plant of origin.

4.9.5 Location and Numbers

Standards do not mention the location of flammable liquid storage cabinets, although OSHA 29CFR1910.106, p. 232, states that "Flammable or combustible liquids . . . shall not be stored so as to limit use of exits, stairways, or areas normally used for the safe egress of people."

Many institutions locate these cabinets under the fumehoods, with the assumption that these chemicals will be used in the fumehood and that the travel distance from the point of storage to the point of use will, therefore, be the shortest. Many fumehood manufacturers have cabinets that meet the standards and fit under the hood. However, other users consider the location under the hood potentially too dangerous, since the cabinets will be very close should a fire occur in the hood—the most likely place for a fire in a laboratory.

There is a reference to the number of cabinets allowed per NFPA Standard No. 30: No more than three such cabinets may be located in a single fire area. Exception: In industrial occupancies three additional cabinets in a group are allowed if separated by at least 100 ft (30 m) from the first group of three cabinets.

REFERENCES

Factory Mutual Research, Revised December 12, 1975. Standard Class Number 6050, Norwood, MA: FM.

Fresina, John M., 1980. Flammable Liquid Storage Cabinets Vents. Unpublished memo. Cambridge, MA: Massachusetts Institute of Technology.

National Fire Protection Association, 1984. Standard No. 30, Chapter 4–3, Design, Construction, and Capacity of Storage Cabinets. Quincy, MA: NFPA.

U.S. Occupational Safety and Health Administration. 1987. 29CRF 1910.106. Washington, D.C: U.S. Government Printing Office.

5

Systems

5.1 LABORATORY FACILITIES AS A TOTAL SYSTEM   *T. Ruys*

5.1.1 Potential Conflicts

Laboratory facilities are sophisticated environments. Many components are interrelated. It is therefore important to look at the facility in its totality as one system with many components that serves the needs of laboratory users and laboratory equipment.

In planning, designing and constructing a laboratory building, many individuals with different backgrounds and training are involved. The possibility of combining systems is limited only by the imagination. However, this section deals with the most common conflicts encountered between systems in a laboratory facility.

Structure and Mechanical Conflicts

The most obvious coordination conflict involves the need to accommodate the large air-handling system necessary for a laboratory building. The structure not only must support the extra loads but must provide the extra floor space and headroom. The issues of space and headroom have been dealt with in greater detail elsewhere in this handbook.

Coordination between the structure and piped services and drainlines is also very important. The structural system must allow penetration during initial construction and in the future. Figure 5.1-1 shows several possibilities with various structural systems.

Support Conflicts

Most mechanical systems are supported by the structural system. Since there often are large ducts in the way, it may be difficult at times to support ceilings, lighting and other mechanical systems, particularly if the location of distribution systems has not been carefully planned.

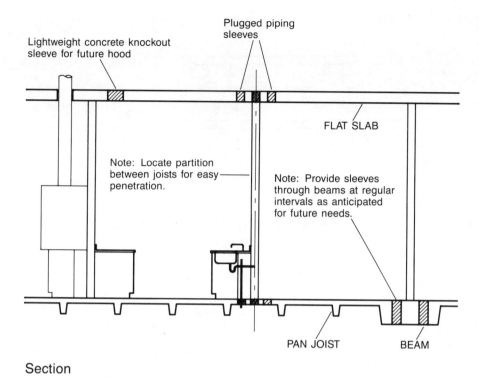

Lightweight concrete knockout sleeve for future hood

Plugged piping sleeves

FLAT SLAB

Note: Locate partition between joists for easy penetration.

Note: Provide sleeves through beams at regular intervals as anticipated for future needs.

PAN JOIST

BEAM

Section

Fig. 5.1-1. Mechanical penetration through structural systems.

Mechanical and Electrical Conflicts

Liquids and electrical power do not mix. Even potential conflicts must be avoided. Drainlines and waterlines must not be distributed through electrical transformer vaults and switch gear rooms. Avoid electrical outlets above sinks, and separate emergency showers and electrical devices.

Mechanical and Mechanical Conflicts

Most mechanical systems for air, gases and fluids can bend and flow uphill. Drainlines and steam condensate returns cannot bend as easily and must flow downhill. These are therefore the controlling systems in a ceiling plenum space and pose special problems below a floor slab on grade.

5.1.2 Distribution

There are many utilities, ducts and electrical services that must be distributed throughout the building. Providing orderly pathways for these will reduce space and make maintenance easier in the future. Distribution can be horizontal and vertical in several ways.

Interstitial Floor

A distinction must be made between ventilation air and piped/electrical services distribution. Ventilation air is typically distributed above the laboratory space it serves. This is most often above the ceiling, although interstitial space and mechanical loft space have been used for laboratory buildings. Figures 5.1-2 and 5.1-3 show such examples. Access for changes and maintenance in both cases is excellent, and these same spaces can be used for piped and electrical distribution systems. The disadvantage over other approaches is the high cost.

Utility Corridor

A similar distribution system can be accommodated between laboratories instead of

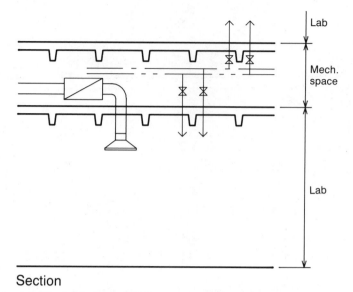

Section

Fig. 5.1–2. Interstitial floor—mechanical distribution space.

above laboratories. Figure 5.1-4 shows a cross section. The advantages of easy access and serviceability are the same as for the interstitial system. The disadvantages are the additional floor area required and a constraint on the ability of the back-to-back laboratories to communicate or expand.

Utility Shafts

The distribution systems mentioned so far are horizontal. There are several vertical systems, which all have vertical shafts in common. Some of these are large, walk-in shafts centrally located or on the building's perime-

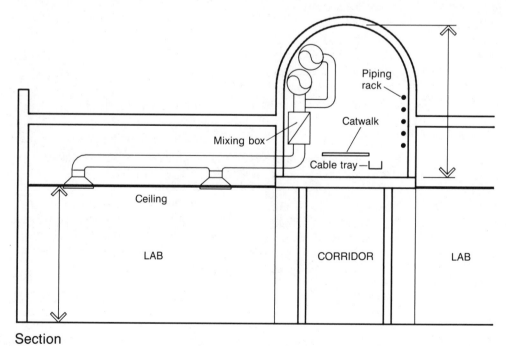

Section

Fig. 5.1-3. Mechanical loft distribution space.

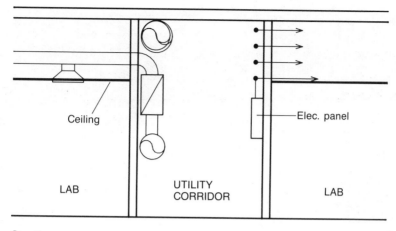

Section

Fig. 5.1-4. Utility corridor mechanical distribution space.

ter; others are multiple small shafts along the corridor wall or on the exterior wall. Figures 5.1-5 to Figure 5.1-9 show these options and the advantages and disadvantages of each.

The multiple utility shafts along the corridor are readily accessible for service without entering the laboratory; this is not possible for the exterior shafts. The corridor shafts can create spaces into which the laboratory door can swing. See Figure 5.1-10. Multiple interior shafts generally require less piping

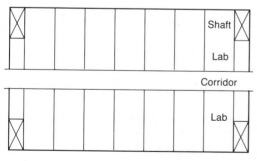

Plan

Fig. 5.1-5. Ceiling and shaft distribution. Ducts, pipes and conduit rise or drop vertically through the building and branch horizontally into ceiling spaces for distribution. Systems feed down to work level or, in the case of drainlines, up to required locations. Advantages: economical. Disadvantages: (1) requires larger ceiling space; (2) Access may be through suspended ceilings.

than exterior shafts or interstitial floors, but not always.

Exterior shafts, on the other hand, can be used as sunscreens and can free the laboratory space, making it more flexible for laboratory use and future changes.

Access

Access to mechanical systems is important:

- For service of moving parts and adjustment of dampers
- For control of valves and electrical breakers
- For changes and additions to utility services

Access has to be provided to mains and utility service branches. If mechanical systems are organized in a network of pathways, installation and renovation costs will be lower and the laboratory user will be served with fewer and shorter disruptions. Building height increases the cost; so, in general, the fewer the crossovers of systems, the lower the cost.

Figure 5.1-11 shows such a network of systems successfully used in a number of laboratory facilities. This particular network uses the ceiling space for distribution and vertical shafts for the mains located outside the labo-

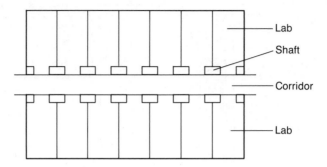

Plan

Fig. 5.1-6. Multiple interior utility shafts—vertical distribution. Ducts, pipes and conduit rise or drop vertically in individual smaller shafts. The horizontal distribution is in the ceiling space of a much smaller area (smaller ducts) or, for piping, immediately from the shaft to the bench. Advantages: (1) shorter horizontal runs mean smaller ducts and pipes; (2) below-eye-level access to shutoff valves; (3) lower floor-to-floor height due to smaller ducts and pipes. Disadvantages: (1) multiple shafts cause multiple obstructions and reduced flexibility; (2) difficulty in making future duct additions: multiple shafts increase the net to gross ratio in a negative direction.

ratory suite. This arrangement keeps the construction cost down and provides the fewest obstructions in the laboratory area. No mains cross; only small run-outs and conduits do. Access to mains is in the corridor; access to run-outs is in the ceiling space above aisles in the laboratory space so that they can be reached without climbing on benches or equipment.

All utilities except drainlines are downfed for four reasons:

- Renovation and changes will not affect the laboratory space on the floor below.

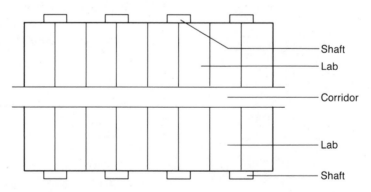

Plan

Fig. 5.1-7. Multiple exterior utility shafts—vertical distribution. Advantages: (1) shorter horizontal runs and multiple shafts mean smaller ducts and pipes; (2) below-eye-level access to shutoff valves; (3) lower floor-to-floor height due to smaller ducts and pipes. Disadvantages: (1) multiple shafts cause multiple obstructions and reduced flexibility; (2) difficulty in making future duct additions; (3) multiple shafts increase the net to gross ratio in a negative direction; (4) strong influence on building design.

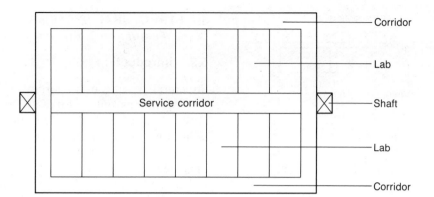

Plan

Fig. 5.1-8. Service corridor. Laboratory spaces back up against an accessible "service corridor" which houses horizontal duct and pipe runs above head height and distributes horizontally into individual labs in ceiling space (ducts, pipes) or may directly service lab benches through the wall from the service corridor. Vertical shafts for ducts and pipes to rise or drop to mechanical spaces are still required. Advantages: (1) continual access for maintenance through service space without entering research spaces; (2) shutoff valves and electric panels easily accessible; (3) service corridor could house shared or moist or heat-producing lab equipment (pumps, transformers). Disadvantages: (1) service corridor affects net to gross ratio negatively. (2) service corridor impairs or prevents space flexibility.

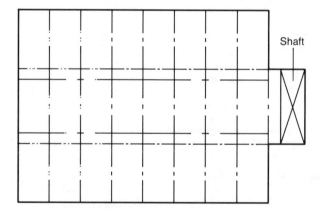

Figure 5.1-9. Interstitial space. Laboratory space is essentially an unobstructed open area with structural members (columns) placed where they relate favorably to the planning module. A horizontal distribution of systems is totally accomplished in an accessible space above the ceiling plane. The services drop vertically from this space into the laboratory envelope and connect to the benches or equipment through umbilicals. Vertical shafts at the perimeter or in a central core connect interstitial space services with the entire building. Advantages: (1) unobstructed floor plan, infinitely adaptable space; (2) minimum disruption in lab during routine maintenance and alternations; (3) services available from above (below) at any point on the planning module. Disadvantages: (1) adds to ceiling height; (2) adds to building's gross space; (3) requires additional structures (access floor, catwalk, etc.); (4) may require additional sprinkling of the interstitial cavity; (5) adds to the cost of the building (depending on the system used, 6–20% of the total building cost).

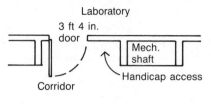

Plan

Fig. 5.1-10. Multiple interior shaft and door combination.

- It does not require two people to figure out which shutoff valve below the floor controls a fixture above the floor.
- It minimizes floor penetration where floods, common in laboratories, can find their way down to lower laboratories.
- It may eliminate the need for a crawlspace below the ground floor.

5.2 STRUCTURAL SYSTEMS
D. Pekrul and T. Ruys

5.2.1 Introduction

Structural systems are important to laboratory operations only insofar as they minimize vibration and allow penetration for utilities and mechanical systems in the future. Not all structural systems qualify to the same degree.

Steel and precast concrete structural systems are not as rigid as cast-in-place concrete systems, and deflection may be a problem with steel beams. However, short spans and structures with a lot of mass generally reduce vibration.

Structural systems must be integrated with mechanical and electrical systems in order to reduce floor-to-floor heights and to ensure an orderly arrangement. Both of these factors reduce costs and may facilitate mainte-

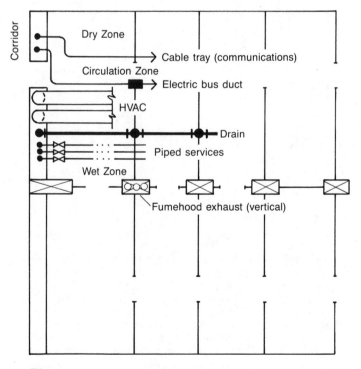

Plan

Fig. 5.1-11. Mechanical systems network. Access to mains is in the corridor. Access to runouts is in the ceiling above the aisles in the laboratory.

nance. The important factor in laboratories, however, is that thought is given to how future fumehood exhaust, waste lines, utility piping and electrical conduits can be added or upgraded where and when the need arises.

5.2.2 Vibration Control

Vibration can be caused by events both outside and inside the building. Traffic, construction, wind and seismic disturbances are examples of exterior causes; mechanical equipment, pedestrians and laboratory operation are examples of internal causes.

External causes are difficult to deal with but must be considered and anticipated in locating a new laboratory building or evaluating an existing building for possible laboratory use.

Internal causes are easier to deal with, but the data necessary to establish acceptable levels of vibration are hard to find. As a result, the usual pragmatic approach is to minimize the vibration caused by known sources such as mechanical systems and to make the building as stiff as possible to counteract vibration by unknown sources. Any instrument that is still affected must then be mounted on isolators, which are either provided as part of the equipment or separately. Unfortunately, overcoming vibration problems is often a matter of trial and error. Laboratory equipment vendors can be very helpful in suggesting preventive or corrective action.

In order for the laboratory user to make a value judgment, a few principles must be understood:

- Several related pieces of equipment, such as those for optical experiments, are best placed on a common base so that differential movement between components is minimized.
- There are three vibration quantities that may be considered: displacement, velocity and acceleration. In practice, the measurement of acceleration is by far the most common, with a large assort-

ment of acceleration-sensitive instruments (i.e., accelerometers) being commercially available. Since velocity and displacement are the first and second integrals of acceleration, these parameters may be obtained from the acceleration by processing the data in real time with an electronic integrator.

- Although one may measure the overall vibration level (i.e., all frequencies taken together), it is usually much more useful to perform a frequency analysis whereby the vibration level is measured in discrete bandwidths, such as octave bands, one-third octave bands, or even narrower bandwidths. This type of analysis is especially useful when the source of excess vibration must be determined.

In order to evaluate the vibration environment in an existing building, assess the ground vibration at a proposed site, or set design goals for a new facility, some criterion for vibration levels is required. As might be expected, the acceptable limits for vibration in a laboratory facility are much more stringent than those in almost any other type of building. This is especially true in the case of laboratories containing sensitive equipment such as optical balances and bench microscopes.

These limits are indicated graphically in Figure 5.2-1. The maximum velocity level in decibels (referenced to 1 microinch/second) is shown for the one-third octave band frequencies between 4 and 125 Hz. In terms of the absolute level for frequencies between 8 and 125 Hz, vibration levels must be kept below 2,000 microinches/second (0.002 in./second). This criterion rises in a straight line up to 4,000 microinches/second at 4 Hz.

The key to minimizing the vibration in laboratory facilities is to provide proper resilient mountings for equipment that produces vibrational forces of a sufficient magnitude to excite the supporting structure. This equipment includes (but is not necessarily limited to) the following:

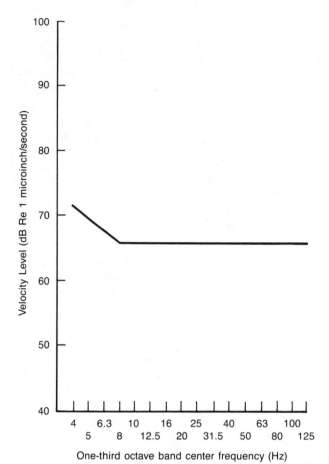

Fig. 5.2-1. Recommended maximum allowable vibration for laboratory equipment (BBN Laboratories, Inc.)

- Fans and air-handling equipment
- Air conditioning equipment
- Refrigeration units and chillers
- Condensing units
- Pumps
- Air compressors
- Cooling towers
- Transformers

In addition to the above equipment, there is laboratory equipment (fumehoods, centrifuges, etc.) that is capable of introducing vibration into the building structure.

Isolation efficiency, i.e., how well a particular resilient mounting system isolates equipment vibration from the supporting structure, is primarily a function of the ratio between the isolator natural frequency and the frequency of the vibration produced by a given item of equipment. A practical limit to isolation efficiency is reached when the isolator's natural frequency is approximately one-fifth of the disturbing frequency. Increasing the ratio beyond this point yields very little additional vibration isolation. As an example, a piece of equipment that produces a fundamental vibrational frequency of 50 Hz should be supported on an isolator that has a natural frequency no greater than 10 Hz.

Rather than specify the natural frequency of a vibration isolator, it is usually more convenient to denote the static deflection. The static deflection is related to the natural frequency of the isolation (f_n) by the following equation:

$$f_n = 3.1 \sqrt{1/\text{static deflection}}$$

The static deflection is a function of the stiffness of the isolator and the weight of the supported equipment. In practical terms, the static deflection is the distance (usually expressed in inches) that a piece of equipment compresses the isolators that support it.

Vibration isolators usually consist of two basic types: neoprene (or rubber) and steel springs. The actual configuration of these isolators varies greatly according to the application, and some vibration isolators combine neoprene and springs in one unit. In general, neoprene isolators provide less static deflection and are therefore effective for equipment producing high-frequency vibration. Equipment that produces relatively low-frequency vibration (e.g., a large fan or cooling tower) must be mounted on high-deflection steel spring isolators to fulfill the requirement of an isolator with a natural frequency that is one-fifth the disturbing frequency.

ASHRAE (1987) has a vibration isolator selection guide in Chapter 52, Table 27; the reader is encouraged to refer to it.

The connections to isolated equipment must not negate the resilient mounting by forming a rigid attachment to the structure. This is often referred to as "shorting out" the vibration isolators. Equipment connected to piping must either incorporate a flexible connector in the line or have the piping itself isolated from the structure. Electrical power connections should include a length of flexible conduit for the same reason.

5.2.3 Mechanical Systems Penetrations

Many laboratory buildings make it impossible to add fumehood exhausts in the future. Adding piping and electrical conduit is usually not a problem, although the results may resemble a bowl of spaghetti. Drainlines pose a bigger problem because of the pitch, but fumehood exhaust ducts and possibly makeup air ducts are large and cause the greatest difficulty.

The difficulty of running the exhaust duct up to the roof, where they should be exhausted, is most often due to the low floor-to-floor heights and the interfering beams

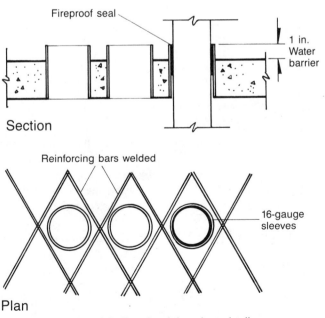

Fig. 5.2-2. Fumehood duct sleeve detail.

between the hood location and the vertical shaft.

Sometimes, however, the structural floor itself does not allow future penetration because the structural strength is affected. Penetration through beams and two-way slabs is of this type. The result often is that fumehood ducts are routed through window openings and up the side of the building. Even worse, if aesthetic reasons prevent exterior ducts, no fumehood may be provided to the laboratory worker.

The obvious solution is to design the building with future changes in mind and to plan for vertical penetration. This can be done as follows:

- Provide large shafts (see Section 5.3) and adequate headroom to get there.
- Provide knockout sleeves filled with lightweight concrete (see Figure 5.2-2) in locations where future penetrations would affect the structural integrity.
- Provide a structural floor which will allow penetration in most locations, such as a pan-joist system or T-flange system.

REFERENCES

ASHRAE, 1985. *Fundamentals,* Chapter 7. Sound and Vibration Fundamentals Atlanta, GA: ASHRAE.

ASHRAE, 1987. *HVAC,* Chapter 52, Table 27. Vibration Isolator Selection Guide. Atlanta, GA: ASHRAE.

Baranek, L. L., ed, 1971. *Noise and Vibration Control.* New York: McGraw-Hill.

Harris, C. M., and Crede, C. E., 1979. *Shock and Vibration Handbook,* 2nd ed. New York: McGraw-Hill.

5.3 MECHANICAL SYSTEMS   *D. K. Lyons, B. H. Atkinson and J. Kasica*

5.3.1 Mechanical Equipment Spaces

Central Utilities Plant

Primary systems, refrigeration and boiler plants are often centrally located either in a fan room or in a central utilities plant (CUP). In the latter case, support services such as air compressors, vacuum, water treatment, emergency and cogenerating equipment are also often included. Isolating fuel storage, delivery of supplies, fumes from stack exhaust, noise and pollution from the working environment is an additional advantage which has an impact on the decision to provide a CUP, particularly when the CUP is built far from the main campus.

When serving multiple buildings, CUPs also permit diversities of 80 to 90% to be used in the selection of primary equipment, chillers, boilers, etc. Although similar diversities may be achieved by cross-connecting satellite chillers and boilers within individual buildings, they are usually more difficult to operate and often require additional operating personnel.

Space requirements for a CUP depend on the type of energy system, configuration of the equipment and provisions for future expansion. A guide for central cooling and heating plants is 2 to 7% of the total gross space, 16 to 25 ft clear height and a minimum width of 25 to 40 ft. These areas can double when electrical generating and other process equipment are included.

Distribution of Primary Utilities

Whenever practical, utilities should be looped, preferably with intermediate cross-connections and main isolating valves. This arrangement will permit the maximum use of diversity, reduce pipe sizes by providing alternate paths and, should a pipe fail, allow the majority of the facility to remain on-line by selectively closing isolating valves.

Often the location of a utility distribution network coincides with materials distribution and maintenance access, and a common service tunnel can be built to provide all of these services. An additional advantage when this occurs is that service of distribution valves, expansion joints and future connections is made easier.

Fan Rooms

The majority of the mechanical space is occupied by the fan rooms which house the air-handling and associated equipment. Assuming that the cooling, heating and other primary plants are installed far from the fan rooms, the space required for this equipment is usually between 10 and 20% of the gross building area. The optimum clear height of a fan room is about 16 to 18 ft, and the width is about 50 to 60 ft. Within certain limits, reducing the height of the fan room will add to the floor area of the fan room, and vice versa.

In the case of certain systems, such as clean rooms and UDF rooms, the percentage for mechanical equipment spaces is considerably higher: up to twice the amount quoted above.

The routing of large air ducts from fan rooms is not as flexible as for small pipes and other services. The location of the fan rooms should be studied to minimize loss of space due to an inefficient duct distribution system. The location should also take into account the geometry of the distribution system, as crossing large ducts or equipment will result in wasted space and increased height of a facility. Additional considerations are the location of outside air intakes and discharge outlets.

A fan room in the basement, compared to one above grade, will require 20% more space due to outside air intake and exhaust configurations.

The area of shafts for the ductwork and piping is from 3 to 4 sq ft/1,000 gross sq ft of floor area served by the shafts.

Ideally, air intakes should be at a low level, with the exhaust discharged at the roof. In practice, this is not always possible. Provided that the engineer is careful in locating intakes and discharges, outside air intakes and discharge ducts can be located at the same level.

Finally, the location and arrangement of the mechanical equipment room must consider the possible use of heat recovery, particularly those types which employ close-contact equipment, such as plate air-to-air heat exchangers where outside and exhaust air are required to run side by side.

5.3.2 Supply Systems

General Considerations

In the overall design of the laboratory building, a module is the smallest repetitive unit in which research is performed and which requires all services to be available. Consequently, air supply systems are designed with the module as the basic unit, and terminal devices are usually sized on this basis.

Research programs are subject to change, and the occupancy and arrangement of laboratory space are often altered over time. Many methods of distribution are available to the designer.

Ideally, each laboratory should have individual temperature control, as requirements vary greatly, with the system available 24 hours/day, 100% outside air to avoid cross-contamination, and a terminal/control system capable of providing positive or negative pressures within the laboratory module.

Systems available are single duct reheat, variable air volume, dual duct and supplemental air systems.

Air may be introduced into the laboratory through ceilings, through sidewalls and under the windows.

Stable face velocities are critical to the proper functioning of the fumehood. Air supplied to a laboratory must be arranged to minimize temperature gradients and air turbulence adjacent to hoods.

It is important that the face velocity of fumehoods not be affected by supply air outlets. A rule of thumb is that terminal velocities of the supply air in the vicinity of a hood should be 50% of the hood's face velocity.

Sidewall grilles are applicable to the laboratory air supply if their terminal velocity, location and air distribution patterns are analyzed and are consistent with the above parameters. It is usually very difficult to achieve this. Distribution below the window or at floor level is usually from fan-powered devices.

The building may be heated either by baseboard heat or by using reheat coils within the control boxes. Either method is acceptable. Care, however, should be used when fan coils which have a cooling coil are provided. When this system is used, dehumidification should be from the interior air systems to ensure a dry coil. If the fan coil cooling coil provides latent cooling, the coil is wet and bacterial growth is possible.

It is not advisable to use suspended ceiling spaces for return air, which is usually ducted. However, each facility has to be analyzed to determine how adjacent spaces are treated for both supply and return/exhaust air.

With the need to conserve energy and the high cost of energy, industry is considering variable air volume systems with true tracking of the supply and exhaust quantities. That is, for negative-pressure labs, the exhaust leads and the supply lags; for positive-pressure labs, the reverse is true.

One of the key elements of a successfully designed laboratory is a minimum response time for controls associated with ever-changing room and fumehood pressures. The faster the response time, the safer the room

design. Section 5.5 deals more fully with this subject.

Outside and Inside Conditions

Outdoor design conditions are usually selected to not be exceeded more than 1% of the time using the ASHRAE handbook.

Inside design conditions vary but are usually on the order of:

Laboratory temperature	72°F ± 3°F
Relative humidity	50% in summer
	35% in winter

When labs are humidified, care must be exercised to avoid condensation on inside window surfaces during the colder months.

Inside heat gains vary, depending on the use of the lab. Table 5.3-1 presents some check values which may be used as a preliminary guide.

Single-Duct Systems

A single-duct system with individual lab reheat control is perhaps the simplest and least expensive first cost of available supply systems. It provides accurate room control with little or no instability. This system, however,

Table 5.3-1. Check Values for Heat Gain From Bench-type Laboratory Equipment*

Equipment Loading	Typical Occupancy Examples	Net Internal Heat Gain From Lab Equipment Total BTU/sq ft/hr[†]		
		Base Maximum[‡]	Peak Maximum[‡]	Sensible Heat Ratio
Low	Chemistry, biology, physics	15	30	0.8–0.95
High	Physics, physical chemistry	30	60	0.8–0.95
Very high	Electronics[δ]	140	0.95–1.0	

*Based on heat release from bench-type laboratory equipment in a 250-sq-ft module. Large individual items should be evaluated separately.

[†]Includes net gain to space after deductions for diversity and hooding.

[‡]Base maximum rates are design values for the majority of spaces. Peak maximum rates are design values for few laboratory spaces with especially high concentrations of equipment.

[δ]Recent trends are to lower heat loads.

Source: ASHRAE.

is the greatest user of energy, and no diversity is possible.

Variable Air Volume (VAV) Systems

Most laboratories today consider VAV with reheat. This has been made possible by the development of economical and reliable hood controls and the ability to accurately track the quantity of supply and exhaust air locally in order to maintain constant pressure relationships.

Many terminal devices are available today. Essentially, each hood or group of hoods controls its respective VAV box. A matching supply box or boxes, depending on air quantities, is provided, with controls to permit tracking.

In all systems which employ VAV, the relative humidity in the space is difficult to control. Calculations must be made to ensure that design limits are not exceeded. Also, even though the exhaust requirements of the hoods within the lab are satisfied, the load within the space may require additional air. Several control methods are available and are discussed in Section 5.5. Operating diversities of 70 to 85% are possible.

Stepped Control Systems

A variation on VAV is to provide each hood with a two-position box set for minimum flow and maximum flow, operated from a manual switch on the hood face. Each exhaust box is matched with a supply box (with a reheat coil) to provide varying flow, depending on the use of the hood. In large systems, the overall effect on the air-handling equipment is similar to that of true VAV, and operating diversities of 80 to 90% can be expected. As with the VAV system, minimum flow has to be calculated to ensure that space temperatures can be achieved during periods of minimum flow.

Dual-Duct Systems

Dual-duct systems are relatively costly to install, since two ducts are required. They also tend to consume more fan horsepower than single-duct systems.

The VAV dual-duct system is viable, but again, the terminal boxes are more expensive than those of the single-duct system.

The primary advantage of the dual-duct system is that no reheat pipe work or control valves are required in the space. Control is provided by mixing hot and cold decks.

Supplemental Air Systems

In order to reduce the amount of conditioned supply delivered to a laboratory, a special hood has been developed. A separate tempered air supply is delivered to a grille above the hood face. The design of these systems depends on the hood; up to 80% of the exhaust requirements are supplied from the tempered, non-cooled supplemental system. The conditioned air supplied to the room is constant volume reheat.

The space requirements for this type of hood sometimes cause a problem. Each lab requires two duct systems, similar to the dual-duct system, and under certain conditions, condensation occurs inside the hood.

When large quantities of unconditioned makeup air are supplied, the user can be uncomfortable. There is also some effect on the conditions within the lab.

Air-Handling Equipment

In all facilities where the operating hours are longer than normal working hours, it is advisable to consider the quality and reliability of equipment. This is true of both hospitals and laboratories, and as with hospitals, higher-quality equipment should be specified.

Since all laboratories are required to be flexible, consideration should be given to providing spare capacity for main headers and air-handling equipment. A reasonable figure is 15%, depending on the type of facility. The cost of this spare capacity is negligible at the bidding stage if designed correctly.

As mentioned earlier, operating diversities of 75 to 90% are common. Under no circumstances should air-handling equipment be reduced in size to accommodate diversities, since during an emergency, 100% design quantities may be required.

Humidification is usually required and is provided by steam generated in central plants. When this is the case, the user must be advised of any treatment of the boiler feed water, since it may contaminate experiments. An alternative is to provide a hospital-quality steam generator using specially treated water. Small canister-type electric boilers are available for localized humidification.

Alternatives to steam are spray air washers, pad type and other equipment. In this type of equipment, particular care has to be exercised to avoid contamination due to bacterial growth.

Humidification using compressed air to atomize water can be used, but the treatment of the water supply is critical to avoid "dusting" when the water evaporates. This method is relatively energy intensive insofar as compression horsepower requirements (i.e., electrical energy usage) are concerned.

Filters in air-handling equipment depend on the type of space served and usually consist of a prefilter and a main filter, 30% and 80%, respectively. Due to the number of operating hours, high dust-holding-capacity filters should be used. Some labs require terminal filters; the user should be consulted for any special requirements.

Most labs require some form of standby equipment. Although this is often critical for hood exhaust, it is often a requirement for the supply equipment as well. A simple method is to provide multiple fans in parallel, sized so that if one fails the remaining fans can continue to operate until a safe shutdown time can be scheduled.

When multiple air-handling units are used, they must be interconnected. If the facility is designed properly, it is possible to operate it with one air-handling unit shut down and isolated from the building systems for maintenance.

Distribution ducting is normally arranged so that all headers are in areas which are not expected to change to permit future additions and modifications without affecting occupied labs, usually in public or service corridors.

5.3.3 Distribution Systems

General Considerations

The success of the facility, both economically and operationally, will depend on how well the mechanical systems are organized. These systems affect the architectural and structural designs and represent 30 to 60% of the total cost of a project.

The single greatest impact on a building is made by the size, type and number of hoods or exhaust connections. They affect the design of air distribution, shafts and ceiling space conditions, which in turn determine the height and overall configuration of the facility.

Distribution of services using multiple vertical shafts requires less building height, since the shafts split the supply and exhaust ductwork; however, as the service shafts are fixed in the plan, future modifications and additions are limited. Many new facilities use some form of horizontal distribution for reasons of economy and to provide greater flexibility, since the floor space is kept essentially clear.

Distribution systems should permit:

- Economical design for the initial laboratory layout.
- Economical design for future laboratory additions.
- Modifications to existing layouts without disruption of services to surrounding areas.
- Economical, safe and easy maintenance.

The impact of various distribution schemes on the initial construction cost depends on the building's geometry, number of floors, and type of structural system. Any additional cost suggested in the interests of flexibility has to be justified. Also since the engineer's involvement in a project is usually limited to 3 years, while the operating and user groups must live with the facility for 20 years, their input on layout is essential.

Vertical Distribution

When vertical distribution is employed, the risers can be integrated with the structural elements (columns) or with elements which are fixed in the plan, such as the core or permanent partitions. Vertical risers can also be located on the exterior of the building, in which case the building facade will be affected by the placement and size of the risers. When this method is used, care must be taken to prevent freezing. This arrangement can also make it very expensive to add to or modify existing systems.

With vertical distribution, horizontal runs can be reduced to a point where the major interaction in the ceiling space is limited to structural elements, lighting systems, and sprinkler systems. Vertical distribution systems require more area but allow the least floor-to-floor height. About 12 ft is possible, although difficult to achieve, and future flexibility may be limited.

Examples

Scheme 1: Multiple-Corridor Shafts. This system is most commonly used in multistory buildings. Services are provided to each floor and at each planning module.

Advantages: Waste and fumehood duct runs can be short. Piping is easily accessible from the corridor, without interfering with laboratory operation, and allows shutoff valves to be accessible from the corridor. Shafts also provide door recesses so that doors can swing out without interfering with corridor traffic. Services can easily be added or replaced, and floor-to-floor heights are minimal.

Disadvantages: Net-to-gross efficiency is lower than for horizontal distribution, and the location of the service shafts limits the flexibility of plan layouts.

Scheme 2: Utility Service Corridor. Vertical utility mains and ducts go to each floor inside a utility corridor, to which the planning modules are backed up, usually on both sides of the corridor to make maximum use of the space. Runouts are exposed along the corridor walls.

Advantages: There is easy access to utilities for maintenance, replacement and addition of mains, without disturbing the laboratory proper. Waste runs are short. Utility mains can be looped, entering the utility corridor at one end and returning at the other. Public corridor ceilings can be used for electrical and communications raceways and utility corridors for piped services and air-handling ducts, helping to reduce floor-to-floor heights.

Leakage in water mains is confined to utility corridors. If the corridors are wide enough, they may be used, if allowed by Code, for common equipment usage between labs (centrifuges, refrigerators, etc.).

Disadvantages: Net-to-gross efficiency is poor; a separate corridor for personnel is required. Waste disposal facilities for island benches have to be coordinated with the lab or with the spaces below.

Scheme 3: Multiple Exterior Utility Shafts. This system is often used in multistory buildings. Utility piping is provided at each floor and at each planning module, either running along the window walls or exposed at the ceiling and down to the benches.

Advantages: This system is well suited for fumehood locations; waste and fumehood duct runs to the shaft can be short. It provides space layout flexibility similar to that of systems using a horizontal distribution.

Disadvantages: Access to shafts is more difficult and may interfere with laboratory benches, equipment or laboratory operation. The main piping runs from the mechanical room are usually longer and more complicated than those to corridor shafts. Runouts may interfere with secondary doors to adjacent laboratories, and care must be exercised to prevent freezing.

Horizontal Distribution

If the distance from the exterior to the core of the building exceeds 40 ft or if the usable space must be kept free of all obstructions, a horizontal distribution system should be considered. When a horizontal distribution system is used, the location of the main vertical risers is critical for proper organization of the total system, particularly the location of drainage.

Horizontal distribution systems require less floor area than vertical systems but make the floor-to-floor height greater: usually 15 ft minimum.

Examples

Scheme 1: Horizontal Distribution. Large central shafts provide services to each floor, with horizontal runouts distributing services to each module. Usually horizontal runs, pipes and ducts have valved and capped connections from 10-ft to 20-ft centers to permit easy future connections.

Advantages: Net-to-gross efficiency is high. It is easy to add or replace utilities, without affecting adjacent labs, because of the exposed runouts and large shafts. This system provides the greatest flexibility in plan layouts, and is often least expensive mechanically and electrically.

Disadvantages: Waste and fume hood exhaust may require short horizontal runs, so additional vertical shafts may have to be provided. Greater floor-to-floor height is required; therefore, the cost is higher.

Scheme 2: Interstitial Floor. A separate level between two laboratory floors is provided for all services.

Advantages: Utilities are up- or downfed at any location. Space is available for noisy equipment and servicing. Access to utility piping is provided for maintenance, modification or replacement without entering laboratory spaces.

Disadvantages: Net-to-gross efficiency is poor. Building height is increased, and some vertical shafts may be required for fume-hood exhaust.

5.3.4 Hood Exhaust

Two basic exhaust systems are available: individual and central. Although reference is made throughout to hood exhaust, it is important to understand that other types of exhaust are used—surface, "elephant trunks," etc. The following discussion applies to all types of exhaust.

Hoods should not be permitted to shut off, since they are often used to store potentially dangerous or objectionable materials. The user should review the need for emergency power with the facility safety engineers together with any other safety requirements.

Most towns and states have codes regulating discharge from a research facility. To ensure proper distribution of exhaust, it is advisable to use the many inexpensive computer-based models which calculate dissipation rates based on the geometry of the surrounding buildings and the prevailing winds.

As a general rule, air should be discharged at 4,000 to 5,000 fpm above the highest point within 20 ft of the discharge stack. These velocities should be maintained for all operating conditions—a matter of particular concern when variable air volume hoods are used.

In practice, there are many instances where this may not be possible and intermediate exhaust is required. When this occurs, the engineer must exercise considerable care in the design to avoid construction in the surrounding area and the possibility of short-circuiting with the intake louvers.

Individual Systems

Individual exhaust systems utilize a separate exhaust connection, exhaust fan and discharge duct for each fume hood. This arrangement is flexible in that it permits selective application of:

1. Special exhaust air filtration.
2. Special duct and fan construction for corrosive fumes.
3. Emergency power connections to small fan motors.

4. Inexpensive off-hour operation.
5. Different levels of velocity requirements.
6. Different static pressure requirements.
7. Hoods may be added or removed without affecting other hoods.

Individual exhaust fans are simple to balance and, when coupled with a constant air volume supply, provide a stable, easily controlled system.

This method of exhaust is, however, expensive due to the number of duct runs and the additional floor and roof space required for shafts and fans. It usually precludes the possibility of energy savings from diversity in the operation of equipment. Heat recovery devices are also not usually practical due to the many exhaust points. Finally, it may be necessary to provide standby fans for certain users, which considerably increases cost and space requirements.

Central Systems

Central exhaust systems consist of one or more fans, a common suction plenum, a system of header ducts and branch connections to multiple exhaust terminals. Central systems are generally less costly than individual systems in terms of installation and maintenance. They are, however, more difficult to balance and present the difficulties of parallel fan operation when more than one fan is employed.

A disadvantage is that a single hood within the system may dictate the system velocity, materials of construction and static pressure characteristics for the entire system. Usually, however, a booster fan is added to accommodate any special filter requirements.

Installed brake horsepower is usually lower than the brake horsepower installed for individual systems. It is also easier to add hoods to a central system, since the increase in flow is often negligible. As exhaust from all sources is exhausted at a common point, heat recovery devices are economical and effective.

Hood Exhaust Filtration

The treatment of exhaust air to remove hazardous contaminants or unpleasant odors is required to meet environmental standards and "good neighbor" practices. Fumehoods handling radioactive and most bacteriological material and be efficiently cleaned using high-efficiency air air filters. However, exhaust systems for hazardous biological and certain types of chemical research can be made safe only by incineration of the exhaust air. The air is usually heated to about 650°F or more to destroy the material.

Small glove cabinets handling no more than 100 cfm usually have individual electric incinerators, while larger units use natural gas fired central incinerators.

The incinerator for exhaust air requires a high-temperature chimney and must be constructed accordingly. When locating these systems, care must be exercised to avoid potential fires in surrounding materials.

Exhaust systems handling odors can be made less unpleasant by treatment with activated carbon, although it is usually more practical to locate the exhaust away from occupied spaces and air intakes to minimize the problem. Air can also be diluted by mixing it with exhaust from other areas or by induction-type discharge outlets which promote rapid mixing and dissipation of odors and fumes.

Mechanical and centrifugal dust separators are available for exhaust which is laden with particulate materials. Other types of filtration devices are also available, such as scrubbers, bag filters and electrostatic filters. Custom-designed equipment is available for special applications.

Material for Exhaust Systems

Selection of materials for an exhaust system will depend on the nature and concentration of contaminants or chemical reagents, space conditions, cost, accessibility for installation and maintenance. Whatever material is selected, the duct joints should be airtight (sometimes welded) and the ductwork should have ample supports. Large exhaust systems should have inspection and cleanout facilities. No single material is suitable for all exhaust materials.

- Asbestos-Cement: Asbestos-cement, or "Transite," is not used today due to its asbestos content. Many older installations do have this material, and care should be exercised when making modifications to these systems.
- Galvanized Steel: Still by far the most common material used.
- Stainless Steel: Usually type 304 or 316 stainless steel is used for bacteriological, radiological, perchloric acid and other special chemical processes. The material is easy to work but is not suitable for certain chemical hoods—for example, those handling highly concentrated hydrochloric and sulfuric acids.
- FRP (Fiberglass-Reinforced-Polyester Resins): Easy to handle and fabricate. The material can also be used for general chemical duty, except for where a high-solvent vapor such as acetone or potent oxidizers are handled. It has to be specified to be self-extinguishing.
- Black or Galvanized Plastic-Coated (PVS) with Acid-Resistant Materials: Used extensively today. It is easy to fabricate and inexpensive.
- Fans and other moving parts of the exhaust system, including constant and VAV boxes, are protected by special coatings. Several protective coatings are available, but none is suitable for all chemicals. Selection of the coating will depend on the majority of the reagents handled in the exhaust system. Bearing surfaces should be outside the air stream and separated by the shaft seals.

5.3.5 Laboratory Plumbing Systems

General Considerations

Laboratory design offers the greatest challenge to the plumbing designer due to the critical nature of the facility and the large number of systems that are usually required.

Myriad utility requirements must be addressed in the programming phase of the project; these will be discussed in the following paragraphs. One of the most important early issues to be resolved is the type of distribution systems that will be used, since these affect ceiling space requirements, shaft spaces, etc.

Utility Distribution

Utility distribution will be routed either vertically or horizontally, or by a combination of these schemes. This decision must be coordinated with other members of the design team, since each system has its advantages and disadvantages. Whichever system is selected, there are key elements which must be addressed:

- Flexibility: Systems must be designed so that changes can be made in a laboratory space without shutting down the facility. Particular attention to pipe sizing is important. The impact of the additional cost for increased piping, materials, etc. must also be addressed.
- Reliability: Some research projects may be a culmination of years of research, and failure of mechanical systems could be disastrous. Use of backup or redundant equipment is a small price to pay compared to the consequences of failure.
- Expansion Capability: Many facilities are constructed with future expansion in mind. Systems should be selected and designed to accommodate this requirement.
- Adaptability: A typical laboratory contains many pieces of equipment, depending on the type of research or activity. Piping systems should be arranged and sized to accommodate future utility requirements.

The most common distribution configurations are discussed in Section 5.1.

Utility Sizing

The following example is used to illustrate how a plumbing distribution system is developed and sized for a three-story university building which is part of a large complex of buildings. The distribution is basically a horizontal scheme modified with a floor loop configuration. The loop provides additional flexibility on each floor by adding quarter-point sectionalizing valves to permit shutting off of sections of a floor for anticipated changes.

In order to understand how individual systems are designed, it is necessary to look at a building floor plan. See Figure 5.3-1. A building is broken up into three sections with both primary and secondary cores. The cores contain mechanical rooms, toilets, stairs, elevators, electric closets, etc. The longitudinal middle of the building is the mall, which contains the utility tunnel and circulation areas. To determine how plumbing systems for a building should be designed, the first step is to know what the loads are and how they are distributed. Based on the desirability of total flexibility, the physical layout of the building and other decisions made by the design team, a loop was selected as a distribution scheme.

The physical location of a single loop allows hot water branches off of the loop without hot water return branches, since the farthest run to a fixture is approximately 30 ft. In addition, branch takeoffs are spaced approximately every 12 ft off of the loop. These spacing criteria were established in order to allow the smallest room its own services without disrupting adjacent rooms. Now that a loop distribution has been established, a supply source has to be established. Even though some floor areas are designed strictly for administrative functions— i.e., laboratory-type services are not required— actual service outlet counts for each services are taken for all areas to determine the density and magnitude of the potential load.

Actual counts of outlets will also be needed later for sizing the systems. Based on these counts, it was determined that either two- or three-loop systems were the most economical and practical solution. Single-loop systems were not used as a rule, since the loop in many cases would not warrant the size of the equipment. This was particularly true for vacuum pumps. On the other hand, loops larger than three became impractical due to long runs and pressure losses.

The sizing of piping for the various loop systems in a large complex can be tedious. Outlet counts must be taken for all laboratory areas and broken down into regular laboratory usage and teaching or classroom usage. Unfortunately, there are no shortcuts with this method. As an example, in determining criteria for pipe sizing of the loops and risers of a laboratory vacuum system, the following procedure is used: Actual outlet counts are taken on a floor-by-floor and loop-by-loop basis for each section in a building. By making a breakdown in this manner, the largest count for any floor can be tabulated. Usage factors are now applied to the outlet counts, as shown in Figure 5.3-2.

Usage factors are included in the pipe sizing sections of each system. Demands with different use factors should be carried separately in the calculations; that is, classroom or teaching laboratories carry twice the normal laboratory use factor. These separate factors are then added only at the end of the calculation. In the preceding example, the classroom use factor was used throughout, since the actual layout had a large percentage of classrooms and the requirement for flexibility warranted this method.

Pressure Piping

The routing of piping systems into the labs will depend on whether or not a ceiling is provided, the type of lab bench and casework, the partition type, etc. Usually the room distribution will be located in the ceiling and drop into a partition wall or chase; alternatively, when an island or peninsula

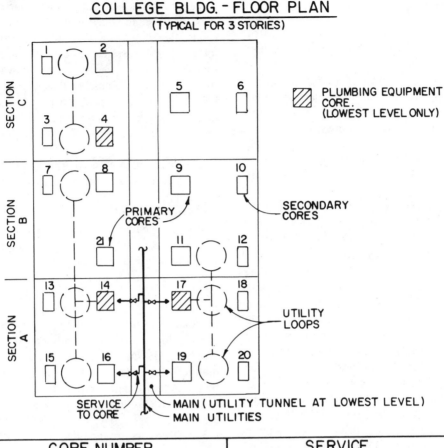

COLLEGE BLDG. - FLOOR PLAN
(TYPICAL FOR 3 STORIES)

CORE NUMBER	SERVICE
1,3,6,7,10,12,15,18,20	GAS (ALL SECONDARY CORES)
2,4,5,8,9,11,14,16,17,19,21	DOMESTIC WATER (ALL PRIMARY CORES)
4,14,17	VACUUM EQUIPMENT, H.W. HEATER, DRINKING WATER CHILLERS, DEIONIZERS

Fig. 5.3-1. Typical lab floor plan.

bench is used, an umbilical or free-standing pipe enclosure provides a location for piping drops. Normal space is provided behind lab benches for pipe runs, and piping is supported by various methods utilizing metal channels. The designer must determine what the best arrangement of piping and take-offs to bench outlets is and verify what space is required behind the bench. In the case of fumehoods, it is necessary to coordinate with the architect, since the depth of the hood may not be the same as that of the bench and utility space behind the hood may not be available.

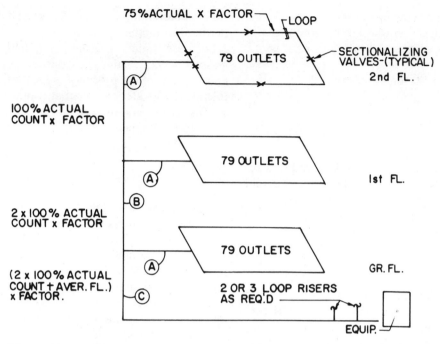

(1) LARGEST ACTUAL COUNT FOR RISER (SECTION B, LOOP NO. 3) = 270 OUTLETS ÷ 3 FLOORS = 90 OUTLETS/FL. AVERAGE.

(2) LARGEST ACTUAL COUNT FOR ONE FLOOR = 132 OUTLETS, LOOP = 75% OF LARGEST FL. = 0.75 x 132 = 99 OUTLETS, 99 x 80% (FACTOR FOR TEACHING LAB'S = 79 OUTLETS → LOOP SIZE.

(A) LARGEST FL. (132) x (80%) FACTOR = 106 OUTLETS

(B) 2 x (132) = 264 x (70%) FACTOR = 185 OUTLETS

(C) 2 x (132) + AVER. FL. = 132 + 132 + 90 = 354 x (60%) FACTOR = 212 OUTLETS.

Fig. 5.3-2. Criteria for sizing a loop system.

Drainage Piping

With regard to drainage and vent systems, a vertical distribution system provides advantages, since gravity piping is mostly concealed in walls and connected to stacks above the floor. Only the island benches and floor drains require penetration through the floor slabs, with horizontal lines in the ceiling to the closest stack. Minimizing horizontal piping in the ceiling avoids coordination problems in the ceiling cavity and may decrease the ceiling space requirements. Underground piping placed under the basement or lowest floor affords little flexibility. Obviously it is preferable not to locate labs on a grade slab. If this is unavoidable, it is possible to provide trenches or access floor arrangements, but these are not preferred.

Valving

The provision of valves should be carefully thought out. They must be located where they are readily accessible; otherwise, they will not provide shutoff when it is needed. The use of good-quality ball valves where possible is important, since they required less maintenance than the globe or gate type.

Many laboratories undergo constant modifications. Branch piping should be arranged so that relocation of a lab bench outlet will not affect adjacent lab spaces.

Domestic Water Systems

Domestic water systems in laboratories are not very different from those for other types of projects. Code requirements and good engineering practice notwithstanding, extra attention must be paid to pressure and flow requirements for special equipment. Certain types of equipment, such as animal cage washers, are high water users, and the load requirements must be included in the pipe sizing. Laboratory outlets with water saver devices are available and should be used whenever possible.

Water flow requirements are determined by using water equipment flows and a fixture count of all outlets. The outlet count includes values for flexibility and future expansion. However, since all outlets will not be used at the same time, calculations are based on diversity, as described in the preceding section.

Most codes require the water supply to a laboratory facility to be provided with a reduced-pressure backflow preventer immediately downstream of the meter assembly. The backflow preventer must be located in an accessible area and provided with a floor drain for water discharge from operation and testing.

All laboratory fixtures with serrated tips must also be provided with vacuum breakers integral with the fixtures. Faucet and removable-type vacuum breakers should be avoided.

Water Softeners

Principles of Design. Most water supplies require softening for certain uses, such as makeup water for boilers. Softeners work by exchanging calcium and magnesium cations for sodium cations (removal of hardness). Softening does not decrease the amount of total dissolved solids (TDS) or alkalinity. The sodium zeolite softening process is the most common exchange reaction involved in

water conditioning. It is capable of reducing hardness to 0 ppm.

Softened water is usually required for glasswashers, steam generators, boiler makeup, or other processes which cannot tolerate hard water or potential scaling conditions. However, softened water can cause corrosion of copper or brass piping if velocities are high enough to cause velocity impingement corrosion. If copper or brass is used, velocities should be limited to less than 5 fps.

The presence of calcium and magnesium salts causes water to be hard. Hardness causes excessive soap consumption in laundries and the formation of scale in hot water pipes, heaters and boilers. It is also generally a problem in piping and heating systems.

The classification of waters in terms of hardness varies in the industry; however, a general classification is as noted in Table 5.3-2. Hardness is expressed in grains per gallon (gpg) as calcium carbonate ($CaCO_3$) equivalents (1.0 gpg—17.1 ppm) (parts per million). Recommended acceptable hardness levels for various applications are as indicated in Table 5.3-3. However, a water consultant should be contacted for all recommendations of required treatment and final hardness for the particular process.

Equipment. Softening equipment consists of resin exchange units (usually with automatic regeneration) complete with brine tanks, interconnecting piping and all required accessories and controls. Normally, units are sized on the gpm flow requirements of the system or equipment served. However, where gallons per minute (gpm) re-

Table 5.3-2. Classification of Water for Hardness

Hardness (ppm)	Classification
0–15	Very soft
15–50	Soft
50–100	Medium hard
100–200	Hard
Over 200	Very hard

Table 5.3-3. Water Hardness Levels

Process	Recommended Values (ppm)
Boiler feedwater (psi)	
0–150	80
150–250	40
250–400	10
Over 400	2
Glasswashing equipment	10
Laundries	0–50

quirements are high compared with gallons per hour (gph) requirements (as for laundry washers), it may be more practical to base the size of the unit on the gph requirements (average gpm) and provide a storage tank with pumps to provide for the peak gpm flows.

Normal resins have a softening capacity of 30,000 grains per cubic foot when regenerated with 15 lbs of salt per cubic foot of resin. Softening capacity between regenerations equals the cubic feet of resin × 30,000 divided by the grains per gallon of water softened.

The acceptable period between regenerations depends on the operating schedule of the system or equipment being served. The minimum should be 1 day.

If 100% continuous supply is required, multiple units must be provided to maintain the supply during regeneration of one of the units.

Automatic regeneration can be actuated by the quantity of water used or by a time clock.

Makeup Water (for Boilers, Humidifiers, Etc.). Normally makeup water for equipment specified in the HVAC specifications consists of a valved and capped outlet within 10 ft of the equipment. However, it is important to ascertain the quality of water required for makeup purposes. Untreated domestic water for boilers can cause excessive scale buildup, inefficient heat transfer and possible eventual breakdown of equipment. The hardness of the domestic water must be determined to decide whether softening is required.

Do not view the use of corrosion inhibitors (normally recommended by the water treatment consultant) as an alternative to the makeup water quality. These are two separate requirements, and the use of one does not exclude the other. Makeup water quality will determine the cycles of concentration (amount of dissolved solids in boiler water) and the blowdown amounts.

Autoclaves may have local electric steam generators for the steam supply. The equipment manufacturers may limit the water makeup to the generator to a hardness of less than 2 grains per gallon. In most cases this will require softened water; this should be reviewed with the equipment supplier so that the equipment warranty will not be voided.

Pure Water Systems

General Considerations. Water treatment is essentially the application of equipment and treatment chemicals to replace, remove or stabilize various impurities in water. Water is classified, depending on its usage, by setting maximum limits on the various constituents or impurities. Gases and solids are dissolved in water in various concentrations with the majority of solids, including ionized metal salts and nonionized organic matter. A water analysis will determine the TDS, pH value, acidity, alkalinity, hardness and concentrations of impurities such as nitrates, sulfates, iron, chlorine, etc.

Purity. There are five major types of contaminants in water:

1. Particulate matter (suspended solids)—dirt, colloids, etc.
2. Dissolved solids, ions of salt—e.g., Na^+, Ca^+, Mg^+ (sodium, calcium, magnesium).
3. Organics—viruses, bacteria, pyrogens, organic molecules.
4. Dissolved nonionic gases, e.g., oxygen.
5. Dissolved ionizable gases, e.g., carbon dioxide.

The degree of water purity required depends on the intended use of the water. Equipment or treatment chemicals are used to remove, replace or stabilize the impurities found in water. High-purity water (in organic and nonorganic forms) is usually used by hospitals, clinical laboratories, colleges and universities, and industrial and laboratory researchers.

Grades of Water. Universities and research laboratories may need various grades of water for many different departments. These may include reagent grade water, purified water or sterile water for injection and irrigation.

Attempts to define "pure" water have been made by several professional societies in the analytical and clinical fields. Each organization has established standards that relate to its own methods of analysis. Because of this, variations between standards exist. Some organizations that have standards in the clinical fields are the National Committee for Clinical Laboratory Standards (NCCLS), the College of American Pathologists (CAP) and the United States Parmacopeia (USP). Other standards have been established by the American Society for Testing and Materials (ASTM) and the American Chemical Society (ACS). Tables 5.3-4 and 5.3-5 provide a tabulation of information from the published standards for reagent-grade water.

The following is a description of the uses of reagent water and suggested methods of preparation of (ASTM):

- Type I Reagent Water (Ultrapure): Used when maximum accuracy and precision are required. Produced by distillation of feed water with a maximum resistivity of 0.05 megohm-cm at 25°C followed by polishing with a mixed-bed ion exchange system to 16.7 megohm-cm and a 0.2-um filter.
- Type II Reagent Water: Used for all procedures (including most analytical ones) requiring organic-free, sterilized, pyrogen-free water. Produced by distillation through the use of still designed with special baffling and degassing features or by double distillation to produce product water with a resistivity greater than 1.0 megohm-cm at 25°C.
- Type III Reagent Water: Recommended for general laboratory purposes, including preparation of solutions, routine quality control tests, washing and rinsing of lab glassware. Produced by ion exchange, distillation, or reverse osmosis followed by polishing with a 0.45-um membrane filter.
- Type IV Reagent Water: Used when

Table 5.3-4. CAP and ASTM Reagent-Grade Water Specifications

Characteristics	CAP Type			ASTM Type			
	I	II	III	I	II	III	IV
Spec conductance (micromhos/cm)	0.1	5	10	0.06	1.0	1.0	5.0
Spec Resistance (megohms/cm)	10	2.0	0.1	16.6	1.0	1.0	0.2
Silicate (mg/liter)	0.05	0.1	1.0				
Heavy metals (mg/liter)	0.01	0.01	0.01				
Potassium permanganate reduction (minutes)	60	60	60	60	60	10	10
Sodium (mg/liter)	0.1	0.1	0.1				
Hardness	Neg.	Neg.	Neg.				
Ammonia	0.1	0.1	0.1				
Bacterial growth (cfu/ml)	10	10					
pH				5.0–8.0		6.2–7.5	5.0–8.0
CO_2 (mg/liter)	3	3	3				

Table 5.3-5. NCCLS Reagent-Grade Water Specifications

Characteristics	Type			
	I	IIA	IIB	III
Bacterial content (colony-forming units per ml/maximum)	<10	10	10	N/A
pH	N/A	N/A	N/A	5.0, 8.0
Resistivity (megohms/cm), 25°C	10	1.0	1.0	0.1
Silicate (mg/liter max.)	0.05	0.1	0.1	0.1
Particulate matter	0.22 micron filter	N/A	N/A	N/A
Organics	Activated carbon	N/A	N/A	N/A

large amounts of moderate-purity water are required, particularly in the preparation of test solutions for wash tests or ion exchange resin evaluation. Produced by ion exchange, distillation, reverse osmosis or electrodialysis.

Purity Measurement. Specific resistance is used as a basis for comparing water purity and is expressed in ohm-centimeter units. It is important to remember that resistivity is a measure of ionic impurities alone; it is not affected by particulates, bacteria or other organic contaminants. The electrolytic content of water is often expressed as conductivity (micro-ohms at 25°C), which is the reciprocal of resistivity. Therefore a conductance of 20.0 micro-ohms is equivalent to 0.05 megohm-cm. Table 5.3-6 is a generally accepted classification of water purity.

Water usage in pharmaceutical laboratories can range from various grades of purified water in typical laboratory applications to purified water used in the manufacture of pharmaceutical products. United States Pharmacopeia (USP) XXI defines the water quality standards for two major categories,

water for injection (WFI) and USP purified water. See Table 5.3-7.

While the specific quality of the water is dictated by the user's needs, the design of the purification system is determined by the quality of the raw water, constraints of equipment technology, economic considerations, etc. A particular equipment application, such as multiple-pass distillation, may not produce the desired end product. Usually, combinations of applications (ultrafiltration, softening, etc.) in addition to distillation will be required.

Based on contaminant removal characteristics of the available technologies, WFI quality water may require distillation and reverse osmosis (RO). USP purified water systems may require distillation, RO, deionizers (DE) or ultrafiltration (UF). Sterile water is designed with a terminal sterile process such as heat or ultraviolet (UV) sterilization.

Sterile water for injection or irrigation is used as a solvent for the preparation of pharmaceutical and parenteral sterile solids and for oral or irrigation use during surgical procedures. Sterile water must be free of all biologically active substances, including spores, bacteria, fungi and viruses. There are various Food and Drug Administration and USP guidelines which must be adhered to in the design of sterile water systems.

Processes. A brief description of the various processes used in water treatment is as follows:

Table 5.3-6. Water Purity Classification

Classification	Resistivity (Megohms/Cm)
Absolute purity	18.3
Ultra-pure	>1.0
High purity	1.0
Low purity	<1.0
Bio-pure	Pyrogen free, sterile, >1 ppm TDS

- Ion Exchange (Deionization/Demineralization): Removes impurities by

Table 5.3-7. Water Quality Standards

	Quality Standard	
Contaminants	Purified Water	Water for Injection
Specific conductance (micromhos)	—	—
Specific resistance (megohms)	—	—
Silicate (mg/liter)	—	—
Heavy metals (mg/liter)	1.0	1.0
Oxidizables (mb/liter)	0.3	0.3
Sodium (mg/liter)	—	—
Hardness (Mg/liter)	—	—
Ammonia (Mg/liter)	3.0	3.0
pH (@25°C)	5.0–7.0	5.0–7.0
CO_2 (mg/liter)	—	—
Chloride (mg/liter)	0.3	0.3
Sulfate (Mg/liter)	0.3	0.3
TDS (mg/liter)	10.0	10.0
Bacteria (colony court)	100/ml	Sterile
Pyrogenicity	—	None

passing water through synthetic resins which have an affinity for dissolved ionized salts and gases. It will not remove bacteria, pyrogens, particulates or dissolved organic compounds. Capable of 15–18 megohm-cm purity. Requires regeneration with sulfuric acid and caustic.

- Distillation: Removes impurities from water by converting a liquid to a gas and then recondensing it as distilled water. Distilled water is free of all pyrogens, bacteria and viruses except dissolved ionized gases. Capable of 800,000 ohms-cm to 1 megohm-cm purity if the feedwater has been pretreated. Higher values are difficult to achieve due to volatile impurities such as CO_2.
- Reverse Osmosis: Utilizes hydraulic pressure to force pure water through a membrane. Usually used in waters having high TDS. This process removes some bacteria, pyrogens and viruses, but not completely. It will not remove dissolved ionized gases.
- Electrodialysis: Separates the components in a salt solution by passing an electric current through one or more ion-permeable membranes. The use of electrodialysis equipment may be suitable where the raw water is in the range of 100 to 7,000 ppm TDS and where the desired product water purity is a maximum of 50,000 ohm-cm (10 ppm TDS).
- Filtration: Separates larger particles from water by passing the water through a porous membrane or medium. Types include sand filters, diatomaceous earth, cartridge filters, etc. The prefilter range is usually 5 to 25 um. Good for bacteria removal but will not remove any dissolved solids, gases or pyrogens.
- Adsorption: Adherence of a gas or liquid on the surface of a solid. Activated carbon is used to remove dissolved organics or for dechlorination or other residual disinfection.

Piping Materials. High-quality water is very aggressive and therefore corrosive. The impurities in the pipe material in contact with the water must also be considered. These impurities can leak out into the product water and may be unacceptable to the user or end process. The selection process of materials must be reviewed with the user, since cost may be a determining factor in some cases.

The following are some recommended materials in contact with high-quality water:

Stainless steel tubing
Stainless steel pipe (type 304L or 316L)
Polyvinylidifluoride
Polypropylene
Polyethylene
Glass
Polyvinylchloride
Aluminum (type 3003)

The following is a brief description of the recommended materials:

- Plastics: Due to its better corrosion resistance and temperature characteristics, Polypropylene is preferred over polyethylene and polyvinylchloride. Plastics will shed molecules or organic matter; also, filler materials may be a source of contamination. Polyvinylidifluoride is the preferred plastic, since it sheds very few contaminants; however, the cost of this system is much higher than that of other systems.
- Glass: Hard glass (borosilicate) is subject to breakage. It will not stand up to shock conditions, such as where solenoids are used for glasswasher equipment.
- Stainless Steel Pipe (304L and 316L); Used whenever heavy metal contamination by iron nickel, lead and chromium can be tolerated. Sometimes these impurities cannot be accepted in critical medical and research applications. Welded stainless steel tubing (316LSS) is widely used in the pharmaceutical industry. It is normally supplied with an electropolished inside surface to ensure product purity.
- Aluminum (type 3003) forms an oxide surface layer when exposed to oxygen. This layer may inhibit water contamination after long-term exposure.

It is emphasized that the potential contamination characteristics of both equipment and piping system materials must be discussed with the user so that there are no surprises when the water is tested for quality parameters. Many times a system can be designed as a lower-purity central system, and point-of-use polishing units (cartridge-type deionizers, filters, etc.) can be provided to obtain the desired water quality.

Demineralized (Deionized) Water Systems

Principles of Design. Review with the user and document exactly the quality of water (purity) that is required. Where the requirements warrant, a central system should be considered. Where the requirements are few or isolated, local cartridge-type units can be provided. The choice between a local and a central system is usually driven by economics, operating costs and maintenance preferences.

Demineralizers are usually located in the basement, with a pressure feed to the outlets. Check the pressure drop through the equipment to ensure adequate pressure at the outlet.

For larger distribution systems, piping should be arranged in a loop and/or continuously recirculating configuration to eliminate stagnant water conditions. Stagnant water is an ideal medium for bacteria to multiply and must be avoided.

Particular care should be made to eliminate dead ends. A dead end is any uncirculated section of pipe more than two times the diameter of the pipe.

Check the capacity of the floor drain receiving the backwash from the demineralizers. This backwash rate is normally several times higher than the demineralizer flow rate, and the backwash is discharged under pressure.

Caustic and acid solutions are used to regenerate the resins. Thought must be given to the delivery of and access to these solutions, as well as safety and maintenance. Improper venting of solution tanks can cause severe corrosion in adjoining spaces and equipment.

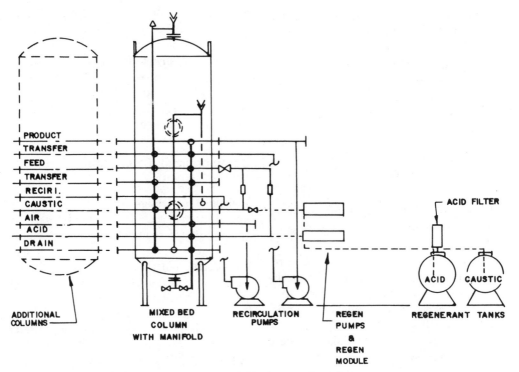

Fig. 5.3-3. Deionized water schematic.

Equipment. Demineralizers should be completely automatic two-bed or mixed-bed ion exchange units complete with required accessories to produce water that conforms to the user's requirements. An analysis of the incoming (raw) water is required. The basic difference between two- and mixed-bed units is that the two-bed unit has cation resins in one column and anion resins in the other. The mixed-bed unit has both cation and anion resins in one column. The mixed-bed type is more suitable for meeting pH requirements; however, it is more difficult to regenerate properly.

Factors for sizing demineralizers:

- Allow 0.5–1 gpd per student station for classroom laboratories (assume two classes per day).
- Allow 1–1.5 gpd per person (technicians, etc.) for other laboratories.
- Allow 5 gpd for classroom preparation room outlets.

- Allow 25 gpd for the pipette washer.
- Add loads for feeding stills or glass-washers. Since loads vary due to the size of the equipment, check with the manufacturer.

See Table 5.3-8 for sizing based on laboratory outlet counts.

Given the chemical content of the water and the gpd load, the time between regenerations can be calculated. Select equipment with a 7- to 14-day run between regenerations. Next, calculate the average peak flow rates of the system. If the selected equipment or equipment that is slightly larger can handle the expected flow rates, that is the proper choice. However, if the equipment to handle the flow rate is considerably larger, use this equipment plus a storage tank.

If raw water booster pumps are required, they can be normal iron body bronze-mounted (IBBM) units. If deionized water booster pumps are required, they must be all

Table 5.3-8. Deionized Water Pipe Sizing

No. of Outlets	Simultaneous Usage (%)	Maximum Demand (gpm)	Pipe Diameter (In.)
1–2	100	1.5	$\frac{3}{8}$
3–4	100	3	$\frac{1}{2}$
5–10	90	7	$\frac{3}{4}$
11–20	75	11	1
21–40	60	18	$1\frac{1}{4}$
41–65	50	24	$1\frac{1}{2}$
66–99	40	30	$1\frac{1}{2}$
100–150	30	34	2
151–300	20	45	2
300–500	20	75	$2\frac{1}{2}$
500–750	20	112	3

Basis of sizing
Flow of 0.75 gpm per outlet
Maximum velocity approximately 5 fps.

stainless steel or plastic (required with tank systems). The water distribution piping should be recirculated back to the tank.

Tanks are available in tin-lined copper and steel, stainless steel or plastic. The selection is based on size availability, economic considerations and water purity requirements.

Depending on the raw water conditions, a carbon filter and/or a softener is usually required as pretreatment before deionization.

Distilled Water Systems

Principles of Design. Distillation units are available in a variety of types, including flash evaporation, multiflash and vapor compression. Each has advantages and disadvantages and should be matched to the application. Basically, the vapor compression unit is used for high loads; it requires lower-pressure steam but more maintenance. The multiflash type uses less energy but is more costly.

Review with the user the exact quality of water (purity) required.

Where the requirements warrant, a central system should be provided. The choice between a local and a central system is usually driven by economics and maintenance preferences. Where requirements are few and isolated, local units should be provided.

It is preferable to locate central systems in

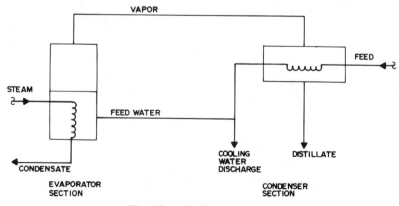

Fig. 5.3-4. Distillation principle.

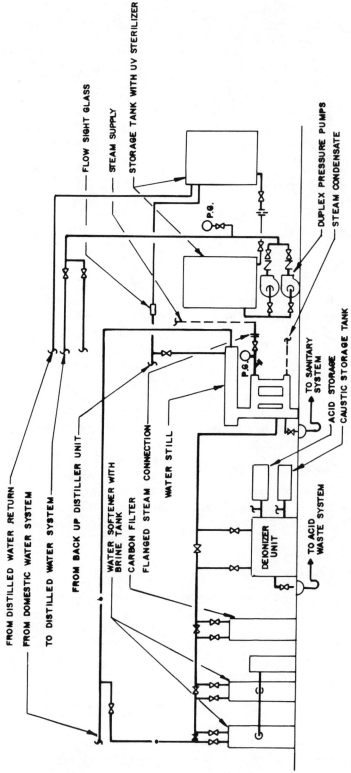

Fig. 5.3-5. Distilled water schematic.

the penthouse and feed by gravity to outlets. If they are located in the basement, a pumping system and storage tank will be required.

Piping should be arranged in a loop and/or a continuously recirculating configuration.

Particular care should be taken to eliminate dead ends and stagnant piping arrangements. Drain valves should be located at accessible low points for drainage and quality testing.

Equipment. Central units should be of the duplex (each half-size) hospital type, steam or electricity heated, completely automatic stills, and storage tank.

As a rule of thumb, the tank should be sized at 5 to 10 times the hourly capacity of the stills; otherwise, the size of the still will be excessive. Select the stills to generate daily requirements in 20 hours.

The following are some of the available tank materials and sizes:

- Tin-lined copper (round vertical), 10–300 gallons.
- Tin-lined (steel and finished in aluminum bronze) rectangular, 100–1,000 gallons.
- Type 304 or 316 stainless steel (round vertical), 30–1,000 gallons.

Lacking detailed requirements from the user, size the stills on the basis of two people per 10 × 20-ft module. Allow 1.5 gpd per person, plus 25% wastage and 50% for growth. Allow 1.5 gph per corridor outlet. For glasswashers, allow 45 gph (total, 160 gpd).

Stills can be operated on water pressures as low as 10 psi. However, where less than 40 psi is used, automatic valves on the still must be obtained from the control air system.

Reverse Osmosis (RO) Water Systems

Principles of Design. The RO process utilizes hydraulic pressure to force water through a membrane by osmotic pressure.

The membrane configurations include hollow fine fiber, spiral-wound and thin-film composites, each available in various materials. Each has advantages and disadvantages. RO units can operate at 350 to 450 psi pressure to produce 50 to 90% product water recovery, depending on the feed water. Single-pass RO units can remove 95% of dissolved solids and 99% of bacteria and pyrogens. RO systems have high power needs due to the high pressure pumping requirements and can vary from 7 to 15 kwh per 1,000 gallons of product water.

The design of an RO system should take into account the life expectancy of the RO membranes. These membranes are susceptible to scaling, bacteria attack and contamination.

RO product flows usually discharge at atmosphere pressure; therefore, a storage tank and pumping arrangement will be required. Sizing of the system is done on the basis of daily or hourly usage requirements, with a pumping system handling the peak flow requirements.

See the preceding section on deionized water for guidelines in sizing based on outlet counts and other factors.

Laboratory Drainage and Vent Systems

Principles of Design. The types and quantities of laboratory waste water must be identified. Specific wastes may be regulated by state or local authorities due to the nature of the hazard (radioactive, biohazard, etc.), and appropriate containment or treatment must be addressed. Review this matter with the authorities at the early stage of the program, since permits may be required.

Waste treatment concepts can range from simple dilution to full-scale on-site treatment facilities, depending on the nature of the waste.

Neutralization is accomplished by chemical reaction or dilution. Wastes normally discharge to sumps filled with limestone or marble chips, or to a treatment tank using an injected sodium hydroxide (NaOH) solution to raise the pH and sulfuric acid

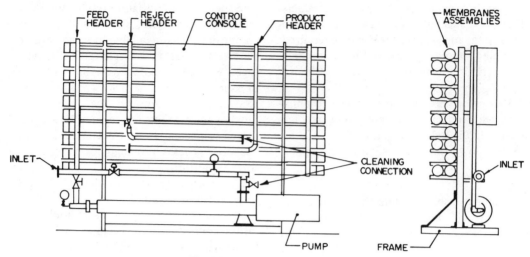

Fig. 5.3-6. Reverse osmosis unit.

(H₂SO4) to lower the pH. Some states or localities do not allow the use of limestone systems. See Figures 5.3-7 and 5.3-8.

In a laboratory drainage system, every fixture should be individually trapped. Where accepted by code, individual neutralizing sumps should be provided for isolated sinks. Individual neutralizing sumps replace the fixture trap.

All waste piping from laboratory sinks and cup drains to neutralizing sumps and all vent piping for these fixtures should be made of acid-resistant materials.

Where floor drains are provided in areas that are susceptible to trap evaporation, means for maintaining the seal should be addressed. Infrequently used drains can be provided with solid gasketed tops. The traps can

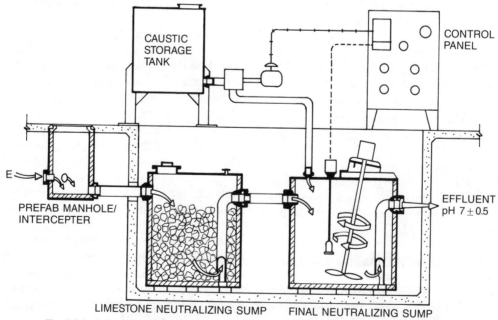

Fig. 5.3-7. Laboratory neutralization sump (Koch Engineering Co., Inc., Knight Division).

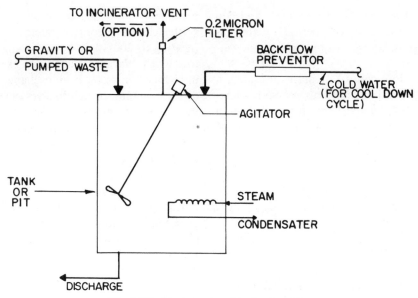

Fig. 5.3-8. Waste treatment tank schematic.

be filled with mineral oil to reduce the evaporation rate, or priming devices can be utilized. Deep seal traps should be used. A deep seal trap is normally 5 in. deep compared to the standard 3-in. seal. See Figure 5.3-9.

Piping. Acid-resistant piping should consist of extra-heavy silicon iron (Duriron) pipe and fittings (either a mechanical joint or a hub and spigot, with only the hub and spigot underground) or of regular-schedule borosilicate glass pipe and fittings with mechanical joints (extra-heavy underground, with a protector jacket supplied by the manufacturer). Fire-resistant polypropylene pipe and fittings may also be used where allowed by code. Check with the manufacturer for the recommended spacing of supports. Long runs of piping should also take expansion and contraction into consideration.

Glass piping in locations where it is subject to accidental damage should be extra heavy and provided with protective guards. Alternatively, one should specify a more sturdy pipe material in these locations. Glass piping through sleeves or construction should be completely protected by aluminum foil tape.

Stacks and branch vents should be offset before going through the roof, with an acid-resistant, plastic-lined, threaded cast iron or malleable iron elbow at the base of the vent terminal. Vent terminals through roofs should not be glass pipe, as these are too vulnerable to breakage.

Equipment. Acid-neutralizing sumps are usually constructed of chemical stoneware; acid-proof, tile-lined steel tanks; or high-density polyethylene. Sizing of tanks is usu-

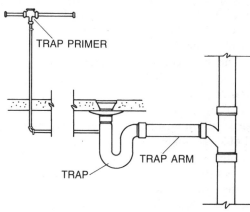

Fig. 5.3-9. Trap primer.

ally based on the number of sinks and cup drains used during peak periods. Sizing tables are found in various manufacturers' catalogs.

Where close control of pH is desirable, a two-stage neutralizing sump system is sometimes used. A standard limestone-filled sump neutralizes the majority of acidity, and final polishing with caustic or soda ash is accomplished in the second sump.

Radioactive Waste Drain Systems. Waste water drainage from fixtures or equipment which may be radioactive should run separately from other types of drainage. Treatment and/or disposition of radioactive waste water must be determined on an individual basis, based on the degree of radiation and the quantities involved, in accordance with the requirements of all authorities and current regulations. Discussions should be held with the user and the local authorities regarding the design of this system and the disposal of its effluent.

The horizontal drainage piping carrying radioactive waste water should not be run on or in ceilings of occupied rooms, kitchens, or food preparation, food serving, or food storage areas unless adequate lead shielding is provided in the ceiling construction. Piping material should be selected on the basis of the hazard involved.

Infectious Waste Drain Systems. Waste water drainage and vent piping from fixtures or equipment which might contain highly infectious waste material should be run separately from other types of drainage and should be effectively decontaminated before disposal into the sanitary drainage system. Treatment and/or disposal of highly infectious waste water vent piping from the same system must be determined on an individual basis, based on the degree of contamination and the quantities involved, after consultation with the user.

Generally, high-temperature heating followed by cooling is required for the waste, and electric incineration of the vapors in the vent terminal is required for the vents. De-

pending on the degree of contamination, wastes can be decontaminated by sanitizing (heating to 200°F) or by sterilizing (heating to 280°F). Various techniques using steam introduced through heat exchange coils or direct steam injection into a vessel or pit may be applied. Appropriate control and monitoring instrumentation is normally required.

Chemical decontamination in lieu of heat treatment is sometimes applicable due to the nature of the waste.

Stainless steel drainage and vent piping is normally used for untreated wastes. Particular attention should be paid to the location of and access to the piping distribution. Long-radius fittings should be used to minimize potential clogging.

Gas Systems

Principles of Design. Gas is normally supplied from the utility company's street mains. Where no street mains are available, it must be provided by a liquefied petroleum "bottled" (LP) installation. The local utility company should be questioned about the availability of street (natural) gas in the area. Obtain drawings showing the locations and sizes of local gas mains. In addition, obtain the pressure and BTU/cubic foot content of the available gas.

Gas service is usually low pressure (0.5 psi or less). However, it may sometimes be medium or high pressure and may require pressure reduction.

Gas systems should be designed in accordance with the utility company's requirements, NFPA Standard 54 and the requirements of applicable codes.

The requirements for equipment using gas should be carefully investigated, and the branch piping as well as the mains and risers carefully calculated on the basis of equipment requirements. Loads for equipment should be taken from the manufacturer's ratings.

As a rule of thumb, loads for laboratory outlets should be 5,000 BTU/hr for small burners and 10,500 BTU/hr for large burners. Find out from the user which type is preferred. Generally, schools use small burners and research laboratories use large ones. If in doubt, assume large burners. Laboratory gas demands should be calculated on the basis of the simultaneous use factors shown in Table 5.3-9.

Branches serving one or two teaching laboratories should have a 100% use factor regardless of the number of outlets. The use factor for more than two class labs may be 80%, and thereafter twice the normal laboratory use factor if this is less than 80%. Simultaneous use factors must be used judiciously and modified to adapt to special conditions as they occur in the system.

Gas piping should pitch back to the meter wherever possible, and risers and trapped sections should be provided with drip pockets consisting of a pipe nipple and cap. Otherwise, pockets of condensation will occur and rusting conditions will permit rust flakes to carry over to gas orifices and other areas.

All risers and branches should be valved so that piping modifications can be made without shutting down the entire system. Mains should be provided with sectionalizing valves at strategic locations. All connections for future extension shall be valved.

In piping up gas meters, the inlet is always on the left and the outlet is on the right.

Wherever possible, gas mains and risers should be run exposed rather than concealed in shafts or hung ceilings. This prevents the possible accumulation of gas in these closed

Table 5.3-9. Laboratory Gas Demand

No. of Outlets	Use Factor (%)	Minimum No. of Outlets
1–8	100	—
9–16	90	9
17–29	80	15
30–79	60	24
80–162	50	48
163–325	40	82
326–742	35	131
743–1,570	30	260
1,571–2,900	25	472
2,901 and up	20	726

spaces due to leakage from the gas piping system, which may explode if it occurs in the proper concentration and is subject to an igniting spark. Where it is impossible to keep gas piping out of ceiling plenums, shafts and wall recesses, ventilation for these spaces to prevent the possible accumulation of gas should be provided. Installation of a gas detector system should also be considered. Gas piping should not run in or through air plenum ceilings, laundry chutes, air ducts, dumb waiters, stair enclosures or elevator shafts. Gas risers in air shafts should be encased or separated by masonry construction. Gas piping passing perpendicularly through air plenum ceilings or ducts, without connections, should be sleeved over its full length. Some authorities may not permit gas piping in ceiling plenums under any circumstances. The designer must check with local officials for any special requirements.

Pipe Sizing. Piping after the meter should be sized on the basis of the cubic feet per hour (cfh) loads and simultaneous use factors given above. Demands with different use factors should be carried separately in calculations and added together at the end.

Pipe size selection should be based on a maximum friction loss of 0.3 in. of water from the meter to the farthest horizontal point of use. A credit of 0.1 in. of water gauge per 15 ft of rise may be taken in sizing risers. The actual run of piping should be converted to the equivalent developed length before calculating friction losses.

Piping should be sized to include future anticipated loads and to provide for normal flexibility in laboratory areas. Sizes should be used for laboratory bench piping as shown in Table 5.3-10. Use Table 5.3-11 to determine friction loss in piping.

Low-pressure piping should be steel pipe with threaded malleable iron fittings. For larger sizes and for medium- and high-pressure piping, welded fittings should be used.

Cylinders and Special Gases. Depending on the type of laboratory space, typical gases

Table 5.3-10. Gas Sizing for Laboratory Benches

	Small Burners		Large Burners	
	Nat. Gas (5 cFH)	LP Gas (2 cFH)	Nat. Gas (10 cFH)	LP Gas (4 cFH)
⅜ in.	1	2	—	1
½ in.	2	3–6	2	2–3
¾ in.	3–6	7–18	3–4	4–10
1 in.	7–16	19–40	5–8	11–21
1¼ in.	17–30	—	9–16	22–37

Notes
1. One duplex outlet equals two single outlets.
2. Branches to equipment should be at least the size of the connection on the equipment.

found in laboratories include nitrogen, oxygen, helium, carbon dioxide and nitrous oxide.

Some special or high-purity gases are usually required for gas chromatic graph work. Terminal filtration with a 0.22-μ filters is employed when contamination by particulates from the piping or tubing is a concern.

Unless large quantities are required, local cylinder rooms are usually provided and local piping manifold arrangements, etc., are piped to outlets as required.

In the semiconductor industry, high-purity toxic and nontoxic gases are used. Designing these systems requires experience and the assistance of a semiconductor gas manufacturing company.

Where flammable or hazardous gases are

Table 5.3-11. Sizing of Piping (Friction Table for Steel Pipe)

Gas Flow (Cfh)	Nominal Pipe Size (In.)							
	½	¾	1	1¼	1½	2	3	4
	Pressure Drop (inches of Mercury per 100 ft)							
5	.01							
10	.04							
15	.08	.01						
20	.15	.02						
25	.23	.03						
30	.33	.04	.01					
40	.59	.07	.02					
50	.94	.12	.03	.01				
75		.25	.06	.02				
100		.45	.11	.03	.01			
125		.69	.17	.05	.02			
150		1.10	.24	.08	.03			
175			.33	.11	.04	.01		
200			.44	.14	.05	.01		
250			.68	.21	.08	.02		
300			.99	.31	.13	.03		
350				.42	.17	.04		
400				.55	.22	.05		
500				.87	.34	.08	.01	
750					.78	.19	.02	
1,000						.34	.04	.01
1,250						.53	.07	.02
1,500						.79	.09	.02
2,000							.17	.04
3,000							.40	.09

required, they are usually stored in special safety gas cabinets. Gas cabinets are normally ventilated, and custom-fitted units have features such as purge panels, leak-tight seals, special regulators and valves. Good sources of information for regulatory compliance are private organization such as the Compressed Gas Association and the Chemical Manufacturer Association. See Figure 5.3-10.

Compressed Air Systems

Definitions. Various terms are used for air-flow rates:

Free air	cfm
Compressed air	cfm
Standard air	scfm*
Actual air	acfm

*Standard cubic feet per minute.

It is essential to know what basis you are working with and to use the proper friction tables and equipment selection.

Standard air is based on the following conditions:

60°F temperature
50% relative humidity
29.92 barometric pressure in inches of mercury (Hg) or 14.7 psia

The proper terminology for airflow at these conditions is scfm.

To change this air to any other set of conditions, apply the basic gas law:

$$\frac{P_1 V_1}{T_1} = \frac{P_2 V_2}{T_2}$$

where P_1 = absolute pressure (29.92 in. Hg or 14.7 psia)
V_1 = initial volume of air, in cubic feet, at standard air conditions
T_1 = 460° + 60° = 520° (standard air conditions) at absolute temperature in °F
P_2 = absolute pressure other than standard (in Hg or psia)
V_2 = volume, in cubic feet, other than standard
T_2 = absolute temperature in °F

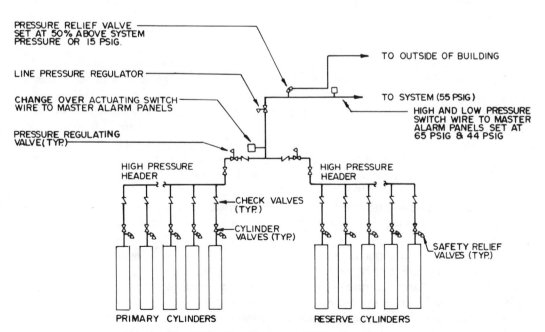

Fig. 5.3-10. Gas cylinder manifold schematic.

- Absolute Pressure: Existing pressure (as read on a gauge) plus atmospheric pressure. Atmospheric pressure at sea level is 14.7 psia; therefore, for 100 lbs gauge, the absolute pressure (psia) is 100 plus 14.7, or 114.7 psia.
- Free Air: Generally described as air at room or ambient temperatures and pressures, that is, normal atmospheric conditions. In other words, the term "free air" describes the air actually taken into the suction of a compressor which takes air from the surrounding atmosphere.
- Standard Conditions: Not universally defined; therefore, since compressor capacities are sometimes expressed in standard cubic feet per minute (scfm), it is necessary to identify, before the compressor can be sized, (1) the standard pressure condition, (2) the standard temperature condition, (3) the compressor suction pressure condition and (4) the compressor suction temperature condition. The most popular identification for standard pressure and temperature conditions is 14.7 psi and 60°F.

Table 5.3-12 illustrates how different air pressures affect the volume.

Principles of Design (Figure 5.3-11). Outlets connected to a central system should be provided in laboratories as required. Most laboratories are designed to provide either 50 or 15 psi at the outlets. If there are a few outlets with lower pressure requirements, they can be accommodated by pressure-reducing valves. Isolated higher pressure requirements can be provided by small air compressors in the lab room.

Ample provision should be made in compressors and in the piping for anticipated future building expansion.

Central compressed air plants should be located below the areas they serve, with upfeed risers so that any moisture in the piping drains back away from the outlet.

Compressed air piping should pitch back to the central plant wherever possible.

Table 5.3-12. Equivalent Air Volumes at Various Pressures

psig	psia	Standard Volume (Ft³)	Compressed Air Vol. at Designated Pressure (Ft³)
0	14.7	100	100
5	19.7	100	74.6
10	24.7	100	59.5
15	29.7	100	49.5
20	29.7	100	42.4
25	39.7	100	37.0
30	44.7	100	32.9
35	49.7	100	29.6
40	54.7	100	26.9
45	59.7	100	24.6
50	64.7	100	22.7
55	69.7	100	21.1
60	74.7	100	19.7
65	79.7	100	18.4
70	84.7	100	17.4
75	89.7	100	16.4
80	94.7	100	15.5
85	99.7	100	14.7
90	104.7	100	14.0
95	109.7	100	13.4
100	114.7	100	12.8

Drains should be provided at the low points and trapped sections of the mains. The drains should be manual petcocks or automatic drain traps, depending on the extent of the system served.

All risers and branches should be valved. Mains should be provided with sectionalizing valves at strategic locations. All connections for future extension should be valved.

Where especially dry air is requested or where the air piping runs through cold spaces (as in outside shafts), an air dryer should be added.

Pipe Sizing. Piping is sized on the basis of the cfm loads and simultaneous use factors. Allow 1 cfm (free air) (scfm) for each each laboratory outlet with the use factors noted in Table 5.3-13.

The branches serving one or two classrooms should use a 100% simultaneous use factor regardless of the number of outlets. The use factor for more than two classrooms

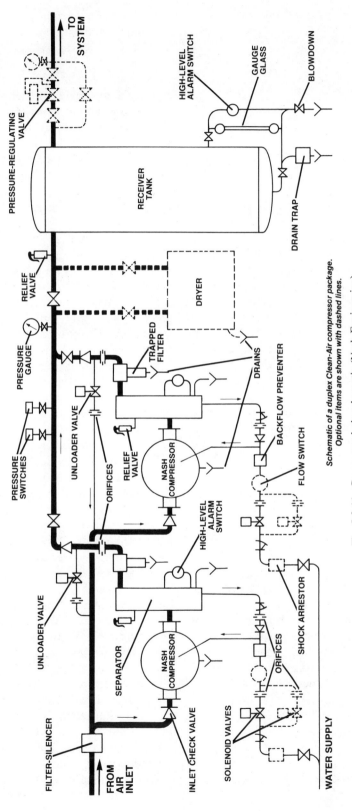

Fig. 5.3-11. Compressed air schematic (Nash Engineering).

Schematic of a duplex Clean-Air compressor package.
Optional items are shown with dashed lines.

Table 5.3-13. Laboratory Compressed Air Demand

No. of Outlets	Use Factor (%)	Minimum cfm
1–2	100	—
3–12	80	3
13–38	60	10
39–115	40	25
116–316	30	50
317–700	20	95
701–1,880	15	145
1,881–4,400	10	285
4,401–16,000	5	445
16,001–80,000	2	800

may be 80%, and thereafter twice the normal laboratory use factor regardless of the number of outlets. Simultaneous use factors must be used judiciously and modified to adapt to special conditions as they occur in the system. Demands with different simultaneous use factors must be carried separately in the calculations and added together at the end.

Piping should be sized to include future anticipated loads and to provide for normal flexibility in the laboratory area. Minimum pipe sizes should be:

3/8 in. branch to single or duplex outlet (short run)
1/2 in. (other branches)
1/2 in. (riser)
3/4 in. (main)

Outlets should be of the appropriate type for their location and use.

All cfm values referred to above are cfm (free air) at atmospheric pressure and are not the actual volumes of compressed air in the piping. The latter will be less due to compression and will vary depending on the pressure in the piping.

Pipe size selection should be based on the more stringent of the following requirements:

• Maximum friction loss rate of 1 psi per 100 ft.

• Maximum friction loss to the farthest outlet of 5 psi.
• Maximum velocity of 4,000 ft per minute.

Table 5.3-14 gives the friction losses in 55-psi compressed air piping. The actual run of the piping should be converted to equivalent developed length by adding fittings and valve allowances before using the tables. For friction losses in other than 55-psi systems, consult tables available from compressed air equipment manufacturers.

Piping. For medical air systems, piping should be Type L copper tubing with wrought copper or cast brass fittings with silver brazed joints, or red brass pipe with threaded cast brass fittings. All pipe, fittings and valves should be specifically washed for medical gas and protected from contamination thereafter.

For other lab systems, piping 1 in. or smaller is usually Type L tubing. Larger sizes are sometimes found in galvanized steel pipe with galvanized, threaded, malleable fittings. Copper solder joints are normally used in other than medical systems.

Buried piping should be adequately protected against frost, corrosion and physical damage by installation within a pipe or conduit, with proper cover and an adequate corrosion protective coating.

Control (shutoff) valves should be ball valves. Check valves are normally of the spring-loaded type.

Equipment. Air compressors should be sized to carry the peak anticipated load with one compressor out of operation. Where future loads are involved, if the proportions are workable, a three-compressor installation may be more practical, with the third compressor installed later. The advantages are that this installation will require a smaller standby unit and will provide a smaller unit for operation during low-demand periods.

For laboratory and medical applications, a reliable source of oil-free air is essential. Compressed air is usually supplied at either

Table 5.3-14. Compressed Air Sizing (55 psi)

		Pressure Drop (psi per 100 ft)								
cfm	acfm	½	¾	1	1¼	1½	2	2½	3	4
5	1.1	0.15	0.04	0.01						
10	2.2	0.51	0.13	0.04	0.01					
15	3.3	1.04	0.27	0.09	0.02	0.01				
20	4.3		0.45	0.14	0.04	0.02				
25	5.4		0.67	0.21	0.06	0.03	0.01			
30	6.5		0.93	0.29	0.08	0.04	0.01			
35	7.6			0.39	0.10	0.05	0.02	0.01		
40	8.7			0.49	0.13	0.06	0.02	0.01		
45	9.8			0.60	0.16	0.08	0.02	0.01		
50	10.9			0.73	0.20	0.09	0.03	0.01		
60	13.0			1.01	0.27	0.13	0.04	0.02	0.01	
70	15.2				0.36	0.17	0.05	0.02	0.01	
80	17.4				0.45	0.22	0.07	0.03	0.01	
90	19.5				0.56	0.27	0.08	0.03	0.01	
100	21.7				0.68	0.32	0.10	0.04	0.02	0.0
110	23.9				0.81	0.38	0.12	0.05	0.02	0.0
120	26.0				0.94	0.45	0.14	0.06	0.02	0.0
130	28.2				1.09	0.52	0.16	0.07	0.02	0.0
140	30.4					0.59	0.18	0.08	0.03	0.0
150	32.6					0.67	0.20	0.09	0.03	0.0
175	38.0					0.89	0.27	0.11	0.04	0.0
200	43.4					1.13	0.34	0.14	0.05	0.0
225	48.8						0.42	0.18	0.06	0.0
250	54.3						0.51	0.22	0.08	0.0
275	59.7						0.60	0.26	0.09	0.0
300	65.1						0.71	0.30	0.11	0.0
325	70.5						0.82	0.35	0.12	0.0
350	76.0						0.94	0.40	0.14	0.0
375	81.4						1.06	0.45	0.16	0.0
400	86.8							0.51	0.18	0.0
450	97.7							0.63	0.22	0.0
500	108.5							0.76	0.27	0.0
550	119.4							0.90	0.32	0.0
600	130.2							1.06	0.37	0.1
650	141.1								0.43	0.1
700	151.9								0.49	0.1
750	162.8								0.56	0.1
800	173.6								0.63	0.1
850	184.5								0.70	0.1
900	195.3								0.78	0.2
950	206.2									0.2
1,000	217.0									0.2
1,100	238.7									0.3
1,200	260.4									0.3
1,300	282.1									0.4
1,400	303.8									0.4
1,500	325.5									0.5

Notes
1. Friction table for Type L copper tubing.
2. Values in table limited to a velocity of 4,000 fpm.

55 or 15 psi, depending on the user's preference.

The principal types of compressors that are widely used are reciprocating, screw and rotary displacement. Most laboratory applications use reciprocating or rotary units, since screw machines are normally used for high volumes. Basic considerations in making a selection will fall into the following categories:

- Package vs. Bare: Fully preassembled, prewired and tested units will normally avoid installation problems. Nonstandard sizes or conditions will sometimes dictate a field-erected system.
- Air Quality: Reciprocating compressors are available as either oil-less or lubricated units. Some oil-less types do use oil in the crankcase, and consideration should be given to the possibility of gaseous hydrocarbons in the air stream. This is normally a consideration only with medical or clinical air. Rotary compressors use water or another liquid as the compressant and, therefore, are oil-less units.
- Materials of Construction: Different units should be investigated to find materials which have longer wear and heat resistance.
- Utility Costs: Power costs are the largest life cycle costs of the compressor set, and factors such as efficiency and selection should be taken into consideration. Water usage and the cost of water for rotary units should also be addressed.

Moisture in compressed air is eliminated by the use of air dryers. Moisture in air systems can cause:

- Freeze-up where systems are exposed to low temperatures
- Clogging and malfunctioning of control valves and instruments
- Damage to or chemical reaction of certain processors
- Rust and flaking in equipment and piping

Air dryers are either of the refrigerated air or the desiccant dryer type. A refrigerated air dryer is basically a chiller unit which maintains a pressure dew point of 33° to 39°F in an ambient temperature range of 45° to 100°F. Dew point is the temperature at which air is saturated with water vapor.

Where dry compressed air to pressure dew points as low as -100°F are required, desiccant-type dryers must be used. Some desiccant models require constant replacement (regeneration). Replaceable, self-contained cartridges are also available.

Particulate after-filters are recommended downstream of air dryers for most applications.

Filters on the discharge main from the compressor should be duplex, each sized for approximately one-half to two-thirds the ultimate load. If the proportions are workable, it may be desirable to use three filters with one for future use. Provide automatic drain traps on the filters.

Vacuum Air Systems

Principles of Design (Figure 5.3-12). For most plumbing applications, vacuum is measured in inches of mercury (Hg): 14.70 psia = 29.92 in. Hg absolute = 0 in. Hg. In some laboratory process work the torr is a commonly used unit: 1 in. Hg = 25.40 torr. Standard atmosphere is measured as 760.0 torr. Vacuum systems are divided into four major divisions:

Rough vacuum	760 to 1 torr
Medium vacuum	1 to 10^{-3} torr
High vacuum	10^{-3} to 10^{-7} torr
Ultra-high vacuum	10^{-7} torr and below

Standard laboratory vacuum systems are designed for the rough vacuum category; however, some facilities require a medium vacuum system for distillation and degassing applications. Some laboratory processes have high condensable loads. Condensables may be harmful to the pump materials or may contain valuable process materials

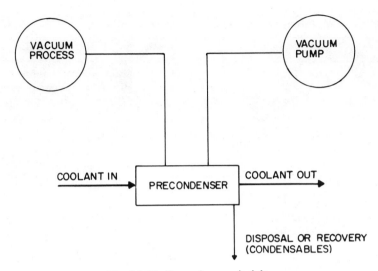

Fig. 5.3-12. Precondenser principle.

which must be recovered. In such cases, the use of a precondenser should be examined. A precondenser can reduce the size of the vacuum pump required.

Four types of vacuum are used in the industry: steam ejectors, liquid ring pumps, rotary pistons and rotary vane pumps. Each type has specified operating and capacity ranges and recommended applications. Table 5.3-15 gives the general characteristics of these pumps.

Factors to consider in installing vacuum air systems are as follows:

- The central vacuum pumps should be located below the areas served with upfeed risers so that if vacuum is lost, any moisture carryover in the piping drains away from the outlets.
- The vacuum pump discharge should be run up through the roof far from all compressed air and other intakes, win-

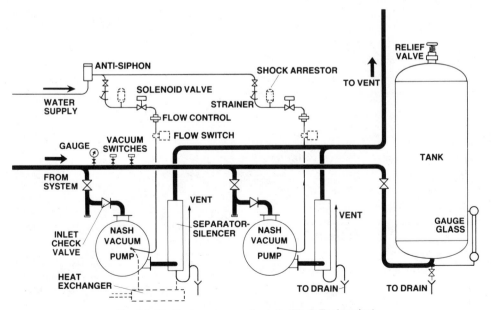

Fig. 5.3-13. Vacuum pump schematic (Nash Engineering).

Table 5.3-15. Vacuum Pump Classifications

Type	Constant Range	cfm	Characteristics
Steam ejectors, 1-stage to 6-stage	75 torr–3 μm	10–1,000,000	Simple, reliable, low first cost. High capacity, down to 3-μm range. Tolerates corrosive chemicals. Liquid slugs, and solids. High operating cost.
Liquid ring	75–10 torr	3–18,000	Rugged construction. Tolerates entrained liquids. Good for wet vacuum applications.
Rotary piston	100–10 μm	3–800	Oil-sealed. Commonly used in semiconductor industry.
Rotary vane	50–2.0 torr (760–50 torr for dry type)	20–6,000	Oil-sealed. Nonmetallic vanes can be provided as a dry compressor, eliminating use of oil. Commonly used in semiconductor industry.

Note: 1.0 μm = 0.001 torr.
Source: J. L. Ryans and D. L. Roper, 1986. *Process Vacuum System Design and Operation*. New York: McGraw-Hill.

dows, etc., to minimize cross-contamination.

- The vacuum piping should pitch back to the receiver wherever possible. Valved drain pockets and drain cocks should be provided at low points and trapped sections of the main.
- Plugged cleanout connections should be strategically located throughout the system to allow removal of stoppages.
- The branches to risers should connect to the risers with a drop leg to facilitate draining of piping contents back to the central equipment.
- The branch piping to inlets should feed up rather than down to the inlets wherever possible.
- Wherever downfeed branches are unavoidable, they should be connected to the top of the main branch to minimize drainage back to the inlet.
- All risers and branches should be valved. Mains should be provided with sectionalizing valves at strategic locations. All connections for future extension should be valved.
- The laboratory inlets should be of an appropriate type for their location and use, as specified.

Pipe Sizing. Allow 0.5 scfm for each laboratory inlet with simultaneous use factors as noted in Table 5.3-16.

Minimum pipe sizes are:

1/2 in. (branch to single or duplex inlet—short run)
3/4 in. (other branches)
1 in. (mains)

Table 5.3-16. Laboratory Outlet Use Factors

No. of Outlets	Use Factor	Minimum scfm
1–5	100	—
6–12	80	5
13–33	60	10
34–80	50	21
81–150	40	40
151–315	35	61
316–565	30	111
566–1,000	25	171
1,001–2,175	20	251
2,176–4,670	15	436
4671 and up	10	701

Note: The branches serving one or two classrooms should have 100% simultaneous use factor regardless of the number of outlets. The use factor for more than two classrooms may be 80%, and thereafter twice the normal laboratory use factor if this is less than 80%.

Simultaneous use factors must be used judiciously and modified to adapt to special conditions as they occur in the system.

Refer to Tables 5.3-17 and 5.3-18 for sizing pipes based on scfm flow rates. These tables indicate pressure drop in Hg per 100 ft for L tubing.

Piping. Piping 2 in. or smaller should be Type L copper tubing with wrought copper long-turn solder joint fittings or red brass pipe with threaded cast brass long-turn fittings. Piping 2.5 in. or larger should be galvanized steel pipe with threaded galvanized cast iron long-turn drainage pattern fittings. Piping should be designed using "Y" or "TY" fittings instead of tees. Control (shut-off) valves should be ball valves. Check valves should be soft-seated swing-type valves.

Equipment. Vacuum pumps should be of the rotary liquid ring, rotary vane or rotary piston type. In installations where chilled water is always available, recirculated seal water systems should be considered for liquid ring pumps to conserve water usage. For total water conservation, consider using oil-sealed, rotary sliding vane units or the oil-less reciprocating type.

Vacuum pumps should be sized to handle the peak demand with one pump out of service.

Consideration should be given to a duplex

Table 5.3-17. Vacuum Air Sizing

	Pipe Diameter							
scfm	¾	1	1¼	1½	2	2½	3	4
1	.08							
2	.27	.08						
3	.53	.15						
4	.88	.25	.09					
5	1.3	.36	.14					
6	1.8	.50	.19					
7		.65	.24	.11				
8		.82	.30	.13				
9		1.01	.37	.16				
10		1.22	.45	.20				
15			.91	.40	.11			
20				.66	.18			
25					.26	.09		
30					.36	.13		
35					.47	.17		
40						.21	.09	
45						.26	.11	
50						.32	.14	
60						.44	.19	
70							.25	.06
80							.31	.08
90								.10
100								.12
125								.18
150								.25

Notes
1. Friction table for type L copper tubing.
2. Limit maximum velocity to 5,000 fpm.
3. Pressure drop in inches of Mercury per 100 ft.

Table 5.3-18. Vacuum Air Sizing

	Pipe Diameter							
scfm	¾	1	1¼	1½	2	2½	3	4
1	.07							
2	.22	.07						
3	.45	.14						
4	.75	.24	.06					
5	1.1	.35	.09					
6	1.56	.48	.13					
7		.63	.17	.08				
8		.81	.21	.10				
9		1.00	.26	.13				
10		1.21	.32	.15				
15			.66	.31	.09			
20				.52	.15			
25				.78	.23	.10		
30					.32	.14		
35					.42	.18		
40					.54	.23	.08	
45						.28	.10	
50						.34	.12	
60						.47	.16	
70							.22	.06
80							.28	.07
90							.34	.09
100								.11
125								.17
150								.23

Notes
1. Friction table for schedule 40 steel pipe.
2. Limit maximum velocity to 5,000 fpm.
3. Pressure drop in inches of Mercury per 100 ft.

or triplex system. Greater operating efficiencies are obtainable with a triplex or quadraplex system under many circumstances, and horsepower requirements for these systems should be analyzed.

Back pressure losses, such as friction in the discharge piping from the pump to the atmosphere plus the loss through the discharge filter-silencer, should be considered when selecting a vacuum pump.

In a duplex pump system with 14-in. Hg at the farthest inlet, start and stop conditions should be as follows:

	Start (in. Hg)	Stop (in. Hg)
Lead pump	18	21
Lag pump	17	20

In a triplex pump system with 14-in. Hg at the farthest inlet, start and stop conditions should be as follows:

	Start (in. Hg)	Stop (in. Hg)
Lead pump	19	21
Second pump	18	20
Third pump	17	19

Vacuum pumps are rated on acfm, while calculations for the system are based on scfm. Therefore, it is necessary to convert to acfm when choosing a vacuum pump. The formula for the conversion is as follows:

$$\text{ACFM} = \text{SCFM}\,\frac{(29.92)}{(29.92\ \text{vac})} \times \frac{(T + 460)}{(528)}$$

Therefore, based on the previous example, it was determined that 82.5 scfm was the estimated demand. Pumps should be sized to operate on the lead pump start setting.

For a duplex pump system where the lead pump starts at 18-in. Hg:

$$\text{ACFM} = 82.5 \frac{(29.92)}{(29.92 - 18)} \times \frac{(68 + 460)}{(528)}$$

ACFM = 207.

In medical research laboratory systems, filters are recommended in the discharge. Filters should be duplex, and the filter pressure drop must be added to pipe friction losses in calculating discharge losses.

If flammable gas is intended to be evacuated through the vacuum pumps, it is necessary to specify nonsparking motors.

5.4 ELECTRICAL SYSTEMS
R. E. Marshall

5.4.1 Power

Site/Building Voltage Selection

Selection of a building or site electrical distribution voltage is based on several factors:

- Size of the building(s).
- Size of the site (several building).
- Function of the building(s).
- Local utility requirements.

Rules of thumb for various building types in watts/sq ft of connected load are noted in Table 5.4-1.

Once the building's functions are defined, an estimated load can be established. The numbers presented in Table 5.4-1 are for connected loads, and a diversity factor should be applied for an estimated real power consumption load. Diversity factors vary among building types and load types. Generally a diversity of 0.8 to 0.85 is used with lab areas; 0.4 to 0.5 for power; and 0.5 to 0.6 for animal facilities, due to the large number of backup systems involved. Since most utilities apply a similar factor, it is recommended that both the connected and an-

Table 5.4-1. Rules of Thumb: Watts/Sq Ft Connection Loads

Bldg. Type	Lighting	Power	Motors	Total
Office	3	5	10	18
R&D	3	10	15	28
Computer	3	50	60	113
Warehouse	3	1	5	9
Animal	3	2	20	24

ticipated demands be included for the local utility company loads. See Table 5.4-2 for an example of a multiuse building-type facility and load breakdowns to be sent. In some locations, it is also beneficial to break down the utility loads for HVAC into a summer and a winter electric load.

Normal Electrical Service

Incoming service has more impact on system reliability than other aspects of the total electrical design. The number of primary feeders, the number of transformers, equipment arrangement and configuration, automatic versus manual schemes—all most be carefully weighed to provide reasonable reliability consistent with cost constraints. There are several types of power distribution systems which are familiar to electrical designers and can be found in most design manuals. For those not involved in the details of design, it might be well to discuss the following four basic designs, recognizing that other schemes can be derived from the basics.

Radial System (Figure 5.4-1). The radial system is the simplest, most economical and least reliable system. Power is received from a single primary source; voltage is stepped down through one transformer; feeders distribute power from one central point such as a panelboard or switchboard. Because all loads are supplied through new transformers, maximum diversity can be used, resulting in minimum installed transformer capacity. The major drawback is the lack of redundancy; a fault ahead of the switch-

Table 5.4-2. Example of a Multiuse Facility: Connected and Demand Loads

Bldg. (Sq. Ft.)	Lights (KW)		Power (KW)		HVAC (KW)	
	Conn.	Dem.	Conn.	Dem.	Conn.	Dem.
Office 100K	300	250	500	300	1,000	750
Lab R&D 100K	300	250	1,000	500	1,500	1,200
Animals 50K	150	100	100	50	1,000	600
Storage 50K	50	75	50	30	250	200
Computer 25K	75	50	1,250	1,000	1,500	1,200
Total	975	725	2,900	1,880	5,250	3,950

Total Load (KW)

	Connected	Demand
Lights	975	725
Power	2,900	1,880
HVAC	5,250	3,950
Total	9,125	6,555

board or a primary feeder outage will deenergize the entire system.

Primary Selective Radial System (Figure 5.4-2). There are several steps between the radial system and the primary selective radial system which offer increasing degrees of reliability. The biggest jump in reliability, however, results from adding a source of primary power. Assuming that either primary feeder is adequate to carry the entire load, a power outage in one feeder can easily be overcome by switching to the second feeder, thus maintaining service to the entire building. If primary service is provided by a utility company, there will frequently be an "extra facilities" charge for the second feeder. As with the radial system, a transformer failure will deenergize the entire system.

Secondary Selective Radial System (Figure 5.4-3). The next way to achieve increased re-

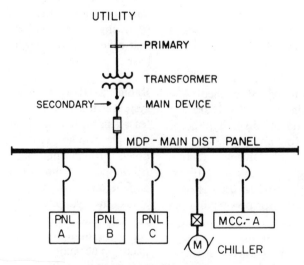

Fig. 5.4-1. Radial system.

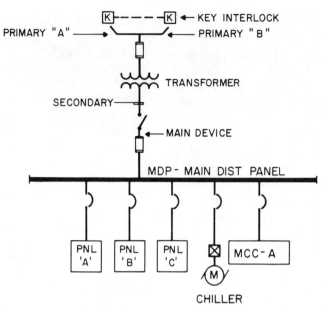

Fig. 5.4–2. Primary selective radial system.

liability is to duplicate transformer capacity so that there are two paths all the way through the transformers to the secondary bus. In the primary selective system, the duplicate paths terminate ahead of the transformer.

In Figure 5.4-3, note that the duplicate systems are connected by a tie breaker or a switch is normally open. In this mode the two systems operate separately, completely independent of each other. In the event of an outage in feeder A, the main service device A opens, the tie breaker closes, and both loads are supplied from feeder/transformer B.

In the writer's judgment, the secondary

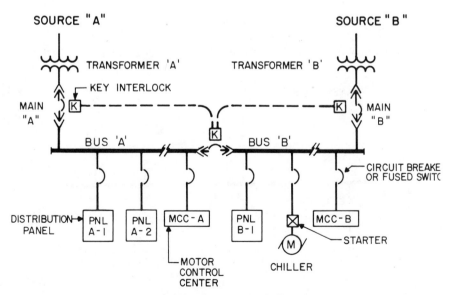

Fig. 5.4-3. Secondary selective radial system.

selective radial system provides a desirable degree of reliability for research facilities.

Network System. For further reliability, there is one major step beyond the secondary selective system: a network system. This system configuration is similar to that of Figure 5.4-4, except that the tie breaker is normally operated in the closed position so that the transformers are in parallel, equally sharing the load. If an outage occurs in feeder A, a network protector (a special circuit breaker mounted on the network transformer—not shown) will open and the entire load will be served from transformers B and C, with no interruption in power. The network scheme is appreciably more costly (approximately 65% more on the switchgear) than the secondary selective radial system and may be difficult to justify on small installations. A second factor to consider is the added resources needed for this system, not only in physical space but in construction dollars (approximately $150–200/sq ft).

Emergency Power

The history of commercial power in recent years includes both brownouts for load reduction and blackouts resulting from system and equipment failure. There is no guarantee that such failures won't recur, and many feel that the situation may deteriorate before any major improvements can be realized. Thus, on-site generation must be provided for critical loads in research facilities.

Ideally, engine-generators should be located in a building enclosure with access to the outside for equipment replacement and adequate ventilation for cooling and combustion. The equipment should be as far as possible from animal spaces in order to eliminate noise and vibrations, which may disturb the animals.

In sizing generator capacity, it is difficult to give a "watts/square foot" for lab buildings in general, because of the nature of the various functions associated with laboratory buildings. Each facility must be examined individually in sizing the emergency system.

Generally, loads that are essential for personnel safety, for preservation of research projects, and for protection of the building and contents should be supplied from the emergency system.

The term "emergency power" has a wide variety of meanings for various levels of personnel within a laboratory facility. In general, the following systems should be considered suitable for connection to an emergency source:

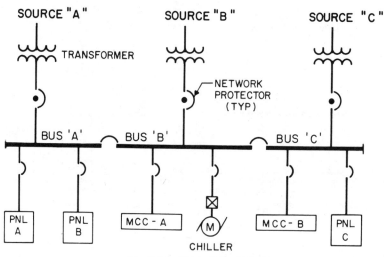

Fig. 5.4-4. Network system.

Life Safety

- Egress lighting (stairs, halls, etc.)
- Fire alarm
- Fire pump
- Smoke control (if applicable)
- Elevator(s) for handicap

Critical Systems

- Critical or hazardous fumehoods
- Sump pumps
- Freeze protection system(s)
- Environmental rooms (long-term samples or experiments)
- Selected refrigerators/freezers within lab areas
- Fuel pumps
- Boiler

In animal facilities, make provisions for that portion of the facility needed to maintain the animals. Assume that a facility of this type has multiple units of the following systems:

- Cooling tower (one cell)
- Chilled water pump (one pump)
- Air-handling system(s) associated with life support of the animal areas, supply and exhaust

Electrical Service and Distribution Systems

Electrical systems in research facilities should be designed to provide adequate, flexible, uniform, reliable and cost-effective power. See Figure 5.4-5. These systems must accommodate a wide range of requirements for power. These needs can range from 75 to 100 watts/sq ft, depending on the equipment and its frequency of use. In addition, periodic reconfiguration of laboratories may change overall power needs. Consequently, designers should estimate power needs not only for short-term projections, but also with long-term needs in mind.

Because of these short- and long-term needs, electrical distribution should provide the laboratory with as much flexibility as possible. The most important considerations

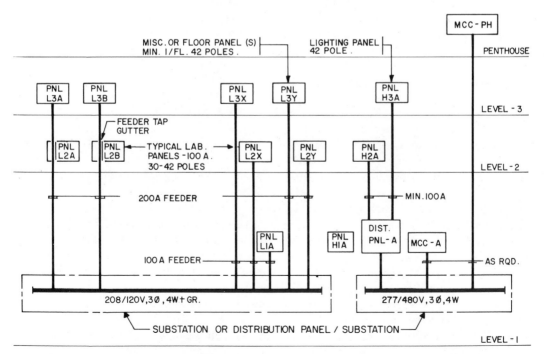

Fig. 5.4-5. Distribution system.

are quantity of power, frequency, and voltage levels. Generally, most laboratory equipment is designed for the normal "clear" power provided by the utility ($\pm 10\%$).

One method of providing flexibility of distribution is with a bus duct. The duct, however, cannot be concealed (lay-in ceiling conceal). Ready access to the plug-in disconnect means is a National Electric Code requirement. This requirement also applies to mechanical spaces where ducts and piping can interfere with ready access to the plug-in disconnect.

A second method is to provide a substation with a distribution section(s). The only drawback to this scheme is that in the vicinity of the distribution section, all feeder conduits come together. These alone require considerable space, and if a pullbox is needed (due to the number of bends and pulling distances), even more space is required. This space, however, is not added floor space, just ceiling cavity space which requires close coordination among mechanical systems.

General laboratory power should be as free from transients, harmonic distortion and ground circuits as practical. To provide uniformity, designers should employ one or more of the available methods of ensuring a reliable power supply. One method of accomplishing this is to provide a separate 120/208 volt distribution system. This should be separate from any noise-generating system, such as a mechanical area or areas with motor loads. See Figure 5.4-5.

The presence of sensitive instrumentation and hazardous materials makes the reliability of a laboratory's electrical service and distribution especially important. Examples of electrical distribution systems which were mentioned earlier (from lesser to greater degrees of reliability) are:

- Simple Radial Service: Consisting of a single service feeder, a single transformer and a single switchboard. This arrangement provides a basic service with no standby capabilities. See Figure 5.4-6.

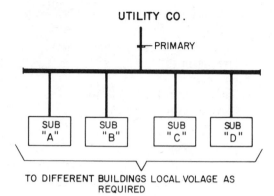

UTILITY CO.

PRIMARY

SUB "A"   SUB "B"   SUB "C"   SUB "D"

TO DIFFERENT BUILDINGS LOCAL VOLAGE AS REQUIRED

Fig. 5.4-6. Simple radial system.

- Multiple Services: Consisting of two or more feeders into the building. These feeders terminate in substations arranged either in parallel or in double-ended fashion, with automatic transfer of half of the building's load to the surviving feeder if one feeder or transformer fails. The disadvantage of this system is that during a utility service failure, part of the facility will experience a momentary outage. See Figure 5.4-7.
- Cogenerator or Parallel: Consisting of a generator to a turbine-driven machine operating in parallel with the utility. That is, both the utility and the power produced by the generator are connected to the same distribution system. See Figure 5.4-8.
- Network System: Consisting of multiple feeders operated in parallel. Loss of a single feeder or transformer will not affect the operation of the facility. See Figure 5.4-9.

The typical means of providing flexibility in a lab building is to provide a 120/208-volt, four-wire panel within each lab area or maximum space of 1,000 sq ft. Panels should all be uniform in size—i.e., 30 or 42 total spaces, depending on the size and function of the lab—with an initial goal of having 65% of all available space programmed or "active." Larger labs or labs with a large amount of equipment may require multiple

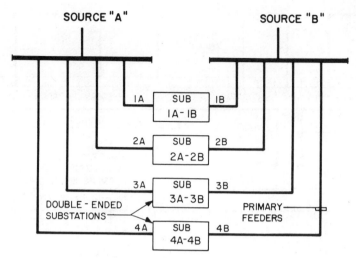

Fig. 5.4-7. Multiple service.

panels. These should remain standard in size, as per smaller labs. See Figure 5.4-5.

Distribution within a lab should be as flexible as possible. This can be accomplished by means of a metal raceway with duplex receptacles spaced 1 ft 0 in. to 3 ft 0 in. on center with an occasional 208-volt, one-phase outlet, generally one per lab bench. See Figure 5.4-10.

Redundancy

Redundancy in laboratory facilities is generally located at the substation level, with a

double-ended configuration and automatic transfer schemes. In this scheme (see Figure 5.4-7), if either source fails—i.e., a feeder, a primary switch/fuse or transformer—the main secondary breaker of the failed side opens and the normally open tie breaker closes.

A second method to supply redundant power to the labs is by means of automatic transfer switches. This method is as reliable as the above method, and many may consider it easier to maintain and troubleshoot. However, this method requires a considerable amount of wall or floor space and closer

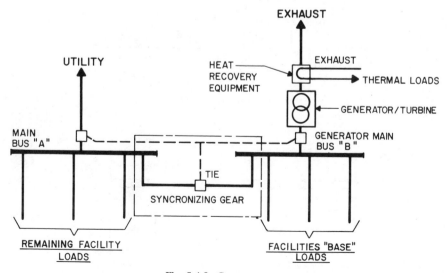

Fig. 5.4-8. Cogen system.

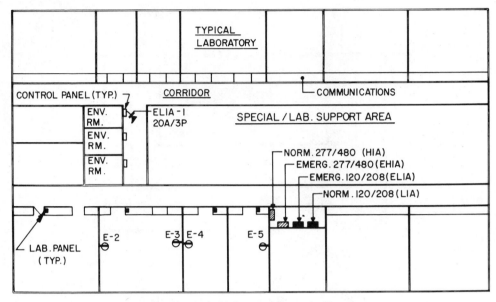

Fig. 5.4-9. Typical laboratory floor panel location.

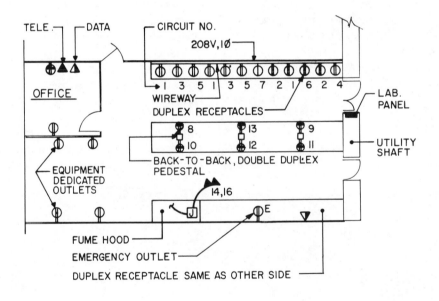

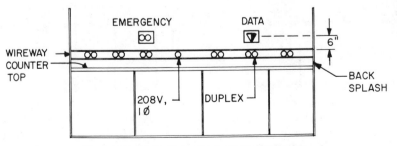

Fig. 5.4-10. Typical laboratory power distribution.

coordination due to the added conduits entering and leaving the transfer switches. It is also more expensive to install.

The need for redundancy in an animal facility is considerable. This is due primarily to the need for minimal service interruptions, especially in mechanical systems which are needed to meet regulatory requirements. With this required amount of mechanical redundancy, there must be a related amount of redundancy in the electrical system.

Special Systems

Dependency on the level of reliability and/ or power conditioning, some of the special systems that may be required are:

- Uninterrupted power supply
- Line conditioners to regulate power to ±1% or 2%
- Isolation transformers
- Special shielding—radio frequency, lead (for X-ray areas), etc.

5.4.2 Lighting

Lighting controls in any area can be implemented in several ways. Offices and laboratories should be provided with local switches. Stairs and corridors should be provided with unswitched fixtures which serve as egress lighting, and all others may be switched by means of a locking (key) switch or timer; both methods should be accessible to qualified personnel only.

Open office area lighting can be controlled by means of low-voltage switching. The low-voltage switch(es) should be located at the entrance to these areas and should operate relays or contactors in or near the lighting panels. Most low-voltage controls can be interfaced to the building's automation system so that these areas can be controlled from a single point.

Lighting in mechanical equipment rooms can also be controlled by low-voltage switching. In certain application, it can be controlled by means of motion detectors which control a smaller area of fixtures.

Tables 5.4-3 and 5.4-4 describe the foot-

Table 5.4-3. Foot-Candle Levels by Area Type

Area	Foot-Candle Level
General office	50
Secretarial	75
Library/archives	75
Laboratory	75–100
Animal labs	
Night	0
Day	30–50
Cleaning	75–100
Corridors	20–30
Storage	10–200
Mechanical	20–30
Computer rooms	30–50
Conference rooms	30
Walk-in environmental rooms	50–100
Fumehoods	100
Stairs	20

Table 5.4-4. Types of Lighting Fixtures and Lamps by Area

Area	Fixture-Lamp Type
General office, secretarial, laboratory	Recessed fluorescent with parabolic or prismatic lens
Open office	Indirect metal halide or recessed fluorescent
Library/archives	Fluorescent aisle lights
Laboratory (wet)	Prismatic lens Fluorescent fixtures
Animal labs	Gasketed, prismatic lens Fluorescent fixtures
Corridors	Similar to that of surrounding areas
Storage	Strip fluorescent
Mechanical	Industrial fluorescent
Computer rooms	Recessed parabolic or indirect fluorescent
Conference rooms	Parabolic fluorescent and incandescent wall washers/down lights
Fumehoods	(By hood manufacturer; fluorescent lens)
Walk-in environmental rooms	Surface, fluorescent or incandescent lens
Stairs	Wall-mounted fluorescent up- and down-lights

candle levels and fixture types generally used for various areas within a facility.

Lighting requirements in a laboratory environment generally are the same as for an office: 75–100 foot-candles at the bench top. However, some lab functions require higher or lower levels.

Animal rooms require a two-level lighting arrangement. Since most laboratory animals are nocturnal, a night cycle of 0–1 foot-candles and a day cycle generally of 30–50 foot-candles with a wide-spectrum fluorescent light source and a cleaning cycle with 70–100 foot-candles are required. Night levels should be as low as possible, with as few light leaks as possible from corridors or adjacent rooms.

The fixture construction in an animal facility is critical due to the extensive cleaning and vermin control requirements. A recessed fluorescent fixture with triple gasketing is utilized in these areas. Gaskets are located between the lens and frame, frame and housing, and housing and ceiling. All lenses must be mounted smooth side out to provide an easily cleanable surface.

Animal rooms designed specifically for primates, monkeys, chimps, etc., should be similar to other animal rooms, but with a high-security fixture designed with concealed hardware, tempered lens, etc.

The lighting control for the animal rooms has been a local time clock-controlled system. This, however, is being replaced with a more sophisticated, computer-controlled system. The reason for this is that a central control point for all rooms provides accurate logs for documentation purposes.

Sensory evaluation labs and food products/packaging labs require special lighting for the visual appearance and taste of a product. The visual appearance of a product is critical in its packaging. If it does not appear pleasing under certain light sources, consumers will not purchase it. Lighting also plays an important part in the appearance of foods. Under certain light sources, if a product doesn't look good, chances are that it will not taste good (usually a psychological relationship).

The location of fixtures in any type of lab has to be coordinated with the equipment within the area. The ideal location is at the edge of and parallel to the lab bench. See Figure 5.4-11. This location minimizes shadows from lab personnel, tall equipment and reagent shelves.

Lighting at a fumehood generally is not

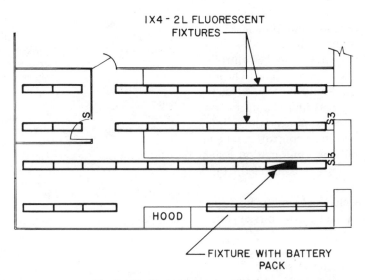

Fig. 5.4-11. Typical laboratory lighting.

needed, since all fumehoods have internal lighting and since ambient light from elsewhere in the lab area provides an adequate amount of light in front of the hood.

Emergency lighting within a lab is not required by any codes. However, good practice provides at least one fixture near an exit, with an emergency battery pack and independent of the switched lights within the lab. This fixture also serves as a night light for security purposes.

5.4.3 Coordination with Other Systems

Coordination of the electrical system with other systems in a laboratory facility is critical. Making sure that the correct mechanical system is connected to the correct electrical distribution system is very important for proper function of the system.

Certain owner-furnished systems and equipment may require a separate electrical system. Examples include all refrigerators and freezers in equipment or instrument rooms and selected pieces of equipment in laboratory spaces.

Architectural elements within a laboratory facility are the most challenging to coordinate electrically. Location of motors for doors and controls, projection screens, interlocked areas (air locks), kitchenette areas and special lighting are sometimes required.

5.4.4 Cogeneration

A cogeneration system for a facility must be looked at in terms of both thermal and electrical loads in order to optimize the efficiency of the system and be economically justified.

Electrically, the system has to be carefully coordinated with the local electrical utility. The utility generally requires extra relays and controls to prevent feedback into their network and paralleling with the utility services.

Once the utility company's requirements are met, the next step is to meet local environmental requirements for noise and emissions.

Size selection of a cogeneration system capacity does not normally exceed the base load for the site, i.e., off-peak demand. Also, the thermal side of the system has to be reviewed to make optimum use of the heat output.

Generally, the electrical side can be utilized as a load-shedding base. The thermal capacity is the deciding factor in determining the cogeneration plant's size.

5.4.5 Maintenance and Operation

The electrical design and layout of systems should be carefully coordinated with all other trades.

In a mechanical area, an aisle should be provided to an outside access point in order to replace any piece of equipment. The largest electrical piece of equipment (or component) is generally smaller than most mechanical components. Therefore, if the mechanical designer has allowed access for his equipment, the electrician need only get from his area to the mechanical access aisle.

The electrical distribution system should be designed for flexibility, so that maintenance can be performed on any component with minimal interruption to the facility.

On emergency systems, automatic transfer switches should be provided with an isolation bypass switch which enables the load to be switched to a preselected source. The transfer switch mechanism can be withdrawn and serviced or replaced, with no interruption in service.

Operation of the electrical distribution system should be as simple as practical, while maintaining a safe and reliable system. In an electrical distribution system with multiple power sources, extreme care should be taken to prevent cross-connection between systems. Provide safety switches, breakers or transfer switches in a foolproof manner to prevent this from happening.

5.4.6 Electrical Construction Costs

In general, electrical costs for a lab project are approximately 11% of the total cost, or about $20/sq ft based on 1987 prices. Factors that add to this cost are special systems, site distribution, size and type of emergency systems, amount of redundancy within the system, and proprietary manufacturers of equipment.

The proprietary manufacturer or the only one named (no alternates accepted) is generally used on existing sites. The owner generally does not want to bring in new manufacturers because this adds to his inventory of replacement parts. This proprietary manufacturer also has no competition during bidding and, in some cases, may not provide a competitive bid.

REFERENCES

Illuminating Engineering Society of North America, 1984. IES *Lighting Handbook*. NY.
Illuminating Engineering Society of North America, 1987. IES Application Volume. NY.

5.5 ELECTRONIC INFRASTRUCTURE
A. Lyons

5.5.1 General

The electronic infrastructure is an integral part of today's modern laboratory. The comfort, productivity and, most important, safety of laboratory occupants depend upon the ability of the electronic infrastructure to support the needs of the lab.

The electronic infrastructure consists of:

- Voice communication systems
- Data communications systems
- Monitoring systems
- Control systems
- Cabling (i.e., cable plant) required to support the above systems

Design coordination of the electronic components and infrastructure can result in considerable cost savings, increased operating efficiency, improved flexibility and enhanced reliability. For example, the voice communications system can provide redundant data links for monitoring/control transmissions.

5.5.2 Communication

Cable Plant

The cable plant (i.e., the set of communications and control cables and wires that interconnect these systems) is the most critical part of the laboratory's electronic infrastructure. When properly designed and documented, a cable plant can remain useful long after the originally supported systems are obsolete. Obsolete electronic components are easily removed and replaced with components incorporating the latest technologies, but the replacement of the hidden communications cables interconnecting these components is both time-consuming and expensive. Many direct and indirect costs (labor, material, downtime, etc.) are associated with upgrading (or replacing) a laboratory's electronic infrastructure to support the latest technologies.

The cable plant built into today's modern laboratory must frequently support a combination of proprietary (single-vendor) and open (multivendor) communications networks. Often it must also support both administrative and scientific needs.

In order to determine the communications requirements of all present and future occupants of a laboratory, a communications design professional should be involved in the early stages of design programming. Meetings with representatives of the occupant's administrative and scientific communication groups must be held to help obtain an overview of their communications requirements and systems currently in use.

All current, planned and future systems should be identified by the engineer to determine whether a common communications medium can be used to integrate several different vendors' systems. Systems can become more expensive and difficult to replace when the many different proprietary cables and connectors frequently specified by vendors are used.

With careful analysis, the communications design professional can develop a uniform cable plant standard for each area type which can satisfy 70 to 90% of the communications requirement of most laboratories. The remaining 10 to 30% (see Figure 5.5-1) can then be satisfied with additional drops.

Specifically, after the optimal communications medium to meet the user's needs and budget is selected, cable plant standard designs are developed and documented. Although a universal cabling system standard is always desirable, the unique requirements of each laboratory often demand some customization, typically in the form of cable drops added to satisfy the unique needs of the occupants.

The use of uniform design standards reduces costs and improves efficiency by simplifying the operation. These advantages are also realized in a standardized modular communications closet design. Typically, at least one closet is required per floor. The number of systems and applications that these closets must support necessitates standardization in order to reduce design and installation costs and shorten installation time. Furthermore, maintenance is improved when personnel develop a quicker and more thorough understanding of a consistent system layout. Finally, modular flexibility reduces the effort of expansion and/or retrofit and increases the likelihood that the electronic infrastructure will be capable of supporting future systems and technologies. Design standardization includes termination panels and the interconnecting "backbones" to these closets.

Voice Communications Systems

Voice and analog data are frequently transmitted from wall- or bench-mounted telephone/analog receptacles in the lab to the

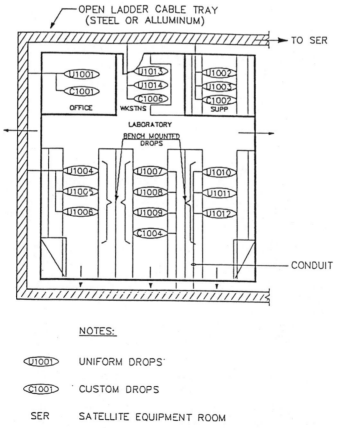

NOTES:

⊲U1001▷   UNIFORM DROPS

⊲C1001▷   CUSTOM DROPS

SER   SATELLITE EQUIPMENT ROOM

Fig. 5.5-1. Data and telephone/communications systems in a laboratory.

telephone room via 22-gauge telephone cables.

These cables are terminated at "horizontal" intermediate distribution frames (IDFs). Vertical IDFs interconnect analog communications risers to the central telephone room of the facility. Cross-connects between vertical and horizontal IDFs depend on users' needs and are usually provided by a telecommunications vendor. As a general rule, telephone cables are run separately from data cables.

Data Communications Systems

A local area network (LAN) is a data communications system with high-speed communications channels to interconnect processing equipment. A variety of transmission speeds and performance characteristics are available for LAN designs that can be based on the specific needs of a user.

Ethernet is a high-speed LAN which is frequently able to support most scientific data communication applications. Ethernet networks provide high-speed access to data in remote locations and can be implemented on baseband (coaxial) or broadband (CATV) cable systems.

In baseband Ethernet, a single network cable (coaxial backbone) replaces the numerous interconnecting cables in traditional data networks. Baseband Ethernet is recommended for scientific environments, particularly where a high density of users (labs) are distributed throughout the building.

Broadband Ethernet LANS combine Ethernet with video, voice and other data communications on a single network wiring system. However, the cost of the modems and the other electronic equipment required to get on a broadband Ethernet is greater than the cost of the transceivers required to get on a baseband Ethernet; therefore, it may not be cost effective for a high density of users. Often the most effective copper-based Ethernet architecture consists of a combination of broadband and baseband systems. The broadband system is used to interconnect islands of high-density users where baseband

is the most effective system. (See Figure 5.5-2).

Ethernet products support the IEEE 802.3 LAN standard. The basic method for accessing the baseband or broadband Ethernet channel is called "carrier sense multiple access with collision detection (CSMA/CD)." Carrier sense (CS) delays transmission until a clear channel is available or selects an unoccupied channel; multiple access (MA) allows equal access for all users to the cleared channels; and collision detection (CD) prevents transmission if two users use the same channel at the same time. Data are automatically retransmitted after a selected period of time.

Both broadband and baseband Ethernet LANs have limitations in terms of the:

- Length of the Ethernet backbone
- Quality of transceivers
- Length of transceiver cables
- Quantity of repeaters
- Distance between transceivers and repeaters

These limitations make it difficult to implement a uniform cabling system with a coaxial cable-based Ethernet.

Recently, several manufacturers have developed systems which allow Ethernet communications over twisted pairs and/or fiber-optic media. These systems should be configured so that the low-cost twisted-pair cabling is used to connect users to communication rooms (where equipment is used to convert the signals from copper twisted-pair media to fiberoptic media) and fiber is used for communications between communication rooms and between buildings.

Using twisted-pair and fiberoptic media for Ethernets and other LANs has several advantages over conventional coaxial cable copper media:

- Twisted-pair and fiberoptic media are readily and cost-effectively incorporated into uniform cabling systems.
- These systems are easily reconfigured to

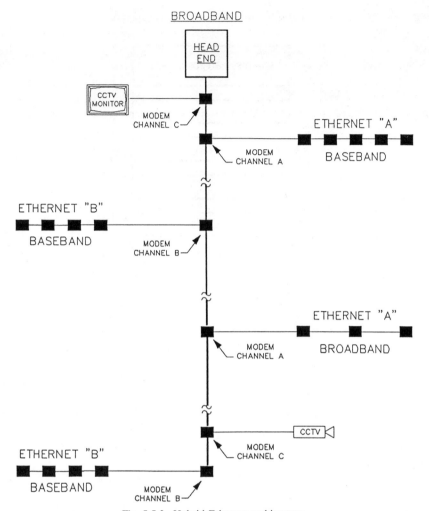

Fig. 5.5-2. Hybrid Ethernet architecture.

incorporate new technologies and re-cover from system failures.

- Fiber is immune to the electromagnetic interference (EMI) and radiofrequency interference (RFI) emitted from sophisticated scientific equipment such as magnetic resonance imaging (MRI) machines.

In addition to the above advantages, utilizing fiber for the communications backbone helps to ensure that the electronic infrastructure built into the modern laboratory will be able to support future generations of scientific equipment.

To facilitate the adoption of future technologies and maintenance of the original systems, the fiber backbone interconnecting the communications rooms should be terminated at a fiber patch panel located in a 19-in. rack in each communications room. The rack should be designed with adequate space for both the electronics and the patch panels required to connect the cables from the work stations to the system. See Figure 5.5-3.

Audiovisual Systems

The audiovisual facility's objective is to provide audiovisual support for training of lab-

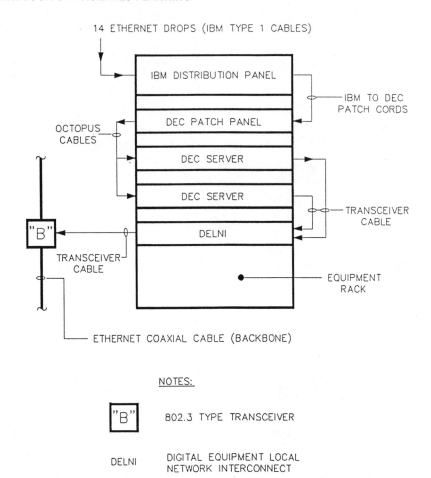

Fig. 5.5-3. Ethernet communications system equipment rack.

oratory personnel. Multimedia presentations are the most efficient way to conduct seminars in training rooms and meetings in board rooms.

An especially attractive and comprehensive audiovisual form of presentation is the projection of computer data (ordinarily displayed on a cathode ray tube at an individual's desk) on a big screen of an audiovisual communication system. This presentation surpasses most other forms of communication between instructors and trainees and is particularly useful in training technical personnel in the use of new, sophisticated, computer-based equipment.

Among the considerations affecting the desired picture and sound quality of an audiovisual facility are distance requirements, optics quality, illumination factors, acoustical characteristics, architecture, and screen, speaker and amplifier qualities.

Depending on the user's needs, audiovisual systems can be front or rear projection types, consisting of the following equipment:

• 35mm slide projectors
• Audiotape recorders/players
• Videotape recorders/players (1/2-in. VHS, 3/4-in. VHS, U-matic)
• 16mm movie projectors
• Overhead projectors
• Video projectors
• Amplifiers
• Preamplifiers
• Mixers

- Microphones
- Speakers
- Intercoms
- Control panels
- Teleconferencing bridges
- Speech enhancement system
- Video monitors

See Figures 5.5-4 through 5.5-7.

5.5.3 Instrumentation and Control

Sophisticated laboratory environments can approach the technical demands of elaborate process control. Temperature, humidity, and air pressure requirements can exceed some commercial direct digital controller (DDC) capabilities. Additionally, many types of equipment frequently interact within a common control loop.

A common example in laboratory design utilizes airflow to maintain precise static pressure gradients between clean and dirty spaces and to control temperature and humidity levels. This flow of air may be affected by modulating levels of fumehood exhaust and by possibly isolated high-pressure zones which require more refined sources of airflow. Control is extended to supply airflow, exhaust airflow, the supply fan speed, the exhaust fan speed, the temperature and humidity of the discharge air. Each of these outputs is adjusted to maintain the tight specifications of the environment, and all must compensate for any change. Many labs require different operation sequences for different tasks. All labs require complicated emergency operations.

Clearly, these systems demand an expertise beyond that of most commercial control installations. As a minimum, vendors must be required to provide control devices which can fully interact with a common system to coordinate operation.

Monitoring Systems

General Considerations. New regulatory requirements have made laboratory occupants

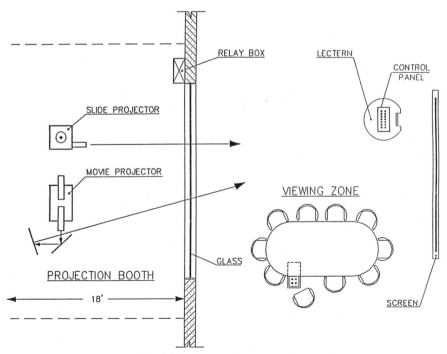

Fig. 5.5-4. Front-projection system.

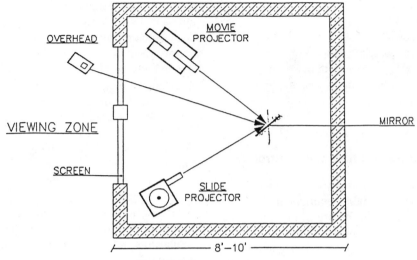

Fig. 5.5-5. Rear-projection system.

some of the first to adopt new technologies to satisfy their monitoring needs. These fall into the following categories:

- Animal room environmental monitoring systems.
- Chemical tracking systems.
- Mechanical alarms.

Animal Room Environmental Monitoring Systems. Monitoring systems are usually integrated into automatic watering and access control system packages, allowing environmental conditions such as temperature, humidity and airflow to be monitored along with automatic watering and trough flush systems. These integrated systems are stand-alone, microprocessor-based systems connected to a central computer for historical log storage and central monitoring, and typically cannot be connected to a building management system by another vendor. Frequently, redundant sensors are monitored by the building management system, resulting in an inefficient use of equipment.

Chemical Tracking System. One technique for improving safety and security in labora-

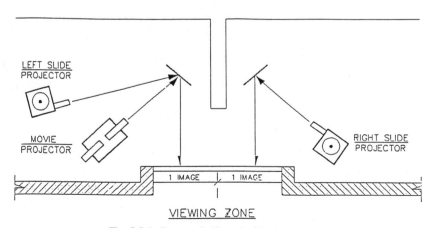

Fig. 5.5-6. Rear-projection, dual-image system.

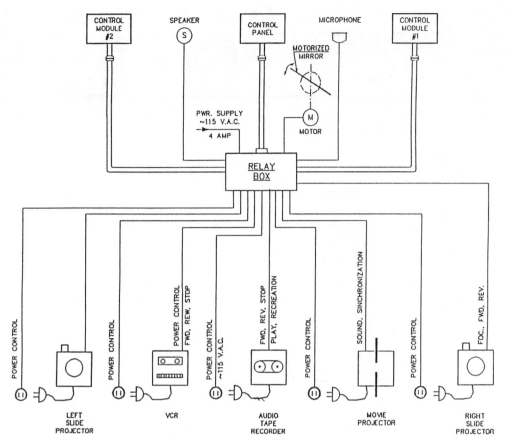

Fig. 5.5-7. Block diagram of AV-COM systems—remote control.

tories utilizes monitoring systems to control the locations of hazardous chemicals and controlled substances around the facility. These chemical tracking techniques ensure that hazardous and controlled materials are confined to areas where safety and security operations are adequate for their use and storage. Bar code labels have been established as an efficient and inexpensive system for material monitoring and control.

The labels used in this operation encode information about chemical type, quantity, toxicity, flammability, security rating and other qualities needed for a material control. This information is written into a standard form of parallel lines whose relative thicknesses are distinguished by bar-code readers. The readers may be contact or noncontact types attached to "satellite wand stations" located at strategic control points through-

out the laboratory complex. The satellite wand stations contain microprocessors for decoding and are linked to the data communications network. Once the information collected by these stations is organized and stored in a central processing unit database, it is available for use by the laboratory's material control personnel. See Figure 5.5-8.

Environmental Alarms. Laboratories, clean rooms and environmental rooms ordinarily require constant control of the following air-quality factors: temperature, humidity, airflow and particle contamination. Sensitive experiments usually impose very tight restrictions on these factors. A reliable system is needed to distinguish an undesirable condition quickly and report an alarm to the shift supervisor. Additionally, when hazardous processes or chemicals are used, sensors are

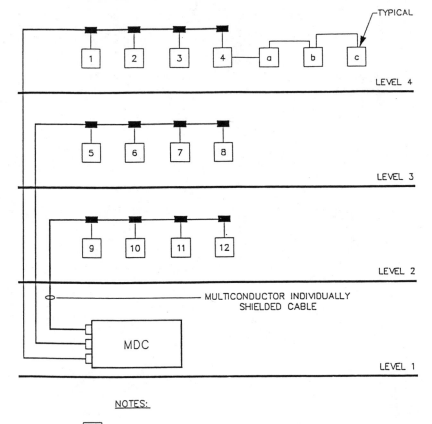

NOTES:

1	BAR CODE TERMINAL
a	BAR CODE SATELLITE WAND STATION
MDC	MULTIDROP CONCENTRATOR
■	SPLICE

Fig. 5.5-8. Chemical tracking system.

needed to alert a response should these chemicals be spilled.

Alarm systems are broken into three components critically selected for their respective tasks. The first segment in the communications link consists of the field sensors, which require maximum sensitivity and accuracy. The sensors transmit signals for decoding, interpretation and retransmission by remote processing units—intermediate devices selected primarily for reliability. The final segment is termination at the human-machine interface. Here essential information must be conveyed clearly and in an un-complicated form; shift supervisors need simple, decisive and thorough directions for a quick and adequate response.

Control Systems

General Considerations. Often new OSHA and NFPA regulations for laboratory facilities can be most efficiently satisfied with state-of-the-art control-system technology. Today all major control system vendors offer direct digital stand-alone microprocessor systems. These microprocessor systems, further enhanced with industrial-grade analog sensors and transmitters, offer one control option that produces one of the safest and most comfortable environments for the laboratory occupant to work.

DDC systems are microprocessor-based systems that accurately control dampers, valves and other mechanical equipment directly, without the need for conventional pneumatic valve and damper control systems. While electronic operators with adequate torque to modulate the terminal unit (VAV boxes, reheat, etc.) have been introduced and are cost effective, pneumatic operators are still used for air-handling systems. This is because much more torque is required to position large air-handling unit dampers and control valves, and the industry has yet to develop cost-effective, reliable electronic operators with adequate torque for these applications.

These systems replace conventional mechanical or electromechanical HVAC control systems with a single piece of equipment capable of performing control, energy management and system diagnostic functions, as well as providing direct compatibility with extension to a centralized computer network. A DDC unit accepts analog and digital input directly from remote sensors, processes the data and directly controls remote mechanical equipment. Therefore, DDC systems offer more accurate control, reducing the drift, maintenance and recalibration problems common with pneumatic control systems.

Control Theory. The computer revolution has had a great impact on the control industry. Modern DDC utilizes the microprocessor and communication technologies developed during the last 20 years. Previously, pneumatic and electronic signals drove the control process and effected a counterbalance using a complex network of hardware, a cumbersome application which could not support the sophisticated control sequences currently used in laboratories. As discussed below, DDC technology has greatly improved the safety and efficiency of laboratory environments. Installed with pneumatic

valve and damper operators, DDC systems combine powerful control capabilities and inexpensive, reliable operation.

Basically, all control algorithms are a combination of three constituent control calculations: proportional, integral and derivative. Error (or offset) signals, the difference between the controlled medium and the desired set point, are the essential variables in these calculations. The error signal integrated with time is the driving force in integral control systems, and the derivative of the error signal by time is the driving force in derivative control systems.

Proportional control signals vary linearly with the error signals. Integral and derivative control signals vary linearly with their integral or derivative factors, respectively. The slopes of these linear functions are the proportional, integral or derivative gain. Gain values are unique to every control loop. The determination of optimal gains, those which minimize the system's response time without causing instability, is the most critical segment of control system design.

Proportional, or P, control is a simple and effective control technique. Valve or damper position, the output of the controller, is proportional to the error signal. See Figure 5.5-9. In order for the operator to maintain a required position, a nonzero error signal may be necessary. Unfortunately, P controls are unable to maintain an exact set point. P systems are designed to maintain a control point within a given range. The location of the range is specified by the set point; the width of the range is called the "throttling range." See Figure 5.5-10. Another term used by some vendors is "offset"—the difference between the control point and the set point.

Throttling range is a form of proportional gain. If a selected throttling range is too small, the gain is too large and the controller overreacts, resulting in a form of instability known as "hunting." The valve or damper continuously overshoots between open and closed when the controller responds faster than the medium.

Proportional integral, or PI, control is be-

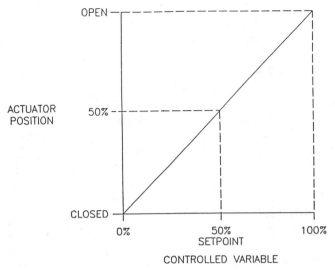

Fig. 5.5-9. Proportional control.

coming more popular because of the ability to maintain an exact set point. Cost and complexity, the major disadvantages of pneumatically performed integration, have been eliminated with DDC technology. Computational methods simplify integration, using an approximation based on repetitive calculation. The more frequent the calculation, the more precise the approximation. The amount of precision is determined by the sampling time between calculations, which is selected to be as small as possible.

The integral signal is simply a total of P calculations multiplied by sampling time. The valve or damper continues to change position unless offset and successive P calculations equal zero. PI control calculates an initial position based on the error signal. Successive calculations are based on previous offsets. These combined calculations

continue to refine the operator's position until the offset equals zero. See Figure 5.5-11.

PID control combines a PI control signal with derivative (D) control. D control is also referred to as "rate control"; the controller responds to reduce the rate of change. Most thermal systems have a small rate of change. Space temperature, return air temperature and mixed air temperatures change very slowly and require nothing to reduce their rates. Discharge air temperature should change quickly when needed and does not benefit from D control.

On the other hand, a static pressure system changes very quickly. A clean room begins to depressurize immediately if a door is opened or a fumehood is started. A D controller monitoring this static pressure will respond immediately, while the P control signal changes slowly after a noticeable change

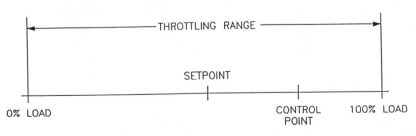

Fig. 5.5-10. Proportional control.

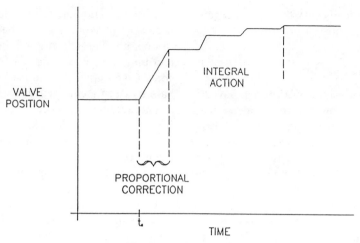

Fig. 5.5-11. PI control.

in the static pressure is detected; I control is the slowest of all. The D constituent is most significant in the initial seconds after a disturbance in order to speed up the controller's response. See Figure 5.5-12.

When safety depends on the control systems of a laboratory environment, PID control will eliminate the dangers caused by a slow response. In these critical applications, the control system must be designed carefully. Because PID utilizes three dimensions of control, these systems have three times the

potential to become unstable. A control loop consists of many components, and each of the following must be carefully selected for response, accuracy and reliability: sensors, sensor locations, transmitters, controllers, transducers, transmission media (particularly pneumatic tubing) and operators. Additionally, the precision of the controller, as measured by the sampling time, must be evaluated to ensure a fast, stable system.

Recently, some vendors have developed "adaptive" control algorithms. these algo-

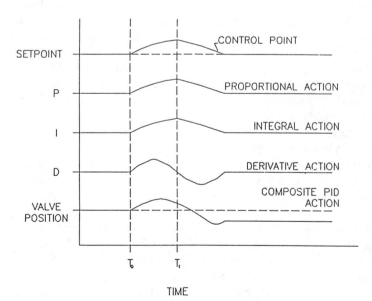

Fig. 5.5-12. Derivative action.

rithms automatically vary the PI and D gains as required to control a process.

Central HVAC Systems

Recently, advances in HVAC design have enabled laboratory owners to install systems which provide critical ventilation at greatly reduced costs. These advances reduce energy consumption by minimizing the exhaust flow of conditioned air and maximizing heat transfer between the exhaust air and the incoming makeup air.

Modern fumehood designs account for many of the advantages realized in today's systems. New fumehoods incorporate an adjustable sash to isolate the protected bench space from the atmosphere inside the workrooms. The hood fans exhaust only the air needed to maintain a safe air velocity across the sash opening. By lowering the sash position, a smaller airflow is needed to maintain a constant velocity. A reduction in this exhausted air yields a reduction in the energy used to condition makeup air.

Another advantage of velocity control lies in the much smaller probability of contaminants escaping from the hood. However, a variable exhaust flow necessitates a sophisticated control system to vary the flow of makeup air. The control process is further complicated by the negative pressurization required in laboratories to reduce the possibility of building contamination.

Systems designed to control the ambient static pressure needed to maintain gradients between clean and dirty areas require sophisticated automatic controls. Static pressure is highly volatile; static pressure control systems must respond quickly to even small disturbances such as those caused by an opened door. PID control is particularly well suited to this application. The previous section explains PID in detail.

An additional criterion of laboratory HVAC design is emergency operation. Equipment failures are little more than a nuisance in most commercial installations but can be life-threatening when potential contamination is involved. Backup equipment is not enough. A reliable processor is necessary to command the backup systems to operate. The selection of the control system hinges on two major factors: ability to control a complex mechanical system and reliability during emergency circumstances.

The airflow diagram shown in Figure 5.5-13 illustrates the scope required of a DDC system. This figure indicates the media monitored and the locations of sensors, as well as controlling devices and safety mechanisms. Multiple supply and exhaust fans are utilized in this design to minimize the effects of a single failure. Another technique uses bypass dampers to integrate into another system when a failure occurs. In either case, the safety of laboratory occupants is enhanced by providing a minimum flow of air during an emergency.

Terminal Unit Control.   State-of-the-art control technology continues to improve laboratory safety and efficiency. Solid-state airflow sensors and controllers recently introduced by terminal box and fumehood manufacturers offer considerable advantages over the more conventional pneumatic devices. A substantial advantage is realized in calibration and maintenance, but an even greater advantage lies in the accuracy and reliability of the device. Pneumatic airflow sensors typically lose accuracy at 25% of their span, resulting in a 4:1 turndown ratio. Capitalizing on the energy-savings opportunity offered by variable air volume (VAV) hoods typically requires an approximately 8:1 turndown ratio. The solid-state (or industrial-grade) sensors used in such sensitive low-flow applications provide the requisite precise airflow control.

Many terminal box manufacturers offer an integrated package combining sensors, a controller and an operator. The controller is microprocessor based and has the advantages of a stand-alone programmable logic controller (PLC); control does not depend on the reliability of (or communication with) a central processor. With proper coordination, the terminal box and fumehood manufacturers are encouraged to provide sensors

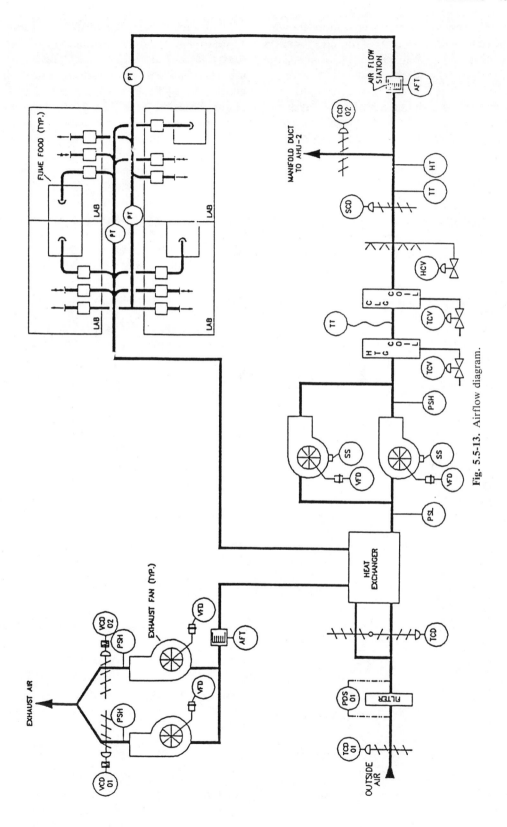

Fig. 5.5-13. Airflow diagram.

and/or controllers which communicate with the central DDC system. If this coordination is initiated early in the design process, the owner can avoid the installation, maintenance costs and operational complexities associated with redundant monitoring systems. The selection of PLC versus DDC control of terminal boxes and fumehoods depends on many criteria. Figures 5.5-14 and 5.5-15 show the installation of both systems.

5.5.4 Fire Alarm Systems

The sophistication of modern laboratories requires sophisticated fire protection systems to protect equipment and enhance occupant safety.

While most laboratories are fully sprinklered, these systems should often be supplemented with smoke detection systems to pro-

vide an earlier warning of fire. Recently, several manufacturers have developed "addressable" fire alarm systems. These systems are able to identify not only the zone in alarm, but also the individual device in an alarm or trouble condition. Thus, these systems not only advise occupants of alarm conditions but also identify the exact location of the alarm condition. This allows the fire brigade to respond more rapidly, minimizing the damage and disruption to scientific research caused by the trouble.

When integrated with other electronic systems, addressable fire alarm systems can further enhance the safety of laboratory occupants and fire-fighting personnel. For example, integrating the fire alarm system and the chemical-tracking system can generate alarm messages advising fire-fighting personnel of the chemicals present in the laboratory where the alarm condition exists.

5.5.5 Security Systems

Laboratories also often need security systems to protect companies from industrial espionage and possibly to protect occupants from terrorist acts. The extent of these systems and their potential integration into the other laboratory electronic systems clearly depend on the location of the laboratory and the type of research conducted.

To determine the scope of the security system, a requirements analysis must be performed. This analysis documents:

- Regulatory requirements
- Potential threats
- Image of occupants
- Philosophy
- What needs to be protected

A good requirements analysis contains all the information needed for the security design professional to determine whether these requirements are best met by:

- Architectural features (doors, walls, fences, etc.)
- A guard force

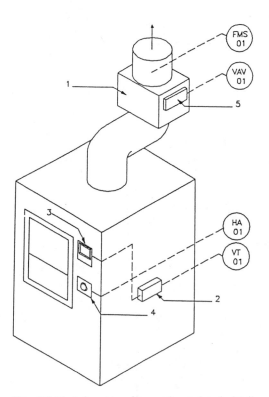

Fig. 5.5-14. Laboratory fume exhaust hood detail. *Note:* (1) exhaust air VAV box; (2) hood velocity sensor; (3) digital face velocity (FPM) display; (4) hood emergency visual/audible alarm (low hood flow); (5) electronic air valve actuator (mounted at factory by box manufacturer).

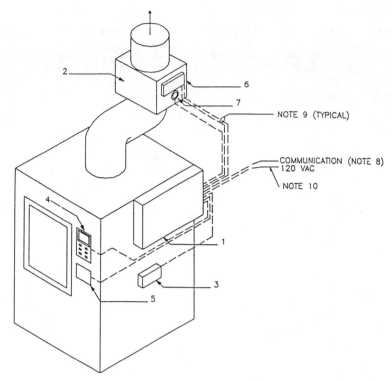

Fig. 5.5-15. Laboratory fume exhaust hood detail. *Note:* (1) PLC controller (mounted at factory by hood manufacturer); (2) exhaust air VAV box; (3) hood velocity sensor (mounted at factory by hood manufacturer; (4) keypad communications unit (mounted at factory by hood manufacturer); (5) hood emergency module (mounted at factory by hood manufacturer); (6) electronic air valve actuator (mounted at factory by box manufacturer); (7) differential pressure transmitter; (8) twisted pair to lab and office pressure controllers; (9) typical low voltage wiring (twisted pair); (10) line voltage wiring from junction box mounted and wired at factory by hood manufacturer.

- Electronic monitoring and control systems
- A combination of the above

Generally, the security requirements of most research facilities are such that a combination of all of these systems is required.

Electronic monitoring and control systems include intrusion detection (motion detectors, door monitor switches, etc.), access control systems (card access, cypher locks, etc.), watch tour systems, paging systems, scream alarm systems, intercom systems, two-way radio systems, and closed circuit television systems. It is important that the design professional be familiar with all of these systems and cognizant of the unique security requirements of the facility.

6

Energy Conservation

6.1 INTRODUCTION
N. Nelson

One of the greatest challenges facing building system design consultants is that of designing safe, energy-efficient, cost-effective laboratory environmental control systems—the energized and nonenergized systems that interact within a laboratory facility to provide the necessary environment for myriad research, development, or production purposes. The energized systems referred to herein are the fans, pumps, chillers, boilers, etc. that are "energized" in order to provide the function intended. Nonenergized systems are those that passively or actively influence the use of energized systems (the building occupants, thermal envelope, etc.). Both systems are a vital part of an energy conservation and management plan. However, this section concentrates on the energized systems, leaving the nonenergized systems to the other energy management textbooks that are available from the applicable engineering societies.

This chapter is concerned with the energized systems and how energy conservation considerations should be applied to laboratory energy systems—in particular, the reduction of energy and the recovery of energy through good design practice for new or retrofit energy-using systems.

One commonly misused term is "energy consumption." Energy is not consumed. In fact, the law of conservation of energy states that energy can only be changed from a higher to a lower level; it cannot be destroyed. Therefore, the term "energy use" will be used in this chapter.

The primary energy conservation opportunities in a laboratory building can be further categorized as those associated with building loads, distribution loads and primary equipment loads.

Building loads are influenced by the building envelope, the climatic conditions and the occupancy patterns of the building. A brief look at the typical energy use profile of a laboratory is of benefit when trying to decide where energy is used. Figure 6.1-1 is an energy use pie chart of a research laboratory located in the Pacific Northwest. The building area is about 120,000 sq ft, and the local climate has 4,750 heating degree days per year.

Building loads are an important part of the total energy use of the facility, but they represent only a small percentage (10%) of the total facility's energy use. A detailed discussion of this issue will therefore not be presented here. However, the issues of site orientation, local climatic conditions, solar gain and heat loss need adequate attention during the early stages of a new design or retrofit application.

Figure 6.1-1 shows that most of the energy use is attributable to the heating and cooling of ventilation air. This will be a major source of discussion in energy use reduction and recovery.

6.2 REDUCING ENERGY USE
N. Nelson

As mentioned, building load energy reduction will not be addressed here. The local climate is a given, and prudent design considerations of fenestration areas, the thermal envelope and site orientation will help keep the energy use impact of these systems to a minimum. Selection of internal environmental design conditions (i.e., temperature, relative humidity, etc.) will also require close scrutiny in order to minimize energy use.

6.2.1 Distribution System Loads

Distribution system loads are typically referred to as "parasitic" loads because they do not directly affect space environmental or comfort conditions for the occupant. They consist of the energy loss or gain in convey-

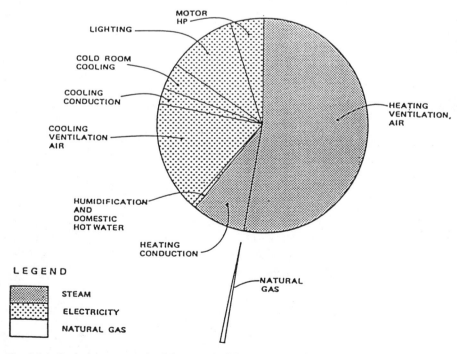

Fig. 6.1-1. Typical energy use for laboratory building (120,000 gsf; location: Northwestern United States).

ing fluids (air and water) from primary equipment (air handlers, boilers, chillers) to their intended point of use. The loads may be in the form of energy input to pumps and air handlers, or energy loss or gain from the distribution system (pipe or duct). The major distribution systems in a laboratory are:

- Air handling
- Heating/chilled/condenser water
- Domestic hot water
- Power distribution
- Special laboratory systems

The principle way to save energy in any energized system is to turn the system off. This will result, in most cases, in the largest amount of energy savings because energy is not needed. In some cases, it may not reduce the overall energy use. For instance, thermal energy storage systems lose energy to the environment when they are off. The energy is lost to the ground, to adjacent spaces or through the distribution systems, and the lost energy must be replaced. In general, turning systems off by automatic means is the best method of saving energy. For distribution systems, this is especialy true. Additional methods for reducing energy use in the distribution systems will be discussed next.

6.2.2 Air-Handling Systems

Air-handling systems, which include the laboratory's ventilations system, are one of the largest sources of energy use in a laboratory facility. Therefore, considerable discussion will focus on reducing the ventilation system's energy use.

The role of the ventilation system is to provide adequate dilution and exhaust of contaminants that may be present in the working environment. Contaminants may include those resulting from the laboratory processes that are taking place or from the materials and methods used to construct the building. In most cases, the latter is of less concern. The purpose of providing ventilation air is to protect the lab worker. Lab ventilation systems often require the use of

fumehoods, biological safety cabinets, laminar flow hoods, canopy hoods and other types of special equipment to improve worker protection or to meet the functional needs of the work (e.g., providing dust-free work areas). Equipment needs are more thoroughly discussed in Chapter 4, and systems are discussed in Chapter 5. Most important, the requirement for worker safety must never be compromised to achieve energy conservation.

As previously mentioned, turning systems off will save the largest amount of energy. In the case of ventilation systems, this may be difficult, undesirable or impossible, depending on the characteristics of the lab operations. If possible, one should organize the systems in such a way that only the smallest number of systems must remain active continuously. For example, the fume exhaust systems of most labs are used for research only during the day. At night and on weekends, they may not be required to operate. If a particular type of project or experiment must be continuously operated, one should provide a separate system for this area, keeping the needed systems to an absolute minimum. Laboratories have been designed and operated so that all of their major heating, ventilating and air conditioning systems are operated only during the hours of lab occupation. This is not under the control of the designer, but it must be discussed with the building owner and the lab user and a decision made with the full knowledge of all parties. It will have a significant impact on the energy use and operating cost of the facility.

If the ventilation system cannot be turned off, the next best approach is to reduce the airflow to the minimum required at all times. In the past, the airflow through laboratories was set at constant supply air and exhaust air volumes in order to ensure that the room remained at the desired temperature, humidity and pressure (relative to an adjacent space). A simple schematic diagram of this approach is shown in Figure 6.2-1. The amount of supply air is set at a relatively high rate of 10 to 12 air changes per hour in order to satisfy the dilution requirements, to

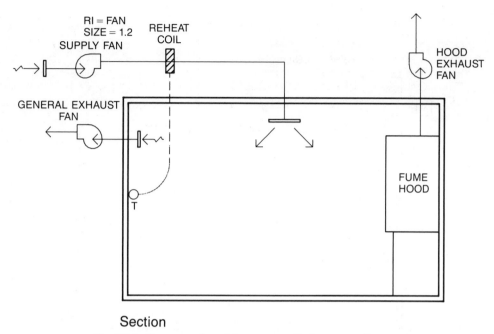

Section

Fig. 6.2-1. Constant-volume laboratory ventilation system diagram.

handle the high heat gain dissipated into the lab space, and to provide makeup air for the air exhausted through fume and canopy hoods. Normal fumehood maintenance at annual or semiannual intervals requires testing for proper supply and exhaust air flows. The system is simple and relatively easy to maintain. The primary disadvantage of this approach is the large amount of energy required to operate this system.

Several attempts have been made to reduce the amount of ventilation air required for exhaust by modifications to the fumehood. This included adding supplemental untempered or tempered (heated only) air directly at the fumehood face or, more recently, reducing the amount of air required for exhaust based upon the fumehood's sash position. The first method, called "add-air hoods," may in fact reduce the overall energy use of the systems, but it may also reduce the reliability of the fumehood in protecting the lab worker. The reason for the lower reliability is that the makeup air fan adds another air control device to the system. If the makeup air fan is not maintained properly, it may reduce the capture effective-

ness of the fumehood by introducing adverse air currents at the fumehood face. In some cases, where waste heat was available or where there was no need to temper the makeup air, this type of hood did result in energy savings.

Most recently, a more innovative concept for lab ventilation and fumehood exhaust systems is the use of the variable air volume (VAV) approach. With this approach, the amount of fumehood exhaust air is allowd to vary as the sash position is open or closed. When the sash is open, the amount of air exhausted is maximum, and when the sash is closed, the amount of air exhausted is minimum. The VAV fumehood concept puts an additional requirement on the space temperature and pressurization control systems. The systems must vary the air volume and temperature to maintain set points. A simple diagram of this system is shown in Figure 6.2-2. Although the initial cost is higher, when properly applied, maintained and operated, this ventilation system will provide the maximum amount of energy savings for the ventilation system by reducing the supply air, makeup air and ventilation air to a mini-

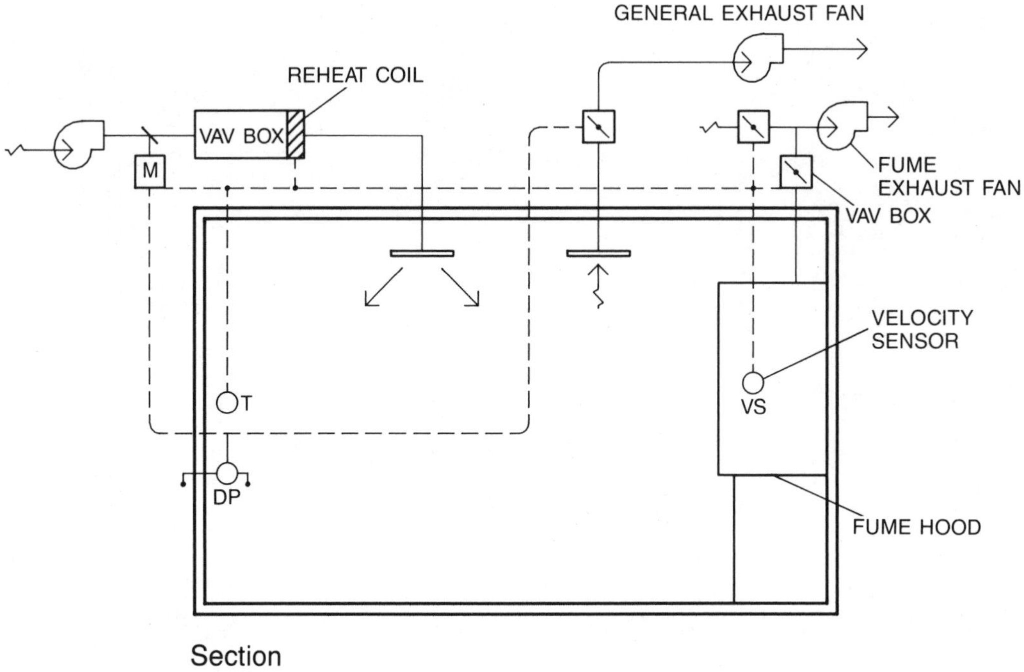

Section

Fig. 6.2-2. VAV laboratory ventilation system diagram.

mum. During off-hour operation, the system should be functioning at its minumum settings if required to function at all.

In addition, the VAV system reduces the airflow for air-handling systems. The ductwork design should be optimized for the least life cycle cost (LCC) for this system. LCC analysis for energy conservation is discussed briefly later in this chapter and in Chapter 8. An LCC analysis will determine the optimum duct size to achieve the smallest amount of energy use while at the same time comparing the cost of construction materials and installation costs. This will require the use of computer software to analyze the effect of changes in duct design parameters and the resultant installation cost changes. A newer method for duct optimization, named the "T-duct method," developed by Dr. Robert J. Tsal (1989), was presented at the 1988 annual meeting of the American Society of Heating, Refrigeration and Air Conditioning Engineers (ASHRAE). This method provides LCC analysis for optimizing duct design in a relatively simple and straight-

forward manner. The calculations can be completed by using a computerized spreadsheet for optimal duct selection.

The next method of reducing energy use in air ducts is to reduce the resistance to airflow by selecting the right filters, coils, and terminal devices and by optimizing the general duct arrangement.

Filters should be selected for the amount of arrestance required with the least amount of pressure drop practical and the minimum initial, maintenance and operating costs. Again, this implies an LCC analysis. The operating cost for filters includes the energy used by fans to overcome the static pressure, operating hours vs. filter life, and labor costs for installation and maintenance. This information is available from fan manufacturers and filter suppliers. An example of the use of this technique is provided in the Architects and Engineers Guide (U.S. Department of Energy, 1980). This guide provides ready nomographs to assist the designer in assessing the impact of energy conservation opportunities. The guide provides step-by-step procedures for completing the analysis. A word of caution to users: The assumptions that have been used to prepare the nomographs may not be applicable to the intended system.

Heating and cooling coils provide considerable resistance to airflow in air distribution systems. The selection of the coils may be optimized by considering the cost of energy for an air handler for the added resistance versus the cost of the installed coil. Several coil manufacturers provide a computerized selection program for optimizing coil sizing. If this is not provided, with the use of a manufacturer's catalog, several coil selections may be completed by hand.

Reduction of energy loss or gain through the air duct system is also accomplished by adding proper insulation to the inside and outside of the duct. The optimal selection of insulation type and thickness can be made through consultation with insulation system manufacturers. They will provide the data necessary to select the insulation thickness and determine the installed cost. This must be compared with the cost of energy that must be added to provide for heat gains or losses from the duct if the insulation is not applied.

6.2.3 Heating/Chilled/Condenser Water Systems

Reducing energy use from heating, chilled, or condenser water distribution systems is very similar to reducing it from the air-handling systems. These methods are:

- Reduce operating hours.
- Reduce water flow.
- Reduce resistance to flow.
- Reduce heat loss or gain.

Reduction of operating hours is the first consideration. Operating hours are normally a function of occupancy loads and outdoor air temperature. Normally, water flow for any system is required whenever ambient outdoor air temperature exceeds a set point for heating or cooling functions to begin and the building is occupied. Turning systems on or off automatically is the preferred method for reducing the hours of operation.

Water flow rates are a function of water temperature and equipment loads. Assuming that the loads are minimized through proper design, the selection of the appropriate water temperature is a function of the heat transfer device, the water temperature rise/drop and the size of piping required. By increasing the total temperature rise/drop of the water system, the water flow is reduced and, consequently, the installation and operating costs are decreased. This reduction has practical limits because of the availability of terminal heat transfer devices. Available information on equipment must be reviewed in order to determine what limiting factors govern the system's selection.

Another method of varying the flow rate is by the use of variable-speed pumps. The flow rate must be varied to match the load on the system. This can be accomplished in a variety of ways. A common method is to provide two-way valves at the terminal devices to control the liquid flow. This, in effect, throttles the flow required by the distribution system to match the load. The flow is reduced to the minimum, and the result is a reduction in the horsepower required to drive the pump. Some systems have used a flow-balancing fitting to reduce the flow by throttling the pump. However, this does not reduce the energy use that will result from reducing the flow through a speed control device.

The resistance to flow may be reduced by the proper selection of terminal devices, the proper design of piping layout or the use of primary-secondary pumping arrangements when the system layout has a remote terminal device or a higher than typical pressure drop. If the system pump must meet a widely variable pressure requirement, it may use less energy to separate the lower-pressure, high-flow-rate primary system pump from the individual secondary loops which require high pressure with lower flow. A simple schematic of the piping arrangement is shown in Figure 6.2-3. Again, an LCC analysis should be

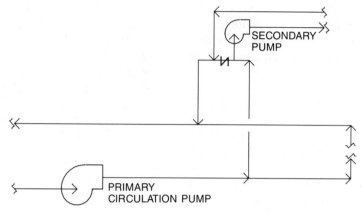

Fig. 6.2-3. Primary-secondary pumping diagram.

completed to compare the two system arrangements.

Heat gains/losses from piping distribution systems are minimized through the selection and application of insulating materials. The optimum thickness of insulation is a function of the installed material costs and operating savings. The insulation manufacturers have the data necessary to complete this type of analysis, based upon the liquid temperature, ambient temperature, hours of operation per year and energy unit cost data. Most manufacturers will provide this analysis for the designer.

6.2.4 Domestic Hot Water Systems

Domestic hot water systems for laboratory buildings do not normally have a significant impact on the total energy budget for a facility. However, some opportunity does exist for reducing energy use. The main methods discussed here are:

- Reduction of heat loss
- Central vs. point-of-use heaters
- Fuel and equipment selection

Heat loss from the system is reduced through the optimal use of piping insulation. This subject was discussed earlier in considering the distribution system.

Many larger laboratory buildings have large domestic hot water distribution systems that consist of heater(s), storage tank(s), distribution piping and a circulation pump(s). A simple diagram of a typical system is shown in Figure 6.2-4. The pump should be controlled by a time clock and a temperature sensor. The time clock allows the pump to operate according to the schedule set on the clock, and the temperature sensor located in the return line energizes the pump when the water temperature drops below the set point. The system provides a single-temperature hot domestic water supply for the various users.

In contrast to the central system, the point-of-use system provides a supply of hot water where needed. This type of system is normally considered when:

- There is a great distance between points of use.
- The water temperature requirements vary.
- The schedule of water needs varies, so that large systems must remain operating for small hot water demands.

An LCC analysis will allow comparison of installation, operating and maintenance costs.

Many types of domestic water heaters are available. Each type has its own operating efficiency and may use a different fuel type. Electricity, gas, oil, steam, and propane are the primary fuel choices. Each fuel type

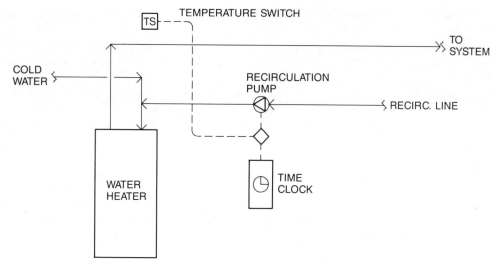

Fig. 6.2-4. Domestic hot water diagram.

source and operating efficiency must be considered for a particular application. The energy conversion efficiencies of the various types of heating devices are listed in ASHRAE Standard 90 (1980). This standard is referenced in or the basis for most energy codes in effect in the United States.

6.2.5 Power Distribution Systems

There are more opportunities to save electrical energy in existing laboratories than in newly designed ones. Existing labs may have poorly designed distribution systems and systems that have been modified extensively since the original installation. Some of the primary ways to save energy are:

- Using the proper voltage.
- Reducing peak demand.
- Using efficient transformers.
- Providing correct motor sizes for various applications.
- Correcting the power factor.

Selecting the proper voltage for power distribution systems is similar to reducing flow resistance in liquid piping systems. This produces lower line losses, which result in more efficient energy use and a subsequent lower operating cost. Using the highest voltage

available may or may not be the appropriate solution to a design problem. An LCC analysis will help to determine the optimum distribution voltage.

The selection of new transformers or the replacement of existing transformers should be made with the highest guaranteed efficiency available. For example, if a dry-type transformer has an efficiency range from 93 to 98%, complete the economic analysis in order to determine the optimal selection.

Electrical utility companies almost everywhere have filed, or are about to file, rate schedules which reflect a demand charge added to the monthly billing process. (That is, they charge the customer either a fixed or a variable amount for each kilowatt [KW] that the customer requires from the utility system during the peak period.) Therefore, efforts to limit the maximum KW demand for a facility during the peak time can result in significant cost and energy savings. In order to determine the effect of limiting the KW power draw, it is necessary to look at each specific case and not to generalize.

Motor selections should be made in accordance with the needs of the project. The motor must perform the intended function without exceeding the nameplate rating. If a selected motor is considerably oversized, the motor's operating efficiency and the distribution system's power factor can be greatly affected. The result is a decrease in the facility power factor, which typically means a higher cost for electricity due to the reactive power which the utility company must provide to correct the power factor.

Power factor is a function of the amount of reactive power required to offset the lack of efficiency in transmitting the real power required in a motor from the serving utility company. A facility power factor of unity (1.0) is desired. The power factor below which a utility may penalize the user varies but normally occurs with values between 0.80 and 0.90. If the facility power factor is less than the penalty value, the user is assessed an additional charge for the entire billing period. In order to maintain a power factor of at least 0.80, motors should be selected to operate above 80% of their full load rating.

Another factor in the proper selection of drive motors is the selection and specification of a *high-efficiency* motor in lieu of a standard motor. The motor manufacturers list in their catalogs the minimum guaranteed full load efficiency at which the motor will operate. By comparing the energy saving due to the difference in operating efficiency, a simple economic analysis will determine the time required to offset the higher capital cost for the high-efficiency unit. Motors larger than 1 horsepower that operate for more than 2,500 hours per year, with average energy rates, should be analyzed for energy reduction.

6.2.6 Special Systems

There are many special systems associated with laboratories. These include:

- Special gases (argon, hydrogen, etc.)
- Special liquids (distilled water, etc.)
- Clean rooms
- Environmental chambers
- Cage-washing systems

Each of these special systems offers the lab designer unique and creative opportunities to reduce energy use. For example, the common practice of evaporating liquid nitrogen to obtain dry nitrogen gas requires a lot of energy. This can be a very inefficient process if the gas is to be used for drying or part cleaning. Parts may be cleaned just as effectively using compressed and dried air. The energy and cost savings are dramatic, and the return on the capital investment is very quick.

Cage-washing systems for animal facilities usually require large quantities of heated water. The wastewater that is discharged from these systems is contaminated with detergents, fecal matter and other undesirable components. However, the heat that resides in the waste stream can be recovered through the use of a heat recovery system. Most of these systems use a waste sump to collect the wastewater, which is then pumped through filters and heat exchangers before being discharged to the sewer. The low-grade heat is transferred to the incoming fresh water before it is heated. Typically, these units can reduce the temperature of the wastewater to within 15°F of the temperature of the incoming fresh water. An LCC is required to determine if the installation is cost effective.

The distilled water system for lab use is another special system that needs to be reviewed for energy reduction. The first question that must be addressed is whether distilled water is required. Perhaps another grade of reagent water could be supplied that does not require the heat of vaporization and condensation to produce. A possible alternative is to provide reagent-grade deionized water by using a cartridge filtration system. This does not require heat energy to produce and could result in substantial energy savings to the owner.

In general, it is prudent for the designer to review all energy-using special systems in the building and try to determine what, if anything, can be done to reduce energy use.

6.2.7 Primary Equipment Loads

Primary equipment loads are those loads attributable to the conversion of energy from a purchased fuel to a usable form of heat energy. This conversion process is not 100% efficient and must be considered during the design process in order to determine the best fuel supply for the laboratory.

In most locations, more than one fuel will be available. Therefore, it is vital to complete an LCC analysis in order to determine the optimum selection. Readily available energy sources typically are:

- Natural gas
- Electricity
- Propane
- Fuel oil

In some facilities, such as college campuses, a district (or campus) heating or cooling system may provide heated/chilled water or steam/condensate systems for cooling and heating. But the raw energy source is one of the types listed above. An exception would occur where geothermal, solar or another fuel is the source of choice.

For the purposes of this section, the energy sources considered will use the energy units listed in Table 6.2-1.

The average purchase costs for these energy units will vary considerably, depending on the area of the country. The U.S. Department of Energy publishes a list of the average energy prices for each type of energy, based on the region. In addition, the list includes the expected energy use escalation that will occur over the next 20 years. This list is expected to be used when completing an LCC analysis for federal agencies. For most design purposes, it is an accepted source for energy rates.

It is important to note that the purchased energy units shown in Table 6.2-1 do not have the same amount of useful energy for heating or cooling the facility. Table 6.2-2 compares the useful energy available from each source based upon assumed average costs for each.

Table 6.2-2 does not address the conversion efficiencies of the primary equipment that is required to convert the energy to a usable form. In other words, boilers are used to heat water; chillers or air conditioners are used for cooling; and these devices vary in terms of the usable energy they provide for the intended purpose. Table 6.2-3 shows the useful energy for heating and cooling buildings based upon the end-use energy cost in dollars per million BTU ($/MMBTU).

It is evident from Table 6.2-3 that the differences between fuels can be significant. Therefore, the designer must consider which source will be the best match for the systems required. This can be completed by calculating the cost per MMBTU, similar to Table 6.2-3, for the available fuels and the primary equipment that is being considered. A word of caution regarding the information presented in these tables is appropriate: Verify the energy rate schedules that will be in effect from the serving utilities, and the conversion efficiency of the primary equipment being considered, before making a final selection. The energy costs shown above do not reflect other utility costs such as those for on- or off-peak demand, standby heating requirements, etc.

6.2.8 Selection of Primary Equipment

Based upon the energy costs for the particular location and the fuel conversion effi-

Table 6.2-1. Energy Source Units

Fuel	Purchased Unit	Btu/Unit
Natural gas	Therm	100,000
Electricity	Kilowatt-hour	3,413
Propane	Gallon	91,500
Fuel oil, No. 2	Gallon	140,000
Coal, bituminous	Pound	14,000

Table 6.2-2. Energy Costs (1988 Prices)

Fuel	Unit Cost	$/MMBTU
Natural gas	$0.70	$7.00
Electricity	$0.06	$17.58
Propane	$0.95	$10.38
Fuel oil, No. 2	$1.05	$7.50
Coal, bituminous	$0.10	$7.14

Table 6.2-3. Energy Cost Comparison

Fuel	Efficiency (%)	$/MMBTU
Natural gas, direct	95.0	$7.37
Natural gas, indirect	80.0	$8.75
Natural gas, cooling	12.0	$58.33
Electricity, resistance	100.0	$17.58
Electricity, heat pump	200.0	$8.79
Electricity, cooling	300.0	$5.86
Propane, indirect	80.0	$12.98
Fuel oil, boiler	70.0	$10.71
Coal, boiler	60.0	$12.50

ciency, preliminary selection of the primary equipment can be made. This selection needs to be confirmed after the secondary systems have been considered. The secondary systems involve air distribution, final temperature control devices, ventilation schemes and makeup air requirements. These systems were discussed at length in the section on distribution loads.

In order to determine how to achieve the greatest reduction in energy use, it is necessary to analyze the interaction between the building and the primary/secondary HVAC systems. A simple analysis such as the heating degree day (HDD) method is not appropriate for such a complex engineering problem. The analysis should at least model the systems using the "temperature bin method," developed by ASHRAE. This method uses historical data of annual occurrences, expressed in hours, in which the ambient temperature falls within 5°F "bins." The bins begin at below-zero temperatures and continues in 5°F increments to over 100°F. These data are available from ASHRAE and *Air Force Manual AFM-88*. However, it is better to model the energy systems using a computerized modeling program that simulates the actual operation of the HVAC systems for an entire year of weather data. This will account more accurately for the occupied/unoccupied modes of operation; temperature variation on an hourly basis; and the intersection of the primary and secondary systems. The results should define more realistically the annual energy use compared to that of other meth-

ods. The results of this analysis will be used together with the operation and maintenance costs over the assumed life of the facility in order to determine the optimum system. Neuman (1987) used this methodology for a 200,000-sq ft research laboratory in southern California. He analyzed several specific systems in order to determine the lowest life cycle cost. In this application, the results favored a two-fan, dual-duct system over the other four systems compared, including constant and variable volume systems. This result would not necessarily apply to a laboratory located elsewhere. The designer needs to determine this for the specific arrangement, climate and design criteria for each building.

6.2.9 Primary Equipment

Once the type of primary equipment has been determined, it is necessary to select particular features of the equipment to meet the lab needs and criteria developed. Particular attention should be paid to optimizing the conversion efficiencies.

Boiler energy can also be improved by reducing the losses due to blowdown, flue gas and fuel oil supply temperature, and, most importantly, by selecting the boiler for operation at its highest point on the efficiency curve. Significantly oversized boilers are usually quite wasteful of energy. In fact, most boilers have an operating curve over time that is bell-shaped. See Figure 6.2-5. This figure shows that boilers typically operate at about 50% of their load. Therefore,

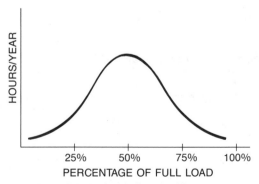

Fig. 6.2-5. Typical boiler operating curve.

the use of one boiler to meet the maximum load requirement would not allow it to operate at its most efficient point. Several boilers must be selected and sized to operate consistently at the high end of their performance curve.

Water chillers require about 0.6 to 1.5 KW per ton of refrigeration, depending on several factors. The two factors which can be controlled are condenser pressure and evaporator pressure. By lowering the condenser (tower water) temperature/pressure, the refrigeration machine efficiency will increase proportionally. This effect is shown in Figure 6.2-6. Similarly, if the evaporator

(chilled water) temperature/pressure is increased, the machine will operate more efficiently. This effect is shown in Figure 6.2-7.

The increase in efficiency is noted on the previous two figures as the percent increase in the coefficient of performance (COP). This term defines the operating efficiency of refrigeration machines. Generally, it is defined as the ratio of the refrigeration effect produced by the machine to the energy input to the machine. The higher the number, the more efficient the refrigeration process. Normally, the COP for a refrigeration machine will be in the range of 2.5 to 3.5, with higher and lower values possible. By lowering the condensing temperature or raising the evaporator temperature, a higher COP (or efficiency) is realized. The higher COP is the result of a more efficient operating point of the refrigeration system.

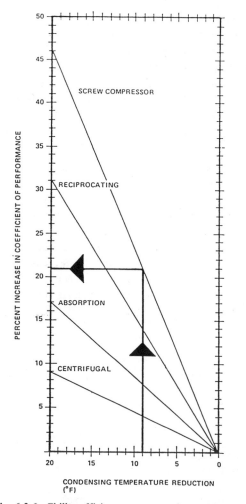

Fig. 6.2-6. Chiller efficiency versus condenser temperature.

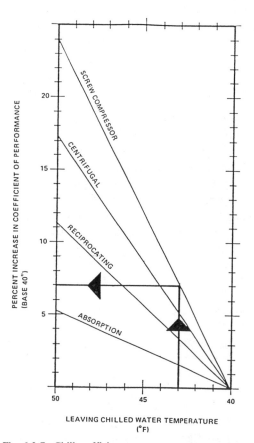

Fig. 6.2-7. Chiller efficiency versus evaporator temperature.

Primary pumping systems, discussed previously, may be designed or modified for reduced energy use by selecting and designing a variable-flow distribution system. This will require modulating control valves that use two-way patterns. A flow or pressure sensor can then be used to modulate the flow of water as the capacity required varies.

There are ways of reducing energy use even further in primary equipment which are not discussed here. Some of them involve the use of heat recovery systems. These systems are the subject of the next section.

6.3 RECOVERY OF ENERGY
N. Nelson

6.3.1 Heat Recovery

Laboratories, in general, are large energy-using facilities. This is especially true if little effort is made to recover heat that would otherwise be wasted. The single most important application of heat recovery will normally occur in the laboratory exhaust and air supply systems. This is the direct result of the large volume of ventilation air required to keep the working environment safe for the occupants. Recovery of exhaust heat to preheat the ventilation air is the most important topic discussed in this section.

Many other opportunities exist for heat recovery from waste streams. Many of these opportunities should be considered in the design of specific laboratories. A list of the other opportunities includes the following:

- Boiler flue gas
- Steam condensate return systems
- Chiller condenser water
- Groundwater or geothermal energy
- Cogeneration systems
- Incinerator systems
- Hot wastewater
- Heat from lights

Most of these opportunities will be discussed in the following paragraphs. However, boiler flue gas recovery and recovery from steam condensate systems are not usually options in a properly designed heating system.

Similarly, the amount of hot wastewater in laboratories and recovery of light heat are of little importance in a well-designed laboratory. These areas will not be discussed here because of the limited recovery of heat energy that may be expected in a well-designed laboratory. Similarly, renovation or retrofit of existing laboratories should minimize the amount of waste heat recoverable from these sources.

6.3.2 Exhaust Air Heat Recovery

Exhaust air heat can be recovered in a variety of ways. The most conventional methods use two basic types of recovery in laboratory facilities:

- Air-to-air heat recovery
- Air-to-water heat recovery

Air-to-air heat recovery provides heat transfer from one air stream (exhaust) to another air stream (supply) without using a liquid for the heat energy to be transferred. As the name implies, air-to-water heat recovery uses a liquid as part of the heat transfer system.

6.3.3 Plate-Type Recovery Devices

Several manufacturers offer plate-type air-to-air heat exchange devices. These consist of thin metallic sheets, either flat or embossed, which separate the air stream into thin "slices" of air in order to increase the effectiveness of heat transfer. A schematic of this type of heat recovery device is shown in Figure 6.3-1. These recovery devices have the following features:

- Heat transfer effectiveness of 60 to 75%
- Air pressure drop between 0.75 and 1.25 in. water gauge
- Sensible heat transfer only

These features indicate that the unit can recover approximately 60 to 75% of the heat from the exhaust air and transfer it to the supply air stream. The additional airflow resistance imposed by the heat exchanger is in the range of 0.75 to 1.25 in. water gauge. The additional airflow resistance requires

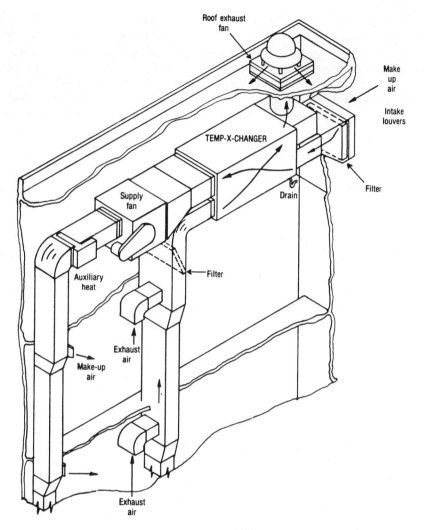

NOTE: Suggested built-up system; conceptual drawing only. Maintain 4' straight run at entrance to TEMP-X-CHANGER.

Fig. 6.3-1. Plate-type heat recovery system. (Source: Temp-X-changer).

additional energy use in order to recover the exhaust air heat. Finally, only sensible heat may be transferred; latent heat (moisture) will not be transferred between air streams when using this type of heat exchanger.

The main advantages are:

- Positive separation between supply and exhaust, which precludes contamination of the supply air system.
- Moderate cost per cfm compared to that of other heat transfer systems.
- Modular design for application to systems of various sizes.

- No moving parts for increased reliability.
- Available in corrosion-resistant materials.
- Low maintenance requirements because of few moving parts and minimal adjustments.

The disadvantages are:

- The air streams must be side by side, which may be very difficult to accomplish due to space restraints.

• More space is required than with other types of systems.

This type of heat recovery device is relatively easy to apply to a new lab facility. If space is available and the air streams are in the same location, it may also be applied as a retrofit project.

6.3.4 Heat Wheel-Type Device

Another type of air-to-air heat exchanger is commonly known as the "heat wheel." A diagram of this system is shown in Figure 6.3-2. It consists of a rotating, cylindrical, heat-absorbing disc. As the disc rotates about its longitudinal axis, it passes sequentially through the exhaust air stream and then through the supply air stream. The surfaces of the wheel alternately absorb energy from the exhaust and dissipate or transfer this same energy into the supply air stream as the wheel rotates. The rate of heat transfer is controlled by the rate at which the wheel rotates.

In applying this device to laboratory sup-ply/exhaust systems, special care must be taken to avoid potential contamination of the supply air stream by air leakage from the exhaust air. This may occur because of the air leaks around the baffle which separates the air streams. In order to avoid this, the exhaust air should be pulled through the heat wheel (which means that the exhaust side is under negative air pressure) and the supply air should be blown through the wheel (which means that the supply side is under positive air pressure). In addition, a purge air section can be provided which further aids in separating the air streams. The purge air section is located at the separation between air streams, is under positive pressure, and allows fresh outside air to flow into the exhaust air stream downstream of the heat wheel.

The chief characteristics of the heat wheel recovery equipment compared to those of the flat plate type are:

• Heat exchanger heat transfer effectiveness of 70 to 80%.

ENRECO SYSTEM AIR FLOW SCHEMATIC

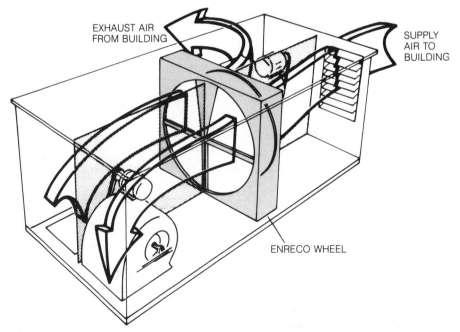

EXHAUST AIR FROM BUILDING

SUPPLY AIR TO BUILDING

ENRECO WHEEL

Fig. 6.3-2. Heat wheel unit diagram (ENRECO).

- Air pressure drop of 1.0 to 1.5 in.
- Can provide some latent as well as sensible heat transfer.

The main advantages are:

- Higher amount of recovered heat compared to flat plate devices.
- Good temperature control for supply air.

The disadvantages are:

- Higher cost per cfm compared to the flat plate type.
- Air streams must be side by side, which may be difficult in retrofit applications.
- Potential cross-contamination of air streams even with the purge section.
- Corrosion-resistant materials are less often available due to construction requirements.
- Many moving parts, which reduces reliability.
- Higher maintenance costs due to the need to adjust and maintain many parts.

6.3.5 Refrigerant Heat Pipe

A third type of air-to-air heat exchanger is normally called a "heat pipe." This device uses horizontal tubes that extend through both exhaust and supply air streams. Inside the tubes is a lining that is used as a wick to transfer liquid refrigerant from one side to the other. The tube is pressurized with a refrigerant and uses an evaporation/condensation process to transfer heat between the air streams. The refrigerant evaporates and cools the air stream at the warm end of the tube. The refrigerant vapor then migrates to the cool end, where it condenses back to liquid and rejects the heat to the cool air stream. The liquid refrigerant then flows back to the warm end to repeat the process. A sketch of the device is shown in Figure 6.3-3. Many of these tubes are combined into a coil (or heat exchanger) and inserted into the supply and exhaust air streams. The heat pipe unit may be tilted in order to con-

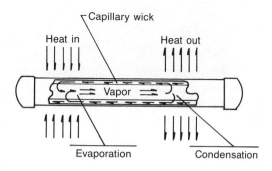

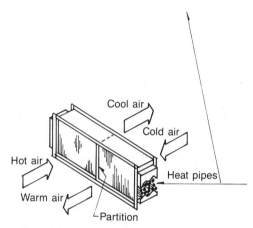

Fig. 6.3-3. Heat pipe recovery unit diagram.

trol the amount of recovered energy or to reverse the flow between summer and winter operations. This will require a flexible connection between the unit and the connecting air ductwork. The characteristics of this system are:

- Heat transfer effectiveness of 50 to 70%.
- Air pressure drop of 1.0 to 1.5 in.

The main advantages are:

- Moderate cost per cfm compared to that of the other devices discussed.
- Good temperature control of the supply air.
- Corrosion-resistant materials available.
- Few moving parts for increased reliability.
- Low maintenance cost.

The disadvantages are:

- Air streams must be side by side.
- Tubes may fail and lose heat transfer effectiveness.

6.3.6 Runaround Coil System

This heat recovery system is found in both an air-to-liquid and a liquid-to-air type. It consists of two air-to-liquid heat exchangers placed into the supply or exhaust air. The exchangers are connected to a pumped liquid piping system that circulates the heat transfer liquid from one exchanger to the other. Due to its relative cost and ease of use, the more common heat transfer fluid is water. In colder climates, the liquid may need to be of a type that is not subject to freezing. If this is the case, a glycol-water solution can be used. However, heat transfer effectiveness is significantly reduced as the concentration of glycol increases. Therefore, only enough glycol to limit the freezing potential should be used. A simple diagram of this system is

shown in Figure 6.3-4. The characteristics are:

- Heat transfer effectiveness of 45 to 65%, which is lower than that of the air-to-air types described earlier.
- Air pressure drop of 0.75 to 1.0 in.
- Sensible heat transfer only.

The main advantages are:

- Supply and exhaust air streams do not have to be together; they can be far from one another.
- Moderate cost per cfm compared to that of the previously described systems.
- Good supply air temperature control.
- Corrosion-resistant materials available.
- Few moving parts for good reliability.

The disadvantages are:

- Slightly lower effectiveness.
- Heat transfer liquid requires pumping.
- Higher maintenance costs due to pumping system.

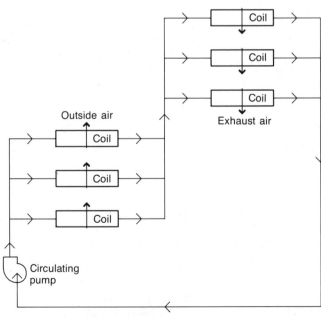

Fig. 6.3-4. Runaround heat recovery system with multiple coils—diagram.

Applying a runaround heat recovery system to a particular application will require special care in selecting the equipment. In order to determine the best combination of heat transfer effectiveness and operating cost, trial and error must be used. The analysis must account for the capital costs of various coil, piping and pumping options, in addition to the operating and maintenance costs of the air handler and the pumping system. This can be done with computer simulation software that is available from several coil manufacturers. Their software programs allow user input for the energy and operating costs and will perform a reasonably accurate cost comparison for the lowest LCC.

In addition to air-to-air and air-to-liquid heat recovery, there are other methods for transfer of heat energy. One of the most widely used system is commonly known as a "heat pump."

6.3.7 Heat Pumps

Heat pumps can be considered for a variety of applications in laboratories. A heat pump can be described as an application of a refrigerant system between two heat sinks (sources) that are at different temperatures. The heat pump is the system that recovers or transfers heat from one heat sink to the other. A simple schematic is shown in Figure 6.3-5. The heat sink or sources of heat en-

ergy can be liquids, gases or solids. The refrigeration system uses the evaporation and condensation cycles of the refrigerant gas, through a gas compressor, together with the necessary appurtenances that complete the system.

Some common heat sources from which heat may be recovered are:

- Ground-coupled heat pumps, where heat is recovered from the earth.
- Air-to-air heat pumps, where heat is recovered from the outdoor ambient air.
- Geothermal heat pumps, where heat is recovered from underground liquid streams.
- Waste heat pumps, where heat is recovered from a lower-temperature heat source and transferred to a higher-temperature heat source.

The refrigeration cycle uses an electrically driven compressor to transfer the heat with a refrigerant cycle COP of 2.5 to 3.5 or more. This means that for every watt-hour of electrical energy input to the compressor, 2.5 to 3.5 watt-hours of energy is transferred.

6.3.8 Heat Exchangers

If the waste heat source has a high or low enough temperature to transfer the usable energy for use at another temperature, this may be accomplished through the use of a heat exchanger. Air-to-air processes were previously discussed. Typical heat sources are:

- Steam/condensate systems
- Hot gas from refrigerant systems
- Hot wastewater

The more common types of heat exchangers are plate and frame or shell and tube types.

Shell and tube heat exchangers consist of a tube bundle through which one gas or liquid passes and a shell surrounding the tube bundle through which the other gas or liquid passes. Shell and tube exchangers have been used for many years in the heating industry.

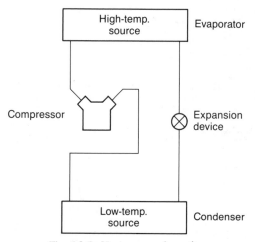

Fig. 6.3-5. Heat pump schematic.

They typically have an approach temperature of about 15°F, which is the temperature difference between the entering hot liquid and the exiting cool liquid. The heat exchanger typically contributes about a 10-psig pressure drop to the flow stream.

Plate and frame heat exchangers have been used much more frequently in the last 5 to 10 years because of their high heat transfer effectiveness, compact size and moderate cost. They consist of many thin metal plates separated by corrugated flow paths that are less than 0.5 in. wide. This thin, turbulent flow path between two flow streams allows very high heat transfer to occur. Therefore, the approach temperature is between 2° and 5°F, with a pressure drop similar to that of the shell and tube units. The heat transfer plates can be fully and easily dismantled for cleaning of the heat transfer surfaces. These advantages, plus the wide range of metals available for construction, make this a highly desirable device for corrosive streams that might be encountered in the lab facility.

6.3.9 Cogeneration

Another system that can be effectively applied to labs, but that does not necessarily save energy budgets, is a cogeneration system.

Cogeneration is traditionally defined as the simultaneous generation of electrcity and useful thermal energy from the same fuel input. The advantage of a cogeneration (cogen) system is that it converts up to 80% of its fuel input to both useful electricity and thermal energy, while conventional electric power generating plants convert only 30 to 35% of the fuel input to useful electricity, with essentially no recovered thermal energy. With the rising cost of power provided by the primary local utilities, and with the deregulation of natural gas, cogen systems are becoming increasingly cost effective. As a result, laboratories which have both thermal and electrical energy demands are often finding it more cost effective to generate their own power through cogeneration.

The cogen systems that are most applicable to laboratory building application include the following:

- Gas turbine generators with heat recovery boilers. See Figure 6.3-6.
- Reciprocating engine-generators with jacket water and/or exhaust heat recovery equipment. See Figure 6.3-7.

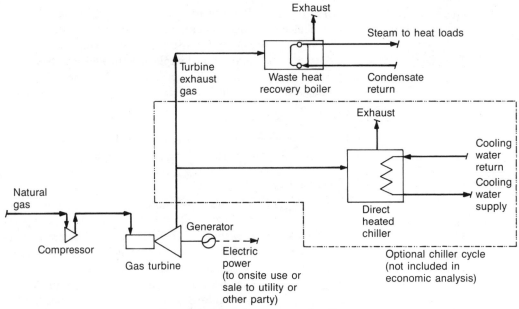

Fig. 6.3-6. Gas turbine cogeneration diagram.

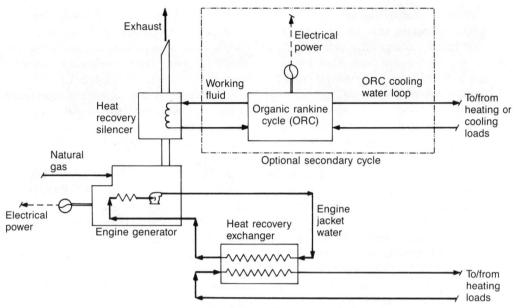

Fig. 6.3-7. Reciprocating engine cogen cycle diagram.

• Rankine steam cycles employing a boiler (or waste incinerator), steam turbine generator, and condensing heat exchangers for recovery of heat from the low-pressure steam. See Figure 6.3-8.

Gas turbines should be considered when a large thermal load exists in comparison to the electrical load. Reciprocating engines should be considered when the thermal load is low compared to the electrical load. Rankine cycles should be considered when steam needs to be available for a process system.

Cogen systems can also be used to meet large cooling loads through the use of absorption chilling equipment while generating electricity. Some of the more specialized system arrangement options are shown in the figures. They include:

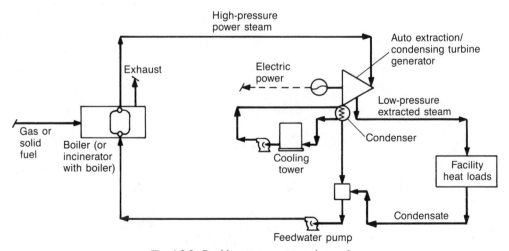

Fig. 6.3-8. Rankine steam cogeneration cycle.

- The direct-heated chiller, which uses turbine or engine exhaust gases to generate heating and chilled water.
- The organic rankine cycle (ORC), which uses a closed-loop heat transfer fluid to operate turbine generators.

Direct-fired chillers use an absorption process to produce the chilling effect with heat energy.

The ORC can operate from the exhaust heat available from a gas turbine or engine to produce additional electricity from the waste heat. This arrangement can increase the overall electrical generation efficiency to more than 42% from an average value without an ORC of 30 to 35%. Each case must be studied independently in order to determine whether this option is economically viable.

In order to illustrate the significant economic impact of cogeneration, Tables 6.3-1, 6.3-2 and 6.3-3 present a set of model economics for two typical cogen systems. The two systems, one at 620 KW and one at 1,200

KW, are sized and estimated based upon previous experience, although the requirements for a specific application can change the economic feasibility requirements. The assumptions used are noted in the work sheets.

As an alternative to using a cogen system to generate electricity for on-site use, contracting arrangements are available for the sale of the electricity to the utility at "avoided cost" rates, which were established by the federal Public Utility Regulatory Policies Act of 1978 (PURPA) Guideline legislation. These rates set the value of cogenerated power at the rate that would be necessary for the utility to generate that incremental amount of power had the cogen system not be installed. The avoided cost rate allows the lab installing the cogen system to sell back the power it produces at a higher rate. In evaluating the benefit of a cogen system, the user has the opportunity either to sell back the power at an avoided cost rate or to offset power purchases, depending on which is more cost effective.

Table 6.3-1. Model Economics for the Life of a Typical Cogen System

	Percent Return on Investment			
	720-KWH Plant (Before Taxes)		1,200-KWH Plant (Before Taxes)	
Year	$0.065/KWH	$0.09/KWH	$0.65/KWH	$0.09/KWH
1	45	123	59	147
2	48	127	62	152
3	50	131	65	156
4	53	136	68	161
5	56	140	71	166
6	59	145	75	171
7	62	149	77	176
8	65	154	81	182
9	68	159	84	187
10	71	164	87	193

Notes

1. The following equation was used to calculate return equity, using data from Tables 6.3-2 and 6.3-3:

$$\text{Return on equity} = \frac{\text{power revenues} + \text{heating fuel savings} - \text{maintenance} - \text{fuel cost} - \text{debt service}}{\text{down payment}}$$

2. Debt service assumes a 10-year loan at 12% annual interest.

Table 6.3-2. Revenues and Disbursements for the Life of a 720-KW Model Cogeneration Plant (Before Taxes)

Year	Down Payment (2)	Fuel Cost (1)	Maintenance Cost	Debt Service (3)	Heating Fuel Savings (1)	Electrical Power Revenues (1) Rate $/KWH $0.090	Rate $/KWH $0.065	Net Revenues Net Revenue @ $0.090	Net Revenue @ $0.065
0	($190,000)								
1		($312,035)	($32,300)	($134,508)	$180,020	$531,878	$384,134	$233,055	$85,311
2		(318,276)	(32,300)	(134,508)	183,621	542,516	391,817	241,053	90,354
3		(324,642)	(32,300)	(134,508)	187,293	553,366	399,653	249,210	95,497
4		(331,134)	(32,300)	(134,508)	191,039	564,434	407,646	257,530	100,743
5		(337,757)	(32,300)	(134,508)	194,860	575,722	415,799	266,017	106,094
6		(344,512)	(32,300)	(134,508)	198,757	587,237	424,115	274,674	111,552
7		(351,402)	(32,300)	(134,508)	202,732	598,981	432,598	283,503	117,119
8		(358,431)	(32,300)	(134,508)	206,787	610,961	441,250	292,509	122,798
9		(365,599)	(32,300)	(134,508)	210,923	623,180	450,075	301,696	128,590
10		(372,911)	(32,300)	(134,508)	215,141	635,644	459,076	311,066	134,498

Notes: All revenues are shown as positive numbers, and disbursements are enclosed in parentheses. The analysis is based upon a model plant and is for illustration only. All costs and revenues are shown in constant 1987 dollars.

1. Fuel costs and electric power revenues are inflated at an incremental inflation rate of 2% per year above the general inflation rate. Since the analysis is in constant 1987 dollars, it is not necessary to include general inflation in the numbers presented. The natural gas price is assumed to be $0.30/therm in 1987. Revenues are computed on a 95% duty factor.

2. The cost is 20 percent of the construction cost, which is estimated at $950,000 (order of magnitude).

3. Based on a 10-year loan at 12% annual interest. Loans with lower interest rates may be available.

Table 6.3-3. Revenues and Disbursements for the Life of a 1,200-KW Model Cogeneration Plant (Before Taxes)

Year	Down Payment (2)	Fuel Cost (1)	Maintenance Cost	Debt Service (3)	Heating Fuel Savings (1)	Electrical Power Revenues (1)		Net Revenues	
						Rate $/KWH $0.090	Rate $/KWH $0.065	Net Revenue @ $0.090	Net Revenue @ $0.065
0	($280,000)								
1		($542,516)	($47,600)	($198,222)	$312,990	$886,464	$640,224	$411,116	$164,876
2		(553,366)	(47,600)	(198,222)	319,250	904,193	653,028	424,255	173,090
3		(564,434)	(47,600)	(198,222)	325,635	922,277	666,089	437,656	181,468
4		(575,722)	(47,600)	(198,222)	332,147	940,723	679,411	451,326	190,014
5		(587,237)	(47,600)	(198,222)	338,790	959,537	692,999	465,269	198,730
6		(598,981)	(47,600)	(198,222)	345,566	978,302	706,859	479,490	207,622
7		(610,961)	(47,600)	(198,222)	352,478	998,302	720,996	493,997	216,690
8		(623,180)	(47,600)	(198,222)	359,527	1,018,268	735,416	508,793	225,941
9		(635,644)	(47,600)	(198,222)	366,718	1,038,634	750,124	523,885	235,376
10		(648,357)	(47,600)	(168,222)	374,052	1,059,407	765,127	539,279	245,000

Notes: All revenues are shown as positive numbers, and disbursements are enclosed in parentheses. The analysis is based upon a model plant and is for illustration only. All costs and revenues are shown in constant 1987 dollars.

1. Fuel costs and electric power revenues are inflated at an incremental inflation rate of 2% per year above the general inflation rate. Since the analysis is in constant 1987 dollars, it is not necessary to include general inflation in the numbers presented. The natural gas price is assumed to be $0.30/therm in 1987. Revenues are computed on a 95% duty factor.

2. The cost is 20 percent of the construction cost, which is estimated at $1,400,000 (order of magnitude).

3. Based on a 10-year loan at 12% annual interest. Loans with lower interest rates may be available.

6.4 Economic Considerations
N. Nelson

Chapter 8 of this handbook will discuss in depth the cost issues of laboratory facilities. This section presents several concepts that need to be considered for energy conservation potential in laboratories.

In comparing several different potential energy conservation projects, several comparison methods are used. Some of the more common methods are:

- Cost/benefit ratio
- Simple payback
- Discounted payback
- Savings/investment ratio
- Life cycle cost analysis

The last method, life cycle cost (LCC) analysis, is the more inclusive analytical tool; it compares the total costs of ownership over a project's life. This is discussed more completely in Section 8.4.

In general, the factors considered in evaluation are:

- Time value of money
- Inflation
- Opportunity cost or discount rate
- Initial investment (captial) costs
- Operating and maintenance costs
- Replacement costs
- Salvage value

Not all analysis or comparison methods take all of these factors into account, except for the LCC. Therefore, the LCC is the best method for comparing alternative energy conservation opportunities.

6.4.1 Cost/Benefit Ratio

As its name implies, the cost/benefit ratio method consists of determining the cost of implementing a particular alternative in the numerator and the benefits attributable to the owner in the denominator. Any ratio less than 1.0 means that the benefits exceed the costs. The lower the value, the more desirable the option.

6.4.2 Simple Payback

Simple payback (SPB) is the total time in which the annual energy savings will pay back the initial investment, exclusive of the time value of money. A simple example would be: If an energy-saving motor costs an additional $300 and the annual savings is $100, then the SPB would be:

$$\text{SPB} = \frac{\$300}{\$100} = 3 \text{ years}$$

Generally, the shorter the number of years, the more desirable the project. This method is not a good comparison method in that it does not always indicate the most cost-effective project. In addition, it does not indicate the payback period when the cost of money is included.

6.4.3 Discounted Payback

Discounted payback (DPB) is very similar to SPB except that the time value of money is added. It is easiest to use available economic tables based upon the applicable discount rate in order to determine the number of years to payback.

6.4.4 Savings/Investment Ratio

The savings/investment ratio (SIR) has as the numerator the reduction in energy costs (delta E) less the differential nonfuel operation and maintenance costs (delta M), and as the denominator the differential investment costs (delta I) plus the differential replacement costs (delta R) less the differential salvage value (delta S). Mathematically, this is expressed as:

$$\text{SIR} = \frac{\text{delta } E - \text{delta } M}{\text{delta } I + \text{delta } R - \text{delta } S}$$

The differential is used because normally alternative solutions are being compared, and the difference between them is the best method of ranking the alternatives. It should be pointed out that the SIR method requires that the alternatives be nonmutually exclusive, i.e., that using one alternative does not exclude the use of the other. A source of information for using this ranking technique is NBS Handbook #135, which is listed in the References.

REFERENCES

ASHRAE, 1987. *ASHRAE Handbook 1987—HVAC Systems and Applications.* Atlanta, GA: ASHRAE, Chapter 30.

ASHRAE, 1980. *Standard 90—Energy Conservation in New and Existing Buildings,* Atlanta, GA: ASHRAE.

Chamberlain, R. I., and Leahy, J. E., 1978. *Laboratory Fume Hood Standards, Recommended for the U.S. Environmental Protection Agency.* Contract No. 68-01-4661. Cambridge: MIT.

Davis, S. J., and Benjamin, R., 1987. VAV with Fume Hood Exhaust Systems. *Heating/Piping/Air Conditioning,* August, 75–78.

Koenigsberg, J., 1984. The Laboratory Fumehood: Efficiency and Energy Conservation. *American Laboratory,* Vol. 16, No. 10, 59.

Neuman, V. A., 1987. Master of Science thesis in Mechanical Engineering, Life Cycle Cost Optimization of HVAC Systems for Research and Development Buildings. San Diego State University.

Neuman, V. A., and Rousseau, W. H., 1986. Design and Cost Considerations for Variable Air Volume Fume Hood Operation. Presented at the ASHRAE Annual Meeting, Atlanta, GA, January.

Tsal, Robert J., 1989. T-Duct Method for Duct Optimization. Research Project RP-516. *ASHRAE Transactions,* Vol. 94, Part 2.

U.S. Department of Commerce, Nat. Bureau of Standards, 1980. NBS Handbook #35, *Life Cycle Costing Manual for the Federal Energy Management Programs.* December, Washington, DC.

U.S. Department of Energy, 1980. *Architects and Engineers Guide to Energy Conservation in Existing Buildings.* Washington, DC: U.S. Government Printing Office.

7

CODES, REGULATIONS AND STANDARDS

7.1 INTRODUCTION *T. Ruys and S. Bettge*

Standards and codes are typically generated by nonprofit organizations that set up committees made up of volunteers with detailed knowledge of their field. These standards may be adopted by local, state and federal agencies and then become law. The Uniform Building Code (UBC), the National Building Code (BOCA) and the Standard Building Code (SBC) are considered consensus codes. Anyone can propose amendments; however, only the active membership (i.e., building officials) can vote. There are, however, public hearings. NFPA standards are documents prepared by committees of volunteers for the National Fire Protection Association. These are examples of widely adopted standards.

Most groups that develop the codes and standards have no power or authority to enforce compliance. That power is entrusted to the "authority having jurisdiction (AHJ)." The AHJ authority may be an individual, office, or organization on a federal, state or local level. In addition, there may be other groups that have an interest in compliance, such as insurance companies and lending agencies.

Code-writing bodies maintain a committee to interpret their codes and/or standards. This is done to provide assistance to the AHJs when questions arise. Depending on the code, interpretations may be rendered only to building officials; however, some committees (e.g., the NFPA) will respond to all questions and publish official interpretations. The purpose of this is to achieve conformity in application.

Public authorities often make compliance mandatory through the process of "adoption by reference." This is defined by the NFPA as "citing of title and publishing information only." Changes required by the adopting authority must be documented separately. "Adoption by transcription," however, is adoption in part or in total, including changes. At times, this license is given to public agencies with lawmaking powers.

Users of codes and standards must ascertain that they are using the correct one(s) being enforced for their project. Normally this will be a state or local building code and will include a fire protection code. In some cases, OSHA regulations will cover an issue not regulated by a local or state code. All applicable codes, regulations and standards, as a matter of practicality, incorporate by reference other codes, standards and regulations. This results in apparent conflicts, as each code-writing body has its own agenda and timetable for republishing a revision of its code or standard. From a legal standpoint, the latest edition of a code or standard may not be enforceable, as legislative action is required to change references from an earlier edition. As a matter of practice, some AHJs follow the latest edition of a code or standard, as it reflects the latest thinking or available technology.

Codes and standards are not enforceable unless they have been adopted by law or through an ordinance process.

Standards that have become law are often called "codes." Regulations, on the other hand, are most often generated by governmental agencies and have by legislative action become laws, such as the Occupational Safety and Health Act (OSHA), the Good Laboratory Practices Act (GLPA) and the Good Manufacturing Practices Act (GMPA).

This chapter does not attempt to deal with all aspects of these codes, regulations and standards. Its purpose is to emphasize those sections that deal with issues specific to laboratory facilities or have been interpreted a certain way to be applicable with laboratory facilities.

Where appropriate, references have been made to other codes or standards dealing with the same subject matter. Some of the more important ones are covered in this chapter.

Codes and standards which may assist in the design of laboratory facilities are published by the National Fire Protection Association. These are:

NFPA 30	Flammable and Combustible Liquids Code
NFPA 45	Fire Protection for "Laboratories Using Chemicals"
NFPA 49	Hazardous Chemicals Data
NFPA 68	Venting of Deflagrations
NFPA 70	National Electrical Code
NFPA 99	Standard for Health Care Facilities, Chapter 10—"Laboratories"
	Note: This was previously 56C—Standard for Laboratories in Health-Related Institutions
NFPA 101	Code for Safety to Life from Fire in Buildings and Structures, commonly referred to as the "Life Safety Code"

NFPA 325M   Fire Hazard Properties of
                    Flammable Liquids, Gases,
                    and Volatile Solids
NFPA 491M   Manual of Hazardous Chem-
                    ical Reactions

Additional standards are listed in the appendix in each of the above publications.

7.2 OCCUPATIONAL SAFETY AND HEALTH ACT (OSHA)   *T. Ruys*

7.2.1 Introduction

The Occupational Safety and Health Act, Public Law 91-596, was signed December 29, 1970, became effective April 28, 1971, and has been revised ever since. The extracts presented in this section come from the July 1, 1988, edition.

Executive departments and federal agencies publish general and permanent rules in the *Federal Register*. The Code of Federal Regulations (CFR) is a codification of these rules divided into 50 titles. Title 29, Labor, Chapter XVII, part 1910, contains the OSHA standards in four volumes.

The basis of OSHA regulations relative to laboratories is the employer-employee relationship. Every employer covered by the act is required to provide employees with a workplace which is free of recognized hazards that cause or are likely to cause death or serious physical harm.

Many OSHA standards deal with procedures, labeling and record keeping, which fall outside the scope of this handbook. Other regulations deal with facilities but are not directly related to laboratory facilities. Only those that have a direct or indirect impact on laboratory facilities are discussed in this section.

It should be noted that OSHA regulations include other standards, i.e., those of the NFPA and ANSI. As a result, OSHA regulations may not be as current as those of the code- or standard-setting body, which may create conflicts.

Many states have been given the authority to enforce OSHA regulations. Some have added more stringent rules and regulations.

1910.36 Means of Egress: General Requirements

Laboratories are inherently hazardous spaces. All hazardous laboratories should have two exits. NFPA No. 45 requires laboratories of 500 sq ft or larger to have two exits.

OSHA 29CFR 1910.36(b)(8)

Every building or structure, section, or area thereof of such size, occupancy, and arrangement that the reasonable safety of numbers of occupants may be endangered by the blocking of any single means of egress due to fire or smoke, shall have at least two means of egress remote from each other, so arranged as to minimize any possibility that both may be blocked by any one fire or other emergency conditions.

Doors should swing out in the direction of exit travel from hazardous areas. NFPA No. 45 requires doors that swing out from the laboratory for all Class A and B laboratories:

OSHA 29CRF 1910.37(f)(2)

A door from a room to an exit or to a way of exit access shall be of the side-hinged, swinging type. It shall swing with exit travel when the room is occupied by more than 50 persons or used for a high hazard occupancy.

This statement has been interpreted to mean that sliding doors between a laboratory and an exit corridor or in any egress path are not acceptable.

The following statement has been interpreted to mean that flammable storage cabinets and fumehoods should not be located at primary exit doors. Fumehoods should not be located at exit doors for an additional reason: backdraft is created from the hood into the laboratory due to people walking by.

29CFR 1910.37(f)(5)

Exit access shall be so arranged that it will not be necessary to travel toward any area of high hazard occupancy in order to reach the nearest exit, unless the path of travel is effectively shielded from the high hazard location by suitable partitions or other physical barriers.

The following paragraph reinterates that prohibition:

29 CFR 1910.106 (p. 229)

(5) *Storage inside building*—(i)*Egress.* Flammable or combustible liquids, including stock for sale, shall not be stored so as to limit use of exits, stairways, or areas normally used for the safe egress of people.

29 CFR 1910.106: Flammable and Combustible Liquids. Page 228 of this document contains standards for the fabrication of storage cabinets. See also NFPA No. 30.

(3) *Design, construction, and capacity of storage cabinets*—(i) *Maximum capacity.* Not more than 60 gallons of Class I or Class II liquids, nor more than 120 gallons of Class III liquids may be stored in a storage cabinet.

(ii) *Fire resistance.* Storage cabinets shall be designed and constructed to limit the internal temperature to not more than 325° F. when subjected to a 10-minute fire test using the standard time-temperature curve as set forth in Standard Methods of Fire Tests of Building Construction and Materials, NFPA 251–1969. All joints and seams shall remain tight and the door shall remain securely closed during the fire test. Cabinets shall be labeled in conspicuous lettering, "Flammable—Keep Fire Away."

(a) Metal cabinets constructed in the following manner shall be deemed to be in compliance. The bottom, top, door, and sides of cabinet shall be at least No. 18 gage sheet iron and double walled with 1 ½-inch air space. Joints shall be riveted, welded or made tight by some equally effective means. The door shall be provided with a three-point lock, and the door sill shall be raised at least 2 inches above the bottom of the cabinet.

(b) Wooden cabinets constructed in the following manner shall be deemed in compliance. The bottom, sides, and top shall be constructed of an approved grade of plywood at least 1 inch in thickness, which shall not break down or delaminate under fire conditions. All joints shall be rabbetted and shall be fastened in two directions with flathead woodscrews. When more than one door is used, there shall be a rabbetted overlap or not less than 1 inch. Hinges shall be mounted in such a manner as not to lose their holding capacity due to loosening or burning out of the screws when subjected to the fire test.

Nowhere do the standards call for ventilated cabinets or exhausts from these cabinets. The purpose of these cabinets is to separate flammable material from fire in the laboratory and to reduce the fuel in the laboratory in case of a fire. The author has seen flammable liquid cabinets vented into fumehood chambers. This may be a dangerous practice, potentially capable of causing a flashback into the cabinet.

On page 229 are requirements for the design and construction of inside storage rooms. NFPA No. 30, which has been approved by reference by OSHA, contains similar information.

29 CFR 1910.106

(4) *Design and construction of inside storage rooms*—(i) *Construction.* Inside storage rooms shall be constructed to meet the required fire-resistive rating for their use. Such construction shall comply with the test specifications set forth in Standard Methods of Fire Tests of Building Construction and Materials, NFPA 251–1969. Where an automatic sprinkler system is provided, the system shall be designed and installed in an acceptable manner. Openings to other rooms or buildings shall be provided with noncombustible liquid-tight raised sills or ramps at least 4 inches in height, or the floor in the storage area shall be at least 4 inches below the surrounding floor. Openings shall be provided with approved self-closing fire doors. The room shall be liquid-tight where the walls join the floor. A permissible alternate to the sill or ramp is an open-grated trench inside of the room which drains to a safe location. Where other portions of the building or

other properties are exposed, windows shall be protected as set forth in the Standard for Fire Doors and Windows, NFPA No. 80–1968, for Class E or F openings. Wood at least 1 inch nominal thickness may be used for shelving, racks, dunnage, scuffboards, floor overlay, and similar installations.

(ii) *Rating and capacity.* Storage in inside storage rooms shall comply with Table H-13.

(iii) *Wiring.* Electrical wiring and equipment located in inside storage rooms used for Class I liquids shall be approved under Subpart S of this part for Class I, Division 2 Hazardous Locations; for Class II and Class III liquids, shall be approved for general use.

(iv) *Ventilation.* Every inside storage room shall be provided with either a gravity or a mechanical exhaust ventilation system. Such systems shall be designed to provide for a complete change of air within the room at least six times per hour. If a mechanical exhaust system is used, it shall be controlled by a switch located outside of the door. The ventilating equipment and any lighting fixtures shall be operated by the same switch. A pilot light shall be installed adjacent to the switch if Class I flammable liquids are dispensed within the room. Where gravity ventilation is provided, the fresh air intake, as well as the exhaust outlet from the room, shall be one the exterior of the building in which the room is located.

(v) *Storage in inside storage rooms.* In every inside storage room there shall be maintained one clear aisle at least 3 feet wide. Containers over 30 gallons capacity shall not be staked one upon the other. Dispensing shall be by approved pump or self-closing faucet only.

The following paragraph applies to all buildings or structures. Laboratory live

Table H-13. Storage in Inside Rooms

Fire Protection Provided	Fire Resistance	Maximum Size	Total Allowable Quantities (Gals./Sq ft./Floor Area)
Yes	2 hours	500 sq. ft.	10
No	2 hours	500 sq. ft.	5
Yes	1 hour	150 sq. ft.	4
No	1 hour	150 sq. ft.	2

[1]Fire protection system shall be sprinkler, water spray, carbon dioxide, or other system.

loads are typically higher than those of many other occupancies (see Section 5.2), and buildings used as laboratories may not have been designed for the additional capacity. Noting the allowable loads in a conspicuous place is a very good idea.

29 CFR 1910.22d

(d) *Floor loading protection.* (1) In every building or other structure, or part thereof, used for mercantile, business, industrial, or storage purposes, the loads approved by the building official shall be marked on plates of approved design which shall be supplied and securely affixed by the owner of the building, or his duly authorized agent, in a conspicuous place in each space to which they relate. Such plates shall not be removed or defaced but, if lost, removed, or defaced, shall be replaced by the owner or his agent.

(2) It shall be unlawful to place, or cause, or permit to be placed, on any floor or roof of a building or other structure a load greater than that for which such floor or roof is approved by the building official.

Backflow preventers or vacuum breakers are often missing from individual water fixtures, which can cause the laboratory water system to be contaminated. A separate, protected water system must be provided to water fountains, lavatories, showers and lunchroom counters.

29 CFR 1910.141(b)(1)

Water supply—(1) *Potable water.* (i) Potable water shall be provided in all places of employment, for drinking, washing of the person, cooking, washing of foods, washing of cooking or eating utensils, washing of food preparation or processing premises, and personal service rooms.

Nonpotable water outlets must be so labeled. Laboratory water systems without vacuum breakers on each water fixture should be classified as nonpotable.

29 CFR 1910.141(b)(2)

Nonpotable water. (i) Outlets for nonpotable water, such as water for industrial or fire-fighting purposes, shall be posted or otherwise marked in a manner that will indicate clearly that the water is unsafe and is not to be used for drinking, washing of the person, cooking, washing of food, washing of cooking or eating utensils, washing of food preparation or processing premises, or personal service rooms, or for washing clothes.

The main water system must be protected from the nonpotable water system.

29 CFR 1910.141(b)(2)

(ii) Construction of nonpotable water systems or systems carrying any other nonpotable substance shall be such as to prevent blackflow or backsiphonage into a potable water system.

Until the revisions of 1978–1979, safety equipment (e.g., eyewash fountains, emergency showers, first aid cabinets) and/or their locations were colored green. The only colors now required are noted below, along with their meaning.

29 CFR 1910.144(a)

Safety color code for marking physical hazards.
(a) *Color identification*—(1) *Red.* Red shall be the basic color for the identification of:
(i) *Fire protection equipment and apparatus.* [*Reserved*]

Appendices to § 1910.145, Accident Prevention Tags

Appendix A—Recommended Color Coding

While the standard does not specifically mandate colors to be used on accident prevention tags, the following color scheme is recommended by OSHA for meeting the requirements of this section:
"DANGER"—Red, or predominantly red, with lettering or symbols in a contrasting color.
"CAUTION"—Yellow, or predominantly yellow, with lettering or symbols in a contrasting color.
"WARNING"—Orange, or predominantly orange, with lettering or symbols in a contrasting color.
"BIOLOGICAL HAZARD"—Fluorescent orange or orange-red, or predominantly so, with lettering or symbols in a contrasting color.

Eyewash fountains and emergency showers are standard equipment in laboratory facilities.

29 CFR 1910.151(c)

Where the eyes or body of any person may be exposed to injurious corrosive materials, suitable facilities for quick drenching or flushing of the eyes and body shall be provided within the work area for immediate emergency use.

It is interesting to note that reference is made to corrosive materials only; caustic and flammable materials are not mentioned. The reference to suitable facilities is not very specific. In 1981 the ANSI Z358.1–1981 standards were published. These have not yet been adopted by OSHA but very likely will be.

The reference to immediate emergency use if generally intepreted to mean that no door must obstruct the path of travel between the site of the accident (i.e., the laboratory) and the emergency shower or eyewash fountain.

The distance to the nearest eyewash fountain is generally assumed not to exceed 25 ft. The distance to the nearest emergency shower is 50 ft. However, ANSI standards are much more lenient (see Section 4.8).

7.2.2 OSHA Health and Safety Standards; Occupational Exposures to Toxic Substances in Laboratories; Proposed Rule 1910.1450

The proposed rule was published July 24, 1986, but has not been adopted. It was proposed to add to OSHA Standards 29 CFR 1910, Section 1910.1450, Subpart Z. The paragraphs concerning laboratory facilities are as follows:

29 CFT 1910.1450(a) Definition

"Closed system" means a device such as a glove box or other system which physically encloses an operation or procedure involving the laboratory use of toxic substances; is constructed and maintained to provide a physical separation between the employee and the substances used in the workplace; is designed to prevent vapors from escaping from the closed system into the laboratory environment; and allows manipulation of chemicals to be conducted in the enclosure by the use of remote controls or gloves which are physically attached and sealed to the enclosure.

"Laboratory" means a facility where the "laboratory use of toxic substances" occurs. It is a workplace where relatively small quantities of toxic substances are used on a non-production basis.

"Laboratory-type hood" means a device located in a laboratory, enclosed on five sides with a moveable sash or fixed partial enclosure on the remaining side; constructed and maintained to draw air from the laboratory and to prevent or minimize the escape of air contaminants into the laboratory; and allows chemical manipulations to be conducted in the enclosure without insertion of any portion of the employee's body other than hand and arms.

Walk-in hoods with adjustable sashes meet the above definition provided that the sashes are adjusted during use so that the airflow and the exhaust of air contaminants are not compromised and employees do not work inside the enclosure during the release of airborne toxic substances.

"Regulated area" means a laboratory, an area of a laboratory or device such as a laboratory hood for which access is limited to persons who are aware of the hazards of the substances in use and the precautions that are necessary.

29 CFR 1910.1450d: Chemical Hygiene Plan

(iii) A requirement that fume hoods and other protective equipment are functioning properly and specific measures that shall be taken to ensure proper and adequate performance of such equipment:

The proposed standard does not include requirements for face velocities of laboratory-type hoods. It requires only that hoods function properly at all times. The reason for this is twofold: First, much controversy exists regarding what the optimum velocities should be, considering differences in the design of general ventilation systems and the concern for energy conservation. Recommendations for minimum face velocities for effective containment have ranged from linear velocities of 60 to 125 fpm. OSHA has insufficient data at this time to establish that one recommendation is superior to another. The second reason for not specifying face velocities is that this standard has adopted a performance-oriented approach, which leaves many of the decisions to the employer regarding how best to protect employees in a particular laboratory.

(x) Provisions for additional employee protection for work with carcinogens or potential carcinogens as defined herein. Such provisions shall include, as a minimum, the following elements:

(A) Establishment of a regulated area:

(B) Requirement that such work be conducted in a properly functioning laboratory type hood, closed system or other device which provides equivalent employee protection:

(E) Specification of appropriate procedures to be employed to protect vacuum lines and vacuum pumps from contamination:

29 CFR 1910.1450: Appendix A. This appendix contains nonmandatory recommendations taken from "Prudent Practices for Handling Hazardous Chemicals in Laboratories" published in 1981 by the National Research Council.

"Prudent Practices" is cited because of its wide distribution and acceptance and because of its preparation by members of the laboratory community through the sponsorship of the National Research Council. However, none of the recommendations given here will modify any of the requirements of the laboratory standard. This appendix merely presents pertinent recommendations from "Prudent Practices," organized into a form convenient for quick reference during operation of a laboratory facility and during development and application of a Chemical Hygiene Plan. Users of this appendix should consult "Prudent Practices" for a more extended presentation and justification for each recommendation.

The recommendations from "Prudent Practices" have been paraphrased, combined, or otherwise reorganized, and headings have been added. However, their sense has not been changed.

Section C. The Laboratory Facility

1. *Design.* The laboratory facility should have;

(a) two exits for each laboratory (225):

(b) an appropriate general ventilation system (see C4 below) with air intakes and exhausts located so as to avoid intake of contaminated air (194);

(c) adequate, well-ventilated stockrooms/storerooms (218, 219);

(d) laboratory hoods and sinks (12, 162);

(e) other safety equipment including eyewash fountains and drench showers (162, 169); and

(f) arrangements for waste disposal (12, 240).

2. *Maintenance.* Chemical-hygiene-related equipment (hoods, incinerator, etc.) should undergo continuing appraisal and be modified if inadequate (11, 12).

3. *Usage.* The work conducted (10) and its scale (12) must be appropriate to the physical facilities available and, especially, to the quality of ventilation (13).

4. *Ventilation.*

(a) General laboratory ventilation. This system should: provide a source of air for breathing and for input into local ventilation devices (199); it should not be relied on for protection from toxic substances released into the laboratory (198); ensure that laboratory air is continually replaced, preventing increase of air concentrations of toxic substances during the working day (194); Direct air flow into the laboratory from non-laboratory areas and out to the exterior of the building (194).

(b) Hoods. A laboratory hood with 2.5 feet of hood space per person should be provided for every 2 workers if they spend most of their time working with chemicals (199); each hood should have a continuous monitoring device to allow convenient confirmation or adequate hood performance before use (200, 209). If this is not possible, work with substance of unknown toxicity should be avoided (13) or other types of local ventilation devices should be provided (199). See pp. 201–206 for a discussion of hood design, construction and evaluation.

(c) Other local ventilation devices. Ventilated storage cabinets, canopy hoods, snorkels, etc. should be provided as needed (199). Each canopy hood and snorkel should have a separate exhaust duct (207).

(d) Special ventilation areas. Exhaust air from glove boxes and isolation rooms should be passed through scrubbers or other treatment before release into the regular exhaust system (208). Cold rooms and warm rooms should have provisions for rapid escape and for escape in the event of electrical failure (209).

(e) Modifications. Any alteration of the ventilation system should be made only if thorough testing indicates that worker protection from airborne toxic substances will continue to be adequate (12, 193, 204).

(f) Performance. Rate: 4–12 room air changes/hour is normally adequate general ventilation if local exhaust systems such as hoods are used as the primary method of control (194).

(g) Quality. General air flow should not be turbulent and should be relatively uniform throughout the laboratory, with no high velocity or static areas (194, 195); airflow into and within the hood should not be excessively turbulent (200); hood face velocity should be adequate (typically 60–100 lfm) (200, 204).

(h) Evaluation. Quality and quantity of ventilation should be evaluated on installation (202), regularly monitored at least every 3 months) (6, 12, 14, 195), and reevaluated whenever a change in local ventilation devices is made (12, 195, 207). See pp. 195–198 for methods of evaulation and for calculation of estimated airborne contaminant concentrations.

Section D. Components of the Chemical Hygiene Plan

6. *Protective Apparel and Equipment.* These should include for each laboratory:

(a) protective apparel compatible with the

required level of performance for substances being handled (158–161);

(b) an easily accessible drench-type safety shower (162, 169);

(c) an eyewash fountain (162);

(d) a fire extinguisher (162–164);

(e) access to a nearby respiratory (164–9), fire alarm and telephone for emergency use (162); and

(c) location signs for safety showers, eyewash stations, other safety and first aid equipment, exits (27) and areas where food and beverage consumption and storage are permitted (24); and

(b) There should be an alarm system to alert people in all parts of the facility including isolation areas such as cold rooms (172).

Always use a hood (previously evaluated to confirm adquate performance with a face velocity of at least 60 linear feet per minute) (40) or other containment device for procedures which may result in the generation of aerosols or vapors containing the substance (39); trap released vapors to prevent their discharge with the hood exhaust (40).

(d) Exiting: On leaving a controlled area, remove any protective apparel (placing it in an appropriate, labeled container) and thoroughly wash hands, forearms, face, and neck (49).

7.3 NFPA STANDARD NO. 45*   T. Ruys

7.3.1 Introduction

NFPA Standard No. 45 specifically deals with fire-related issues in laboratories using chemicals. It has been widely adopted by AHJs, although it has not been adopted by reference by OSHA.

This standard deals with both educational and research laboratories, but it specifically excludes health care laboratories, which are covered in NFPA No. 99; pilot plant and manufacturing facilities and incidental testing facilities or those that use small quantities of chemicals for incidental purposes are also excluded. NFPA No. 101 is an integral part of NFPA No. 45 by reference. NFPA No. 101 is referred to for means of egress requirements (3–3, NFPA No. 45):

---

*The 1986 edition was used for this discussion.

• Instructional laboratories for grades 1 through 12 are covered under Educational Occupancies in Chapters 10 and 11 (A3–3, NFPA No. 45).

• Instructional laboratories for grades 13 and above are covered under Business Occupancy in Chapter 26 and 27.

• Other laboratories are covered under Industrial Occupancies in Chapter 28.

The key to applying the standard is an understanding of the concepts of laboratory, laboratory work area and laboratory unit. "Laboratory" is a generic term and has generally been used somewhat loosely. For the purposes of this standard, the standards committee therefore, provided the following definitions:

• Laboratory: a generic term denoting a building, space, equipment or operation.

• Laboratory building: a structure consisting wholly or principally of one or more laboratory units.

• Laboratory work area: a room or space for testing, analysis, research, instruction, or similar activities that involve the use of chemicals. This work area may or may not be enclosed.

• Laboratory unit: an enclosed space classified as A, B or C based on the limitations established in NFPA No. 45, Tables 2–2 and 3–1. The space within a laboratory unit may include a number of work areas, offices and support space used by laboratory unit personnel. The laboratory unit separation consists of walls, floors and ceilings, including protected openings such as doors and ducts between adjacent laboratory units.

7.3.2 Laboratory Unit Design and Construction

The concept of a laboratory unit was created to allow maximum flexibility of operation and layout, limited by (1) the amount of flammables and combustibles present and how they are stored, (2) the lab unit classification, (3) the size of the lab unit, (4) the fire resistance rating of the separation with other laboratory units, (5) the automatic fire suppression system in place, and (6) the exiting.

Amounts of Flammable and Combustible Liquids (See Table 7.3-1)

The amounts of flammable and combustible liquids are difficult to predict, even by those occupying the laboratory, particularly for a long future period of time. Often the best approach is to consider the company's, institution's or department's goals, and the laboratory's long-term purpose, and to classify the laboratory as A, B or C. Upgrading to a higher hazard classification later on is very expensive. It should be noted that for instructional laboratories, smaller quantities of flammable and combustible liquids are allowed; these labs cannot, therefore, be classified as Class A. Academic research laboratories used by graduate students are not considered instructional laboratories.

Flexibility is built into the standard. The quantities allowed can be doubled if stored in approved storage cabinets (see Section 4.3) and safety cans, and doubled again if the laboratory is provided with an automatic fire suppression system. There are, however, cetain limitations. First, the maximum allowable quantity must not exceed an amount calculated for the whole laboratory unit. That includes the areas for offices, circulation spaces and other nonlaboratory support spaces within the laboratory unit. This is where the definition of a laboratory unit is very important. The second limitation is that the maximum quantities of Class I liquids must not exceed those specified for Class I liquids alone.

To illustrate the points above, let us analyze an instructional laboratory. Most building codes assume 50 sq ft per student, and NFPA No. 45 allows only 50% of the quantities listed in Table 7.3-1. That means:

Class I flammables in use equal 2.5 gal/student or 2.5 gal/100 sq ft—Class B unit

Classes I, II, and IIIA flammables in use equal 2.5 gal/student or 5.0 gal/100 sq ft—Class B unit

These quantities are for nonsprinklered laboratory units. They can be doubled for sprinklered areas and doubled again if stored in safety cans and approved storage cabinets. See Table 7.3-2.

These limiting quantities have been tabulated by Fresina (private communication, MIT) in Table 7.3-3 for different sizes of instructional laboratory units and translated into gallons per student in Table 7.3-4. Actual surveys made at different colleges indicate that these quantities are adequate for student use in instructional laboratory units. Additional quantities are, of course, allowed in approved flammable liquid storage rooms (see Section 7.2.1). In general, the larger the laboratory unit, the smaller the quantity per student because the total quantity limitations govern.

An additional limitation is the size of the container itself. Table 7.3-5, reproduced from NFPA No. 45, also limits the maximum capacity for instructional laboratory units in footnote 4.

Laboratory Unit Classification

The laboratory unit fire hazard classification is:

Class A—high hazard
Class B—medium hazard
Class C—low hazard

These classifications are based on the quantities of flammable and combustible liquids; on the way those quantities are stored; and on whether the facility has an automatic fire suppression system in place. See Table 7.3-1.

Size of the Laboratory Unit

The maximum size of the laboratory unit depends on the fire hazard classification, on the type of construction, on whether the laboratory unit has an automatic fire suppression system, and to a great extent on the AHJ.

Table 7.3-1. NFPA Standard 45, Table 2.2: Maximum Quantities of Flammable and Combustible Liquids in Laboratory Units Outside of Flammable Liquid Storage Rooms[7]

Laboratory Unit Class	Flammable or Combustible Liquid Class	Excluding Quantities in Storage Cabinets[7] and Safety Cans			Including Quantities in Storage Cabinets[7] and Safety Cans		
		Maximum Quantity[3] Per 100 Square Feet of Laboratory Unit	Maximum Quantity[3,4] Per Laboratory Unit		Maximum Quantity[3] Per 100 Square Feet of Laboratory Unit	Maximum Quantity[3,4] Per Laboratory Unit	
			Unsprinklered	Sprinklered[6]		Unsprinklered	Sprinklered[6]
A[1] (High hazard)	I	10 gallons	300 gallons	600 gallons	20 gallons	600 gallons	1,200 gallons
	I, II and IIIA[5]	20 gallons	400 gallons	800 gallons	40 gallons	800 gallons	1,600 gallons
B[2] (Intermediate hazard)	I	5 gallons	150 gallons	300 gallons	10 gallons	300 gallons	600 gallons
	I, II and IIIA[5]	10 gallons	200 gallons	400 gallons	20 gallons	400 gallons	800 gallons
C[2] (Low hazard)	I	2 gallons	75 gallons	150 gallons	4 gallons	150 gallons	300 gallons
	I, II and IIIA[5]	4 gallons	100 gallons	200 gallons	8 gallons	200 gallons	400 gallons

[1]Class A Laboratory units shall not be used as instructional laboratory units.

[2]Maximum quantities of flammable and combustible liquids in Class B and Class C instructional laboratory units shall be 50% of those listed in the Table.

[3]For maximum container sizes, see Table 7-2.

[4]Regardless of the maximum allowable quantity, the maximum amount in a laboratory unit shall never exceed an amount calculated by using the maximum quantity per 100 square feet of laboratory unit. The area of offices, lavatories, and other contiguous areas of a laboratory unit are to be included when making this calculation.

[5]The maximum quantities of Class I liquids shall not exceed the quantities specified for Class I liquids alone.

[6]Where water may create a serious fire or personnel hazard, a nonwater extinguishing system may be used instead of sprinklers.

[7]See description of Flammable Liquid Storage Room in Section 4-4 of NFPA 30, *Flammable and Combustible Liquids Code.* See description of Storage Cabinet in Section 4-2 of NFPA 30.

For SI units: 1 gal = 3.785 L; 100 sq ft = 9.3 m².

Source: Reprinted with permission from NFPA 45, Standard on Fire Protection for Laboratories Using Chemicals, Copyright, 1986, National Fire Protection Association, Quincy, Mass. 02269. This reprinted material is not the complete and official position of the NFPA on the referenced subject, which is represented only by the standard in its entirety.

Table 7.3-2. Maximum Quantities of Flammable and Combustible Liquids in Instructional Laboratory Units

Lab Unit Class	Flam. Liquid Class	*Excluding* Safety Cans and Storage Cabinet Quantities — Maximum Quantities — Gal Per 100 Sq Ft	Non-spkd.	Spkd.	*Including* Safety Cans and Storage Cabinet Quantities — Maximum Quantities — Gal. Per 100 Sq Ft	Non-spkd.	Spkd.
A		Not permitted except for graduate and postgraduate laboratories					
B	I	2.5	75	150	5	150	300
B	I, II and IIIA	5	100	200	10	200	400
C	I	1	37.5	75	2	75	150
C	I, II and IIIA	2	50	100	4	100	200

NFPA Standard No. 45 allows a great deal of flexibility in how a laboratory unit is divided into laboratory work areas, offices and internal corridors or circulation pathways. Many building code officials, however, are unaware of this provision, and some may not allow it because other codes under their jurisdiction are perceived to be more stringent. The following four examples in three different states, designed according

Table 7.3-3. Limiting Factors in Typical Class B Instructional Lab Units

Sq Ft	Class	Excluding Storage — Gal/100 Sq. Ft.	Max. Non-spkd	Max. spkd.	Including Storage — Gal/100 Sq Ft	Max. Non-spkd	Max. spkd.
1,000	I	(25)	75	150	(50)	150	300
	I, II, IIIA	(50)	100	200	(100)	200	400
2,000	I	(50)	75	150	(100)	150	300
	I, II, IIIA	100	(100)	200	200	(200)	400
3,000	I	75	(75)	150	150	(150)	300
	I, II, IIIA	150	(100)	200	300	(200)	400
4,000	I	100	(75)	150	200	(150)	300
	I, II, IIIA	200	(100)	200	400	(200)	400
5,000	I	125	(75)	150	250	(150)	300
	I, II, IIIA	250	(100)	(200)	500	(200)	(400)
6,000	I	150	(75)	150	300	(150)	(300)
	I, II, IIIA	300	(100)	(200)	600	(200)	(400)
6,100	I	152.5	(75)	(150)	305	(150)	(300)
	I, II, IIIA	305	(100)	(200)	610	(200)	(400)

Note: Circled numbers denote limits.
Source: John Fresina.

Table 7.3-4. Gallons Per Student for a Typical Class B Instructional Laboratory Unit*

Sq Ft	Flam. Liquid Class	Excluding Safety Cans and Storage Cabinet Quantities Maximum Quantities			Including Safety Cans and Storage Cabinet Quantities Maximum Quantities		
		Gal Per Stud	Non-spkd.	Spkd.	Gal. Per Stud.	Non-spkd.	Spkd.
1,000	I	1.25			2.5		
	I, II, IIIA	2.5			5.0		
2,000	I	1.25			2.5		
	I, II, IIIA		2.5			5.0	
3,000	I		1.25			2.5	
	I, II, IIIA		2.5			3.3	
4,000	I		0.6			1.8	
	I, II, IIIA		1.25			2.5	
5,000	I		0.75			1.5	
	I, II, IIIA		1.0			2.0	4.0
6,000	I		0.6			1.25	2.5
	I, II, IIIA		0.83			1.6	3.3
6,100	I		0.6			1.2	2.4
	I, II, IIIA		0.8			1.6	3.2

*Assumes 50 sq. ft per student.

to the provisions of the standard and reviewed and approved by code officials, illustrate the difference in acceptance of non-rated partitions within the laboratory unit:

Example 1: A Teaching Laboratory for College Chemistry (Figure 7.3-1)

The laboratory unit in this case is a complete floor in a multistory building. The separation is the standard 2 hours between floors, and the stair enclosure is 2 hours. The support spaces are enclosed with nonrated partitions for security reasons and to minimize cross-contamination. The total area is

Table 7.3-5. Maximum Allowable Container Capacity[1]

Container Type	Flammable Liquids[2]			Combustible Liquids[2]	
	IA	IB	IC	II	IIIA
Glass	1 pt[3]	1 qt[3]	1 gal	1 gal	5 gal
Metal (other than DOT drums) or approved plastic	1 gal	5 gal[1]	5 gal[4]	5 gal[4]	5 gal
Safety cans	2 gal	5 gal[4]	5 gal[4]	5 gal	5 gal
Metal drums (DOT)	N/A[5]	5 gal[4]	60 gal[4]	60 gal[4]	60 gal

[1]This table is taken from NFPA 30, *Flammable and Combustible Liquids Code,* except for allowable quantities of flammable liquids in metal DOT drums.
[2]See B-1 for definitions of the various classes of flammable and combustible liquids.
[3]See Exception No. 1 of 7-2.3.2 and A-7-2.3.2.
[4]In instructional laboratory work areas, no container for Class I or II liquids shall exceed a capacity of 1 gallon, except that safety cans may be of 2 gallon capacity.
[5]N/A = Not Allowed. See Exception No. 2 of 7-2.3.2.
For SI units: 1 gal = 3.785 liters; 1 qt = 0.95 liters; 1 pt = .48 liter.
Source: Reprinted with permission from NFPA 45, Standard on Fire Protection for Laboratories Using Chemicals, Copyright, 1986, National Fire Protection Association, Quincy, Mass. 02269. This reprinted material is not the complete and official position of the NFPA on the referenced subject which is represented only by the standard in its entirety.

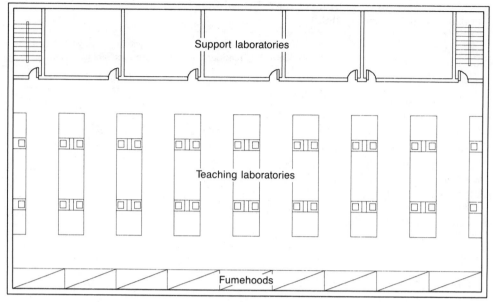

Fig. 7.3-1. Teaching laboratory for college chemistry.

sprinklered and can be 20,000 sq ft, assuming a Class B fire hazard classification for an instructional laboratory based on the quantities of flammables and combustible liquids anticipated. Advantages: lower cost and better visual supervisions of teaching operations.

Example 2: State Public Health Laboratory (Figure 7.3-2)

This one-story building consists of a number of wings, each designed as a laboratory unit. Fire exits are provided to the corridor and directly to the outside. The partitions and doors between labs, offices and circulation pathways are nonrated and stop at the ceilings. The total wing area is sprinklered and is less than 10,000 sq ft for a Class A fire hazard classification. Advantages: lower cost and a feeling of openness due to the

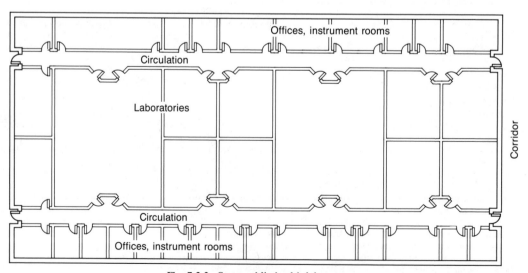

Fig. 7.3-2. State public health laboratory.

many windows between laboratories, circulation pathways and offices.

Example 3: Biomedical Research Laboratory (Figure 7.3-3)

This is a multistory building, with each floor consisting of four quadrants. Each quadrant is a laboratory unit for a Class A hazard classification, fully sprinklered and less than 10,000 sq ft. An equipment alcove is provided in the circulation pathway for noisy and shared equipment. With rated corridors, equipment would not be allowed here. Advantages: lower cost and greater flexibility.

Example 4: State Public Health Laboratory (Figure 7.3-4)

This laboratory, located in California, is governed by Title 29 provisions which are more restrictive. A laboratory unit concept is acceptable only if exit pathways are clear and visible. Large open labs are acceptable.

Enclosed, nonrated work areas on the perimeter, but not in the center, are acceptable.

Fire Resistance Rating of the Separation with other Laboratory Units

Table 7.3-6, which is reproduced from Table 3-1 of NFPA No. 45, makes it very clear that the size and fire hazard classification of the laboratory unit depend to a large degree on the construction of the separation between it and other laboratory units. Construction can be downgraded if the unit is fully sprinklered.

The committee that produced the standard felt strongly that innocent bystanders should be protected from operations in a laboratory unit, hence the provision for a separation between a laboratory unit and nonlaboratory areas equal to or greater than the provisions stated in Table 7.3-6. However, nonlaboratory areas which are an integral part of the units operations, such as research offices,

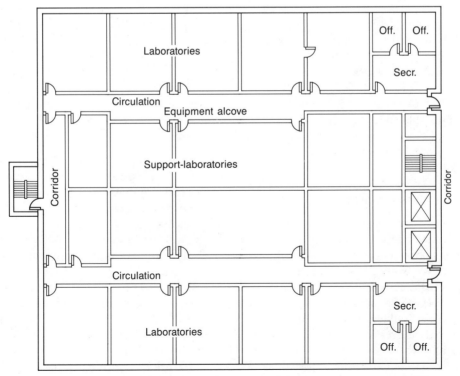

Fig. 7.3-3. Biomedical research laboratory.

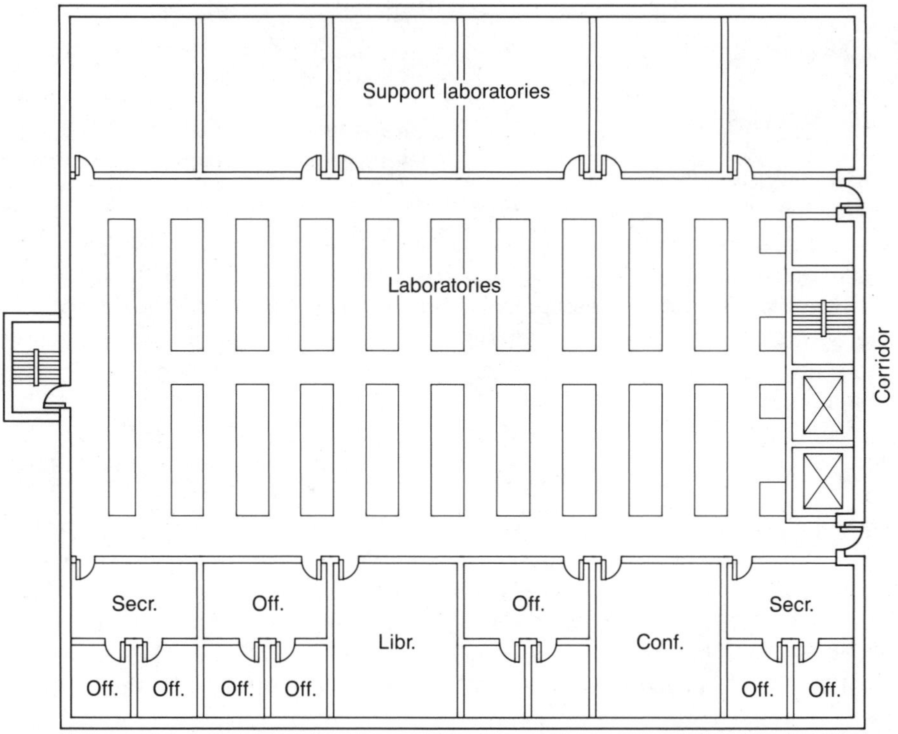

Fig. 7.3-4. State public health laboratory, California.

equipment rooms, locker rooms, and storage areas, can be incorporated in the laboratory unit enclosure.

The standard provides for separation between laboratory units and nonlaboratory areas. The provisions of NFPA No. 101 and other applicable codes dealing with stair enclosures, access to an exit, and separation between floors still apply and must be adhered to.

Automatic Fire Suppression System

The recorded ability of automatic sprinkler systems to extinguish and control the spread of fire has been good (see Section 2.9). The committee was willing to give a great deal of credit for the use of sprinklers. They allowed the quantities of flammable and combustible liquids to be doubled for sprinklered areas and allowed the area to be doubled for a laboratory unit with a standard 1-hour separation between it and other laboratory units of equal or lower classification for a Class A

lab unit in a building with any type of construction.

Exiting

In order to facilitate exiting from a laboratory unit, several provisions are written into the standard:

- The door must swing in the direction of exit for Class A and B laboratory units.
- Every laboratory work area must have a second access to an exit if (1) an explosion hazard exists that could block the only exit, (2) the laboratory work area is greater than 500 sq ft and has a Class A classification, (3) the laboratory work area is greater than 1,000 sq ft and has a Class B or C classification, (4) a fumehood is located adjacent to the exit door, which might prevent its use in case of a fire or explosion in the fumehood, or (5) under certain other conditions re-

Table 7.3-6. Construction and Fire Protection Requirements for Laboratory Units[1]

Laboratory Unit Fire Hazard Class	Area of Laboratory Unit. Square Feet	Nonsprinklered Laboratory Units				Sprinklered Laboratory Units[2]	
		Construction Types I and II[3]		Construction Types III, IV and V[3]		Any Construction Type[3]	
		Separation from Nonlaboratory Areas	Separation from Lab. Units of Equal or Lower Hazard Classification	Separation from Nonlaboratory Areas	Separation from Lab. Units of Equal or Lower Hazard Classification	Separation from Nonlaboratory Areas	Separation from Laboratory Units of Equal or Lower Hazard Classification
A	Under 1000	1 hour	1 hour	2 hours	1 hour	1 hour	NC/LC[3,4]
	1001–2000	1 hour	1 hour	N/A[4]	N/A	1 hour	NC/LC
	2001–5000	2 hours	1 hour	N/A	N/A	1 hour	NC/LC
	5001–10,000	N/A[4]	N/A	N/A	N/A	1 hour	NC/LC
	10,001 or more	N/A	N/A	N/A	N/A	N/A[4]	N/A
B	Under 20,000	1 hour	NC/LC[3,4]	1 hour	1 hour	NC/LC[5,7]	NC/LC
	20,000 or more	N/A	N/A	N/A	N/A	N/A	N/A
C	Under 10,000	1 hour	NC/LC[5,7]	1 hour	NC/LC[5,7]	NC/LC[5,6]	NC/LC[5,6]
	10,000 or more	1 hour	NC/LC	1 hour	1 hour	NC/LC[5,6]	NC/LC

[1]Where a laboratory work area or unit contains an explosion hazard, appropriate protection shall be provided for adjoining laboratory units and nonlaboratory areas, as specified in Chapter 5.

[2]In laboratory units where water may create a serious fire or personnel hazard, a nonwater extinguishing system may be substituted for sprinklers.

[3]See Appendix B-3.

[4]N/A = Not Allowed; NC/LC = Noncombustible/Limited Combustible Construction (See Appendix B-3).

[5]May be ½-hour fire-rated combustible construction.

[6]Existing combustible construction is acceptable.

[7]Laboratory units in educational occupancies shall be separated from nonlaboratory areas by 1-hour construction.

For SI units: 1 sq ft = 0.093 m².

Source: Reprinted with permission from NFPA 45, Standard on Fire Protection for Laboratories Using Chemicals, Copyright, 1986, National Fire Protection Association, Quincy, Mass. 02269. This reprinted material is not the complete and official position of the NFPA on the referenced subject, which is represented only by the standard in its entirety.

lating to the use of gas cylinders and cryogenic containers.

- The benches and equipment in the laboratory work areas must be arranged in such a way that the path of travel to the exit is clear and easy to travel.
- Given the above requirements, one is well advised to consider the need for a second egress from almost all Class A laboratories in order to increase the flexibility of use. Access to an exit through another laboratory work area or unit with the same or a lower hazard classification is generally acceptable.

The means of egress for laboratory units and buildings must comply with the provisions of NFPA No. 101 or any other building code in force.

7.3.3 Conclusions

It was not the intent of this section to repeat in detail the requirements of NFPA Standard No. 45, but rather to elucidate some of the provisions, to emphasize the need to anticipate future requirements of use,and to provide flexibility so that the facility can adjust. The reader is well advised to read the standard in its entirety. This handbook does not deal with emergency, fire prevention and maintenance procedures described in the standard. Fumehood requirements and mechanical systems are dealt with in other chapters in this handbook.

REFERENCES

National Fire Protection Association, 1986. Standard 45: Fire Protection for Laboratories Using Chemicals. Quincy, MA: NFPA.
National Fire Protection Association, 1985. Standard 101: Life Safety Code. Quincy, MA: NFPA.

7.4 NFPA STANDARD NO. 99   T. Ruys

7.4.1 Introduction

The National Fire Protection Association is a nonprofit organization dedicated to establishing standards to protect against the loss of life and property due to fire.

In the past, laboratories in health care facilities were covered in NFPA No. 56C. The 1987 edition of NFPA No. 99, Healthcare Facilities, formerly incorporated NFPA No. 56C. The references in this section are from the 1987 edition.

Health care facilities laboratories, both new and existing, are covered in NFPA No. 101 unless they are considered a severe hazard. In that case, they must comply with NFPA No. 99.

Our interest is in how Standard No. 99 applies to laboratory facilities planning and design. As its name implies, Standard No. 99 covers health care facilities. However, by the definition given in the standard, health care facilities include hospitals, nursing homes, custodial care, supervisory care, clinics, medical and dental offices and ambulatory care facilities. Thus this standard applies to laboratories in any of these types of facilities. However, it applies only to new construction.

The standard defines a laboratory as a building or space which houses activities in which flammable, combustible or oxidizing materials are used for analysis, research or teaching. Medical laboratories, by contrast, are defined as rooms used in direct support of patient therapy. It is not clear whether the standard applies to these types of laboratories, but it is assumed that it does if flammable, combustible or oxidizing materials are used.

NFPA standards are typically revised every 5 years. Any questions or proposed revisions must be addressed to the Standards Committee at the NFPA offices. The address is given in Appendix A of this handbook.

NFPA standards are not codes or regulations unless adopted by a legislative body on a federal, state or local level. The laboratory planner must contact the AHJ in order to ascertain whether this standard applies.

The AHJ most often is the agency responsible for public safety, but insurance companies and building owners may also impose these standards. The prudent laboratory planner should consult all these entities in order to document all standards that apply.

Adoption can be by reference or by transcription. "By reference" means the citing of title and publishing information only. Any changes, deletions or additions to the standard made by the legislative body must be noted. "By transcription" means that the legislative body has received permission from the NFPA to transcribe, in whole or in part, this standard in its own codes, laws or regulations. In that case, NFPA No. 99 does not apply.

This edition of the standard has been approved by the American National Standards Institute and is also known as the "ANSI/NFPA No. 99 Standard."

7.4.2 Laboratories

A great deal of the chapter on health care laboratories in NFPA No. 99 deals with operations, procedures and training. Some of the salient points dealing with facilities are:

- One-hour rated partitions and 45-minute rated openings must separate the laboratories in health care facilities from other occupancies and exit corridors. An exception is made for laboratories protected by an automatic extinguishing system (10-3.11).
- Finishes, means of egress and doors must comply with the requirements of NFPA No. 101 (10-3.1.2 and 10-3.2.3).
- Laboratories larger than 1,000 sq ft (assume net sq ft) must have at least two exit access doors. One door must open into a means of egress (10-3.2.1).
- Travel distance to one of these doors must not exceed 75 ft from any location inside the laboratory space (10-3.2.2).
- Laboratory corridors which are used as exit access must meet the requirements of NFPA No. 101 (NFPA No. 99, 10-3.2.4). NFPA No. 101, 5-1.3.4, states, "Corridors used as exit access and serving an area having an occupant load of more than 30 shall be separated from other parts of the building by construction having at least a one-hour resistance rating." However, internal corridors that are *not* an exit access are probably complying more with NFPA

No. 45, which allows internal corridors within a laboratory unit and without a fire rating.

- If laboratory corridors are used to transport patients in beds, the more restrictive requirements govern. Corridors (access to an exit) must be at least 96 in. clear and unobstructed (10-3.2.5).
- Unattended laboratory operations using flammable or combustible reagents must be protected by an automatic fire extinguishing system (10-4.1.2) This also applies to laboratories that are not separated from surrounding areas by 1-hour rated construction and Class C self-closing fire doors (10-5.1.1) and use quantities of flammable and combustible or hazardous materials considered less than severe. The same applies to laboratories that are not separated from surrounding areas by 2-hour construction and Class B self-closing fire doors (10-5.1.2) and use quantities of flammable and combustible or hazardous materials considered severe. Unfortunately "less than severe" and "severe" are not defined, so a reading by the AHJ is advisable. See Section 7.1.
- The automatic fire extinguishing system must be connected to the facility fire alarm system and sound an immediate alarm (10-5.2).
- Emergency shower and eyewash facilities must be provided within the work area if corrosive materials are used (10-6). The eyewash facility is referred to as the "fixed eye bath," which seems to limit the types of fixtures (see Section 4.8 of this handbook).

7.4.3 Environmental Systems

Some of the salient features for environmental systems are covered here. References are to the 1987 edition of NFPA No. 99.

- "Air exhausted from laboratory areas shall not be recirculated to other parts of the facility" (5-3.1).
- Laboratories must have negative pressure (5-4.3.1). Exception: when the work

must be protected from contamination and is not infectious or noxious.

- "Exit corridors shall not be used as plenum to supply or exhaust air from laboratory areas" (5-4.3.2). The previous statement precludes the use of the corridor as an exhaust plenum.

- Exhaust ducts must be under negative pressure. Fumehood fans *should* be installed outside and not in a mechanical space (5-4.3.3). In many cases, it is not practical to locate fumehood fans on the roof because of high maintenance costs and the difficulty of waterproofing the roof membrane around multiple penetrations. The committee seems to have recognized that need and has allowed "should" instead of a "shall," although the statement is located in the body of the text.

- Fumehoods must not be located at exit doors and must be away from areas causing air turbulence in front of the fumehood (5-4.4.1).

- Fumehood controls must prevent an imbalance in the system if the exhaust is shut off in one hood on the system (5-4.4.5). Not mentioned is the fact that the supply or makeup air should shut off if the exhaust air fails; otherwise, the laboratory will be pressurized in relation to surrounding areas, which is prohibited by Section 5-4.3.1 of the standards.

The reader is encouraged to acquire a copy of NFPA No. 99 when planning a health care laboratory. Several areas of possible concerns are not covered in this handbook.

BARRIER-FREE DESIGN   *T. Ruys*

It is not the intent of this section to repeat all the requirements of the *Guidebook to the Minimum Federal Guidelines and Requirements for Accessible Design* (1981), but only those that have been applied to laboratories. There are no specific references to laboratories in the *Guidebook*. However, the DHEW-TH *Criteria for the Full Accessibil-*

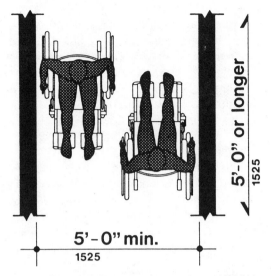

Fig. 7.5-1. Minimum dimensions for wheelchair passing.

ity to HEW-Owned Facilities (1975) specifically mentions dimensions and aisle widths for workstations in laboratories. These will be covered later in this section.

Because of the lack of specifics, a number of practices have evolved over time, and a mumber of barrier-free designs have been applied to benches, fumehoods and safety equipment commonly found in teaching and research laboratories.

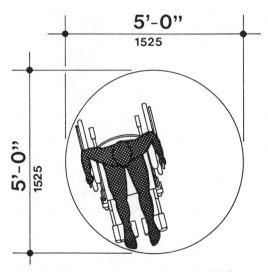

Fig. 7.5-2. Turning radius for a wheelchair.

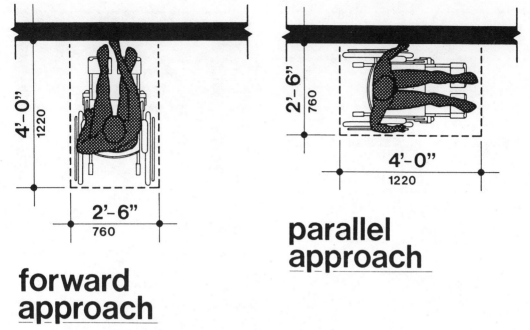

forward approach

parallel approach

Fig. 7.5-3. Minimum space requirements for straight wheelchair access.

The Architectural Barriers Act (Public Law 90-480) of August 12, 1968, as amended, ensures that certain buildings financed with federal funds are designed and constructed to be accessible to the physically handicapped. "Building" means any building or facility whose intended use requires it to be accessible to the public or that may result in employment or residence therein by physically handicapped persons. This building or facility is (1) to be constructed or altered by or on behalf of the United States and (2) for

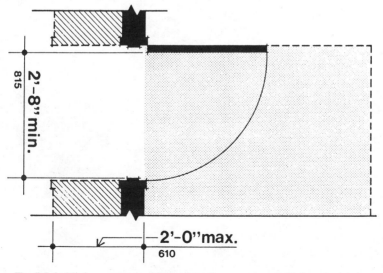

Fig. 7.5-4. Minimum access width and maximum access depth for wheelchair.

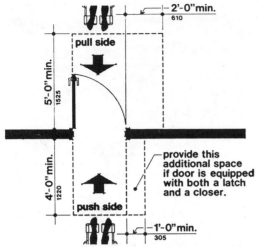

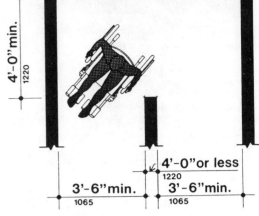

Fig. 7.5-7. Minimum turning requirements for a maze.

front approach

Fig. 7.5-5. Latch-side clearance required for a person in a wheelchair to open a hinged door.

every lease entered into in whole or in part by a grant or loan made by the United States, including any renewal of a lease after January 1, 1977.

The illustrations in this section come from the *Guidebook to the Minimum Federal Guidelines and Requirements for Accessible Design* published by the United States Architectural and Transportation Barriers Compliance Board, unless otherwise noted.

7.5.1 Access

Most laboratory facilities, because of the heavy amount of cart traffic, have corridors

which are at least 5 ft wide. This allows adequate space for two wheelchairs passing each other, for turning or for straight access to laboratory doors. See Figures 7.5-1, 7.5-2 and 7.5-3.

Laboratory doors, because of equipment access, are typically 3–4 ft wide, which is far in excess of the 2 ft 8 in. minimum clear opening required. See Figure 7.5-4. Door opening recesses which are deeper than 2 ft 0 in. shall be a minimum of 3 ft 0 in. wide on the push side, with an additional 1 ft 0 in. if the door is equipped with both a latch and a closer. See Figure 7.5-5. The minimum maneuvering space next to the door, i.e., the latch side clearance for a hinged door is 1 ft 6 in., but a 2 ft 0 in. is space is recommended where available.

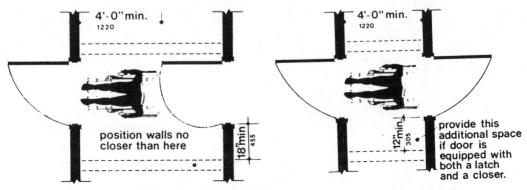

Fig. 7.5-6. Minimum dimensions for a wheelchair to pass in an airlock.

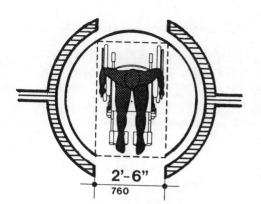

Fig. 7.5-8. Revolving lightlock minimum access requirements (modified).

Certain laboratory facilities have doors in series, such as for air locks to containment or animal facilities. The minimum dimensions for these conditions are shown in Figure 7.5-6. Doors shall not swing toward each other into the intervening space.

Some shielded facilities require a maze for entry. The turns and maneuvering clearances are as noted in Figure 7.5-7.

Dark room and cold room doors are a particular challenge. Dark room doors are difficult to keep light tight and often have a threshold. Although the standard revolving doors are not suitable for handicapped per-

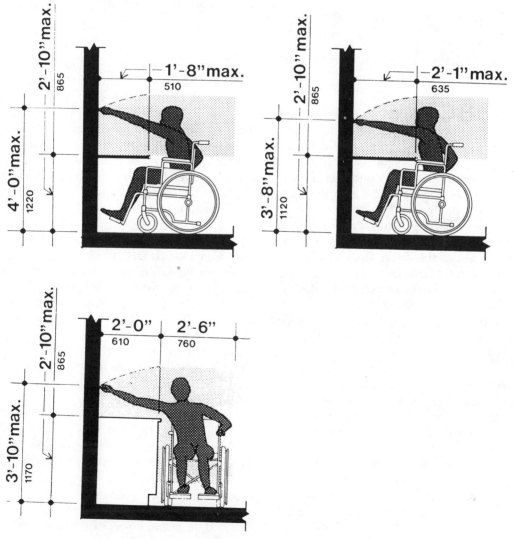

Fig. 7.5-9. Limitations of forward and sideways reach.

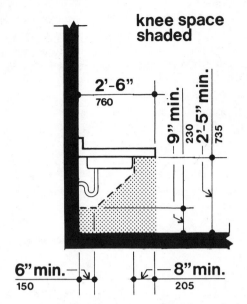

knee space shaded

Fig. 7.5-10. Available plumbing space under a wheelchair workstation.

sons in wheelchairs, there are special light-tight darkroom revolving doors that may be used as long as these meet the clear floor or space requirements required. Note that revolving doors are not permitted as an egress component. See Figure 7.5-8. Another possibility is to apply blackout curtains to the air lock shown in Figure 7.5-6. Cold rooms have a 4-in. insulated floor, which often is installed above the finish floor and not recessed into the structural slab. This requires a ramp which shall not exceed the slope requirements of the *Guide.* That means that a 4-in. insulated floor on 1-in. sleepers which are used to provide an air space below the box will require a 5 ft 0 in. ramp (1:12 slope). This assumes that it is possible to open the cold room door, which always opens out, while maneuvering the wheelchair on the ramp and opening the door at the same time. If this is not practical or if the space for the ramp is not available, the cold box floor must be recessed or deleted, with insulation applied to the bottom of the floor slab below the cold box. This applied insulation is important to prevent condensation on the cold floor slab.

7.5.2 Laboratory Benches

The *DHEW-TH Criteria* (1975) requires workstations for handicapped persons.

- Lab benches for use by persons in wheelchairs should provide knee space at least 32 in wide, with a clear height of at least 28.5 in. to the underside of the bench. The height of the benchtop should not exceed 30 in.
- Aisles between benches or equipment should have a clear width of at least 48 in. Nothing is mentioned about reach limitations. Let's consider each in turn, starting with the last.

The reach limitation depends on the depth of the benchtop and on whether the bench is approached with a forward or parallel motion. See Figure 7.5-9. That means that the bench top height shall not exceed 2 ft 10 in., and any fixtures that must be reached are no further back than 2 ft 1 in. from the front edge. However, in order to reach a shelf over the bench and to turn fixture handles, the configuration shown in Figure 7.5-11 is preferred.

The knee space requirements can be derived from the first DHEW statement above, which are based on the dimensions of the most commonly used wheelchair. However, a slightly higher top allows the wheelchair armrest to go below the bench top. See Figure 7.5-11.

The space below the bench available for plumbing and the armrest is shown in Figure 7.5-10. These dimensions have been incorporated in Figure 7.5-11 as well.

The design of this bench is fixed because of the plumbing. This may be acceptable for a teaching laboratory, where students in wheelchairs may be common. The design in Figure 7.5-12 is better for research labs, where handicapped persons in wheelchairs are rare, and the bench may be used at a standard height until needed.

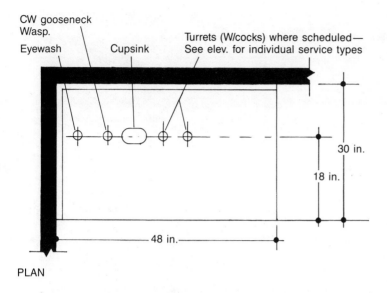

CW gooseneck
W/asp.

Eyewash   Cupsink

Turrets (W/cocks) where scheduled—
See elev. for individual service types

30 in.

18 in.

48 in.

PLAN

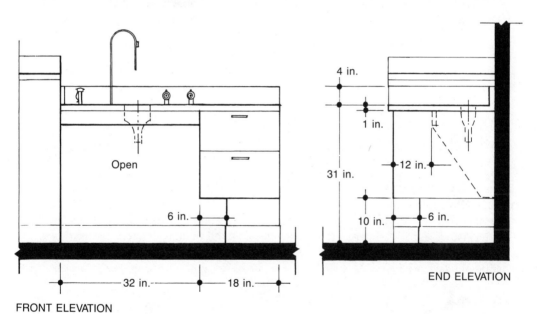

4 in.

1 in.

Open

31 in.

12 in.

6 in.

10 in.   6 in.

6 in.

32 in.   18 in.

END ELEVATION

FRONT ELEVATION

Fig. 7.5-11. Laboratory workstation for wheelchair access: fixed (Theodorus Ruys).

7.5.3 Fumehood Designs

Fumehoods required in many laboratory operations create special problems because they are safety devices. They are therefore difficult to adjust and modify, are expensive and take up a lot of room.

For simple applications and most teaching situations, an adjustable hood can be designed above the handicapped person's workstation, as shown in Figure 7.5-14. For research laboratories and more complex laboratory operations, a standard fumehood must be modified when needed. Modifications consist of deleting the base cabinets and supporting the superstructure and top on a leg frame at the required height. A

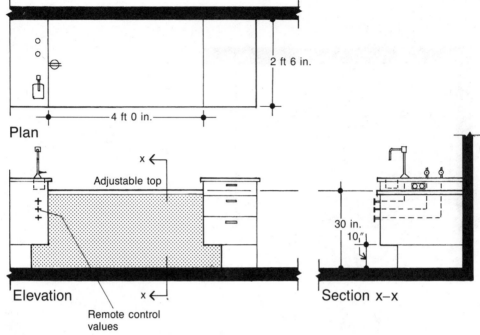

Plan

Adjustable top

Elevation

2 ft 6 in.

4 ft 0 in.

30 in.

10″

Section x–x

Remote control values

Fig. 7.5-12. Laboratory workstation for wheelchair access: adjustable (Theodorus Ruys).

fumehood with remote handle fixtures in the sideposts must be selected. See Figure 7.5-15.

7.5.4 Emergency Safety Devices

Emergency showers and eyewash facilities are common and necessary in laboratory operations. Eyewash facilities can be incorporated as hand-held devices in workstations for the handicapped. Emergency shower handles must be no higher than 4 ft 6 in. and must be of a type which can be pushed up in

order to stop the flow of water. See Figure 7.5-16.

7.5.5 Other Considerations

Nothing has been said about thresholds, hardware types and heights, and closing and opening forces. These are considered standard building requirements for all building types and the reader is encouraged to review referenced standards.

A few comments, however, are in order.

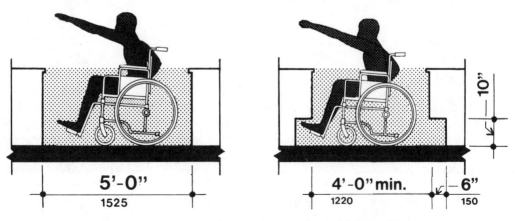

5'-0"
1525

4'-0" min.
1220

10"

6"
150

Fig. 7.5-13. Aisle width to accommodate a single wheelchair (modified).

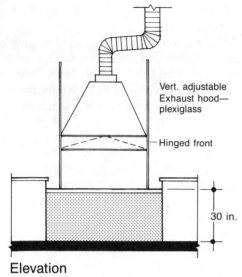

Elevation

Fig. 7.5-14. Adjustable fumehood over a wheelchair workstation (Theodorus Ruys).

Little has been said in this section about individuals with other types of handicaps, such as the blind and the deaf. Although these individuals are rare in laboratory facilities, they do occur. Therefore, as a minimum, the following should be considered:

- Doors leading to hazardous areas such as radioisotope labs and other types of containment laboratories, and to chemical and waste storage vaults, should have a textured surface on the door handle as a signal for the visually impaired.

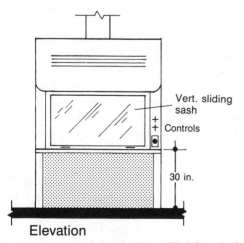

Elevation

Fig. 7.5-15. Standard fumehood modified for wheelchair access (Theodorus Ruys).

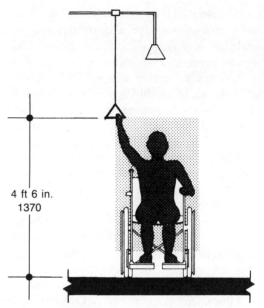

Fig. 7.5-16. Emergency shower maximum reach (modified).

- There are many types of alarms in laboratory facilities. These should be provided with both audible and visual signals for the hearing impaired.

REFERENCES

U.S. Architecture and Transportation Barriers Compliance Board, 1981. *A Guidebook to the Minimum Federal Guidelines and Requirements for Accessible Design.* Wash. DC.

DHEW-TH (1975). *Technical Handbook for Facilities Engineering & Construction Manual.* Part 4, Facilities Design and Construction. Series 4.2. Design of Barrier-Free Facilities. Chapter 2, Criteria for Free Accessibility to HEW-Owned Facilities, pp 3-20, Wash. D.C.

Federal Register, 1982. Part III. Architectural and Transportation Barriers Compliance Board. *Minimum Guidelines and Requirements for Accessible Design.* Vol. 47, No. 150, pp 33862–93.

7.6 Building and Fire Codes
S. Bettge and T. Ruys

7.6.1 Introduction

Every project must begin by establishing the ground rules. Laboratories and their design are no exception.

The initial step is to determine all applicable codes, ordinances and regulations, as each has a direct effect on the design and permit process. This begins by determining each reviewing agency and AHJ. This process may not be readily apparent because the AHJ may not be limited to one jurisdiction; both local and state authorities may be involved. Other agencies may also be involved and may have additional regulations, e.g., lending agencies or insurance groups. Owners may require adherence to codes which have not been adopted locally.

We cannot overstress the importance of ascertaining all AHJs and codes which are applicable to the project. The date of the adopted edition for each code, standard and/or regulation must also be determined. It is not uncommon for two AHJs to use two different editions of the same code or standard.

Some jurisdictions, when writing adoptive ordinances, may choose either total or partial adoption of a code or standard. Also, portions of codes or standards may be deleted or amended. If this is the case, the local adopting ordinances would not be applicable outside of their specific jurisdiction. When two AHJs are involved, it is possible that one AHJ will not accept or recognize another jurisdiction's amendments, adopting ordinances or interpretations.

When two or more codes are applicable, it should be anticipated that there will be conflicts between them. It is not to be construed that the codes' intents are different, only that the means to the same end may differ. Generally, the most restrictive part of each code or standard must be incorporated into the design. However, this may make a project economically unfeasible by forcing the design to meet each code. When a jurisdiction has adopted two or more codes or standards which are in conflict, it is important to determine which one ultimately will govern. In many cases, this may take extensive negotiation between two AHJs, e.g., a building official and a fire marshal.

It may be helpful in the negotiation process to use nationally recognized standards as a guide to assist in resolving conflicts and disputes.

The entire process of negotiation may be accomplished by an architect or an engineer who is well versed in the applicable code issues. In some cases, it may require the services of an outside professional, i.e., a fire protection consultant. There will be times when AHJs will listen only to a recognized professional code consultant or fire protection engineering consultant, while others will rely strictly on an appeal process. Both the professional consultant and the appeal process will be expensive and time-consuming, especially when the project is large and when more than one issue is concerned. The larger the project, the more will be at stake. Through negotiation, trade-offs or code equivalency may be acceptable to the AHJs. This process could offset the cost of the consultant's fee, even if amortized over a few years, including the agreed-upon equivalencies. Regardless of the process, it is extremely important to have all decisions documented, with copies to each participating party. This is recommended for all decisions, especially on projects lasting for several years. It is not uncommon for personnel within a jurisdiction to change over the course of a project. If possible, written confirmation should be received from those making decisions.

When beginning a laboratory project, the first thing to establish is the occupancy classification. This may vary, depending on the AHJ and/or on the hazard rating of the laboratory contents. Laboratories will generally fall into one of four basic occupancy classifications: (1) business, (2) industrial, (3) hazardous or (4) special use. Placement of the occupancy into the correct classification is based on the laboratory use and intended (proposed) quantities of flammable or hazardous materials used or stored. Therefore it is important to establish or obtain from the owner or user a list of materials which will be used and/or stored in the lab. The materials list should include all combustibles and flammables, along with individual quantities and flame spread ratings. In addition, a list is required of those materials which may be considered toxic or hazardous, including those which will react with other substances—especially water, as this is primarily used for fire protection. This list must be accurate, as most jurisdictions require permits for the storage, use and handling of flammables, hazardous materials and/or toxic materials. The AHJ, i.e., the fire marshal, may be able to assist in determining the hazard classification of certain materials.

Once the occupancy classification has been established and approved by the AHJ, the zoning must be reviewed to determine if the site is zoned to accept the proposed use. If not, either a zoning variance and hearing must be undertaken or an alternative site must be selected. This process may take an exceptionally long time, perhaps years.

Generally speaking, high-hazard laboratories or those using highly hazardous or toxic materials are not permitted in or near densely populated or metropolitan areas. These are sometimes referenced under fire districts within applicable codes and ordinances.

Once the occupancy group is established, the type of building construction can be determined. The occupancy has a direct bearing on the allowable construction type, building area, height and zoning restrictions, along with the location of the building on the lot. Placement of the building on the site may be determined by property lines, exit locations, streets, fire department access, easements, setbacks and other buildings on the same site.

For those unfamiliar with the use of codes, each of the three model codes (UBC, SBC, BOCA) has in the introduction a list of steps, procedures or recommended use of the code. Once a person is familiar with one model code, its intent, practices and similar conditions may be applied to other codes and standards. However, a word of caution is in order. There will always be differences among the various codes and/or standards. Some of these differences may be subtle, with requirements spelled out in what appear to be nonrelated areas of an applicable document.

7.6.2 Uniform Building Code (UBC, 1988 Edition)

The UBC is published by the International Conference of Building Officials (ICBO). This code is used predominantly in the western United States; however, several midwestern states have also adopted the UBC.

Occupancy Classification

Depending upon the classification of the materials used, stored or handled, laboratories are placed in either of the following occupancy categories:

B-2—see UBC Chapter 7.
H—see UBC Chapter 9.

Laboratories which exceed the amounts of hazardous materials, liquids and chemicals listed in UBC Table 9–A (Chapter 9) are considered hazardous and are classified as an H (hazardous) occupancy. Other laboratories generally fall under a B-2 classification. This does not prohibit laboratories from being housed in an E (educational) occupancy, provided that they are separated from adjacent areas, as required in Chapter 8 of the code.

Mixed Occupancies

Laboratories are commonly located in buildings classified as "mixed occupancy." These are permitted as long as each occupancy complies with its own occupancy requirements and is separated from adjacent occupancies, as covered in UBC Chapter 5, Section 503 and Table 5.B.

Laboratories using "hazardous production material (HPM)" as defined in Chapter 4 of the UBC are automatically classified as H-6 occupancies. The specific requirements are found in UBC Chapter 9. When an H-6 occupancy is within a mixed occupancy building, that portion of the building housing the H-6 occupancy is limited to three stories in height. Hence, no occupancy is permitted above the H-6 portion of the building.

Uniform Fire Code

This has been written by the Western Fire Chiefs Association for the ICBO. It limits the amount of container and portable tank storage permitted within each occupancy classification. See UBC Article 79. Refer to Article 80 for rules governing the use and storage of hazardous materials.

7.6.3 National Building Code (BOCA, 1987 Edition with 1988 Supplement)

The BOCA Basic/National Building Code is published by the Building Officials and Code Administrators (BOCA). This code is used predominantly in the eastern United States.

Use Group Classification

Similar to the UBC, the "use group" for laboratories is determined by the amounts of hazardous materials, liquids and chemicals used, stored or handled. Laboratories are placed into the following use groups:

Use BOCA Group B—see Section 303.0
Use BOCA Group H (high hazard)—see Section 306

Laboratories which exceed the amounts of materials, liquids or chemicals listed in BOCA Table 306.2.1 are considered Group H hazardous occupancies.

Mixed Use Occupancies

Laboratories are commonly located in buildings classified as "mixed use" occupancy. These are permitted provided that each occupancy or "use" complies with its group requirements and is separated from other "uses" as covered in BOCA Sections 313.1.2 and 902.

Special Use Occupancies

Laboratories using HPM, as defined in BOCA Section 200, are classified as "special use" occupancies. Requirements for HPM use facilities are covered in BOCA Section 603.

The BOCA code, unlike the UBC, makes direct reference to standards published by the NFPA.

BOCA National Fire Prevention Code

This code should be reviewed for the storage, handling and use of flammable or combustible liquids permitted in each use group. See BOCA Article 28, Section F-2805.0.

7.6.4 Standard Building Code (SBC, 1988 Edition)

The Southern Standard Building Code is published by the Southern Building Code Congress International (SBCCI). This code is used predominately in the southern United States.

Occupancy Classification

Similar to both the UBC and the BOCA Codes, the occupancy or use category for laboratories is determined by the types and quantities of flammable and hazardous materials used or stored within the facility. Laboratory occupancies are placed in the following groups:

SBC Group B—see Section 405
SBC Group H—see Section 408

Nonhazardous laboratories for testing and research are classified as Group B occupancies.

Laboratories located in Group I (institution, unrestrained) occupancy, (i.e., hospitals) are permitted with protection and separation, as required in SBC Section 409.16.

Mixed Occupancies

Laboratories are commonly located in buildings classified as "mixed Occupancy Buildings." These are permitted provided that each occupancy complies with its use group requirements and separations are provided per SBC Section 403.

Special-Use Occupancies

Laboratories using HPM are considered as "special occupancies." Special requirements are covered in Section 511 of the code. Specific definitions of HPM areas are found in Chapter 2 of the code.

The SBC, unlike the UBC, makes direct reference to regulation and standards published by the NFPA.

Standard Fire Prevention Code

This code should be reviewed for the storage, use and handling of flammable and combustible liquids permitted in each occupancy group.

7.6.5 NFPA No. 101 (1988 Edition)

Introduction

This code, unlike those discussed earlier in Section 7.6, "does not attempt to address general fire prevention or building construction features. These items are normally a function of fire prevention and building codes" (1-3.6).

The NFPA recognized the special nature of laboratories and published NFPA Standard No. 45: Laboratories Using Chemicals. This section, therefore, only discusses those issues that are not covered in NFPA No. 45 or clarifies apparent conflicts between them.

NFPA No. 101 covers "instructional laboratories" and "laboratories for basic or applied research not including hazardous chemicals" (4-1.8) under the *business* classification of occupancy and "laboratories involving hazardous chemicals" under the *industrial* classification (4-1.9). It is interesting to note that instructional laboratories are covered under business occupancy and that "hazardous chemcials" are not defined; however, they are defined in NFPA No. 45.

In addition to the two occupational classifications, NFPA No. 101 includes the category of "hazard of contents," which can be superimposed on the two previous ones by the AHJ. Definitions of low, ordinary and high hazard are given (4-2.2), and a new set

of "special provisions" must be complied with for high-hazard contents (5-11.1). It behooves the laboratory planner to get a reading from the AHJ early in the planning stages because this affects the number, size, and distance to exits considerably. See Table 7.6.-3.

NFPA No. 101 stipulates that for features of fire protection in laboratories using chemicals, NFPA No. 45 shall be complied with unless otherwise provided for (6-4.4). It also states that laboratories using chemicals in educational occupancies shall also comply with NFPA No. 45 (10-3.2.4).

NFPA No. 45 assumes that all laboratories using chemicals are covered under No. 45, including instructional labs. NFPA standards are written by different committees with different members, so conflicts may arise. However, a mechanism exists to work out these conflicts and for standard users to request clarifications. Until conflicts are resolved, standard users are advised to comply with both or the most restrictive requirements.

This section is intended to facilitate the early planning process and provides an overview of those features that affect the arrangement and location of corridors, stairs and exits. It does not replace the standard, and the reader is encouraged to study NFPA No. 101.

Definitions

The following definitions are important for an understanding of this section. They have been copied from NFPA No. 101.

- Common Path of Travel: That portion of exit access that must be traversed before two separate and distinct paths of travel to two exits are available. Paths that merge are common paths of travel. Common path of travel is measured in the same manner as travel distance but terminates at that point where two separate and distinct routes become available. (Note: Common path of travel in most laboratories is short because NFPA No. 45 requires a second means of egress for most laboratories over 500 NASF).

- Exit: That portion of a means of egress that is separated from all other spaces of the building or structure (by construction or equipment as required in 5-1.3.1) to provide a protected way of travel to the exit discharge.
- Exit Access: That portion of a means of egress that leads to an entrance to an exit.
- Exit Discharge: That portion of a means of egress between the termination of an exit and a public way.
- High Hazard Areas: Areas of structures, buildings, or parts thereof used for purposes that involve highly flammable, or explosive products or materials that are likely to burn with extreme rapidity, or that may produce poisonous fumes or gases, including highly toxic or noxious alkalis, acids, or other liquids or chemicals that involve flame, fume, explosive, poisonous, or irritant hazards; also uses that cause division of material into fine particles or dust subject to explosion or spontaneous combustion, and uses that constitute a high fire hazard because of the form, character, or volume of the material used.
- High Hazard Industrial Occupancy: Includes those buildings having high hazard materials, processes, or contents. Incidental high hazard operations in low or ordinary occupancies and protected (in accordance with Sections 4-2 and 28-3.2) shall not be the basis for overall occupancy classification.
- Means of Egress: A means of egress is a continuous and unobstructed way of exit travel from any point in a building or structure to a public way and consists of three separate and distinct parts: *(a) the exit access, (b) the exit, and (c) the exit discharge.* A means of egress comprises the vertical and horizontal travel and shall include intervening rooms spaces, doorways, hallways, corridors,

passageways, balconies, ramps, stairs, enclosures, lobbies, escalators, horizontal exits, courts, and yards. See Figures 7.6-1 and 7.6-2.

Conflicts with NFPA No. 45: Exiting

NFPA No. 45, Fire Protection for Laboratories Using Chemicals, covers laboratories, as indicated by the title. NFPA No. 101, as outlined earlier, covers both research and instructional laboratories that are not hazardous and laboratories that are very hazardous. This means that NFPA No. 45 and No. 101 overlap for laboratories using hazardous chemicals.

Instructional (educational) laboratories that use chemicals but are not hazardous, and basic and applied research laboratories using chemicals that are not hazardous, are not covered under NFPA No. 45, only hazardous laboratories are.

The following appear to be in conflict, and an evaluation from the AHJ is advisable before proceeding too far with the design. Not all possible conflicts are covered.

NFPA No. 45 allows laboratory units from 2,500 to 10,00 sq ft, depending on the quantities of flammable and combustible liquids in the laboratory and the presence of sprinklers. These laboratory units may contain separate enclosed spaces. These are called "internal corridors" (Appendix D),

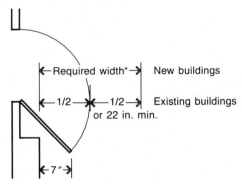

←Required width*→   New buildings
←1/2→←1/2→   Existing buildings
or 22 in. min.

←7″→

*Note: Required width based on calculated occupant load.

Fig. 7.6-1. Allowed obstruction of means of egress by door swing (NFPA No. 101, 5-2.1.4.2).

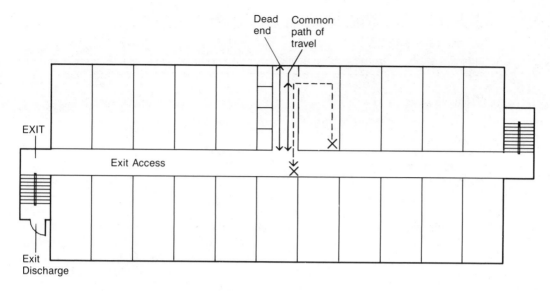

Exit: 1 hour for 3 stories or less; 2 hours for 4 stories or more.
Exit Access: 1 hour serving an occupant load of 30 or more.

Fig. 7.6-2. Means of egress (after NFPA No. 101).

but they can be construed as a means of egress. NFPA No. 101, however, requires corridors used as exit access and serving an area having an occupant load of more than 30 to be separated from other parts of the building by a 1-hour fire resistance rating (5-1.3.4) and 20-minute doors. This requirement is far more limiting.

NFPA No. 45 allows doors to swing into low-hazard laboratories (Class C). NFPA No. 101 requires doors to swing in the direction of exit travel for doors in exit enclosures, in hazardous areas, and for spaces with an occupant load of 50 or more (5-2.1.4.1).

This provision also has a number of exceptions. Exception 6 allows horizontal sliding doors in a means of egress for occupant loads lower than 50 and *if permitted by the occupancy classification.* The business occupancy, which includes instructional laboratories, does not mention sliding doors, so it can be assumed that they are not allowed. However, the industrial occupancy, which includes laboratories involving hazardous chemicals, allows sliding doors (28-2.2.2.3) for low and ordinary hazards. However, for high-hazard occupancies—which, according

to Appendix A, include occupancies where hazardous chemicals are stored or handled—sliding doors are not allowed. NFPA No. 45 does not allow sliding doors as an egress component.

Laboratories in Business Occupancies

Instructional laboratories and laboratories for basic and applied research not including hazardous chemicals are covered under business occupancies (4-1.8, Chapters 26 and 27).

The following general requirements apply:

- Occupant load: For purposes of determining required means of egress, one person per 100 GSF.
- Maximum distance to the exit is 200 ft for nonsprinklered buildings and 300 ft for sprinklered buildings.
- Common path of travel: 75 ft for non-sprinklered buildings and 100 ft for sprinklered buildings.
- Dead-end corridor: 20 ft maximum for nonsprinklered buildings and 50 ft for sprinklered buildings.

Table 7.6-1. Dead-end Corridors Allowed

Code	UBC	NFPA No. 101 (Business)	NFPA No. 101 (Industrial)	SBC	BOCA
New					
Nonsprinklered	20	20 ft	0*	20	20
Sprinklered	20	50 ft	N/A		
Existing					
Nonsprinklered	20	50 ft or more	50*	20	20
Sprinklered	20	NA	NA		

*This occupancy considers laboratories as high hazard.

Table 7.6-2. Minimum Clear Corridor Width

Code	UBC	NFPA No. 101	SBC	BOCA
	44 in.	44 in.	44 in.	44 in.*

*Serving an occupant load > 50.

Tables 7.6-1 through 7.6-5 compare these requirements with those of the standard building codes. Figure 7.6-2 presents the NFPA definitions in a graphic form.

Laboratories in Industrial Occupancies

Laboratories involving hazardous chemicals are covered under industrial occupancies (4-1.9 and Chapter 28). A subclassification places the laboratories under "High Hazard Industrial Occupancy" (28-1.4.1.C). Appendix A states that this includes occupancies where hazardous chemicals or explosives are manufactured, stored or handled. No definition of hazardous chemicals is offered. Low- and ordinary-hazard subclassification do not include labs.

The following general requirements apply:

- Occupant load: For purposes of determining required means of egress. Same as for business occupancy, i.e. one person per 100 GSF (28-1.7).
- Maximum distance to the exit is 75 ft (28-2.6.1, exception 3). No allowance is made for sprinklered buildings.
- Common path of travel is 0 ft (28-2.5.1). No exception is made for sprinklered buildings.
- Dead end corridors are not permitted (28-2.5.2). No exception is made for sprinklered buildings.

Table 7.6-3. Maximum Distance to Exit

Code	UBC	NFPA No. 101 (High-Hazard Content)	NFPA No. 101 (Business)	NFPA No. 101 (Industrial)*	SBC	BOCA Bus.	BOCA Haz.
Nonsprinklered	150	75	200	75	200	200	0
Sprinklered	200	75	300	75	250	300	75

*All laboratories are considered high hazard.

Table 7.6-4. Occupant Load To Determine Means of Egress.

UBC (Educ.)	UBC (B2 Lab)	NFPA No. 101*	SBC	BOCA
50	100 sq.ft./person	100 GSF/person	100 GSF/person	100 GSF/person

*Both business and industrial occupancies.

Table 7.6-5. Maximum Common Path of Travel

Code	UBC	NFPA No. 101 (Business)	NFPA No. 101 (Industrial)	SBC	BOCA
Nonsprinklered	N.R.	75	0*	+	50
Sprinklered	N.R.	100	NA	+	100

N.R. = no requirement.
*All laboratories are considered high hazard.
+See Table 7.6-3.

- No sliding doors may be used in a means of egress (28-2.2.2.3).
- It appears that all laboratories in this category shall have an automatic extinguishing system (28-3.2)

Tables 7.6-1 through 7.6-5 compares these requirements with those of other model building codes.

7.6.6 NFPA No. 30

This code covers the use, handling, and storage of flammable and combustible liquids. Use and handling are governed by the occupancy type, and storage is limited based on how the liquids are stored. Limits are set for flammable liquid storage cabinets and depend on whether liquids are housed in storage rooms or detached buildings. The allowable quantity permitted in storage rooms varies based on the hourly rating of the enclosing walls. The quantity increases permitted for the addition of an automatic sprinkler system.

7.6.7 NFPA No. 68

This code covers the venting of deflagrations. Empirical data and formulas are currently used to establish venting requirements.

The purpose of venting is to prevent total destruction of a building or area should a deflagration occur. The problem is that venting is not an exact science. The size of the vent area varies based on the size and construction of the enclosure. The vent area decreases as the size of the enclosure increases.

When venting is provided, security is sacrificed. However, this problem may be overcome by the use of bars. These are sometimes referred to as "shrapnel bars" to keep containers from becoming deadly missiles.

The requirement for venting is stated in NFPA No. 30.

7.7 CODES USEFUL TO THE MECHANICAL ENGINEER
B. H. Atkinson

There are many codes and regulations (federal, state and local) with which the HVAC designer/engineer has to comply when designing a laboratory facility. Almost all accepted state and local codes refer to the NFPA for the building construction industry.

The NFPA codes are minimum guidelines for design which in specific circumstances may be overridden by state or local codes having more stringent requirements. If and when this occurs, or if interpretation suggests that it may occur, then the designer/engineer should have it clarified and verified by the state or local authorities having jurisdiction before continuing with this part of the design.

The following NFPA codes are applicable to the design of a laboratory facility. Although some codes referenced below may not be required at a specific laboratory facility, they may be required at other laboratory facilities. This is relative to what the client/user needs for experimentation within a laboratory in a safe manner for both people and property.

Item	NFPA Code No.	Description	Vol.	Latest Edition
1.	45	Laboratories Using Chemicals	2	1986
2.	49	Hazardous Chemicals Data	9	1975
3.	69	Explosion Prevention System	2	1986
4.	70	National Electric Code	3	1987
5.	77	Static Electricity	9	1983
6.	90A	Installation of Air Conditioning and Ventilation Systems	4	1985
7.	90B	Installation of Warm Air Heating and Air Conditioning Systems	4	1984
8.	91	Installation of Blower and Exhaust Systems for Dust, Stock, and Vapor Removal or Conveying	4	1983
9.	92A	Smoke Control Systems	9	1988
10.	96	Installation of Equipment for the Removal of Smoke and Grease-Laden Vapors from Commercial Cooking Equipment	4	1987
11.	101	Life Safety Code	5	1988
12.	101M	Alternative Approaches to Life Safety	9	1988
13.	204M	Smoke and Heat Venting	9	1985
14.	321	Basic Classification of Flammable and Combustible Liquids	6	1987
15.	325M	Fire Hazard Properties of Flammable Liquids, Gases, and Volatile Solids	10	1984
16.	491M	Hazardous Chemical Reactions	10	1986
17.	493	Intrinsically Safe Apparatus and Associated Apparatus for use in Class I, II, and III, Division 1, Hazardous Locations	7	1978
18.	497M	Classification of Gases, Vapors, and Dusts for Electrical Equipment in Hazardous (Classified) Locations	11	1986
19.	654	Prevention of Fire and Dust Explosions in the Chemical, Dye, Pharmaceutical, and Plastics Industries	7	1982
20.	801	Facilities Handling Radioactive Material	11	1983

The above codes are noted primarily for within-laboratory design; however, the HVAC designer/engineer has other codes which are related and may be applicable and have to be compiled with. These other codes, to mention a few, are as follows:

There are several more, such as 85A, 85B, 85D, and 85G, which pertain to boilers; however, most of the NFPA codes noted previously are the most common. This does not relieve the HVAC designer/engineer of responsibility for complying with other NFPA

Item	NFPA Code No.	Description	Vol.	Latest Edition
1.	54	National Fuel Gas Code	2	1984
2.	58	Storage and Handling of Liquified Petroleum Gases	2	1986
3.	59A	Production, Storage and Handling of Liquified Natural Gas (LNG)	2	1985
4.	82	Incinerators, Waste and Linen Handling Systems and Equipment	4	1983
5.	86	Ovens and Furnaces—Design Location and Equipment		
6.	214	Water Cooling Towers	6	1988
7.	231	General Storage	6	1987
8.	231C	Rack Storage of Materials	6	1986
9.	232	Records, Protection of	6	1986
10.	232AM	Archives and Records Centers	10	1986

codes, not listed above, that may be applicable to their specific project.

It is imperative that the HVAC designer/engineer know the program for the laboratory facility and understand what has to be accomplished in order to satisfy the need, the code, and the safety requirements of the specific facility.

Other references:

Occupational Safety and Health Administration.
ASHRAE: *Fundamentals Handbook* (1985), *Refrigeration Handbook* (1986), *Systems and Application* (1987), *Equipment Handbook* (1988).
ASHRAE Handbook, 1987. HVAC Systems & Applications. Chapter 58. Fire and smoke control. Atlanta
ASHRAE Standards 110-1985—Method of Testing Performance of Laboratory Fume Hoods.
Kolte J. H, Fothergill J. W., 1983. Design of Smoke Control Symptoms for Buildings. ASHRAE Publication. Atlanta

State codes:

BOCA Codes (Building, Mechanical, Fire Prevention, Plumbing, Energy, Electric).
Uniform Building Codes.
Southern Building Codes.

7.8 National Energy Code *N. Nelson*

7.8.1 Scope and Application

The BOCA National Energy Conservation Code (NECC) has been adopted by many building code enforcement agencies across the United States. Other agencies have also adopted similar codes, such as Chapter 53 of the Uniform Building Code and the *Model Energy Code,* published by the Council of American Building Officials (CABO). Virtually all of the presently adopted energy conservation codes have their origins in or have been adopted from the American Society of Heating, Ventilating, and Air Conditioning Engineers (ASHRAE) Standard 90, Energy Conservation in New Building Design. This landmark standard was first published in 1975, with its latest revision in 1980. It was developed in order to establish minimum acceptable levels of energy use by defining the design and operating standards that should be attainable for new and retrofit constructions in the industry.

The development of new and retrofit designs of laboratories typically are not exempt from the applicable energy conservation standards that apply to other types of facilities. In general, energy conservation regulations apply minimum standards to several important energy-using systems in laboratories:

- Building envelope
- HVAC systems
- Plumbing systems
- Electrical systems

Each of these areas will be addressed separately in the following paragraphs.

The only structures that are not normally required to be in compliance are laboratories that:

- Are neither heated nor cooled.
- Have a peak design energy use rate of 1 watt/sq ft for all purposes.
- Are use group U or F, with a peak annual design rate of energy use less than 29,784 BTUh/sq ft of floor area.

Most laboratories use significant amounts of energy, as discussed in Chapter 6. The annual energy use for laboratories can vary between 200,000 and 500,000 (or higher) BTU per square foot per year (BTU/sq ft/yr). By comparison, a well-designed office building may require less than 100,000 BTU/sq ft/yr. By this comparison, it is easy to understand the desire to conserve energy and why laboratories are usually required to comply with applicable energy-conserving regulations.

7.8.2 Compliance Requirements

The exceptions mentioned in the previous paragraphs are the only structures that do not need to comply with the NECC. All other structures have two alternative ways of demonstrating compliance: (1) by following the criteria cited in Articles 3 through 6 of the NECC or (2) by demonstrating that the proposed building design's energy use is equal to or less than the design energy use that would occur if the structure were designed in strict accordance with the NECC.

The requirement of Articles 3 through 7 of the NECC are briefly described in the next few paragraphs.

7.8.3 Building Envelope

Article 3 describes compliance requirements for thermal transmission and air leakage for the laboratory envelope (walls, floors, windows, etc.) The article includes requirements for residential and "other" buildings. The "other" buildings category is, of course, the appropriate section for laboratories.

Also included is a separate section for heated and mechanically cooled spaces. The minimum thermal transmittance of the building is reviewed for overall walls, roof/ceiling assemblies, floors over unheated spaces and floor slab-on-grade components. The individual components must meet the minimum thermal transmittance, or U-values (BTU/ft²-h-F), for walls and roof assemblies and thermal resistance, or R-values (ft²-h-F/BTU), for floor insulation. The values are adjusted for the local climate by using annual Fahrenheit heating degree days (HDD) to a base of 65°F. Representative values of HDD are included in the appendices of that standard.

Cooling criteria are applied in a similar manner, except that the term used for compliance is "overall thermal transfer value (OTTV)" for the walls (BTU/h-ft²). The roof/ceiling assembly requires a U-value not exceeding those required for heating. However, with roof assemblies, skylights are *not* included in the calculations unless:

- Domed skylights are used and the skylight area is 10% or less of the roof/ceiling area.
- Double-domed skylights are used when the HDD exceeds 2,500.
- Curbs are insulated to a U-value of 0.21 (R = 1/U = 5).
- The infiltration coefficient of the skylight does not exceed 0.05 BTU/h-ft²-F.
- The domed skylight area exceeds 10% of the roof/ceiling area. Energy balance calculations must be made in accordance with the Architectural Aluminum Manufacturers Association (AAMA) Standard 1602.1, Voluntary Standard Procedure for Calculating Skylight Manual Energy Balance, to determine the percentage of skylight permitted.

Cooling criteria are adjusted for solar influences by adjusting the OTTV values based on the latitude of the site.

Exposed floors must meet the heating criteria discussed previously in order to comply with the cooling requirements.

Air leakage criteria apply to all interior spaces that are heated or mechanically cooled and are also exposed to ambient conditions. The standard for measurement of building air leakage is the American Society for Testing and Materials Standard ASTM E283, Rate of Air Leakage Through Exterior Windows, at a pressure differential of 1.567 lbs./ft². The acceptance criteria for air infiltration through various components are as follows:

- Windows: 0.5 cfm/ft of sash crack
- Sliding and swinging doors: 0.5 cfm/ft² of door area for Use Group R.
- Other Doors: 11 cfm/lineal ft of door crack.

The code further requires that all exterior joints or cracks be sealed or caulked in a suitable manner.

If the thermal performance of one component (i.e., wall, roof/ceiling, etc.) fails to comply with the required thermal performance (U-values), the building may still be in compliance if the entire building envelope is still in compliance with NECC requirements. Adjustments may be made to any component in order to compensate for the deficiencies of another.

For example, assume that a laboratory has 20,000 sq ft of roof area, with an overall U-value (Uo) of 0.05, and 7,200 sq ft of wall with a Uo of 0.20. Further assume that the local climate requires a Uo for the roof of 0.08 and a Uo for the wall of 0.15. The proposed wall Uo value of 0.20 is clearly not in compliance with the requirement. However, a simple calculation will show that with the design Uo of the roof, the overall thermal performance of the lab is in compliance.

First, calculate the thermal performance required by the NECC:

$$
\begin{array}{ll}
\text{Uo-roof} \times \text{A-roof} = & 1,600 \text{ BTU/h-ft}^2\text{-F} \\
\text{Uo-wall} \times \text{A-wall} = & \underline{1,080 \text{ BTU/h-ft}^2\text{-F}} \\
& 2,680 \text{ BTU/h-ft}^2\text{-F}
\end{array}
$$

This shows that the allowable heat loss value is 2,680 BTU/h-ft^2-F, which when multipled by the design temperature difference and the area will provide the design heat loss rate. The design heat loss value, using the proposed wall and roof design, is:

$$
\begin{array}{ll}
\text{Uo-roof} \times \text{A-roof} = & 1,000 \text{ BTUh/h-ft}^2\text{-F} \\
\text{Uo-wall} \times \text{A-wall} = & \underline{1,440 \text{ BTUh/h-ft}^2\text{-F}} \\
& 2,440 \text{ BTUh/h-ft}^2\text{-F}
\end{array}
$$

Since the design heat loss value is less than the required value, the lab is in compliance.

7.8.4 HVAC Systems and Equipment

Article 4 of the NECC pertains to warm air heating, ventilating, and air conditioning systems and equipment, and sets minimum criteria for their selection and installation. It does not apply to special ventilation systems such as those required for removal of flammable vapors, dust, etc. The NECC further states: "For such special applications such as . . . laboratories . . . , the design concepts

and parameters shall conform to the requirements of the application at minimum energy levels." This statement allows the designer to exercise professional judgment in the establishment of space environmental requirements and the inclusion of owner preferences in the design criteria for any given space.

The NECC has provisions and requirements pertaining to design conditions, mechanical ventilation, cooling with outdoor air, simultaneous heating and cooling, equipment performance requirements, duct insulation, temperature control, and hydronic piping systems. The reader is encouraged to review these requirements for applicability to the laboratory design. In many cases, the environmental needs of the laboratory spaces will be governed by research needs, but many of the energy conservation regulations are still applicable.

7.8.5 Plumbing Systems

Article 5 describes the regulations that are applicable to plumbing systems in laboratories. The areas covered include water service, fixtures and the hot water supply. All of the regulations in this article should be applicable to laboratories. Therefore, the designer is urged to review this article as well.

7.8.6 Electrical Systems

Article 6 covers electrical systems and is less than one page in length. The NECC does not cover electrical issues in detail. The only item that is applicable to laboratories concerns lighting switches. The lighting system should be provided with adequate switching in order to keep the number of fixtures operating needlessly to a minimum.

7.8.7 Alternative Systems

Article 7 is also a very brief section of the code. If the lab does not comply with Articles 3 through 6, then it must be proven that the lab as designed will use less energy then a similar building that does meet the code. This will require the use of an Energy Analysis prepared in accordance with ASHRAE Standard 90B. When nondepletable energy sources are used, the energy supplied by the alternative system must be excluded from the total energy chargeable to the proposed alternative design. Documentation will require an Energy Analysis.

7.9 Quality Control Standards: GLP and CGMP *T. Ruys*

7.9.1 Introduction

Sometimes the Good Laboratory Practice Act (GLP) for nonclinical laboratories or the Current Good Manufacturing Act (CGMP) may apply to facilities planned by the laboratory planner, so a brief summary is presented here. Both are Federal Regulations published in the Code of Federal Regulations. The Code is divided in 50 titles which represent broad areas subject to federal regulations. Each title is divided into chapters, which usually bear the name of the issuing agency. The GLP and GCMP are covered in the following regulations:

These codes are revised each year and issued on a quarterly basis. Titles 17 through 27 are issued approximately on April 1. This section refers to the April 1, 1988, issue.

For a summary, legal interpretation, or other explanation of any regulation in this volume, contact the issuing agency. Inquiries concerning editing procedures and reference assistance with respect to the Code of Federal Regulations may be addressed to the Director, Office of the Federal Register, National Archives and Records Administration, Washington, DC 20408 (telephone: 202-523-3517). Sales are handled exclusively by the Superintendent of Documents, Government Printing Office, Washington, DC 20402 (telephone : 202-783-3238).

Both acts deal primarily with quality control of products regulated by the Food and Drug Administration, such as pharmaceuticals, food products, research, and manufacturing and medical devices. The code includes operational procedures, record keeping, personnel, maintenance and storage.

Only facilities design and the planning incidental to these requirements are covered here.

7.9.2 Good Laboratory Practices

The regulations of the GLP say almost nothing about laboratory facilities other than the fact that "the testing facility shall be of suitable size and construction" and "shall be designed so that there is a degree of separation that will prevent any function or activity from having an adverse effect on the study." That does not provide much direction. The CGMP regulations are much more detailed and helpful.

However, the GLP covers in some detail the regulations for animal care facilities, which are here reproduced:

58.43 Animal care facilities

(a) A testing facility shall have a sufficient number of animal rooms or areas, as needed, to assure proper: (1) Separation of species or test systems, (2) isolation of individual projects, (3) quarantine of animals, and (4) routine or specialized housing of animals.

(b) A testing facility shall have a number of animal rooms or areas separate from those described in paragraph (a) of this section to ensure isolation of studies being done with test systems or test and control articles known to be biohazardous, including volatile substances, aerosols, radioactive materials, and infectious agents.

Commonly Referred to As:	Title	Code Part	Section	Parts Covered	Cost
GLP Act	21 CFR	1.1	Food and drugs	1 to 99	$5
CGMP Act	21 CFR	200.5	Food and drugs	200 to 299	$12

(c) Separate areas shall be provided, as appropriate, for the diagnosis, treatment, and control of laboratory animal diseases. These areas shall provide effective isolation for the housing of animals either known or suspected of being diseased, or of being carriers of disease, from other animals.

(d) When animals are housed, facilities shall exist for the collection and disposal of all animal waste and refuse or for safe sanitary storage of waste before removal from the testing facility. Disposal facilities shall be so provided and operated as to minimize vermin infestation, odors, disease hazards, and environmental contamination.

[43 FR 60013, Dec. 22, 1978, as amended at 52 FR 33780, Sept. 4, 1987]

58.45 Animal supply facilities

There shall be storage areas, as needed, for feed, bedding, supplies, and equipment. Storage areas for feed and bedding shall be separated from areas housing the test systems and shall be protected against infestation or contamination. Perishable supplies shall be preserved by appropriate means.

[43 FR 60013, Dec. 22, 1978, as amended at 52 FR 33780, Sept. 4, 1987]

58.47 Facilities for handling test and control articles

(a) As necessary to prevent contamination or mixups, there shall be separate areas for:

(1) Receipt and storage of the test and control articles.

(2) Mixing of the test and control articles with a carrier, e.g., feed.

(3) Storage of the test and control article mixtures.

(b) Storage areas for the test and/or control article and test and control mixtures shall be separate from areas housing the test systems and shall be adequate to preserve the identity, strength, purity, and stability of the articles and mixtures.

The separation of animal species and the isolation of projects in Subpart C (facilities) is quite specific denoted by the word shall.

However, in Subpart E (testing facilities operation), the regulations are far more lenient:

(e) Animals of different species shall be housed in separate rooms when necessary. Animals of the same species, but used in different studies, should not ordinarily be housed in the same room when inadvertent exposure to control or test articles or animal mixup could affect the outcome of either study. If such mixed housing is necessary, adequate differentiation by space and identification shall be made.

Common wisdom suggests: If in doubt, apply the more restricted regulations. Testing, calibration, inspection and maintenance of equipment are integral parts of the regulations, along with a written record of these procedures. Manufacturers have responded by providing digital printouts on sterilizers and controlled-temperature rooms to provide a record of temperature behavior during processing or storage of materials.

7.9.3 Current Good Manufacturing Practice

Four parts of the CGMP deal with current good manufacturing practice:

Part	Title
210	Current Good Manufacturing Practice in Manufacturing, Processing, Packing, or Holding of Drugs; General
211	Current Good Manufacturing Practice for Finished Pharmaceuticals
225	Current Good Manufacturing Practice for Medicated Feeds
226	Current Good Manufacturing Practice for Type A Medicated Articles

This section will deal only with Part 210. The other parts are very similar, and the laboratory planner is encouraged to refer to the code itself.

The main concern of the chapters in this area is to *prevent mixup* and *contamination*. This includes mixups between different components, drug products containers, closures, labeling, etc. and contamination from outside sources and from other drugs transmitted through the ventilation system or water supply. In practice, this means that many separate enclosed spaces are provided, particularly for storage of unfinished, finished and returned goods.

The code specifically states that separate and defined areas shall be provided for operations to prevent contamination or mixups as follows (211A2).

- Receipt, identification, storage, and withholding from use of components, drug product containers, closures, and labeling, pending the appropriate sampling, testing, or examnation by the quality control unit before release for manufacturing or packaging;
- Holding rejected components, drug product containers, closures, and labeling before disposition;
- Storage of released components, drug product containers, closures,and labeling;
- Storage of in-process materials;
- Manufacturing and processing operations;
- Packaging and labeling operations;
- Quarantine storage before release of drug products;
- Storage of drug products after release;
- Control and laboratory operations;
- Aseptic processing.
- Operations relating to the manufacture, processing, and packing of penicillin shall be performed in facilities separate from those used for other drug products for human use.

The aseptic processing area shall have the following features:

- Floors, walls, and ceilings of smooth, hard surfaces that are easily cleanable;
- Temperature and humidity controls;
- An air supply filtered through high-efficiency particulate air filters under positive pressure, regardless of whether flow is laminar or nonlaminar;

- A system for monitoring environmental conditions;
- A system for cleaning and disinfecting the room and equipment to produce aseptic conditions;
- A system for maintaining any equipment used to control the aseptic conditions.

HVAC and plumbing systems are covered in 211.46 and 211.48, respectively.

- Adequate ventilation shall be provided.
- Equipment for adequate control over air pressure, micro-organism, dust, humidity, and temperature shall be provided when appropriate for the manufacture, processing, packing, or holding of a drug product.
- Air filtration systems, including prefilters and particulate matter air filters, shall be used when appropriate on air supplies to production areas, measures shall be taken to control recirculation of dust from production. In areas where air contamination occurs during production, there shall be adequate exhaust systems or other systems adequate to control contaminants.
- Air-handling systems for the manufacture, processing, and packing of penicillin shall be completely separate from those for other drug products for human use.
- Potable water shall be supplied under continuous positive pressure in a plumbing system free of defects that could contribute contamination to any drug product. Potable water shall meet the standards prescribed in the Environmental Protection Agency's Primary Drinking Water Regulations set forth in 40 CFR Part 141. Water not meeting such standards shall not be permitted in the potable water system.
- Drains shall be of adequate size and, where connected directly to a sewer, shall be provided with an air break or other mechanical device to prevent back-siphonage.

8

Cost Issues

8.1 INTRODUCTION *S. Matson*

Laboratories are expensive projects. What makes them costly is the laboratory equipment and casework. The structural, mechanical and electrical costs associated with accommodating the laboratory equipment, casework and special laboratory requirements add even more expense. Table 8.1-1 lists other factors. If the project is a renovation or a space conversion, the mechanical costs alone can be as much as 50% of the construction costs. See Figure 8.1-1. The operational costs of a laboratory are also high due to equipment and research updates. For the project to continue to be successful, it must anticipate and accommodate these future changes in its initial design. This also makes a laboratory project more expensive than an office or a school.

The cost estimate is a decision-making tool. Its purpose is not to arrive at the lowest cost but to cost a decision. Since few projects have an unlimited budget, cost estimating is a tool to facilitate trade-offs between various options. The cost savings potential are greatest in the early stages of planning before ideas become progressively more fixed, first in multiple drawings and then in brick and mortar. See Figure 8.1-2.

Unfortunately, at the early stages of planning, the margin of error is also greatest. In laboratory facilities projects, it is therefore crucial to engage the estimator as a member of the planning team so that every idea can be priced and the impact evaluated, instead

Table 8.1-1. Reasons Why Laboratory Costs Are Higher Than Those of Nonlaboratory Projects

Initial Project Phases	Reason
Design	Considerations for specialized equipment
	Considerations for future needs
	Considerations for specialized casework
	Considerations for specialized mechanical systems
	Takes longer to design
	Higher design costs
	Requires more reviews and delays
Construction	Lower net to gsf efficiency to accommodate special equipment and systems
	Structure must be stronger to accommodate heavy equipment loads
	Finishes must be suitable for sanitary conditions
	Welded sheet vinyl flooring
	Epoxy painted drywall
	Special laboratory casework
	Flexible casework
	Acid-resistant surfaces
	Stainless steel surfaces
	Specialized laboratory equipment
	Fumehoods
	Biological safety cabinets
	Autoclaves
	Cold rooms
	Glassware washers and dryers
	Mechanical systems
	Higher ventilation rates
	Up to 100% makeup air
	Highly sophisticated HVAC, controls and filtration
	Plumbing systems
	More utility services
	Acid-resistant sinks and waste lines
	Electrical systems
	Higher power requirements
	Equipment emergency power
	Greater security and communications requirements
	Sitework
	Greater site utility loads
	Bidding
	Qualified contractors less available
	More often negotiated bid
	More change orders due to more elaborate systems and conditions
	More reviews and construction delays
	Fast track more difficult
	Longer construction duration
Project Costs	Expensive equipment and furnishings
	Higher design fees
	Higher project management fees
	Higher insurance costs
	Special consultants' fees
Capital Costs	Property costs—fewer available sites
	Greater legal fees
	Higher moving costs
	Greater interim financing costs

Table 8.1-1 (Continued)

Long Term Project Phases	Reason
Life Cycle Costs	Greater long-term financing costs
	Operational costs
	More energy consumed on a day-to-day basis
	More maintenance required: cleaning and painting
	Higher waste disposal costs
	Security costs
	Renewal costs
	More frequent equipment and process upgrades
	More space configuration changes
	More frequent remodeling and additions
	Work force
	Highly paid laboratory technicians

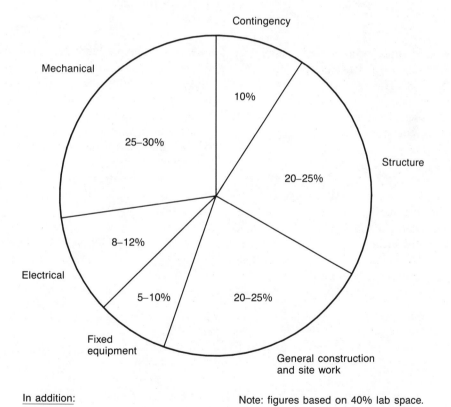

In addition:
Fees
Permits
Surveys
Test borings
Laboratory inspections
Movable equipment
Escalation

Note: figures based on 40% lab space.

Fig. 8.1-1. Typical laboratory construction cost range.

IMPORTANCE OF EARLY DECISIONS

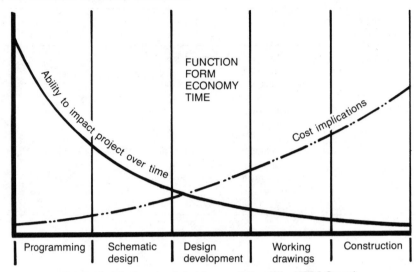

Fig. 8.1-2. The impact of decisions over time (The NBBJ Group).

of the typical method of pricing many decisions at the end of each design phase. See Figure 8.1-3. The estimating costs will be higher, but a better value is assured and this process saves planning time, which in many cases will reduce the construction cost.

8.1.1 Estimating Basics

An estimate is a price that anticipates building costs. Estimating is the act of creating an estimate. An estimator in the early stages interprets the ideas of the designer and converts them into a concept called "cost." Estimating means more than measuring quan-

tities and applying labor and material costs to them. Estimating construction costs means anticipating the general contractor's bid; understanding the market, bidding climate, subcontractors' and suppliers' conditions; being aware of the client's personality; being familiar with the cost of other similar projects; creating design/cost solutions; understanding all construction trades and practices; having local contacts—in other words, the ability to understand the whole picture. Figure 8.1-4 graphically shows the estimating methodology used by the NBBJ Group. The "activity" for each system, the trades involved and the location of the project are

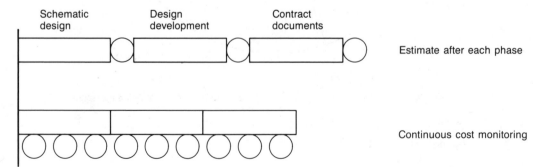

Fig. 8.1-3. Estimating methods (The NBBJ Group).

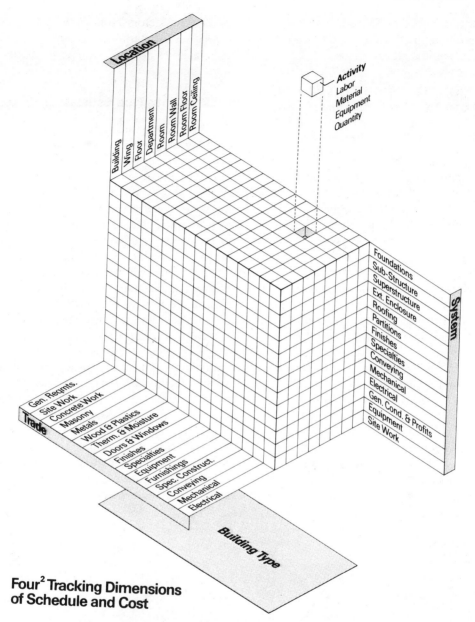

Four² Tracking Dimensions of Schedule and Cost

Fig. 8.1-4. Estimating basics (The NBBJ Group).

evaluated, and the labor, material, equipment and quantity costs are included in the estimate.

An estimator needs to have knowledge, experience, imagination and common sense: knowledge and experience of current building systems, codes, and practices; imagina-

tion to combine the knowledge and experience; and common sense to know what will or will not work.

An estimate can be generated by the architect, the client or the contractor, although all estimates attempt to anticipate the contractor's bid and match this with the budget. See

Figure 8.2-6. The following sections will cover the estimating methodology and accuracy of various design stages.

8.2 CONSTRUCTION AND PROJECT COSTS *S. Matson and T. Ruys*

8.2.1 Estimating Methodology

Design phase estimating determines estimating methodology and estimate accuracy. As illustrated in Figure 8.2-1, the various stages of design require different estimating methods.

There are four basic estimating methods: facility type, space type, systems and detailed. Each type is applicable to different stages of design, with varied accuracy, and varied time and costs to generate. As the design of a project progresses, the estimating method becomes more refined, takes longer to generate and becomes more accurate.

"Accuracy," when referring to an estimate, means how close the estimate will be to the negotiated general contractor's bid or to the competitive low bid. On a competitive bid project, it is not uncommon to have bids spread as much as 30%. The architects' final cost design estimate should be within 5% of the selected low bid. This means that the professional estimator's accuracy is expected to be much better than that of the majority

of the contractors bidding the project. Selecting an estimator experienced in laboratory facilities projects is therefore extremely important.

8.2.2 Facility Type Estimating

At the preprogrammatic, budget concept phase of design, an estimate can only establish a budget by allowing so many dollars per GSF because so little is known about the project at this point. The facility type is known—office, warehouse, school, laboratory, hospital, etc. Either the required GSF or the budget has been established. There is no building design. Normally it is not known what materials will be used. Because so little is known at this point, the budget and/or the size of the project may be the goal of the owners, but they must be correlated and confirmed by a facility type estimate.

Facility type estimating takes into account the type of facility, establishes the GSF and applies facility GSF costs. It can also be worked backward: by using the budget and cost per GSF ($/GSF) to determine the square footage of the project that can be built. Facility type estimating is the most simplistic type of estimating and the least accurate of the four methods. While this method may be a quick (1 to 4 hours) and

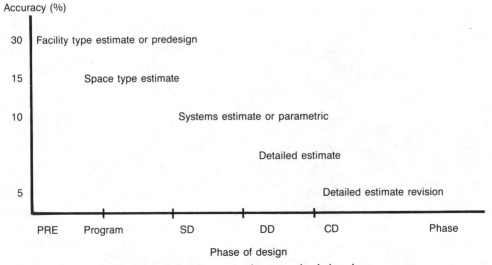

Fig. **8.2-1.** Estimating type and accuracy by design phase.

inexpensive way of generating an estimate, its accuracy range is 30%. It should not be depended upon for later stages of design.

When facility type estimating is used to establish or confirm a budget, the most realistic approach is to compile a $/GSF report of various similar facilities. The $/GSF should come from various sources, such as actual historical data, averages as in the *Means Unit Cost Guide,* and actual published projects such as F. W. Dodge's *Cost and Trends* publication. Historical data, real projects and their costs can come from architects, general contractors and/or the owner. Means unit costs, based upon a very large historical data base, are "cost at bid" average prices which do not take into account special features or conditions. All $/GSF unit prices should then be escalated and factored into current cost at bid $/GSF unit costs for an apples-to-apples comparison. See the following examples.

Example 1: A study (Table 8.2-1) was conducted for a major university in Seattle to assist in budgeting a master plan for laboratory facilities. The cost at bid $/GSF was established by creating "model" projects using parametric costs (costs based on space types) from a historic data base and square feet from a "model" generic design. The $/GSF costs could be more realistically projected by this method than by relying on the means square foot cost guide.

Example 2: The NBBJ Group has classified laboratory facilities into four classes based on degree of complexity. See Table 8.2-2. The complexity affects the conversion from NASF to GSF and, of course, the $/GSF. The NASF to GSF conversion factors have been repeated here. See Table 8.2-3. For a detailed discussion of NAFS and GSF, refer to Section 8.6 and the glossary for definitions.

The $/GSF for these laboratory classes escalated for the different years as noted in Table 8.2-4. These costs are based on bid prices from many projects and have been converted to costs in New York. Future costs have been

Table 8.2-1. Master Plan Study (Seattle Costs)

University in Seattle Washington
Date: April 22, 1988

Building Type	Cost at Bid ($/GSF)	Project Cost ($/GSF)
New high-tech. bldg.	$200	$274
New low-tech. bldg.	150	206
Remodel high-tech. bldg.	140	192
Remodel low-tech. bldg.	95	130

Description
Technical Facilities
   Laboratories
   Glasswash
   Tissue culture
   Media prep
   Electron Microscope Room, etc.

New Buildings
   Includes:
      Standard foundations
      Slab on grade
      Concrete floor and roof structure
      Brick exterior walls
      Elevators and stairs
      Specialties and casework
      Mechanical and electrical
      Fixed lab equipment and casework at lab buildings
      Building sitework and tunnel
      General contractor's markups
      37% project cost (per university staff)
   Excludes:
      Movable equipment and furnishings (Groups 2 and 3)

Remodeling
   Includes:
      Demolition
      Code compliance
      Exterior upgrades
      Specialties and casework
      Mechanical and electrical
      Lab equipment and casework at lab buildings
      General contractor's markups
      37% project cost (per university staff)
   Excludes:
      Movable equipment and furnishings (groups 2 and 3)
      Asbestos removal

escalated using an aggregate trend from the Building Cost Modifier (Boeckh Index Numbers).

Using Tables 8.2-3 and 8.2-4, it is possible to arrive at a reasonably accurate building budget from NASF for a given complexity of laboratory projects at a particular point

Table 8.2-2. Laboratory Facilities Classifications by Complexity

Class 1—highly specialized
  A laboratories building with more than 80% wet labs or a building with a high level of containment facilities.
  Examples: high-hazard laboratories due to carcinogens, toxic substances, biological substances or high level radioisotopes.
  Dual-corridor animal facilities may be considered in this classification.

Class 2—specialized
  A laboratory building with 60 to 80% wet labs or special conditions that require expensive space but not more space than a standard laboratory.
  Examples: double-floor computer rooms, clean rooms, shielded rooms, controlled-temperature rooms, glass and cage wash areas. Single corridor animal facilities.

Class 3—standard
  A laboratory building with 40 to 60% wet labs and no special conditions in a budget building with budget casework.
  Examples: laboratories with only standard utility services and without central glasswash facilities.

Class 4—low lab/office ratio
  A budget building with less than 40% wet labs.
  Examples: an office building with some laboratories.

in time. This point in time is typically the midpoint of construction. Table 8.2-5 will assist in establishing the date in which the cost should be taken. This will establish the cost in New York, which can be converted to the cost at the project location by using the Boeckh Index conversion factors published bimonthly by the Building Cost Modifier and available in most libraries or the City Cost Indexes published in *Means Construction Cost Data* in bookstores.

This will establish the cost at bid at the project location. However, there are a number of other costs, or "owner's costs," that must be factored in to arrive at the project costs for this concept (budget) estimate. These are expressed as a percentage of construction cost and noted in Table 8.2-6.

The following calculation will illustrate the process:

Assuming a 24,000 NASF project in Raleigh, North Carolina, for a university to house technology transfer projects in biotechnology and engineering. Planning starts in October 1988. Using the outline of Figure 8.2-2, we get:

Step	Value	Comments
NASF	24,000 NASF	Given data
×		
Net/gross eff.	60% NASF	Table 8.2-3 (typical laboratory)
=		
GSF	40,000 GSF	
×		
Cost per GSF	$172/GSF	Table 8.2-5
=		Planning 8 months, construction
		12 months, midpoint of construction
		October 1988 plus 14 months is December 1989–January 1990
Cost at bid for New York	$6,880,000	Table 8.2-4 gives the cost at $172/GSF for New York
×		
Means Index Conversion	$\dfrac{166.2}{241.6}$	Data from Means Construction cost data; value for Raleigh (166.2) divided by value for New York (241.6)
=		
Cost at bid @ project site	$4,732,848 or $120 sq. ft.	
+		
Owner's costs	15%	Table 8.2-6. No land cost or demolition. Landscaping, site utilities, roads, moving costs, separate budget. Fees, furniture and administrative costs 15%
=		
Project cost	$5,442,775	

Table 8.2-3. Average Plan Efficiencies for Different Categories of Laboratories

Laboratory Facility Category	Net to Gross Efficiency (% of Assignable Area)
Highly specialized	45–50% assignable
Specialized	50–55% assignable
Typical	55–60% assignable
Low lab/office ratio	60% and up assignable

This type of estimate, based on a conceptual idea, makes many assumptions regarding building efficiency, construction schedule and costs. However, it is far superior to most of the "guesstimates" used to arrive at a budget. As a minimum, it can be useful as a check.

8.2.3 Space Type Estimating

At the programmatic stage of design, more information is known about the project than at the preprogramming or budget phase. A building program of space requirements and a laboratory space module have been established, and the cost must be estimated and/or the budget checked. Since we still do not have a building design, we will cost by space type. A design contingency is not required at this point. The space type costs assume materials and finishes typical for these functions. The degree of accuracy is about ± 15%. See Figure 8.2-1.

The space type estimate (see Figure 8.2-3) converts NASF for each space type to departmental gross square feet (DGSF) and multiplies these by the number given in Table

Table 8.2-4. Average GSF Cost at Bid for Different Categories of Laboratories

Laboratory Facility Category	Cost per Square Foot in Dollars*					
	1987	1988	1989	1990	1991	1992
Highly specialized	194	207	217	228	240	251
Specialized	157	165	173	182	191	201
Typical	149	156	164	172	181	190
Low lab/office ratio	97	102	106	112	118	124

*Average costs for New York escalated 5% per year as predicted.

Table 8.2-5. Arriving at the Midpoint of Construction for Laboratory Facilities

Cost at Bid Range ($ for 1988)	Planning Contract Documents and Bidding Time (Months)	Construction Time (Months)
$1–$5,000,000	8–10	10–12
$5,000,000–$20,000,000	10–12	12–18
$20,000,000–$50,000,000	12–18	18–24

Notes
1. Planners and construction time from the date when the planner or architect and contractor start actual work.
2. Fast-track projects overlap planning and construction times and therefore complicate matters.
3. Public projects take longer than private ones because of the extended review periods required. Use the high part of the range.
4. Renovations require less time. Use the low part of the range.
5. Judge complexity of site, utilities, owner's schedule.
6. For smaller projects, the lead time of some equipment may be the governing factor.

Table 8.2-6. Owner's Costs (New Construction)

Item	Cost (% of Construction Cost)
Land cost	Verify
Demolition	Verify
Landscaping	Verify
Site utilities	Verify
Roads and parking	Verify
Movable equipment	6%
Professional fees	8%
Contingencies	None for concept estimate
Administrative costs	1%
Moving costs	Verify

8.2-7. Since these costs are for New York, they must be converted to the costs for the location of the project and an escalation factor applied to the midpoint of construction.

DGSF includes the exterior wall, interior partitions, columns, shafts, and half of the adjacent corridor. Assuming a 20 × 24 NASF laboratory module, the multiplier is 1.25 to arrive at the DGSF. See Figure 8.2-4. In a similar way, multipliers have been calculated for other types of spaces and noted in Table 8.2-8.

In addition to the DGSF for various types of spaces, there is GSF for main circulation areas such as hallways, stairs, and elevators and for toilets and mechanical rooms. Add 25% to the DGSF to get the total GSF.

Take the same project, in Raleigh, October 1988, as an example. However, a program of space requirements now exists as follows:
The midpoint of construction per Table 8.2-6 is 13 to 16 months. Assuming a 2% escalation per year, or 4%, the construction bid cost will be approximately $4,868,454.

The facilities type estimate is compared with the space type estimate as a check. Several things are noted:

- The NASF is a given and is therefore close (24,000 to 23,334).
- The GSF is substantially lower at 40,000 to 35,429 because the example facility has more large open spaces than the typical laboratory.
- The mix of expensive versus lower-cost spaces is also low, so the construction cost at bid is $4,732,848 to $4,868,454, or 3% of the previous estimate.

Admin. support/conf./library	2,602 NASF×	1.15	=	2.992 GSF ×	$140	=	$ 418,880
Research offices	3,810	× 1.15	=	4,382	× 140	=	613,480
Computer room	990	× 1.15	=	1,139	× 170	=	193,630
Laboratory							
Wet	8,400	× 1.25	=	10,500	× 250	=	$2,625,000
Dry	1,800	× 1.25	=	2,250	× 200	=	450,000
Instrument rooms	972	× 1.25	=	1,215	× 220	=	267,300
Controlled-temp. room	120	× 1.25	=	150	× 200	=	30,000
Animal room							
Wet	720	× 1.19	=	857	× 370	=	317,090
Dry	720	× 1.19	=	857	× 250	=	214,250
Washing facilities	936	× 1.25	=	1,170	× 360	=	421,200
Shops	900	× 1.25	=	1,125	× 150	=	168,750
Storage	1,364	× 1.25	=	1,705	× 120	=	204,600
Subtotal	23,334 NASF			28,343 DGSF			
Circulation				2,243	× 150	=	336,450
Toilets	Note 25% of the total; multiply			800	× 300	=	240,000
Mech. rooms	28,343 × 1.25			3,043	× 100	=	304,300
Total				35,429 GSF			$6,804,930

This is the construction cost at bid for New York. For conversion to Raleigh, we look up the Means Index for Raleigh for October 1988 (166.2), divide by the one for New York (241.6) and multiply this figure by the New York cost:

$$\frac{166.2}{241.6} \times 6,804,930 = \$4,681,206 \text{ (construction cost at Raleigh for 1988)}$$

Input	Question	Date Source
NASF	How many net assignable square feet? Total.	From space users
(x)		
Net to gross efficiency	How sophisticated is the facility planned?	Table 8.2-3
(=)		
GSF		
(x)		
Cost per GSF	What is the midpoint of construction? What is the cost/GSF?	Table 8.2-5
(=)		
Construction cost for New York		
(+)		
Means Index conversion	What is the location?	Building cost index See references
(=)		
Cost at bid at project site		
(+)		
Owners costs	What other costs are included?	Table 8.2-6
(=)		
Project costs		

Fig. 8.2-2. Facility type estimating process at the concept phase.

Input	Question	Date Source
NASF	How many NASF space type?	From Building Program
(x)		
Net to department gross multiplier		Table 8.2-8
(=)		
Dept. GSF		Assume 25% of the total for circulation, toilets and mechanical rooms.
(+)		
Circulation, toilets and mechanical rooms		
(x)		
Space type cost/DGSF		Table 8.2-7
(=)		
Construction cost for New York		
(x)		
Means Index conversion	What is the location?	Building Cost index. See references
(=)		
Construction cost at desired location now		
(x)		
Escalation	What is the midpoint of construction and escalation?	Engineering news record. See references
(=)		
Estimated construction cost at bid		

Fig. 8.2-3. Space type costing process.

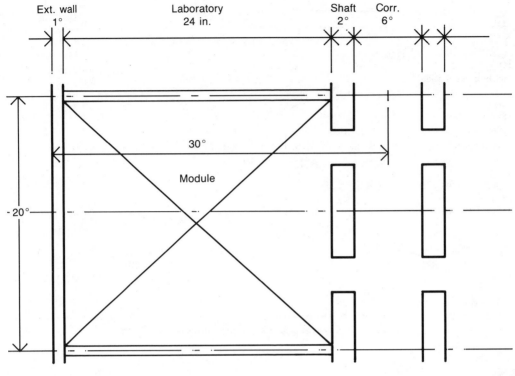

Departmental GSF $\quad 20 \times 30 = \dfrac{600}{480} = 1.25 \times$ NASF
NASF $\qquad\qquad 20 \times 24$

Fig. 8.2-4. D-SF multiplier calculation.

Table 8.2-7. Costs for Various Space Types for New York (October 1988)

Space Type	$/DGSF
Admin. support/conf./library	140
Research office	140
Research office	150
(if convertible to lab space)	
Computer room	170
Laboratory (wet)	250
Laboratory (dry)	200
Instrument room	220
Controlled-temp. room	200
Clean rooms	225
Shielded room (metal)	260
Animal room (wet)	370
Animal room (dry)	250
Washing facilities	360
Shops	150
Locker rooms	150
Storage	120
Circulation	150
Toilets	300
Mechanical rooms	100

Table 8.2-8. Net Assignable Square Feet (NASF) to Departmental Gross Square Feet (DGSF) Multipliers

Space Type	Multiplier
Admin. support/conf./library	1.15
Research office	1.15
Research office	1.25
(if convertible to lab space)	
Computer room	1.15
Laboratory	1.25
(both wet and dry)	
Instrument room	1.25
Controlled-temp. room	1.25
Clean room	1.25
Shielded room (metal)	1.25
(for concrete, verify)	
Animal room (single corridor)	1.19
(both wet and dry)	
Animal room (dual corridor)	1.38
Washing facilities	1.25
Shops (within lab areas)	1.25
Locker rooms (within lab areas)	1.25
Storage (within lab areas)	1.25

A lower cost estimate is, of course, more desirable than a high one. However, if the estimate turns out to be higher a scope adjustment will become necessary. The next phase of planning will make that process much easier with a facilities type estimate.

8.2.4 Systems Type Estimating

Systems estimating, also known as "building component estimating, uniformat and parametric estimating, "involves measuring the different building systems, such as the floor system and the exterior wall system, and then applying unit prices to them.

At the schematic phase of design, a program, a budget and a preliminary building design exist. By measuring the various building systems and applying cost, we can estimate even more accurately ($\pm$ 10%) than at the two earlier phases. We can now use the estimate as a decision-making tool by trading off various types of building materials and systems. See Figure 8.2-5. Cost targets are established for each functional element

or system. We can use systems estimating to compare various design schemes and their costs. Many design decisions and trade-offs will be made during this stage. To assist with these decisions and stay on budget, systems estimating is the most efficient method.

Unit prices can be found in estimating manuals, derived from historical data, or requested from a general contractor. The unit prices applied will be raw cost for the specific building system and will be within the cost range historically established based on actual construction costs. The unit prices may need to be adjusted if the system being priced is not within the normal range. For instance, if the soils condition is known to be poor, it is necessary to increase the foundations unit cost or add special foundation costs.

Markups are then added to the raw costs. See Table 8.2-9. At the schematic stage of design, a 15% contingency is added. This contingency is for design changes and increased detail. It is based upon a historical average that shows that from schematic de-

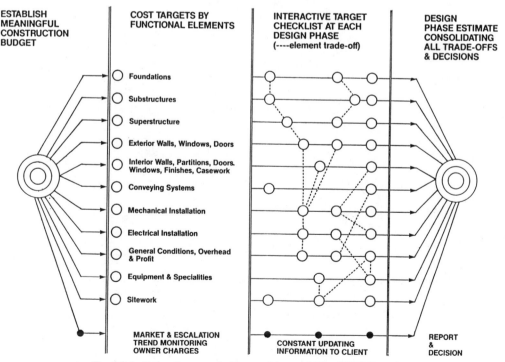

Fig. 8.2-5. Estimating as a decision making tool (The NBBJ Group).

Table 8.2-9. Systems Estimate

Parametric estimate: SD
Project: Research and technical lab

Date: 10/88	Area	Unit	Unit Cost	Total
Building Structure and Shell				
Foundations	12,000	FPA	$5.00	$60,000
Special foundations: piers/pits	12,000	FPA	1.00	12,000
Slab on grade	12,000	FPA	3.00	36,000
Basement excavation	168,000	CF	0.38	63,840
Basement walls	6,160	BWA	12.50	77,000
Floor structure	23,510	UFA	17.00	399,670
Roof structure	12,000	SF	14.00	168,000
Stair structure	6	FLT	3,000	21,000
Exterior wall system	10,560	XWA	18.50	195,360
Roofing	12,000	FPA	6.50	78,000
Interiors				
Partitions	28,800	PSF	6.00	172,800
Finishes	139,180	TFA	0.75	104,385
Misc. specialties & casework	35,510	GSF	2.50	88,775
Conveying				
Elevators	3	STP	12,500.00	37,500
Escalators				
Mechanical	35,510	GSF	38.00	1,349,380
HVAC				
Plumbing				
Fire protection				
Special systems				
Electrical	35,510	GSF	18.50	656,935
Lighting				
Power & signal				
Communications				
Special systems				
Equipment				
Lab equipment & casework	35,510	SF	10.00	355,100
Site Work		LS		400,000
Site preparation				
Site improvements				
Site utilities				
Markups		**12 mos.**		674,519
General conditions				
Overhead & profit				
Contingency				
Escalation				
Total Cost at Bid	35,510	GSF		4,890,264

LEGEND:

BWA = basement wall area	GSF = gross square feet	STP = stop
CF = cubic feet	LS = lump sum	TFA = total finish area
FLT = flight	PSF = partition sq. ft.	UFA = upper floor area
FPA = footprint area	SF = sq. ft.	XWA = exterior wall area

sign to final contract documents, the changes in design average an additional 15%. This may be adjusted depending on available detailed information. This design contingency is necessary to maintain the 10% accuracy margin.

Many public agencies require a systems estimate for their project. This estimating method was established by the General Services Administration (GSA) of the federal government and is called "uniformat" estimating. The GSA has published guidelines for proper measuring of each building system, specifying what is included and excluded in each system.

To perform a systems estimate, all component quantities must be measured and then listed. Parametric unit prices are applied to each system and totaled. Site costs must be either detailed or assigned an allowance. Equipment costs should also be detailed or an allowance assigned. Table 8.2-9 is an example of a schematic design cost at bid systems estimate.

At this point, let us compare the cost at bid estimates:

Facility type at concept
   phase $4,732,848
Space type at program
   phase   4,681,206
Systems type at
   schematic design   4,890,264

These are within 3.3% from concepts to schematic design estimate.
Remember that the accuracy of a systems estimate is ±10% compared to the budget.

8.2.5 Detailed Estimating

At the design development phase of design, a detailed program, a detailed budget and a fairly detailed building design exist. By measuring the quantities of the various building details and applying costs, we can estimate even more accurately (5 to 10%) than at the schematic (±10%) stage. The time to generate a systems estimate is much greater (five times) then the time required to generate a schematic design systems estimate, and the design contingency is reduced to 10%.

At the design development stage, a fairly detailed estimate can be made. Much of the detail will need to be clarified and/or assumed through conversations with the project manager. A detailed estimate can be easily established by using a final bid document of a detailed estimate from a previous similar project as a template. The quantities and unit costs will need to be adjusted. The listed materials may also need to be adjusted. Using historical data to establish a detailed design development estimate will provide a list of design decisions that need to be addressed, will clarify many design decisions, and will make cost allowances for some line items. The design development detailed estimate will need to be formatted so that it can be compared to the schematic design systems estimate. This comparison will show whether the project is on budget, or if any of the building's systems are more or less costly than assumed and why.

A detailed estimate can be performed as early as a schematic design with adequate historical data, but it is normally first performed at the design development phase. A detailed estimate contains all actual and assumed materials and their quantities. Many times a detailed estimate is used as the basis for negotiating the fee or construction cost with the architect and/or contractor. A detailed estimate assists the client and the architect in seeing how the design and/or scope changes affect the budget. It clarifies assumptions, and it assists in deciding what is to be included and excluded in the budget.

Detailed estimates are normally performed by a professional estimator for the architect if the architect is to provide an estimate. The professional estimator will estimate the architectural, structural, site preparation and site improvements portion of the project. A detailed takeoff is performed from the drawings, specifications and discussions with the project manager. The material types and their quantities are input into a computerized estimating system by a uniform system format. The estimating program will price out and summarize the estimate. The unit prices will be adjusted to reflect local conditions.

The estimator will also provide coordination with the mechanical and electrical (M&E) consultants to incorporate their estimates into the main estimate. The M&E portions of an estimate are normally the responsibility of the M&E consultants as part of their design package. Special attention should be given to the M&E estimates, as this portion of a project can exceed 50% of the total construction costs.

Many other consultants may also provide an estimate as part of their design package, such as civil, landscape, kitchen, lab equipment and other consultants.

The professional estimator will incorporate the main detailed estimate with all the subconsultants' estimates. The general contractor's anticipated markups, plus any contingencies, are added to the estimate to derive the bottom line or the anticipated cost at bid. Factors taken into account include the contractor's track record and bidding habits, where the project will be built and any unusual conditions. These factors are normally in the form of a contingency.

The bottom line number is then cross-checked with the past budget record and with other similar facilities for reasonability. The estimate is first summarized by systems. The systems units costs and the systems total cost are looked at for scope change and compared to past budget records and historical data. This is necessary to maintain the design intent.

Detailed Estimating at the Construction Documents Design Phase

At the construction documents (CD) phase of design, the bulk of the project's detail is known and the previously prepared detailed estimate is checked. A design contingency may still need to be added to the estimate, depending on how close to completion of final bid documents the estimate is made. At the completion of bid documents, no design contingency should be necessary.

The CD systems summary uses the same format as the schematic design (SD) parametric (or systems) estimate. The difference is that the SD parametric estimate has unit costs (based upon historical data) applied to the unit measurements, whereas the CD systems summary's unit costs are based upon actual detail. The actual cost of each system is totaled, placed on the CD system's summary sheet and then divided by the unit measurement to arrive at the parametric unit costs. These become part of the historical data base.

A detailed estimate can be formatted into a systems format and/or a Construction Specifications Institute format, also known as a building "trades" format. The trade format summary allows the project manager to negotiate with the general contractor because the final estimate and the general contractor's schedule of values can be compared.

At the CD phase, all the detail will be based upon the documents. The unit prices will be confirmed through conversations with contractors and supplies. The labor rates will be checked with the local labor unions.

The final bid documents estimate will still have an expected accuracy of ±5% of the anticipated low bid or the anticipated negotiated bid.

8.2.6 Cost at Bid

An "estimate" or "budget" normally means the anticipated cost at bid. The cost at bid can be a negotiated bid or a competitive low bid. The scope of the budget must always be clarified with the owner. This cannot be emphasized strongly enough, since the owner's budget may mean total construction costs or total project costs.

The construction cost is the money required to build the facility, including the general contractor's anticipated cost at bid and change orders. An architect's estimate must anticipate the general contractor's cost at bid if it is to be accurate. To do this, one must understand the general contractor's bidding methodology, which is covered in this section. Project costs will be covered in Section 8.3.

"Cost at bid" means the proposed price for which a general contractor will build the project based on the construction documents. It includes the general contractor's and the subcontractors' direct labor and material costs, plus all applicable markups. The cost at bid is normally 97% of the total construction costs, and the remaining 3% are for change orders.

The general contractor becomes the project's construction facilitator once his bid has been accepted by the owner. To prepare his bid, he will estimate his own work, which is normally concrete and rough framing, and will solicit subcontractors' bids or subbids. The general contractor either works with a few select subcontractors and suppliers and negotiates the subbids or solicits competitive bids from several subcontractors. It is assumed that if the general contractor solicits more than one subbid per trade, the bid will be lower. Knowing the bidding habits of local general contractors will increase the accuracy of an architect's estimate.

The general contractor will figure the direct labor plus labor burdens, material and equipment costs, and add these costs to his subbids. These are the "raw costs" or "direct costs." The general contractor will then add the markups.

Markups, also called "add-ons," are the amounts of money added above and beyond direct labor, material and equipment costs or raw costs. There are five basic markup categories: general conditions; taxes, insurance and permits; overhead and profit; escalation; and contingencies.

Markups will vary from contractor to contractor and from job to job. Total markups for a lab project should be in the range of 15% for a competitive bid standard lab project to 30% for a negotiated bid for an extensive lab renovation. That is why it is best to combine all markups into one number and note this as one percentage for comparison with the general contactor's markup. A contractor may have 3% for overhead and profit, 5% for contingency, 10% for general conditions, 5% for taxes and insurance, and 5% for escalation. That is a total of 28% for markups, which is very high for a competitive bid on a standard lab building, but it may be acceptable for a laboratory renovation project.

- General conditions, also known as "site overheads," are the general contractor's site costs relative to the specific project and include costs as noted in Table 8.2-10.
- Taxes and insurance include the sales tax on materials, if applicable to that area; the general contractor's "all risk" insurance"; warranties and bonds; and all required local construction taxes and insurance.
- Permits may include the general building permit, which often is provided by the owner. It may include special permits for items such as a sanitary sewer, storm drainage, street cut, and other local requirements.
- Overhead, also known as "head office overhead," figured on a percentage basis, consists of the general contractor's expenses which are not applicable to the

Table 8.2-10. Typical General Conditions

Cranage	Security
Dumpster fees	Shop drawings
Equipment rental	Small tools
Field engineer	Supervision
Final cleaning	Temp. fence
Job shack	Temp. heat
Layout & survey	Temp. phone
Photographs	Temp. power
Product data	Temp. Storage
Project manager	Temp. water
Project sign	Testing
Samples of labs	Travel
Sani-cans	Trucks
Schedules	

specific job but are required to run the head office on a daily basis. Typical head office overhead costs are for accounting, bookkeeping, marketing, office furniture, office personnel, office insurance, office taxes, office supplies, office telephone, postage and printing.

- Profit is the general contractor's profit on a specific project, figured on a percentage basis. Overhead and profit are normally lumped together in the general contractor's estimate. Many contractors will negotiate their "fee." This should be clarified when selecting a contractor, as it may mean their profit only, not their overhead and profit.
- Escalation is the amount of money added to the cost at bid, figured on a percentage basis, to reflect future anticipated price increases. It is figured from the date of the estimate and then escalated to the bid date. Many estimating guides and publications will assist in determining anticipated escalation.
- Contingencies are amounts of money set aside for unpredictable or unknown future changes—a Murphy's Law type of insurance. The three standard contingencies are (1) design contingency, an allowance to cover predictable design changes, based upon historical data and varying per the design phase (normal design contingencies are as noted in Table 8.2-11); (2) escalation contingency, an allowance to cover possible changes in the forecasted escalation; (3) bidding contingency, an allowance to cover upredictable and/or changing market conditions. This contingency may be a negative contingency when bidding is

predicted to be extremely competitive or the construction market is depressed.

After the general contractor has totaled the markups, he will add them to his raw costs. These costs then total the general contractor's cost at bid: his proposd price to build the project, excluding unforeseen changes.

To determine the reasonableness of your project's markups use the following procedure:

1. Determine the bottom line amount of the contractor's cost of materials and labor.
2. Determine the total dollar amount of all markups.
3. Markups ÷ bottom line × 100 = percentage markups.

To determine if the percentage of markups is reasonable, you can ask a professional estimator or other general contractors.

Change Orders

Change orders are the additional expenses due to changes made in the construction documents after the owner/contractor agree-

Table 8.2-11. Suggested Design Contingencies at Various Phases

Phase	Percentage
Schematic design	15
Design development	10
Contract document at bid	0

Table 8.2-12. Total Construction Cost in Percentages (Standard Laboratory)

Percent	Trades	Categories
20	*Building structure and shell:* foundations, basement, floor and roof structure, exterior wall system, and roofing	
8	*Interiors:* partitions, finishes, ceilings, miscellaneous specialties, nonlab casework	
30	*Mechanical:* HVAC, plumbing, fire protection, and special systems	
10	*Electrical:* lighting, power and signal, communications, and special systems	
11	*Lab equipment and lab casework*	
4	*Site work:* site preparation, improvements and utilities	
14	*Markups:* general conditions, overhead and profit	
3	*Change orders*	
100	Total	

Table 8.2-13. Checklist of Conditions Affecting Construction Costs

Type of Bid

A bid that is negotiated with a single general contractor (negotiated bid) will be higher than a bid selected using several preapproved general contractors (select bid) bidding against each other, and both types of bids will be higher than a competitive bid open to the public. The same applies to the subcontractor selection process. This is due to lack of competition. The less competitive a bid is, the lower the risks that a general contractor has to take to win the bid.

Site Access

Is there an on-site staging area for the general contractor?

YES

- Can it be secured, or will security services be needed?
- Will special permits be required?
- Will flagmen and/or special traffic control be required?

NO

- How far away from the site can the contractors stage?
- Will extra personnel be needed?
- Will extra trucks and deliveries to needed?
- Will extra time to complete the project be needed?

Project Work Area Access

Is the work area a remodel that can be accessed only at night?

Do all workers get paid overtime?

Is the demolition work hand-loaded into carts?

Can equipment and/or tools fit into the work area?

Will hand excavation be required?

Noise Control

Does noise need to be kept down?

Will temporary sound walls be required?

Can work be performed day and night or day only?

Contractor Availability

Are many subconstractors tied up on other projects? Will competition be reduced? (Maybe there has been so little work in the area or the area is so remote that there are no local contractors.)

Are labor disputes or negotiations going on?

Materials Availability

Are specified materials locally available?

Will extra delivery time and costs be required?

Will delays be expected?

Are the contractors qualified to install special materials?

Will special representatives be required?

Materials Quantities

Are small quantities of various materials required?

(If so, unit prices cannot be applied.)

Soils Problems

High water table, underground streams, rock, winter conditions or rainy season during excavation

Dust/Dirt Control

Renovation site, urban site, location of dumpsite, asbestos abatement

Local Code Requirements

Runoff control

Anticipated Contractor Problems

Labor disputes, wage agreement nearing expiration date, financial condition of contractor

Anticipated Owner Problems

Financing delays, multiple owners (slow decision process)

ment is signed, i.e., during the construction phase. These changes include extra work due to construction document errors and omissions, owner-requested changes and unforeseen no-fault changes. Change orders normally run 3 to 5% of the total construction costs. The accuracy of detail in the CDs and the "change order habits" of the general contractor will affect the percentage of change orders, as well as unforeseen difficult site conditions and "acts of God" such as storms, fire and strikes.

Sales Tax

It must be verified whether sales tax is included in the general contractor's cost at bid. Sales tax varies from state to state and city to city and changes frequently. The easiest way to determine the sales tax for a specific project is to phone a general contractor in the project's vicinity.

Total Construction Cost

Once the project has been completed, built and is ready for occupancy, the general contractor and the architect will add all cost at bid costs, all change order costs, and any applicable sales tax to determine the total costs of the project.

Table 8.2-12 provides an average cost distribution for a medium-cost research laboratory. It can be used as a cost check on a project to establish which categories may be out of line. If the percentages of the costs at bid are significantly out of line, consult Table 8.2-13 for possible oversights. Even better, check this list while preparing the estimate to avoid future disputes because conditions surrounding the project were not covered in the contract documents.

8.3 PROJECT AND CAPITAL COSTS
S. Matson

Construction costs of a typical lab project are only 58% of the total initial costs of a specific project. The other 42% are split equally into project costs and capital costs. See Figure 8.3-1. This is also referred to as

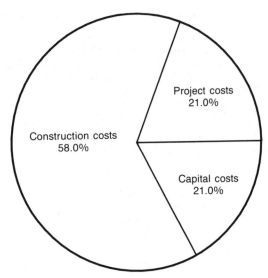

Fig. 8.3-1. Percentages of construction, project and capital costs.

the "initial cost" as opposed to the "life cycle cost," which will be covered in the next section.

8.3.1 Project Costs

Project costs are initial costs that the owner pays to have the project designed, built and completely furnished, excluding capital costs. Project costs vary widely, depending on the type of lab and where it will be built. These costs will add 20 to 60% to the construction costs of a lab project. Table 8.3-1 shows some typical project costs.

Table 8.3-1. Typical Project Costs

Architect's fees
Engineering fees
Furnishings
Furniture
Insurance & permits
Market studies
Movable equipment
Owner's administration
Owner's contingency
Project management
Soils report
Special consultants
Survey fees
Testing, inspections & balancing

Major movable laboratory equipment (5 to 25% construction costs) needs should be identified as early as possible in the planning stages of the design, since these often are the largest percentage of the project costs. This process should include an inventory of existing equipment to determine which lab equipment can be relocated and which equipment needs to be replaced or updated. Equipment items may be owner furnished and excluded from the construction costs to save the general contractor's markups.

Furniture and furnishing are $3 to $7/GSF, including tables, chairs, lab instrumentation and all associated supplies, waste cans, movable casework, window coverings, special floor coverings and artwork. Here again, some items may be part of the construction costs. The most common construction items may be owner furnished are window coverings and carpeting.

Architectural and engineering fees (6 to 15% of construction costs) will vary, depending on the size and complexity of the design. For a standard lab design, the architectural, structural and M&E fees may be as low as 6% of construction costs. For a complex renovation, these fees may be as high as 15% of the construction costs.

Special consultants' fees (0.5 to 10% of construction costs) include fees for design and engineering services provided by lab planning, landscape, kitchen, signage, elevator and acoustic consultants and interior designers.

Project management (3% of construction costs) may be performed by the owner, contractor, architect or engineer. Project management services performed during the construction process include creating and updating a project schedule; monitoring the project for quality of materials and workmanship; monitoring costs, pay requests, and schedule of values; and coordinating the work of the owner, architect and contractor throughout the construction process.

Testing, inspections and balancing (0.01 to 2% of construction costs) typically include continual testing of concrete for slump and soils compaction tests; inspections of structural steel welds, pile placement and curtain wall placement; and a final balancing of the plumbing and HVAC systems. The final balancing of the HVAC system can be critical to a lab project to optimize the operating costs and to ensure the correct air distribution and fumehood face velocity. Many of these project costs may be a part of the construction costs.

Market studies (1 to 2% allowance) include feasibility studies, which will determine if the project is needed, affordable and ultimately profitable.

Owner's administration costs (up to a 2% allowance) include costs for coordination with architects, engineers, designers, contractors, special consultants and financial consultants. Some owners consider these operating costs and do not charge them to the specific project.

A site survey, showing property lines, contours, and existing structures and conditions, must be performed early in the design stages of the project. The survey costs are included in the project costs.

Soils testing to determine the structural capabilities of the existing soil must be performed early in the design stage, since the

Table 8.3-2. Capital Costs

Site Acquisition	Leasing/Occupancy	Interim Financing
Land costs	Moving expenses	Interim financing (net)
Legal fees	Leasing commissions	Permanent financing
Appraisal fees	Tenant inducements	Placement
Surveys for purchase	Property taxes during construction	
Offsite work		

Table 8.3-3. Example of a Construction Cost/Project Cost Worksheet

COST @ BID WORK SHEET				
Phase of Design:	Date:			
Project:	Estimator:			
Architect:				
CONSTRUCTION COSTS	**Area**	**Unit**	**Unit Cost**	**TOTAL**
Building Structure				
foundations		FPA		
special foundations		FPA		.
slab on grade		FPA		
basement excavation		CF		
basement walls		BWA		
floor structure		UFA		
roof structure		SF		
stairs		FLT		
Building Envelope				
exterior wall system		XWA		
roofing		SF		
Interiors				
partitions		PSF		
finishes		TFA		
misc. specialties & casework		GSF		
Conveying				
elevators		STP		
escalators				
Mechanical		GSF		
HVAC				
plumbing				
fire protection				
special systems				
Electrical		GSF		
lighting				
power & signal				
communications				
special systems				
Equipment				
equipment		GSF		
Site Work				
site preparation				
site improvements				
site utilities				
Mark-Ups				
general conditions		MOS		
overhead & profit				
design contingency				
contingency for:				
escalation				
Total "Cost At Bid"		GSF		

Source: Matson/Carlson.

Table 8.3-4. Back of Construction Cost/Project Cost Worksheet in Table 8.3-3

INITIAL COSTS WORK SHEET				
Phase of Design:	Date:			
Project:	Estimator:			
Architect:				
	AREA/NOTES	UNIT	UNIT COST	TOTAL
TOTAL "Cost At Bid"		GSF		
CONSTRUCTION COSTS				
Change Order Allowance		LS		
Sales Tax & Other Applicaple Taxes		LS		
Total Construction Costs				
PROJECT COSTS				
Furniture & Equipment				
major moveable equipment		LS		
furniture & furnishings		LS		
Design & Management				
architectural/engineering fees		LS		
special consultants		LS		
project management		LS		
testing, inspections, & balancing		LS		
market studies		LS		
owner's administration		LS		
survey		LS		
soils		LS		
Contingencies				
general owner's contingency		LS		
contingency for:		LS		
Insurance & Permits				
insurance		LS		
permits		LS		
Total Project Costs				
CAPITAL COSTS				
Site Acquisition				
land costs		LS		
legal fees		LS		
surveys & tests for purchase		LS		
appraisal fees		LS		
off-site work		LS		
Leasing/Occupancy				
moving expenses		LS		
leasing commissions		LS		
tenant inducements		LS		
property taxes during construction		LS		
Financing				
interim financing (net)		LS		
permanent financing placement (net)		LS		
Total Capital Costs				

Source: Matson/Carlson.

structural foundation's engineering depends on it. The costs for soils testing are included in the project costs.

Owner's contingency is a percentage added to the project costs, at the owner's discretion, to cover unforeseen costs such as escalation, changes in scope, unwanted project delays, etc.

Insurance (1 to 2% of construction costs) can be handled many different ways. The owner or the contractor can insure the site during construction. If the project is an addition, the owner may find it less expensive to insure the site through the existing policy.

Permits (0.5 to 2% of construction costs) cost will vary, depending on the size and location of the project. Each city, county and state has different permit requirements and related costs. The owner generally secures the permit, but it becomes a part of the project cost.

8.3.2 Capital Costs

Capital costs are the owner's site acquisition costs, leasing and occupancy costs, and interim financing costs. Costs relating to or dealing with bankers, lawyers and realtors are noted on Table 8.3-2.

- Site acquisition costs: land costs, legal fees, appraisal fees, surveys for purchase, off-site work.
- Leasing/occupancy: Moving expenses, leasing commissions, tenant inducements, property taxes during construction.
- Interim financing: Interim financing (net), permanent financing, placement.

Tables 8.3-3 and 8.3-4 provide examples of a construction cost/project cost worksheet.

REFERENCES

Building Construction Cost Data, R. S. Means Company, Inc., 150 Construction Plaza, P.O. Box 800, Kingston MA 02364-0800. (617) 747-1270.

Building Cost Modifier, E. H. Boeckh Company, 525 East Michigan Street, P.O. Box 664, Milwaukee WA 53201. (414) 271-5544.

8.4 LIFE CYCLE COSTS   *S. Matson*

8.4.1 Introduction

A construction project owner must initially make a large financial commitment for the creation of a building: planning, design, construction and financing. However, greater financial commitment must be made for the continuing life of the building: operating, heating, cooling, maintenance, janitorial service, security services, repainting, remodeling, repairing and replacement costs.

Some initial costs may be traded off against the life costs (or continuing costs). For instance, paying more initially for flexible lab casework may save money in the long run against the continuing costs of moving fixed casework. Typically, the life cycle cost (LCC) analysis is most often used in building energy utilization-related studies.

LCC analysis offers project owners and architects techniques to make investment trade-off decisions. To better comprehend LCC techniques, the following concepts must be understood.

- Life: The life expectancy of a building. Does the building need to last 10, 40 or 60 years? This must be considered when establishing project objectives and goals, as it will affect the cost and design of the facility. Factors affecting the determination of a facility's life for calculation purposes are many. They relate to projected ownership, expected use, applicability of depreciation, financing sources and the purpose of the project.
- Cycle: The building's yearly or monthly cycle in terms of operation and maintenance, and its expected cycle for remodeling and replacement.
- Costs: All present and future costs associated with the project projected over the life of the facility. These costs are factored using projected inflation, interest rates and depreciation, and other factors affecting the cost of money in the future.

Figure 8.4-1 is an average distribution of the total costs of a lab project.

8.4.2 LCC Analysis

LCC analysis can be used to assess the economic consequences of a decision or to compare the consequences of two or more alternatives as input for decision making.

It combines the initial project development costs (construction, project and capital costs) with the projected continuing occupancy or use costs (operating and maintenance, renewal and long-term financing costs, i.e., interest payments). These combined costs are projected over the life of the building. They are analyzed in terms of both present worth and future worth so that a realistic comparison can be achieved. LCCs can be analyzed for various alternatives for comparative purposes. With this information, the most advantageous return on investment can be determined for a given project or project component. See LCCA, A Guide for Architects, A/A.

Initial Costs

Initial costs were discussed in Sections 8.2 and 8.3

Operating Costs

Operating or use costs are customarily estimated on an annual basis. Operating costs are the owner's total building costs for supplies, utilities and building services, excluding any tenant's share of the costs. These costs project the annual costs for supplies that the building needs to operate, such as cleaning supplies, toilet supplies and small tools. Operating costs also project the annual costs for utilities such as electricity, gas, oil, water, telephone bills, garbage collection fees and sewer fees. Finally, operating costs include fees for services such as security, maintenance, and janitorial and cleaning services. For example, security service may cost $250,000 per year. This cost is then projected to the total security service costs based on the life expectancy of the building. When all the annual operating costs are projected throughout the life of the building, this total will be the total operating costs of the life cycle of the building.

Cyclical Maintenance Costs

Maintenance costs, including renewal costs, are costs associated with repainting, remodeling, repairing and replacing. These costs are projected on a cycle. For example, fixed lab casework may have to be replaced every 5 years. Thus costs for replacing the lab casework every 5 years are projected to a total replacement cost based on the life expectancy of the building. When all the cyclical maintenance costs are projected throughout the life of the building, this total will be the total maintenance costs of the building.

Annual Interest Costs

The building's annual interest costs and financing fees are projected throughout the life of the debt. These may be increased as a part of initial construction or renewal costs. These costs then become the total interest costs.

Total LCCs

Total LCCs are the total operating costs plus the total maintenance costs plus the total interest costs plus all of the project's initial costs, as illustrated in Figure 8.4-2. Replace-

Total costs over 25-year building life

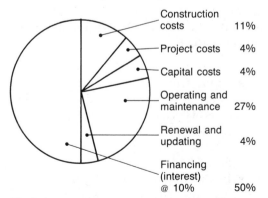

Construction costs	11%
Project costs	4%
Capital costs	4%
Operating and maintenance	27%
Renewal and updating	4%
Financing (interest) @ 10%	50%

Fig. 8.4-1. Total initial and continuing costs of a lab project.

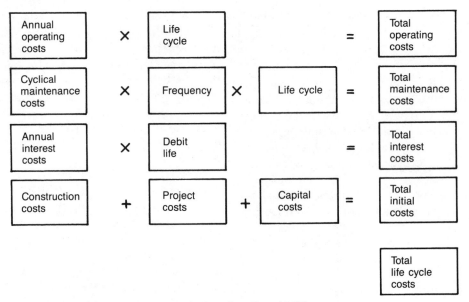

Fig. 8.4-2. Overview of total LCCs.

ment or disposal costs may also be included, depending on the ownership and goals of the project.

Other Cost Factors

Sometimes additional factors can also be considered in determining total LCCs. For example, a functional use factor may be developed based on efficiency studies of personnel in the operations of different systems or components being compared. Since personnel LCCs are very high in general and even higher for laboratories, considering the highly paid personnel who use them, a more functional design or system can produce large LCC savings.

A factor for intangibles can also be used for items such as design, which may help to attract and keep high-quality personnel, thus lowering recruitment, down time and other labor-related costs.

Conceptual LCC Analysis

At the conceptual design stage, a simplistic shortcut LCC comparison which does not consider all the costs and factors of a full analysis may be helpful in order to get an order of magnitude comparison. For example, the lab planner may have suggested to the owner that flexible casework will better suit this project's objectives. The owner can rearrange the lab layout in the future to accommodate new equipment and instrumentation or staffing needs, using the flexible casework for much less than it will cost to reuse the fixed casework or buy new fixed casework. It will cost the owner an increase in his construction budget of 3%, or $400,000. Is is worth it? Lets see:

OPTION A: Use fixed casework and same money initially

- Using fixed lab casework saves the owner $400,000 in initial construction costs. He can put that money in an interest-bearing account. In 10 years, with a 10% interest-bearing account, he will have $1,037,600.
- In the 10-year span of the building's life, the lab layout will have been changed three times. This will cost the owners:

Demolition:	$100,000 × 3 =	$ 300,000
Drywall:	50,000 × 3 =	150,000
Electrician:	500,000 × 3 =	1,500,000
Painter:	5,000 × 3 =	15,000
Cabinets:	750,000 × 3 =	2,250,000
Down time:	500,000 × 3 =	1,500,000
TOTAL		$5,715,000
Less Savings		− $1,037,600
TOTAL COST OF OPTION A		$4,678,000

OPTION B: Use flexible casework and spend more money initially

- Using flexible casework will cost the owner an additional $400,000 initially.
- In the 10-year span of the building's life, the lab layout will have been changed three times. This will cost the owner:

Demolition:	$25,000 × 3 =	$300,000
Drywall:		0
Electrician:	200,000 × 3 =	600,000
Painter:		0
Cabinets:		0
Down time:	200,000 × 3 =	600,000
TOTAL		$1,500,000
Add Initial Investment		$400,000
TOTAL COST OF OPTION B		$1,900,000

This gross level of comparison indicates that by investing $400,000 initially, the owner could save $2,778,000 in the course of 10 years. This quick analysis may be helpful in an early analysis, but it should be verified with a a more thorough LCC analysis before final decisions are made. To be accurate, the cost of money over time and many other significant factors must be clearly defined and applied.

Summary

In summary, LCC analysis may be applicable to many aspects of laboratory design, especially high-cost areas. Functional use alternatives which affect personnel costs are a prime area which has not been investigated using LCC analysis. High maintenance and operations items such as HVAC systems, types of waste piping, energy intensive equipment, etc. may offer opportunities.

Buildings which are financed privately and whose owners are subject to taxation should be analyzed on an LCC basis. For example, property taxation, based on the value of property, may offset savings in operations and maintenance, since the initial expenditure will probably be greater. Careful analysis is required to take into account all of the specifics for each project.   •

REFERENCES

American Institute of Architects, 1977. *Life Cycle Cost Analysis, A Guide for Architects,* Washington, DC: AIA.

Griffith, J. W., 1975. *Life Cycle Cost-Benefit Analysis: A Basic Course in Economic Decision Making.* Springfield, VA: NTIS. Document PB-251-848/LK.

Perkins, Bradford, 1975. Life Cycle Costing: An Approach to Method. *Architectural Record,* August 58–59.

Thorndike, David, 1973. *The Thorndike Encyclopedia of Banking and Financial Tables.* Boston: Warren, Gorham & Lamont.

US Department of Health, Education and Welfare, 1975. *Life Cycle Costing: Processes and Concepts,* Washington, DC: Office of Facilities Engineering and Property Management.

8.5 COST OF FLEXIBILITY
U.M. Lindner

Flexiblity in a laboratory environment increases the cost—or does it? Let's examine first what "flexible" really means. The American Heritage Dictionary* defines "flexible" as (1) "capable of being bent or flexed, pliable" (that's useless in a building); or (2) "Responsive to change, adaptable"; or (3) "capable of variation or modification."

Definitions 2 and 3 state what we are really seeking in a laboratory environment—one that is adaptable, capable of variation or modification.

Why is adaptability so important? A research building, with its multitude of inter-

---

*American Heritage Dictionary of the English Language, William Morris, Editor, 1969. American Heritage Publishing, Inc, NY.

dependent systems, structures, plumbing, air conditioning, controls, etc., is probably the most complicated and therefore the most costly building type encountered. Making any kind of modification to such a building can be an expensive nightmare. The knowledgeable designer will organize and coordinate these sophisticated systems in such a manner that future modification can be accomplished not only expeditiously but also at reasonable cost.

Designing to incorporate flexibility for future modification into a laboratory can range from a fortune to a modest increase in the original budget, depending on how flexible one wishes to be, how knowledgeable the designer is, or how accommodating the budget is. Most often a combination of these three circumstances is needed to design a state-of-the-art facility.

Let's examine the systems individuality.

8.5.1 Structural Systems

Two points always come up for discussion:

1. How susceptible to vibration is the building?

Unless there are definite requirements and reasons, a laboratory should not be built to provide a completely vibration-free environment. A structure should be designed that is reasonably stiff, especially against footfalls, and vibration problems should be treated on an individual basis. Very sensitive pieces of equipment should be located on the bottom floor at grade. Pneumatic tables, mounts or shock-absorbent padding can be used as a localized treatment on upper floors as needed.

This reasonable stiffness could add as much as 0.5% of the structural budget to the building budget or nothing if the budget was knowledgeably established.

2. How does the structural system help to permit access to the system?

This could involve an interstitial access space, which essentially adds a fully accessible space above each lab floor. This might add as much as 15 to 20% of the structural

budget to the building cost. A catwalk system permitting a high degree of access to systems might add 5 to 10% of the structural budget to the building cost. The addition of a comfortable* vertical allowance between the ceiling and the floor above might, depending on the degree of comfort, add 0.25 to 1.0% of the structural budget to the building cost.

The cost of this systems access may be viewed as a drastic and disturbing number in the building budget. However, if this problem is ignored, it may cost many times that amount during the life of the building as access for routine maintenance and modifications becomes a nightmare.

8.5.2 HVAC System

A well-engineered supply and exhaust system, with a control system that does not require a degree in celestial science for operation and maintenance, must include the capability to add hoods, change their location and change air pressurization in any area. This should be the basic philosophy behind the design of any laboratory building. The options that can be added to this system are almost limitless.

The basic design philosophy should give reasonable adaptability and capacity. How much more one can spend is very hard to tabulate. Costs should be carefully and frequently monitored during the early design stages.

8.5.3 Plumbing System

The basic philosophy for research facilities should provide for:

- Future capacity
- Looped and sectionalized systems
- Modular access to mains
- Accessible shafts
- Accessible equipment

These ideas not only facilitate routine maintenance during the life of the building but

---

*"Comfortable" in this case means easy access to install and maintain ductwork and piping.

also have a certain amount of flexibility (adaptability) built in.

Beyond the above considerations, flexibility becomes a matter of choice. It might include such things as piping systems for the future use of lab waste hookups, oversizing of systems for future capacity, etc.

The cost, once more, is hard to tabulate, and should be examined and monitored on a case-by-case basis.

8.5.4 Electrical System

Flexibility in electrical systems is probably the least understood feature and, therefore, the one most complained about by building occupants. The lack of power and the distance needed to pull an additional circuit or two into a heavily used laboratory can be quite costly to the occupant.

Careful planning and programming will suggest a basic building concept that has frequently located panels with adequate spare capacity, backed up properly to the primary system. Plug-in wireways that are accessible and feeds that have been designed for spare capacity will also help to provide flexibility.

Providing additional power capacity for unforeseen future needs can add 10 to 20% to the cost of the electrical base.

Again, it is hard to be specific, since this system could have a wide range of applications. It may also include emergency power, standby power and/or uninterrupted power.

Communications and computer systems are probably the most difficult systems to predict and are subject to much renovation by future occupants. If the original building was knowledgeably designed, it will include such things as cable trays and oversized conduits to permit future adaptability. Depending on the degree of sophistication, this might add 2 to 5% to the electrical base estimate.

8.5.5 Casework

Some words of caution here are advised: There are many so-called flexible casework systems on the market that may provide unnecessary flexiblity (changes being made just because it's easy to make them).

Thorough knowledge of the market and the product will be needed to educate the user and help him select the right casework system.

If one looks at conventional casework (built to the floor) as a base, a reusable system that disassembles and reconfigures in various new ways, such as a simple suspended or C-frame system, may add 10 to 15% to the base lab casework cost. More sophisticated systems can add as much as 25 to 30%.

The 10 to 15% premium for a reusable system is only the first cost over the base assumption. It does not take into consideration:

- Ease of access for installation of plumbing systems during original installation or for maintenance, which would reduce the cost.
- These systems basically are designed to support a work surface. Secondarily they support storage modules or cases (cupboards and drawers). This means that a laboratory could be made fully functional by providing storage modules under 25 to 30% of the bench top. This would also reduce the cost. The cost of additional cases could be saved, as they are not needed to support the work surface.

Flexibility does not have to be expensive if planned properly and with knowledge.

The direct building cost (bricks and mortar) for a hypothetical cost model might be as follows:

	Percent of Total	Add for Flexibility (%)
Site work	2	0–0
Structure	14	5–20
Enclosure and roof	6	
Interior finished and partitions	8	0–0
Specialties (including lab. casework)	23	10–30
Plumbing	10	5–10
Electrical	10	10–20
HVAC	27	5–15
	100	6–17

8.6 NET ASSIGNABLE TO GROSS SQUARE FEET EFFICIENCY
T. Ruys

8.6.1 Introduction

In 1964 the National Academy of Sciences, National Research Council, published Technical Report No. 50, "Classification of Building Areas." The report was the result of an effort to conserve scarce resources, and the need was felt to measure building "efficiency" in order to compare different building designs. A survey revealed that various agencies used their own definitions and ways to measure building areas, and no meaningful comparisons could therefore be made.

The task force, made up of representatives from nine federal government agencies, included the following qualifying principles in the preface:

- "That definite criteria for efficiency of the use of space, as expressed in the recommended 'formula for plan efficiency,' are needed and useful as a guide to planners and building owners."
- "That such criteria must not be used as a absolute measure because many other factors of design and cost must be considered in the evaluation of the plan."

In their recommendations, the task force made the following statements:

- "Buildings should not be arbitrarily evaluated or numerically compared on the basis of area relationships alone. The evaluation or comparison of the plans of different buildings should give due consideration to such factors as the nature of occupancy, intended functions, size, location, and significant mechanical and service features."
- "Any method of evaluating building design resulting from these efforts should not employ the term 'efficiency' in either a qualitative or a quantitative sense, nor utilize an arbitrary scale as a single criterion for assessing adequacy or functional suitability of building plan; rather, it should make possible, as a minimum, comparison of structures of like sizes, location and use."

Since 1964 many federal agencies have made it a practice to list the desired efficiency in their building program of requirements. It is not known how much deliberation precedes these decisions or how the decisions are arrived at.

Different types of laboratories have different net to gross square feet efficiencies. The purpose of this section is to provide a guide to efficiencies for different types of laboratories.

8.6.2 Definitions

These definitions have been the basis for measuring building areas by means of a uniform method and have been employed by many agencies, institutions and individuals; their continued use is highly recommended. However, in practice, some variations have occurred over time. In spite of the task force's objections to the word "efficiency," it is widely used in the term "net to gross square feet efficiency." It is also common that only gross square feet and net assignable square feet are used; the other area classifications—custodial, circulation, mechanical and construction—have not played a significant role in measuring space.

Because uniformity of measurements is so important, we have reproduced the task force's definitions for gross square feet and net assignable square feet verbatim. The reader is referred to the report for the definitions of custodial, circulation, mechanical and construction areas, the other area classifications which in their totality make up all the areas in a building.

Gross Area

Definition. "Gross area" should be construed to mean the sum of the floor areas included within the outside faces of exterior walls for all stories, or areas, which have floor surfaces.

Basis for Measurement. Gross area should be computed by measuring from the outside face of exterior walls, disregarding cornices, pilasters, buttresses, etc., which extend beyond the wall face.

Description. In addition to ground-to-top-story internal floored spaces obviously covered in "Definition" above, gross area should include basements (except unexcavated portions), attics, garages, enclosed porches, penthouses and mechanical equipment floors, lobbies, mezzanines, all balconies—inside or outside—utilized for operational functions, and corridors, provided they are within the outside face lines of the building. Roofed loading or shipping platforms should be included whether within or outside the exterior face lines of the building.

Limitations. Open courts and light wells, or portions of upper floors eliminated by rooms or lobbies which rise above single-floor ceiling height, should not be included in the gross area, nor should unenclosed roofed-over areas or floored surfaces with less than 6-foot 6-inches clear head-room be included unless they can properly be designated and used as either net assignable, mechanical, circulation, or custodial area.

Net Assignable Area

Definition. "Net assignable area should be construed to mean the sum of all areas on all floors of a building assigned to, or available for assignment to, an occupant, including every type of space functionally usable by an occupant (excepting those spaces elsewhere separately defined).

Basis for Measurement. All areas comprising the net assignable should be computed by measuring from the inside finish of perma-

nent outer building walls to the office* side of corridors and/or to permanent partitions.

Description. Included should be space subdivisions for offices, file rooms, office storage rooms, etc., including those for special purposes (e.g., auditoriums, cafeterias, courtrooms, telephone and telegraph rooms, garages), which can be put to useful purposes in accomplishment of an agency mission.

Limitations. Deductions should not be made for columns and projections necessary to the building.

Some clarification is in order, derived from the definitions of gross, net assignable, custodial, circulation, mechanical and construction areas:

- *Gross and net assignable areas* have different meanings and are generally measured differently for leased laboratory facilities.
- *Custodial areas* such as guard rooms, shops, locker rooms, janitorial closets, and maintenance storerooms which are a part of the building's operation and maintenance are not assignable. However, shops, locker rooms, showers and storerooms which are a part of the building's functions are assignable.
- *Circulation areas* permanently assigned to code-imposed exit requirements are never assignable. However, "aisles which are normally used only for circulation within offices or other working areas" are assignable.
- *Mechanical areas* are most often nonassignable, but not always. The mechanical space behind a built-in autoclave is assignable space because it is not a part of the building system and function specific; that is, it can be reassigned when the need for the autoclave ceases.
- *Construction areas* are building walls,

---

*The task force apparently wrote the standard primarily for offices.

columns, etc. that are permanent. Partitions between adjoining laboratories occupy assignable square feet.

- The area classifications should remain the same over the life of a building unless major renovation takes place.

8.6.3 Building Plan Efficiency

The formula for determining plan efficiency is as follows:

$$\frac{\text{Net assignable floor area}}{\text{Gross building area}} = \text{plan efficiency}$$

The task force's report goes on to warn that the results of this formula cannot be applied rigidly because of the many variables that are a part of facility design. Building func-

tion, size, location and site create enough differences in plans to make fixed numbers restrictive. The function, in particular, has a large impact on the plan's efficiency. Table 8.6-1 gives the actual net to gross square feet efficiencies at a major university for various buildings dedicated to different disciplines. It should also be noted that efficiencies were higher in older buildings.

Over the last two decades, a concerted effort has been made to classify laboratory facilities into four categories as noted on Table 8.6-2. An efficiency range for each category has been identified, using the National Academy of Sciences–National Research Council's method of measuring gross and net square feet. Our experience has been based mostly on federal, state and academic laboratory facilities.

Table 8.6-1. Net to Gross Efficiency of Space Utilization as a Factor of Building Age (for science buildings at a major university, 1988)

Building	Bldg. Year Built	Addition Year Built	ASF	GSF	Eff. %
Atmos. sci geophys.	1970	1973	45,095	78,186	58
Chemistry	1937	1963	136,047	224,277	61
Psychology	1973		39,942	74,021	54
Biology/botany/zoo.	1982		62,230	106,372	59
Bio., botany, zoology, geophys.	1930	1948	76,158	124,562	61
Zoology	1971		44,435	86,012	52
Physics	1928	1984/1972	87,683	150,934	58
Aero. & astro, appl. match	1929		38,542	57,949	58
Compsc., phys.	1960		34,529	56,836	61
Aero. & engr. research	1969		21,049	45,327	46
Chem. engr., Nucl. engr.	1966		41,717	80,245	52
Electr. engr.	1948		57,417	101,035	57
Mech. engr.	1959		67,575	94,873	71
Civil	1946		53,964	75,039	72
Civil, mat. SC	1921	1927/1987	37,583		
Fisheries center	1951		64,428	111,086	58
Applied physics	1968		47,839	67,573	71
Marine sciences-oceanography	1966		31,346	60,515	52
Marine studies-fisheries	1983		17,963		
Oceanography teaching	1969		29,015	58,444	50
Communications-math.	1955		62,811		
Astronomy	1896		14,798		
Health sciences Biochemistry-genetics	1964	1985	82,861	155,128	53
Health sciences Mental retardation/child dev.	1970		72,580	141,623	51
Health sciences Chemical medicine	1949	1972	158,069	328,284	48

Table 8.6-2. Average Plan Efficiencies for Different Categories of Laboratories

Laboratory Facility Category	Net to Gross Efficiency (% of Assignable Area)
Highly specialized	45–50% assignable
Specialized	50–55% assignable
Typical	55–60% assignable
Low lab/office ratio	60% and up assignable

The selection of categories was based on the types of laboratory functions and the degree of sophistication, hence the selection of titles. The following is an attempt to define these category titles, but readers are encouraged to expand on this list with their own experience in plan efficiences for other types of laboratories. These efficiencies apply to the total building plan and cannot be applied to individual floors or wings.

- Highly Specialized Laboratory Facility: totally dedicated to research functions requiring containment or isolation, with or without the use of animals.
- Specialized Laboratory Facility: Research laboratory with some containment but with a high ratio of laboratory to office/administrative space.
- Typical Laboratory Facility: As the name implies, those laboratories that occur most often, typically with a labo-

ratory to office/administrative ratio of 3:2.
- Low Laboratory to Office Ratio: Laboratory functions in a building otherwise occupied by office-type functions. The efficiencies typically attainable in office buildings begin to apply.

8.6.4 Reasons for Low Plan Efficiencies in Laboratory Facilities

Many individuals who should know better express shock when confronted with the reality of low net to gross square feet efficiencies. The following will explain some of the reasons, starting with the more obvious ones:

- More air-handling systems, utilities, power, waste lines which requires larger mechanical/electrical rooms and shafts.
- Larger elevators and probably more of them.
- For safety reasons doors swing out from the laboratory, which is now counted as gross square feet even if it requires no more floor area, which is next to impossible to do. See Figure 8.6-1.
- Many other safety features require space: safety showers, airlocks, secondary exists from laboratories.
- Some codes, when applied, require proportionately more space: the number of

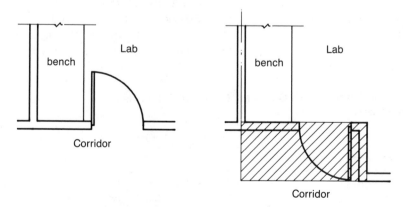

Note: ▨ Net area has become gross area. Not accounted for is loss of bench space as well.

Fig. 8.6-1. The effect of door swing on plan efficiency.

toilets is based on the number of occupants, which is based on gross square feet. Laboratory facilities are equipment-intensive, low-people-density facilities, which at times mandates more sanitary facilities than are normally required.

- Many facilities, particularly for research, have a large proportion of small, enclosed spaces, which requires more space for partitions and doors.

8.6.5 Conclusions

There is a direct correlation between the sophistication of the laboratory facility and its square foot cost, and, as pointed out earlier, an indirect relationship between sophistication and plan efficiency. That seems obvious enough. What is often overlooked, however, is the double effect of lower efficiency and higher cost per square foot on the total construction cost. Section 8.2 shows the relationship between laboratory category and cost, which is repeated here as it relates to efficiency. See Table 8.6-3. The numbers are based on actual projects and bid figures modified for New York using the Boeckh Index and escalated using ENR escalation percentages.

Tables 8.6-2 and 8.6-3 together provide a cost range which can be used in the early stages of planning for budget purposes. For example, assume a 40,000 assignable square feet cancer research facility located in Seattle, Washington, with construction starting in 1991. The facility includes a containment suite, cold rooms, and a small animal colony

and has approximately a 70:30 ratio of laboratory to office-type space.

The facility category is somewhere between specialized and typical, but the facility is on the small side, which makes it less efficient, considering that it will need all the systems of a large laboratory facility. Let's assume 52% assignable square feet, which means:

$$\text{Gross square feet} = 40,000 \times \frac{100}{52} = 77,000$$

Turning to Table 8.6-3, we must select the cost range. However, the costs noted are for New York. We must convert to Seattle costs and take the midpoint of construction rather than the beginning of construction to arrive at a closer approximation of the true cost.

A laboratory facility of that size will take approximately 18 months to construct, so the midpoint of construction is in 1992. Thus the cost is between $190 and $201 per square feet, or $14,630,000 to $15,477,000 for 77,000 gross square feet in New York. The Boeckh Index publishes tables monthly to adjust construction costs from place to place. The index for New York for July-August 1988 is 4.68 and for Seattle 3.98, so the cost range in Seattle is between (3.98 ÷ 4.68) × $14,630,000 = $12,435,500 and (3.98 ÷ 4.68) × $15,477,000 = $13,155,450.

With so many assumptions and guesses, it must be obvious that this is a crude "guesstimate" at best, but with a little practice we have found it to be surprisingly accurate.

Table 8.6-3. Average GSF Costs for Different Categories of Laboratories

Laboratory Facility Category	Cost per Square Foot in Dollars*					
	1987	1988	1989	1990	1991	1992
Highly specialized	197	207	217	228	240	251
Specialized	157	165	173	182	191	201
Typical	149	156	164	172	181	190
Low lab/office ratio	97	102	106	112	118	124

*Average costs for New York escalated 5% per year as predicted.

REFERENCES

Building Cost Modifier (Boeckh Index), American Appraisal Associates, 525 East Michigan Street, P.O. Box 664, Milwaukee, WI 53201. (414) 271-5544

Classification of Building Areas, Report No. 50, Publication 1235, for the Federal Construction Council, Building Research Advisory Board; Division of Engineering and Industrial Research, National Academcy of Sciences, National Research Council. Washington, DC 11964.

ENR, Sept. 29, 1988, published by McGraw-Hill Book Company, 1221 Avenue of the Americas, New York, NY 10020. (212) 512-2000

8.7 HOW TO LOWER COSTS   *T. Ruys*

8.7.1 Introduction

By now, it should be clear that laboratory facilities are expensive to build, renovate, maintain and operate. There are many reasons for this, and an understanding of them will be the first step in an effort to reduce them. Table 8.7-1 summarizes the different cost types and lists the tools typically used to *minimize* these costs and the sections in which they have been covered. The word "minimize" was used deliberately in lieu of "reduce" because most planners, architects and engineers make a conscientious effort to keep the cost down so that there is no cost reduction. Where many of them fail, however, is in their understanding of why these types of buildings are so expensive and the balance between the various entities which will result in the best overall value in acquiring, maintaining and operating a laboratory facility over time.

The single most important thing to understand is that personnel costs far exceed any other cost over the life of a building. This means that the efficiency of workers should never be compromised even though this cost type does not even show up in a typical construction cost or LCC analysis.

Wright State University made a study of the typical cost associated with a typical teaching/research laboratory facility and found that over 25 years personnel costs were on the order of 80% and construction on the order of 10%. See Figure 8.7-1. Over 30 years, personnel costs were 83% and construction costs 6%.

8.7.2 Cost Types

The various cost types, the reasons for these costs and ways to minimize them are covered next in the order in which they occur over the life of a laboratory facility.

Planning Costs

In addition to the standard planning costs—architects/engineers fees, surveys, soils and other tests, permits, taxes, and owners' administrative and financing costs—there are a number of hidden costs as a direct result of the planning process.

The wrong information transferred, if detected before construction begins, may result in delays, which, due to inflation, are a cost. The wrong information or inadequate information, if detected during construction, will result in change orders, which certainly has associated costs which can and almost always are measured. A change after construction is completed, which was the result of inadequate information transfer, can be a very large cost which is most often not attributed

Table 8.7-1. Summary of Cost Types and Ways to Minimize Costs

Cost Type	Cost Checking Tool	Covered in Section
Planning	Develop a POR	2.3
Construction	Value engineering	8.7
Renovation	Built-in flexibility	3.2
Maintenance	Product selection and LCC	4.1 and 8.4
Operating	Energy conservation	6.1
	Monitoring and control system	5.5
Space utilization	Space inventory	2.6

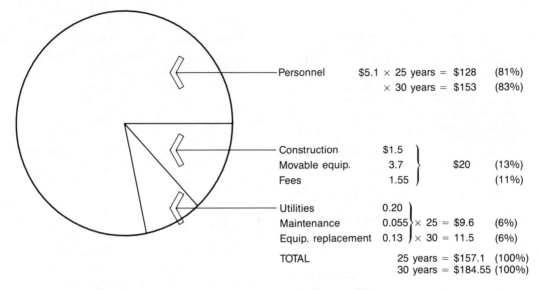

Personnel	$5.1 × 25 years =	$128	(81%)
	× 30 years =	$153	(83%)
Construction	$1.5		
Movable equip.	3.7	$20	(13%)
Fees	1.55		(11%)
Utilities	0.20		
Maintenance	0.055 × 25 =	$9.6	(6%)
Equip. replacement	0.13 × 30 =	11.5	(6%)
TOTAL	25 years =	$157.1	(100%)
	30 years =	$184.55	(100%)

Note: Amount in millions. Does not account for escalation, land cost, or financing cost.

Fig. 8.7-1. LCCs of a typical teaching/research laboratory facility (Fenning, 1988).

to a planning error or inadequacy but is written off as a renovation due to a change in function.

The thoroughness of the planning process is directly proportional to the cost savings. In other words, early decisions have the greatest potential for saving dollars. See Figure 8.7-2. Conversely, the cost of change is indirectly proportional to the time. That is, the later a decision to change is made in the building acquisition process, the greater the cost.

Construction Costs

Laboratory facilities are expensive for several related reasons, some of which reinforce each other. For instance, the square foot cost is higher and, in addition, many more gross square feet are required for the same net or usable square feet; this results in an additional cost increase. Furthermore, items in laboratory facilities not usually found in other types of buildings raise the cost again. Let us consider each of these factors in turn.

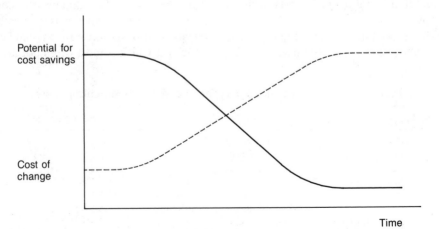

Fig. 8.7-2. The effect of time on cost savings and building acquisition.

- Square foot costs are higher because the structural system must carry heavier loads and be vibration resistant. Finishes, at least in some areas, are moisture resistant, cleanable and sealed against vermin or designed to contain microbes. The HVAC system requires better filtration, more air ventilation and closer environmental controls. There are several types of exhaust systems, some of which have stainless steel ducts and filtration. Typically there are large numbers of piped services for gas, air, vacuum and treated water distributed throughout the building. There are several waste systems for sanitary, acid waste and storm drains. The equipment-intensive work requires extensive power distribution and communications systems, and the type of work requires higher lighting levels. Many areas, because of the special nature of the work, require special walls, ceilings and floors.
- Net-to-gross square feet efficiency is lower or, for the same usable square feet of space, more space is required for the envelope and for structural, circulation and mechanical systems. Most of this is the result of the items listed above: more structure, and more M&E systems, require more space, which accounts for most of the increase in gross space or the decrease in efficiency. But there are two more reasons relating to safety. In most laboratories, doors must swing in the direction of exit—i.e., into the corridor—which is not allowed by building codes unless the path of exit is not compromised. There are several ways to accomplish this, but all of them require more space.

  Because of the nature of laboratory activities, there is a tendency to have more cart traffic, with an associated increase in corridor width, elevator sizes, and number of elevators.
- Items not typically found in other types of buildings are laboratory benches, fumehoods, controlled-temperature rooms, glassware washers and dryers, au-

toclaves and many other types of fixed equipment which are often a part of the construction cost and consequently raises the square foot cost.

Many operations in research and clinical laboratories are irreplaceable. Alternatively, repeating the procedures may be extremely costly in time and services. Because of this, redundancy is often built into the utility services. Dual fans, filters and emergency power generation are common, which, of course, raises the square foot costs.

Laboratory facilities commonly have safety features not found in other building types, such as eyewashes, emergency showers and fire protection systems.

Renovation Costs

Because laboratory construction costs are higher, renovation costs are proportionately even higher since renovation projects also require demolition, and demolition involves many trades and often must be carried out without disrupting ongoing operations. It is not uncommon to find that noise, vibration, dust and utility interruption can only be tolerated after working hours or on weekends, resulting in an obvious increase in labor costs.

It is an established rule of thumb that laboratory facilities are changed, on the average, every 5 years. Most changes require a change in laboratory equipment and utilities, and some require changes in building components such as walls, doors and ceilings.

Maintenance Costs

Many laboratory workers will not tolerate janitorial services inside their space because of the risks involved. That means that janitorial services are restricted to public areas such as corridors, stairs, elevators and toilets, which is a small part of the total building and should be at a lower cost than for office buildings.

However, the cost of maintaining mechanical and electrical systems is much higher because of the many systems, their sophistication, and the 24-hour-a-day, 365-days-per-year operation. It is not uncommon to find a full-time maintenance person with backup specialists for a laboratory building plus security on a full-time or part-time basis.

Operating Costs

Typical costs in this category are associated with maintaining the right environmental conditions and utilities: fuel, power, gas, water and sewage. This category also includes staff and personnel costs, which, as pointed out earlier, constitute the highest cost over the life of a building.

8.7.3 Lowering Costs

For every type of cost, a cost-checking tool has been developed to analyze the cost impact or to minimize the cost of facility acquisition. See Table 8.7-1. These are tools covered below in the order in which the process evolves.

Minimizing Planning Costs

Applying the data-gathering methods described in Section 2.5 provides the best assurance that information is transferred adequately and correctly from the user team to the design team. It should be obvious from the previous discussion on various types of costs that the planning cost is low compared to the construction cost and minuscule compared to the LCC. A program of building requirements (see Section 2.4) is the best assurance of minimizing future costs.

Minimizing Cosntruction Costs

A common tool to minimize construction costs is known as "value engineering." It is an analytical process by which different methods of construction and different systems are compared, based strictly on costs. Their merits are compared with other criteria and prioritized in order of desirability or value and in order of undesirability or compromising functions.

Because value engineering typically deals primarily with the value of construction, it can be a very shortsighted method, causing higher renovation, maintenance and operating costs and thus a higher LCC. This method is most often used for public buildings owned by federal and state agencies. The political pressure to minimize the initial cost may spell the success or termination of a project. Renovating, maintenance and operating costs are long-term costs, and are often hidden and easier to justify.

It is interesting to note that some private research laboratories conscientiously keep initial costs down because renovation, maintenance and operating costs are passed on to the research contract in the form of overhead or project charges. There is, of course, a limit to this strategy in order to remain competitive.

The balance between initial and long-term costs has not been lost on legislative bodies. Many now require an LCC analysis for every capital project.

The greatest benefit of value engineering is in pooling experience and thus getting a second opinion, as is done in medicine for critical operations. A typical value engineering team consists of the owner's representative, the architect and his consultants, and the contractor. The owner will make the final decision in weighing the reduced initial cost against higher maintenance or operating costs. The architect is in the best position to advise on aesthetic implications; the engineers on systems; and the contractor on construction methods and the cost of labor and materials.

Typically, however, the value engineering team consists of individuals who had no role in the design. They are chosen to increase the possibility of unbiased opinions and to get a second opinion. The design team of record should be present in order to explain the reasons for certain design decisions.

The best time for value engineering is after the design development phase, when enough design information is available for evaluation but changes are possible with a minimum impact on the design costs.

There is another way to reduce the construction cost: by purchasing laboratory benches and equipment directly from the supplier or by deferring the purchase until later. Laboratory benches may be treated as furniture. Laboratory benches that are readily disassembled and moved are available. The bench tops are self-supporting; they do not depend on cabinets to support them. This type of lab furniture tends to be more expensive than standard cabinetry, but there are several factors that result in an overall lower cost:

- Many of the components may be purchased directly from the supplier because they are not fixed to the building. This type of purchase can save about 10% of the cost of the contractor's markup.
- Only those storage units known to be required need to be purchased initially. Additional units can be bought later when the real needs are better known.
- The movable units can be exchanged between labs.
- The casework has a high salvage value because it is made for general use, not designed to fit only one company's specific building conditons.

Minimizing Renovation Costs

The obvious way to minimize renovation costs is to lower the cost of renovation. That sounds like double-talk, but since the amount of renovation will remain the same, that means that the cost of renovation has to be lower for the same number of square feet.

In order to make that possible, flexibility is built into the systems. Section 3.2 discusses the various types of flexibilities. See also Ruys (1970). Flexibility typically increases the initial construction cost, and the benefits of a lower future cost must be weighed against the present cost. It should be remembered, however, that there are hidden costs in lost time, and in waiting for and planning the renovation, not to mention the frustration of dealing with the wrong and inefficient space.

Figure 8.7-3 graphically portrays the relative cost of planning, which is fairly low, compared to the construction cost, which is a straight line if the costs are reimbursed to the contractor as the work progresses. The renovation costs occur at shorter and shorter intervals as the building ages, and at a higher and higher cost with inflation, which results in an upward curve. Increased flexibility

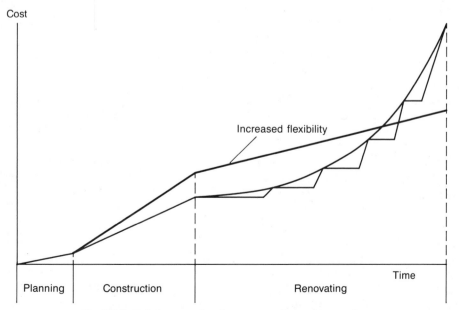

Fig. 8.7-3. Relative cost planning, constructing and renovating.

raises the construction cost but lowers the renovation cost, most often for a life cycle gain.

Minimizing Maintenance Costs

The best way to do this is to lower personnel costs. This involves selecting the best products, which require fewer individuals to clean, watch and serve. Unfortunately, that will increase the initial construction cost.

The LCC analysis method of comparing initial costs against long-term costs is a useful tool to evaluate the best value.

Minimizing Operating Costs

The highest operating cost is the cost of energy, both in fuel and in electrical power. An energy conservation analysis evaluates the best and lowest use of energy. Here again, an LCC analysis will determine the best choice of systems and fuel.

The advance in computer technology and control systems has automated and maximized energy conservation in building systems.

8.7.4 Space Utilization

As costs go up, the need to increase space utilization increases. Laboratories become more and more crowded. There are ways to increase the number of people in the same amount of space by changing the way space is owned and used. The following approaches suggest ways to use existing facilities more fully.

Facility Inventory

It is not uncommon, particularly in academic research facilities, to find that the facilities manager's position is slightly lower in the institutional hierarchy than that of the laboratory user. As a result, it is practically impossible for the manager to reassign or relocate, and especially to reduce space, for an investigator who is not using that space effectively until that person moves, retires or dies. This poor usage of space leads to many complaints from others who would like to use it.

The best way to ovecome inequities is to make space nonproprietary and assign it on the basis of need or grant support generated. The first step is to make a space inventory of the present facility and measure individual space claims against available space standards or institutional consensus standards.

There are standards available for space per principal investigator or equivalent and for bench space for each technician (see Section 2.6). Once space standards have been established, it will be much easier to reassign space on the basis of need rather than status.

Multidisciplinary Space

In the laboratory, many spaces are design specific, with a low occupancy rate per space. By changing our thinking, we can design a laboratory operation in which supplies and equipment are brought to the technician who performs tasks for many disciplines or operations.

At several teaching institutions today, multidisciplinary labs are based on this concept (Ruys, 1973). A variation on this approach is to assign the same space consecutively to different functions, such as chemical synthesis, product formulation, and various kinds of sample preparation.

Shared Space

Using the same thinking, we can cause individuals or departments to share space. Many institutions have conference rooms, libraries, lunchrooms and lounges for each department. These spaces, however, are often shared; the same can be done with other types of facilities, such as those for glass washing, media preparation, equipment storage, animal facilities and controlled-temperature rooms.

This solution is sometimes resisted because of the reluctance of many individuals to depend on services not under their own control. But administrative considerations may overcome this reluctance, particularly in a time of tight budgets.

"Supermarket" Concept

An inventory of the storage units in many labs would show that much equipment stored is used infrequently. There may also be dated chemicals and bulk supplies that are not needed for immediate use. Especially in R&D, there is a reluctance to dispose of equipment or glassware that might be needed in the future. And to take advantage of quantity savings, there is a tendency to buy more supplies than immediate needs dictate.

Rather than use lab space to store equipment and supplies, the institution or company may assign secured storage to each investigator or department in less valuable space outside the working laboratory. In addition, a central area for stocks of chemicals, glassware, and other supplies can be set up as a "supermarket," Here individuals can select what they need on a daily, weekly or monthly basis and charge the cost to a personal R&D account. These accounts can be billed monthly for these charges.

Analysis of Activities

Another way is to organize functions, space and systems to use less space and to reduce the cost per square foot.

A good way to organize functions is to rank needs in descending order of importance. Once the priorities are firmly established, the planners can identify the most needed facilities and reduce or eliminate items of low or no priority to within the established budget.

Another approach considers activities and the spaces in which they occur (Ruys, 1969). By thinking in terms of activity centers, planners can identify those activities and spaces that may qualify for the multidisciplinary approach or those which may be shared.

Activity centers are spaces used for such functions as:

- Administration—offices, conference rooms, computer rooms, typing pools, reproduction rooms and library.
- Dry bench work—electronics labs, bal-

ance rooms, and the like, which require power but not other utilities.
- Wet bench work—chemistry labs and similar facilities which require water and drains.
- Support facilities—animal rooms, electron microsocpy, storage, glass washing, shops and similar facilities.

Once the priorities are established and the activity centers are identified, planners might combine these facilities and functions into zones of spaces to take advantage of similarities in requirements. See Figure 8.7-4. For instance, the administrative activities could be located along the perimeter wall of a building and a communications cable tray provided. Next to this area might be a dry-laboratory zone with access to piped utilities and power.

Adjoining the dry-lab zone might be a wet-lab zone with access to water and drains and a mechanical zone with air-handling systems. A circulation zone between offices and labs would provide internal circulation between these two areas. Such an arrangement results in significant cost savings when compared to other designs because:

- Only the appropriate utilities are provided in each zone. In each case, however, the planners need to establish the proper mix of offices, labs and dry versus wet facilities.
- With this arrangement, fewer fire exit corridors, fire dampers, rated door and closers are needed, and less building area is used.
- Air can be supplied to the administration zone and exhausted from the wet-lab zone, using a less expensive mechanical system.

Removing Barriers

One of the most effective cost-saving steps is the elimination of barriers. The reasons for all walls and partitions should be analyzed. Almost without exception, barriers are expensive; they can cause fragmented treat-

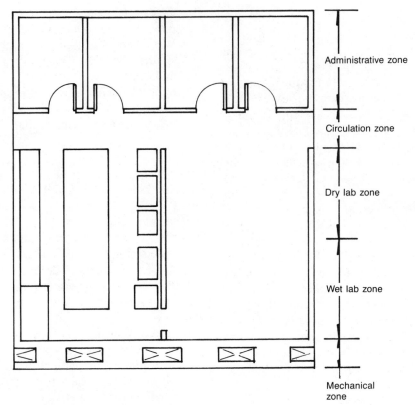

Administrative zone

Circulation zone

Dry lab zone

Wet lab zone

Mechanical zone

Fig. 8.7-4. Space activities combined in zones.

Table 8.7-2. Reasons for Barriers and Ways to Eliminate Barriers

Item	Remarks
Equipment support	Consider freestanding casework.
Territoriality	Make sure that all claims are justified.
Investigator's control	This should be questioned.
Security	This requires hardware to match.
Separation of incompatibilities	
Clean functions and containment	Clean functions can be localized and minimized.
Dust and clean functions	Dust may be localized by capture and exhaust.
Noisy and quiet functions	Equipment rooms can be separate from labs.
Dark and light areas	Separate equipment rooms from labs.
Sensitive and standard functions	Separate special functions from lab.
Public and staff	Only visual separation may be required.
Containment	
Chemical and biological hazards	Provide special suites.
Fires	Barriers must comply with codes but can be reduced in number.

ment of mechanical systems, lighting and ceilings. They may also lead to expensive code interpretations concerning fire dampers, fire-rated doors and door closers.

The laboratory fire code (NFPA No. 45) allows 5,000 sq ft of open area for a Class A laboratory without sprinklers and larger areas for sprinkler-equipped buildings and for Class B and C labs. As a rule, the larger the laboratory units, the lower the cost of the building.

Table 8.7-2 gives some of the reasons barriers are created and ways to eliminate or minimize them.

REFERENCES

Fenning, Robert L., 1988. Capital Improvement Program HB 810. Dayton, OH: Engineering/Computer Science Facility, Wright State University.

Ruys, T., 1969, 37 Keys to Laboratory Design. *Research/Development,* Vol. 20, p 18–25.

Ruys, T., 1970. Flexibility in Laboratory Design. *Lab Manager,* April, May, June, July & September issues.

Ruys, T., 1973, A MultiPurpose MultiDisciplinary Teaching Lab. *American Institute of Architecture Journal,* August p. 46.

Ruys, T., 1983. Plan Ahead and Get the Most Useful Space for Your Money. *Industrial Research and Development,* March, p. 120–124.

Appendixes

A. List of Organizations

Abbreviation	Organization	Comment
AAALAC	American Association for Accreditation of Laboratory Animal Care 9650 Rockville Pike Bethesda, MD 20814–3998 (301) 571-1850	Animal facilities standards
AALAS	American Association for Laboratory Animal Science 70 Timber Creek Drive, Suite 5 Cordova, TN 38018 (901) 754-8620	Workshops on animal facilities planning
ACGIH	American Conference of Governmental Industrial Hygienists, Inc. 6500 Glenway Avenue, Building D–7 Cincinnati, OH 45211 (513) 661-7881	Publications on lab safety
ACIL	American Council of Independent Laboratories, Inc. 1725 K Street N.W. Washington, DC 20006 (202) 887-5872	Equipment labeling
ACS	American Chemical Society 1155 16th Street N.W. Washington, DC 20036 (202) 872-4600	Chemical information
AGA	American Gas Association 1425 Grande Vista Ave. Los Angeles, Ca 90023 (213) 261-8161	Electrical products testing lab
AIA	American Institute of Architects 1735 New York Avenue N.W. Washington, DC 20006 (800) 424-5080	Source for MASTERSPEC
AIA	American Insurance Association 85 John Street New York, NY 10038 (212) 669-0400	
AIHA	American Industrial Hygiene Association 475 Wolf Ledges Parkway Akron, OH 44311 (216) 762-7294	Publication on lab safety
AAMI	Association for the Advancement of Medical Instrumentation 1901 North Fort Myer Drive, Suite 602 Arlington, VA 22209 (703) 525-4890	Sterilizer testing

(continued)

Abbreviation	Organization	Comment
AMMAA	Adhesive Manufacturers Association of America 111 East Walker Drive Chicago, IL 60601 (312) 644-6610	Adhesive information for flooring products
ANSI	American National Standards Institute, Inc. 1430 Broadway New York, NY 10018 (212) 354-3300	Standards for handicapped access, eye-wash/emergency showers
APL	Applied Research Laboratories 5371 NW 161 St. Miami, Fl 33014 (305) 624-4800	Electrical products testing lab
ASA	Acoustical Society of America 500 Sunnyside Blvd. Woodbury, NY 11797 (516) 349-7800	
ASC	Adhesive and Sealant Council 1627 K Street, N.W., Suite 1000 Washington, DC 20006 (202) 452-1500	Adhesive information
ASHRAE	American Society of Heating, Refrigerating and Air Conditioning Engineers 1791 Tullie Circle, N.E. Atlanta, GA 30329 (404) 636-8400	Fumehood testing standards
ASME	American Society of Mechanical Engineers United Engineering Center 345 East 47th Street New York, NY 10017 (212) 705-7722	Engineering standards
ASSE	American Society of Safety Engineers 1800 E. Oakton Street Des Plaines, IL 60016 (312) 692-4121	Safety information
ASTM	American Society for Testing and Materials 1916 Race Street Philadelphia, PA 19103 (215) 299-5420	Test standards for materials
BOCA	Building Officials and Code Administrators International 4051 West Flossmoor Road Country Club Hills, IL 60478–5795 (312) 799-2300	Building code
BOECKH	Building Cost Modifier American Appraisal Associates 525 East Michigan Street P.O. Box 664 Milwaukee, WI 53202 (414) 271-5544	Cost modifier for different cities

Abbreviation	Organization	Comment
CABO	Council of American Building Officials 5203 Leesburg Pike, Suite 708 Falls Church, VA 22041 (703) 931-4533	Building code
CAP	College of American Pathologists 5202 Old Orchard Road Skokie, IL 60077 (312) 966-5700	CAP unit values. Publishes manual of laboratory planning
CAP	Canadian Association of Pathologists Dr. M.D.D. McNeely, Secretary/Treasurer Island Medical Laboratories 4489 Viewmont Avenue Victoria, BC V8Z 5K8 Canada (604) 479-7676	CAP unit values
CCAC	Canadian Council on Animal Care 1105–151 Slater Street Ottawa, Ontario K1P 5H3 Canada (613) 238-4031	Publisher of *Animal Care Guide for Canada*
CDC	Center for Disease Control Atlanta, GA 30333 (404) 639-3883	Containment facilities design
CHI	CHI Systems, Inc. 330 East Liberty Street, Suite 4A Ann Arbor, MI 48104 (313) 761-3912	Clinical laboratories space calculations
CPSC	US Consumer Products Safety Commission 5401 Westbard Avenue, Room 700 Washington, DC 20207	Products quality
CAC	Canadian Standards Association 178 Rexdale Blvd. Rexdale Ontario, Canada (416) 747-2647	Electrical products testing lab
CSI	Construction Specifications Institute 601 Madison Street Alexandria, VA 22314 (703) 684-0300	Specifications information
ENR	Engineering News Record 1221 Avenue of the Americas New York, NY 10020 (212) 512-2000	Construction cost data
EPA	Environmental Protection Agency 401 M Street S.W. Washington, DC 20460 (202) 382-2090	Laboratory design standards
ETL	Electrical Testing Laboratories, Inc. Rt. 11 Industrial Park Courtland, NY 13045 (607) 753-6711	Equipment labeling

(continued)

Abbreviation	Organization	Comment
FCC	U.S. Government Printing Office Superintendent of Documents 941 North Capital N.E. Washington, DC 20002 (202) 275-3015	Federal government publications
FMS	Factory Mutual Systems Factory Mutual Engineering & Research Corporation 1151 Boston-Providence Turnpike P.O. Box 688 Norwood, MA 02062 (617) 762-4300	Equipment labeling
FS	Federal Specifications Superintendent of Documents U.S. Government Printing Office Washington, DC 20234 (202) 275-3204	Product specifications
GSA	General Services Administration General Services Building Eighteenth and F Streets N.W. Washington, DC 20405 (202) 655-4000	Government construction standards
IAPMO	International Association of Plumbing and Mechanical Officials 5032 Alhambra Avenue Los Angeles, CA 90032–3490 (213) 223-1471	Mechanical codes
ICBO	Uniform Building Code International Conference of Building Officials 5360 South Workman Mill Road Whittier, CA 90601 (213) 699-0541	Building code
LIU	Laboratory Investigation Unit Department of Education and Science Room 7, 36 Main Block Elizabeth House York Road, London SE 1 England 01-928-9222, ext. 2248	Publishes standard and articles on laboratories
LOC	Library of Congress 101 Independence Avenue S.E. Washington, DC 20540 (202) 287-5000	Any publication
NAS	National Academy of Sciences National Research Council 2101 Constitution Avenue N.W. Washington, DC 20418 (202) 334-2000	Net and gross square foot standards
NBC	National Building Code c/o American Insurance Association 85 John Street New York, NY 10038 (212) 669-0400	Building code

Abbreviation	Organization	Comment
NBS	National Bureau of Standards Gaithersburg, MD 20899 (301) 975-2000	Building standards
NCRPM	National Council on Radiation Protection and Measurements 7910 Woodmount Avenue, Suite 1016 Bethesda, MD 20814 (301) 657-2652	Radiation protection standards
NCSBCS	National Conference of States on Building Codes and Standards 481 Carlisle Drive Herndon, VA 22070 (703) 437-0100	Building codes
NIH	National Institutes of Health 9000 Rockville Pike Bethesda, MA 20892 (301) 496-4000	Largest user of laboratories in the U.S.
NFPA	National Fire Protection Association Batterymarch Park Quincy, MA 02269 (617) 770-0200	Fire code standards
NFSA	National Fire Sprinklers Association P.O. Box 1000 Patterson, NY 12563 (914) 878-4200	Fire sprinkler standards
NPCA	National Paint and Coatings Assoc. 1500 Rhode Island Avenue, N.W. Washington, DC 20005 (202) 462-6272	Standards for coatings
NSF	National Sanitation Foundation 3475 Plymouth Road P.O. Box 1468 Ann Arbor, MI 48106 (313) 769-8010	Biological safety cabinet standards
NSF	National Science Foundation 1800 G Street NW Washington, DC 20550 (202) 357-5000	Laboratory planning publications
NTIS	National Technical Information Service U.S. Department of Commerce 5285 Port Royal Road Springfield, VA 22161 (703) 487-4600	Technical information service
OSHA	Occupational Safety and Health Administration 200 Constitution Avenue N.W. Room N-3603 Washington, DC 20210 (202) 523-7725	Laboratory safety standards

(continued)

Abbreviation	Organization	Comment
OTA	Office of Technology Assessment 600 Pennsylvania Avenue S.E. Washington, DC 20510 (202) 226-2115	Trends in R & D
PS	Product Standards National Bureau of Standards (Dept. of Commerce) Office of Engineering Standards Services Government Printing Office Washington, DC 20402 (202) 275-3204	Product standards
RFC	Resilient Floor Covering Institute 966 Hungerford Drive, Suite 12-B Rockville, MA 20850 (301) 340-8580	Flooring standards
SAMA	Society of Apparatus Makers Association 1101 16th Street N.W. Washington, DC 20036 (202) 223-1360	Formerly published laboratory case-work, fumehood, fixtures and tops standards and tests
SBC (SBCCI)	Southern Building Code Congress International 900 Montclair Road Birmingham, AL 35213–1206 (205) 591-1853	Building code
SCUP	Society of College and University Planners Central Office 2026 M School of Education Building University of Michigan Ann Arbor, MI 48109–1259 (313) 763-4776	University standards
SEI	Safety Equipment Institute 1901 North Moore Street Arlington, VA 22209 (703) 525-1695	Safety equipment standards
SPE	Society of Plastics Engineers Division of Plastics in Building 14 Fairfield Drive, P.O. Box 0403 Brookfield Center, CT 06804 (203) 775-0471	Information on plastics
SRA	Society of Research Administrators 1505 Fourth Street, Suite 203 Santa Monica, CA 90401 (213) 393-3137	Conducts workshops on laboratory planning
UBC	Same as ICBO	
UL	Underwriters Laboratories, Inc. 333 Pfingsten Road Northbrook, IL 60062 (312) 272-8800	Equipment labeling

Abbreviation	Organization	Comment
USDA	U.S. Department of Agriculture 1776 F Street, N.W. Washington, DC 20437 (202) 447-2791	Animal Welfare Act enforcing agency
USDHHS	U.S. Department of Health and Human Services 200 Independence Avenue S.W. Washington, DC 20201 (202) 245-6296	
USPHS	U.S. Public Health Service 200 Independence Avenue S.W. Washington, DC 20201 (202) 245-6296	Publishes standards for animal care
USTBCB	U.S. Architectural Transportation Barriers Compliance Board 330 C Street, S.W., Room 1010 Washington, DC 20202	Publishes standards for handicapped access

B. Common Fixed-Equipment Manufacturers

Note: Only built-in equipment commonly found in laboratory facilities has been noted. Every effort has been made to list manufacturers in each category that are of comparable quality and competitive. The addresses, contact persons, and telephone numbers were in effect at the time of publication. Contact manufacturers to inquire about local sales and service representatives and suppliers. Manufacturers are listed in alphabetical order.

Equipment Type	Manufacturer's Address	Contact Person	Telephone
1a. Lab casework—metal	American Seating Grand Rapids, MI	Customer Service	(616) 456-0600
	DuraLab Equipment Corp. Brooklyn, NY	Joe Angara	(718) 649-9600
	Fisher Scientific Indiana, PA	Customer Service	(412) 357-5800
	Hamilton Industries, Inc. Two Rivers, WI	Ned Braun	(414) 793-1121
	Kewaunee Scientific Corp. Statesville, NC	Si Pike	(704) 873-7202
	Laboratory Furniture, Inc. Carle Place, NY	Ed Fiance	(516) 294-6300
	Lab Marc Cambridge, MA	Robert Nizel	(617) 547-1700
	Labx System, Inc. North Andover, MA	Customer Service	(508) 975-3336
	St. Charles Corp. St. Charles, IL	Robert Rodgers	(312) 584-3800
	Classic Modular Systems, Inc. Two Rivers, WI	Customer Service	(414) 793-2269 (800) 558-7625
1b. Lab casework—hardwood	Hamilton Industries, Inc. Two Rivers, WI	Ned Braun	(414) 793-1121
	Kewaunee Scientific Statesville, NC	Si Pike	(704) 873-7202
	Laboratory Furniture, Inc. Carle Place, NY	Ed Fiance	(516) 294-6300
1c. Lab casework—plastic laminate	LSI Corp. Minneapolis, MN	Keith Wrobel	(612) 559-4664
	Ly-Line Products, Inc. Enumclaw, WA	Hugh Lyman	(206) 825-1611
	Monitor Tacoma, WA	Customer Service	(206) 475-5800
	TMI Corp Dickinson, ND	Jim Seawert	(701) 225-6716

Equipment Type	Manufacturer's Address	Contact Person	Telephone
1d. Lab casework—plastic	Fisher Scientific Indiana, PA	Customer Service	(412) 357-5800
	Herman Miller, Inc. Zealand, MI	Customer Service	(616) 772-3200
2. Cabinet hardware	National Lock Rockford, IL	Robert Mills	(815) 564-6156
3. Bench tops	All casework manufacturers:	See listing above	
	Durcon Canton, MI	Customer Service	(313) 455-4520
	Prime Resin Elmhurst, IL	Customer Service	(312) 833-6821
	Lab-Resin Taylor TX	Ron Warner	(512) 352-5287
4. Sinks	All casework manufacturers:	See listing above	
Stainless steel	Elkay Manufacturing Co. Oakbrook, IL	Gary Gates	(312) 574-8484
	Just Manufacturing Co. Franklin Park, IL	Dave Lewis	(312) 678-5150
Resin	See Bench tops		
5. Disposal units	Salvajor Kansas City, MO	George Hohl	(800) 821-3136 (816) 363-1030
6a. Laboratory service fixtures	Chicago Faucet Des Plains, IL	Customer Service	(312) 694-4400
	GAM Butler, PA	Gary Cipa	(412) 285-6360
	T & S Brass, Inc. Travelers Rest, SC	Mike Magrino	(805) 834-4102
	Water Saver Faucet Co. Chicago, IL	Don Schoen	(312) 666-5500
	Wolverine Brass Works Grand Rapids, MI	Customer Service	(800) 253-9002
6b. Laboratory safety Fixtures and cabinets	Guardian Equipment Chicago IL	Customer Service	(312) 733-2626
	Haws Berkeley, CA	Customer Service	(415) 525-5801
	Lab Safety Supply Janesville, WI	Customer Service	(800) 356-0783
	Speakman Safety Equip. Wilmington, DE	Customer Service	(302) 764-7100
7. Specialty—gases	Air Products Allentown, PA	Customer Service	(215) 481-8257
	M.G. Industries Valley Forge, PA		(215) 630-5492
	Scott Specialty Gases Plumsteadville, PA	James Strom	(215) 766-8861

(*continued*)

Equipment Type	Manufacturer's Address	Contact Person	Telephone
8a. Fumehoods—metal	All metal casework manufacturers	See listing 1a above	
8b. Fumehoods—plastic	Hemco Independence, MO	Milroy Mitchell	(816) 796-2900 (800) 821-3504
	Lab Conco Kansas City, MO	Mike Wyckoff	(816) 333-8811 (800) 821-5525
	LabShield USA Boxborough, MA		(508) 635-0404
9. Biological safety cabinets	Baker Sanford, ME	Dennis Eagleson	(800) 992-2537 (207) 324-8773
	Forma Scientific Marietta, OH	Customer Service	(800) 848-3080
	NuAire Inc Minneapolis, MN	Diane LaHoud	(800) 328-3352
10. Water-purifying equipment	AMSCO Erie, PA	Paul Kelly	(814) 452-3100
	Barnstead/Thermolyne Dubuque, IA	Harry Myers	(800) 446-6060 (319) 556-2241
	Continental Water Systems Corp. San Antonio, TX	Customer Service	(800) 426-3426
	Corning Medfield, MA	Customer Service	(508) 359-7711
	FinAqua Kirkland, WA	Rolf Hogger	(206) 822-8282
	Millipore Bedford, MA	Customer Service	(800) 225-1380
11. Glassware washers/dryers	AMSCO Erie, PA	Customer Service	(814) 452-3100
	Basil Equipment Corp. Wilson, NY	Don Basil	(716) 751-9365
	Forma Scientific Marietta, OH	Customer Service	(800) 848-3080
	Heinicke Philadelphia, PA	Customer Service	(800) 523-3608
	Pharmetics Hauppauge, NY	Customer Service	(516) 234-5888
12. Autoclaves/sterilizers	AMSCO Erie, PA	Paul Kelly	(814) 452-3100
	M.D.T. Castle Rochester, NY	Customer Service	(716) 475-1400
	Getinge Lakewood, NJ	Richard Roony	(201) 370-8800
13a. Controlled-environment rooms	Bally Bally, PA	Peter Koch	(215) 845-2311 (800) 242-2559
	Environmental Growth Chambers Chagrin Falls, OH	A. Rule III	(216) 247-5100

Equipment Type	Manufacturer's Address	Contact Person	Telephone
	Hotpack Corp. Philadelphia, PA	Nancy Martin	(800) 523-3608 (215) 824-1700
	Kysor-Sherer Environmental Marshall, MI	Customer Service	(616) 781-3911
	Lab-Line Instruments Melrose Park, IL	Customer Service	(312) 450-2600
	Queue Systems Parkersburg, WV	Customer Service	(800) 222-6902 (304) 464-5400
	Forma Scientific Marietta, OH	Customer Service	(614) 373-4763
	Nor-Lake Scientific Hudson, WI	Customer Service	(715) 386-2323 (800) 826-3304
	Tyler Refrigeration, Inc. Seattle, WA	Stanley Young	(206) 323-8940
	Jewett Refrigerator Co. Buffalo, NY		(716) 881-0030
13b. Clean rooms	Clean Room Products, Inc. Ronkonkoma, NY	William Duncan	(516) 588-7000
	Clean Room Technology Syracuse, NY		(315) 437-2152
13c. Soundproof rooms	Integrated Air Systems Valencia, CA	Customer Service	(805) 257-2300
	Compaire Corp. Grand Rapids, MI	Bill Decker	(616) 698-9660
14a. Floor finishes—applied	Desco Chem Co. Toronto, Canada	Customer Service	(416) 741-3830
	Dex-o-Tex Compton, CA	Customer Service	(213) 636-0561
	Stonhard Maple Shade, NJ	Customer Service	(609) 779-7500
	Hubbellite Sewickely, PA	Customer Service	(412) 741-0500
14b. Floor finishes—sheet products	Mipolam Northridge, CA	Customer Service	(818) 886-0439
14c. Wall finishes—special coat- ings	Sanitile St Louis, MO	Customer Service	(314) 644-1000
	Desco Chem Co Toronto, Canada	Customer Service	(416) 741-3830
15. Wall System—clean rooms	Donn Corp. Westlake, OH	Peter Reynard	(216) 871-1000
16. Security	Cardkey Systems, Inc. Chatworth, CA	Customer Service	(818) 998-7560
	Liebert Corp. Columbus, OH	Customer Service	(614) 888-0246
17. Laboratory instrumenta- tion	Lab-Line Instruments, Inc. Melrose Park, IL	Customer Service	(800) 323-0257

(continued)

	Equipment Type	Manufacturer's Address	Contact Person	Telephone
		Napco Scientific Tualatin, OR	Customer Service	(503) 692-4686
		Revco Scientific Ashville, NC	Customer Service	(800) 252-7100
		VWR Irving, TX	Customer Service	(214) 258-6953
18.	Autopsy stations	Lipshaw Corp. Detroit, MI	Customer Service	(800) 547-7429 (313) 834-8855
		Jewett Refrigerator Co. Buffalo, NY		(716) 881-0030
19.	Other	Unistrut Corp Wayne, MI	Customer Service	(313) 721-4040
20.	Many products	VWR Irving, TX	Customer Service	(214) 258-6953
		Labland Industrial Corp. Brooklyn, NY	Customer Service	(718) 625-5440
		AM Kinney, Inc. Cincinnati, OH	Customer Service	(513) 281-2900

C. Specialized Facilities: Radioactive Materials Research Laboratories

R. Baltzo

C.1 INTRODUCTION

In the two decades immediately after World War II, radiation phenomena, particularly radiation effects, were unknown factors, and laboratory studies typically used much higher activity levels than at present. The term "hot lab" was universally used to describe radioactive materials-handling laboratories. In the context of the postwar years, all such research was regarded as dangerously radioactive. In the majority of today's radioactive materials-handling laboratories, the implication "dangerously radioactive" is not true.

In the interim, scientific research, which previously studied radiation's physical and biological effects and explored the possible commercial applications of radiation, has been increasingly redirected to biological and medical procedures. Today's radiation scientists are apt to require smaller quantities of radioactive materials and less dangerous nuclide elements. The radiation hazards which remain are more readily controlled by precautionary designs and time-tested laboratory procedures.

In biological and medical research, the radioactive material procedures most commonly used today were originally described as "tracer experiments." The term "tracer" has a double meaning: radionuclides were used in very small (trace) quantities, and the procedures were designed to track (or trace) biological and chemical reactions at submicroscopic levels, where other forms of testing and measurement cannot be applied.

Use of biological tracer methodology has produced many benefits in biology, agriculture, nutrition and health. In the mid-1970s, an outgrowth of tracer research produced a new medical specialty, nuclear medicine imaging (or scanning), which was built to order around the availability of radioactive technicium-99m and a restricted group of other nuclides with closely related physical properties. The current boom in research, development and production laboratories for molecular biology on campus and in genetic engineering companies is yet another example of the same research trend.

Concurrent with the progress of scientific research involving radioactive materials, a considerable body of information has been refined and developed regarding the design of laboratory spaces which are optimized for well-controlled radiation research.

It should also be noted that over the past 40 years, design features associated with hot labs have influenced nonradioactive laboratory design. Several features formerly associated with hot lab design are now ubiquitous in professionally designed laboratories and, as such, make it reasonable to carry out low-level (submicrocurie) procedures in what is otherwise designated as a general or routine laboratory space.

Having defined the present state of the act of radioactive materials laboratory design, we shall now identify and explain the role of special precautionary features which provide a complete, balanced research environment for radiation workers.

C.2 RADIATION LABORATORY CONTROL FEATURES

C.2.1 Working Surfaces

Bench tops, floors and sinks require durable, easy to clean, seamless surface finishes. Repeated cleaning with harsh decontaminating agents produces surface deterioration of all but the toughest materials, which makes sub-

Table C-1. Comparative Levels of Radioactivity Use

Use Level	Usage	Control Elements
Kilocurie (× 1,000)	Sterilization and cancer treatment	Shielding Containment
Curie (× 1)	Used as baseline reference	
Millicurie (× 0.001)	Nuclear medicine patient doses, biomedical stock nuclides, lab waste accumulations, binding reactions and chemical synthesis	Isolation Local shields Hot lab control
Microcurie (× 0.000001)	Tracer experiments	Selected hot lab controls
Nanocurie × 0.000000001)	Individual measurements	Routine laboratory
Any Level	Accidental lab contamination	No special controls

sequent decontamination progressively more difficult and less effective. The preferred bench top and sink material is type 316 hammered (high nickel). On the floor, good-quality sheet vinyl coverings are preferred over floor tiles because they have no seams. In any area subject to daily decontamination, such as animal room floors, troweled-on epoxy flooring material is even better.

A plastic-laminated bench top is acceptable for routine tracer work where there is little expectation of large spills, provided that the bench top is routinely covered with 24 × 30-in. pads of absorbent paper with a water-stopping plastic back such as baby crib liners. This absorbent paper is routinely disposed as solid waste as soon as it becomes worn or contaminated.

It is also good practice for the worker to renew the paper surface immediately after a major spill in order to maintain an effective spill barrier. Thus, in many biomedical labs, absorbent paper has become the principal item of radioactive waste.

Plastic-laminated bench tops are accept-

able in routine biology tracer laboratories, but when lead brick shields must be moved frequently, as is the case when penetrating gamma ray nuclides are in use, plastic laminate does not pass the durability test. Baked enamel finishes on laboratory instruments and equipment have proven quite satisfactory.

C.2.2. Shielding

The reduction of radiation exposure from gamma rays and high-energy beta nuclides in storage or during research operations can be accomplished by either shielding or isolation, i.e., increasing the distance between the radiation source and workers. Hot laboratories make effective use of outside walls and back corners, where the location and fortuitous presence of a heavy concrete wall or subgrade earth backfill does the job. See Figure C-1. For intermediate- millicurie-level gamma sources, a palisade of lead bricks (2 × 4 × 8 in., 28 lbs. each) provides ample

Table C-2. Radionuclides Used as Scanning Agents in Nuclear Medicine

Agent	Advantages
Technetium-99m	Short half-life and low-energy
Xenon-133	photon emissions which
Gallium-67	are readily shielded and
Thallium-207	collimated to form high-
Indium-111 and -113	quality images
Iodine-123	

Table C-3. Selected Nuclides for Biomedical Applications

Nuclides	Half-life	Radiation
^{3}H	13.3 years	Very weak beta
^{14}C	5730 years	Weak beta
^{32}P	14.3 days	Strong beta
^{35}S	88 days	Weak beta
^{51}Cr	28 days	Gamma
^{125}I	60.2 days	Weak gamma
^{131}I	8.05 days	Beta and gamma
^{137}Cs	30 years	Strong gamma

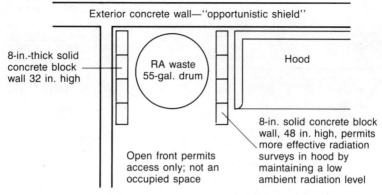

Fig. C-1. Solid concrete block shield for radioactive waste drums.

protection for local personnel. For beta nuclides and low-energy gamma nuclides, upright panels of thinner lead sheet or leaded glass and plastic are used as body and face shields. However, for low-level research shielding requirements (i.e., microcurie level and below), this may not be necessary.

For the designer, the principal considerations are sufficient space, structural strength and durability of the support surface. Inasmuch as research objectives are often redirected daily, equipment and shielding are relocated, with consequent wear and tear on the exposed surfaces. Lab benches which are likely to support shielding at any time must be designed for 400 lbs/sq in.

Shielding is also provided for radioactive waste containers at workstations. Researchers use 2-gallon galvanized garbage cans, fliptop trash cans, plastic buckets or coffee cans lined with vinyl bags for bench to waste collection. Shielding in the form of 1/16- or 1/8th-in. sheet lead is formed around the container. In other laboratories, waste is accumulated in an open-topped 55-gallon drum located in an isolated corner of the laboratory and shielded behind a 3-ft-high wall of solid concrete blocks positioned to "shadow" personnel in the area and on the far side of the wall if necessary.

C.2.3 Working Space

In order to fully accommodate radiation safety procedures, more than average-size work space allowances are essential. The dimensions of typical laboratory furniture modules are generally too small to accommodate radioactive materials workstations.

- Floor space in front of the bench or hood must allow workers to back away a full step (30 in.) from their work whenever they are not directly engaged. This simple avoidance precaution significantly reduces the exposure rate to the worker.
- The space required for the shield is always larger than the space required for the apparatus being shielded by 6 in. in each direction. Therefore, bench top work space must be enlarged to allow for lead bricks, shielded enclosures and/or single-face glass or lucite barriers. See Figure C.2.
- It is often impractical to decontaminate bench top equipment each time it is used. The accumulation of contaminated equipment such as vacuum pumps, eppendorfs and mixers must be stored on bench tops in the work area even when they are not being used. It is unsafe to transport contaminated equipment to and from the workstation to make space for work in progress.
- A worker assigned to carry out radioactive procedures will normally be required to perform related nonradioactive procedures as well. This inevitably

Lead brick storage enclosure

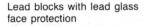

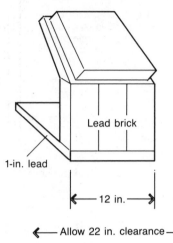

Fig. C-2. Typical bench top shield configuration.

leads to duplication of equipment on the bench top, requiring extra space.

- In general, if 10 to 12 linear feet of bench top is considered a satisfactory module for routine nonradioactive workstations, a radioactive materials work center should encompass 20 to 25 linear feet.

C.2.4 Storage Space

Use of disposable glass and plastic laboratory supplies is encouraged in order to reduce the effort and hazard of decontamination. A ready supply of disposable syringes, vials and pipette tips, gloves and laboratory coats requires storage drawers and shelves at the workstations. A storage cabinet is required to ensure a ready supply of the 24 × 30-in. mats of plastic-backed absorbent paper used to protect the bench top from spatters and spills.

Higher-level hot laboratories also require storage for an emergency spill kit or cart. The spill kit is as essential to radiation work as a fire extinguisher is to routine laboratory activities.

C.2.5 Enclosures

Both the institution and the individual worker assigned to the area have an obliga-

tion to prevent fellow workers from being exposed or contaminated. Posting "Caution: Radioactive Material" or "Caution Radiation Area" signs is required, but a sign by itself is not sufficient to achieve the isolation required by regulations. In many instances, a separate room with a locked door is the only acceptable method of providing isolation, security and enclosure.

An inherent deficiency of modern open laboratory design, which utilizes lab bench modules to replace walls, is that because of the lack of walls, the institution and the worker have difficulty in restricting access to areas where sources of exposure or contaminated surfaces regularly occur.

On the other hand, routine tracer research laboratories and their facilities do not constitute a sufficient threat under routine circumstances to require special precautions such as enclosed space and related restrictions. Each of the activity centers listed below should be reviewed toward this end against the desirability of enclosing and securing radioactive materials-handling procedures.

- Centralized storage and dispensing areas for controlled storage of stock radioactive materials. The area designated for storage/dispensing may simply require a lead brick storage enclosure on the bench top, but locking ready-built cabinets with built-in shielding may also be considered. Lockable file cabinets are often used for nuclide storage without shielding because this arrangement tends to emphasize the importance of security and documentation procedures.

- In biomedical research, the stock of radionuclides consists of labeled biological compounds which require refrigeration or freezer storage. Lead shielded under the counter refrigerators are available for this purpose. To avoid spilling radioactive materials while they are being carried from place to place, the bench top work space for measuring out stock radioactive material should be within arm's reach of the storage cabinet. This one storage and work function often constitutes the only hot lab enclosure for a small laboratory.

- In the event that a laboratory will routinely work with over 0.1-millicurie levels of iodine-131 or -125 to prepare labeled materials (referred to as a "synthetic" or "binding reaction"), these activities should also be centralized and isolated in an enclosed hot lab.

- Support facilities should include an enclosed area for collection, storage, volume reduction procedures, packaging and shipment of solid radioactive waste. The waste area is not referred to as a "hot lab," but the principle is the same.

- A support facility for collection, storage, dilution or solidification of liquid radioactive wastes. See Figure C.4.

- In larger institutions, the daily delivery of radioactive supply items through the receiving department requires monitoring, documentation and unpackaging in a restricted area.

- Certain heavy equipment items such as centrifuges, incubators, cold boxes, water baths and sample/fraction collectors occasionally become contaminated. If these items must be shared and thus cannot be sequestered in the hot lab, a workable alternative is to provide a sep-

arate heavy equipment room which can be secured whenever repeated contamination and necessary cleanup operations dictate a need for enforceable isolation.

C.2.6 The Entry

The hot lab (enclosed or open) must provide space for workers to put on their laboratory coat and to exchange their laboratory coat for regular street wear each time they leave the controlled area. When appropriate space and storage are not provided, it is virtually impossible for researchers to comply with regulations.

To complete the entry exit control picture, a small hand sink, separated from the laboratory sink, with a shelf above it for a Geiger counter and an electrical outlet, is often located near the entry door.

C.2.7 Graduated Levels

Graduated levels of isolation contribute to the overall hot lab concept. Items such as the radiosotope hood, the nuclide storage cabinet and the radioactive waste storage receptacle, where the highest levels of radioactivity are concentrated, are grouped together at the far end, away from the entry, or in a corner of the hot lab. This gradient arrangement tends to emphasize the presence of exposure and contamination for workers while at the same time physically reducing the radiation hazard originating from these high-risk areas, which interferes with sensitive measurements of contamination in other parts of the controlled work areas. Biological research requires the use of large equipment items such as freezers and refrigerators, cold boxes, floor-mounted centrifuges, incubators, water baths, fraction collectors and even cold rooms.

It is common practice to arrange shared-use equipment in clusters located at some distance from the hot lab area. Consequently, radioactive materials must be carried back and forth past uncontrolled workstations, and in due course accidents en route result in "out of assigned area" contamination.

Such accident involving uncontrolled workers are contrary to regulations and are a principal source of aggravation between radiation-controlled workers and their fellow workers. One solution to this recurrent problem is to allow sufficient space for heavy equipment in the hot lab. An alternative solution is to enclose heavy equipment items in their own isolation rooms so that they can be restricted whenever necessary.

C.2.8 Telephone Service

A telephone located in the hot lab was originally justified as a means of summoning outside emergency assistance. Fortunately, this kind of emergency is rare, but telephone accessibility is still essential for other reasons. Radioactive material workers have as many incoming and outgoing communications needs as anyone. It is inconvenient and inefficient for workers to remove their gloves each time they are called to the phone.

Since hot lab telephones are extremely vulnerable to transferred contamination, shared use of a phone out-side the restricted area is a poor idea. A speaker phone which can be actuated without the need to take off contaminated rubber/vinyl gloves is very effective in this regard.

C.2.9 Controlled Ventilation Systems

Hot lab fumehoods require special consideration. Selection of an appropriate hood must take into account accessible work space, airflow characteristics, interior illumination and other auxiliary services, and, as previously discussed, the durability and cleanability of the interior surfaces.

Radiosotope quality hoods are available in 4- 5- and 6-ft models from most fumehood manufacturers. The actual size is often a subjective decision based on previous experience of the users rather than inch-by-inch justification. Hoods with stainless steel interior surfaces and illumination levels equal to or exceeding the illumination in the sur-

rounding space are important. More important than the hood selection is the face velocity of the entering air. The hood fan must maintain a face velocity between 100 and 150 fpm to provide breathing zone protection for the worker.

Lower airflow does not capture and entrain air into the hood with sufficient efficiency. Over 150 fpm has been shown to produce turbulence in the wake of the operator, which allows contaminated air or gases to flow out of the hood toward the operator's face.

Radioisotope quality hoods are equipped with internal dampers, which are linked to the sash and intended to maintain a constant airflow rate whatever the opening of the sash may be.

The hood air discharge must also be engineered to provide sufficient air for the dilution of airborne contaminants released to the environment. A 120 fpm airflow uniform across a 5×2.5-ft opening, offers a dilution capability of 60,000 m^3/day, which is generally sufficient for millicurie levels of all biomedical nuclides except Iodine-131 and -125.

The calculations in Table C-4 are based on permissible concentrations of radionuclides, 10 CFR-20, Appendix 220 as, defined by the U.S. Nuclear Regulatory Commission (USNRC) and agreement states.

In Table C-4, the concentration limit for each nuclide (microcuries per cubic centimeter of air) is as cited in USNRC regulations* and is applicable to the case of airborne releases to the atmosphere by radioactive materials licensees. USNRC limits are calculated using equations based on models of human inhalation and retention which would result in exposure of 500 millirads to a hypothetical person continuously downwind from the point of release. A detailed treatment of the method of evaluating planned and existing air discharge systems is available from the National Council on Radiation Protection (*Commentary 3: Screening Techniques for Determining Compliance with Environmental Standards: Releases of Radio-*

---

*10 CFR 20.220, Appendix C.

Table C-4. Fumehood Discharge Rating

Nuclide	USNRC Concentration Limit (Microcuries/cc)	Acceptable Daily Release (Microcuries)	Rating
^{3}H	2E-7	120	Satisfactory
^{14}C	1E-7	661	Satisfactory
^{32}P	2E-9	1.2	Marginal
^{35}S	9E-9	5.5	Marginal
^{51}Cr	4E-7	244	Satisfactory
^{125}I	8E-11	0.05	Filter required
^{131}I	1E-10	0.06	Filter required
^{133}Xc	3E-7	183	Satisfactory

nuclides to the Atmosphere, March 31, 1986).[†] The screening calculation provides for alternative routes of airborne transport and simultaneous intake from inhalation, food and water. A complete analysis is beyond the scope of this review.

The selection of correct discharge filter systems involves trade-offs between efficiency, service period, and filter replacement convenience and safety. Use of consultants and early negotiation with state or federal regulatory agencies are recommended at this juncture to ensure approval of the system.

Hood exhaust air ducting must be completely separated from room ventilation and should be discharged to the atmosphere above the building roof and as far downwind from any building air intakes as possible, i.e., over 50 ft. The discharge blower should be located near the base of the stack in order to maintain negative pressure in all ducting that passes through the building.

The problem of recirculation of contaminated air leaking out of the hood exhaust system requires months of effort to discover, locate and rectify when it occurs. Therefore, high-quality fumehood discharge lines and installation procedures should be specified.

In any small hot lab, the presence of an acceptable radioisotope hood establishes and dominates the room ventilation characteristics. In larger laboratory areas, the hood exhaust rate will be balanced against conventional room air supply and exhausts rates.

A ventilation requirement of long standing is that the air input and output of the laboratory must be adjusted so that 10 to 12 air exchanges per hour result and the technical space is maintained at a lower air pressure than that of adjacent corridors, offices, supply rooms, libraries, etc. The objective is to avoid any air balance condition which would cause contaminated air to flow outward into the uncontrolled spaces.

Air supply exhaust rates and pressure balance calculation reports are part of the licensing procedure and must be submitted to regulatory agencies when the client applies for a license to operate.

C.2.10 Liquid Waste Control

Water-disposable waste products fall into two regulatory categories. Very low concentrations may be disposed via municipal sewer systems and are identified as "uncontrolled waste." In many small laboratories, the uncontrolled allowance will accommodate a major fraction of the liquid wastes which are routinely generated. No special facility other than a dedicated exclusive-use sink is required for this purpose.

In larger laboratories or those designed to use high-level or especially hazardous radionuclides, the uncontrolled waste quota may only be sufficient to cope with glassware rinse waters and experimental animal excreta. The bulk of liquid waste must then

[†]National Council on Radiation Protection and Measurements, 7910 Woodmont Avenue, Bethesda, MD 20814.

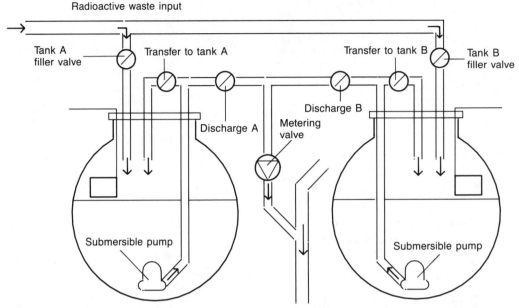

Fig. C-3. Schematic liquid waste retention system.

be classified as "controlled waste," which means waste collected, absorbed on approved solid absorbents,* and transported in solid form to a commercial low-level radioactive waste disposal site.

An alternative liquid waste system consists of an isolated high-capacity retention tank (or dual tanks) and a dilution system for controlled dilution and discharge of radioactive liquids. A pair of 500-gallon retention tanks equipped with submersible sump pumps and crossover plumbing are then used to dilute weekly or monthly increments of liquid waste as required to comply with release limits. See Figure C-3.

In some cases, collection rates and retention times can be balanced to allow complete radioactive decay of short-half-life nuclides, permitting large quantities to be disposed of eventually as uncontrolled waste.

A retention tank system should be provided with sampling ports for radiometric verification of the concentration of the diluted waste before release. USNRC or agree-

ment state review and approval well in advance of licensing is strongly recommended.

Dilution water may be added to waste via a waste input line for batch process dilution or via a discharge line, as shown for the continuous flow rate method.

Single-tank retention systems are most frequently provided. The double-tank arrangement illustrated above is often preferred because it offers four operating modes:

1. Tank I can be the active receptor, and tank II, previously filled, is sampled to determine the concentration of radioactivity and then released at a controlled rate to permit continuous dilution with makeup water while being discharged to the sewer system.
2. Wastewater from tank I, the active receptor, can be transferred in small quantities to tank II, where it is assayed and diluted before discharge.
3. Tanks I and II can be filled alternately while short-half-life radionuclides in the opposite tank are stored and allowed to decay before the tank is discharged.

---

*Regulatory agencies provide lists of approved absorbents for solidification of liquid radioactive waste.

4. Tank I or II can be valved out of the line to permit repair.

REFERENCES

American Standards Association, Inc., 1965. *Design Guide for a Radioisotope Laboratory (Type B)*. NY

ASHRAE, 1987. *Handbook of Heating, Ventilation and Air Conditioning Systems and Applications,* Chapter 40 Atlanta: ASHRAE.

Kathren, Ronald L., 1985. *Radiation Protection,* Vol. 1, 16 *Medical Physics Handbooks.* Boston: Adam Hilger.

Stewart, Donald C., 1981. *Handling Radioactivity. A Practical Approach for Scientists and Engineers.* New York: Wiley.

GLOSSARY

Alpha Particle—Intensely ionizing charged-particle radiation composed of helium nuclei. Alpha particles have limited range (less than 1 mm) and are easy to shield but extremely hazardous when the emitter is inhaled or ingested. Alpha particle radiation is emitted only by heavy elements such as radon, radium, thorium, and plutonium (i.e., exceeding the atomic mass of lead. Where alpha emitters are encountered in research operations, emphasis is placed on air breathing, air supplies and hood exhaust filtration. Alpha emitters are not used in biomedical research.

Becqueral (Bq)—A special unit for defining the quantity of radioactive material representing one radioactive disintegration per second. The becqueral is designated to replace the series of curie units in science, transport and industry.

Beta Particle—Charged-particle radiation composed of electrons moving with a velocity approaching the speed of light. The combination of high velocity and low mass produces moderate ionization density and limited penetration through solids and liquids (i.e., millimeters to inches). In biology and medicine the most useful beta emitters are tritium, carbon-14, phosphorus-32 and sulfur-32.

Curie (Ci)—A special unit for defining the quantity of radioactive material based on the rate at which radium-226 disintegrates to form daughter products (i.e., 3.7×10^{10} disintegrations per second per gram).

Gamma Ray—Very penetrating ionizing radiation from the high-energy end of the electromagnetic spectrum. It has no mass and no charge, and consequently requires inches to feet of concrete or inches of lead for shielding, depending on the energy level and quantity. Most useful gamma ray emitters in biomedical research are Chromium-51 and Iodine-131 (the latter emits both beta and gamma radiation).

Half-Life, Radioactive (T1/2)—The time required for any given radionuclide to lose half of its activity by radioactive transformation and radiation emission. Each radionuclide has a unique half-life.

Health Physics—The science and profession devoted to protecting humans and the environment from unnecessary radiation exposure.

Kilovolt Peak (KVP)—Unit of energy used to express the penetrating power and ionization potential of machine-generated radiation. Equivalent in energy to an electron elevated to 1,000 volts.

Million Electron Volts (MEV)—Unit of energy used to express the penetrating power and ionization potential of nuclear radiation from radioactive materials. Equivalent in energy to an electron elevated to 1 million volts.

Nuclear Medicine Imaging—Medical utilization of physical and optical properties of gamma ray–emitting nuclides to produce video or photographic representations of the human anatomy for diagnostic purposes.

Rad—Quantity of energy imparted to matter by radiation-produced ionization. Used to quantify injuries or other effects resulting from exposure to radiation.

Radioactivity—The property of certain nuclides which emit energy in the form of charged particles or electromagnetic rays.

Radiation—Radioactive materials emit energy in different forms, traditionally referred to as "alpha," "beta," "gamma" and "x-rays." The properties of each form of radiation are distinguishing characteristics which aid in identification and control.

Radiation Hazards—Transport of radiation through living tissues results in deposition of energy in the form of ionization and ultimately in the disruption of normal life processes such as cell division. High-level exposure results in injuries akin to burns with resultant scarring. Continuous or repeated exposures at lower levels but of long duration result in blood cell reduction, interference with the immune response and production of specific types of cancer. Radiation hazards are all the more insidious because the precipitating radiation event may not be detected by the human senses and because the resultant injury may manifest itself out of sight inside the body.

Radionuclide—Generic designation for individual radioactive elements. Scientists use the atomic symbol (abbreviated element name) and a superscript number representing the atomic mass number to specify radioactive elements in terms of radiation and chemical properties, i.e., ^{14}C, ^3H, ^{32}P, ^{135}I and ^{31}Cr.

Roentgen (R)—Quantity of energy imparted to air ionization by radiation as measured by specially designed electronic instruments. The roentgen is used to measure exposure or exposure rate, and thus is an indication of potential hazards resulting from radioactive materials. Submultiples of the roentgen—the millroentgen (mR) = 1/1000th roentgen and microroentgen (uR) = 1/1,000,000 roentgen—are most commonly encountered in laboratory practice.

Submicrocurie—In many practical applications of radioactive material such as research and medicine, the curie is too large to be handled safely. Consequently submultiples such as the microcurie are commonly substituted as the basic quantity reference:

millicuries	one-thousandth curie
microcurie	one-millionth curie
nanocurie	one-billionth curie
picocurie	one-trillionth curie

Nanocuries and picocuries are submicrocurie units typically encountered in biomedical and environmental work situations.

Trace Quantities—Biomedical science depends on the researcher's ability to introduce selected radioactive elements in study samples in order to track or trace biological processes which are otherwise not observable. Some life processes and disease studies do not tolerate high concentrations of foreign materials (which would be measured in grams or milligrams). Radioactive materials are useful because the amount required for measurements (using electronic instruments) is much smaller and is normally measured in micrograms.

Tracer Radioactive—A research technology in which selected radioactive materials are incorporated into samples of biological or medical interest, making it possible to observe and quantify the chemical, biological and physical processes which would not otherwise be observable.

U.S. Nuclear Regulatory Commission (NRC)—The U.S. government currently controls radioactive material hazards through the U.S. Nuclear Regulatory Commission (USNRC). This organization is a direct successor of the original Atomic Energy Commission, which in turn succeeded the U.S. Army Corps of Engineers, Manhattan District, which developed the atomic bomb during World War II. In 26 of the 50 states, USNRC authority has been transferred to state public health or environmental control agencies. The regulations are essentially the same.

X-Rays—Penetrating electromagnetic radiation equivalent to gamma rays in most respects but normally of lower energy and therefore less penetrating. X-rays are produced by electric discharge in special vacuum tubes but also occur in certain radionuclides. Nuclear medicine imaging utilizes X-ray emitters because low-energy radiation is more readily collimated and thus produces clearer images. The most useful x-ray emitters are technetium-99, indium-111, iodine-125, xenon-133, gallium-67 thallium-201.

D. Specialized Facilities: Shielded Facilities

R. Baltzo

D. X-RAY PROTECTION

D.1.1 Introduction

Many medical laboratory facilities require shielded spaces for diagnostic X-ray machines. The annual sale of new X-ray units, over 25,000 in 1987, is a good indicator of the ongoing need for X-ray room shielding.

As with other major equipment sales, it is common practice for X-ray machine vendors to propose a room plan and equipment layout indicating the location of the tube and table, transformer, generator, console and chest film holder. See Figure D-1. The vendor will also specify the electrical service requirements for each component. Occasionally the selection of a given X-ray model is determined by the dimensions of the equipment because of assembly and installation limitations. Clearances are critical, and a mid-design change in equipment may require correction of the plan layout. See Figure D-2.

With few exceptions, x-ray machine manufacturers and their sales representatives prefer to concentrate on their role as electrical engineers. As a result, X-ray shielding calculations, which are a different area of physical science, are performed by outside consultants with appropriate training in physics and medical department experience.

D.1.2 X-Ray Shielding Standards

The National Bureau of Standards (NBS) began addressing generic X-ray shielding safety problems in 1934 and has provided a unifying influence for hospital physicists in the form of a succession of technical reports. However, in 1976, the technical authority of the NBS was transferred to the National Council on Radiation Protection and Mea-surements (NCRP),* whose current recommendation, Report 49, supersedes all earlier NBS shielding reports.

Inasmuch as they are routinely incorporated into state regulations, local building codes and X-ray machine purchase contracts the following three reports, covering dental X-rays, routine health care X-rays and high-energy cancer treatment X-ray machines, respectively, are the indispensable references of the shielding trade.

NCRP Report 35, *Dental X-Ray Protection* (1970).

NCRP Report 49, *Structural Shielding Design and Evaluation for Medical Use of X-Rays and Gamma Rays of Energies Up to 10 MEV* (1976).

NCRP Report 51, *Radiation Protection Design. Guidelines for 0.1 to 100 MEV Particle Accelerator Facilities* (1977).

Each of these reports offers a conceptual (i.e., not excessively scientific) explanation of the overall objectives and strategies of shielding followed by complete coverage of practical options for the use of concrete, lead and a few other possible shielding materials. Report 49 also covers radiation exposure limits, protected space occupancy assumptions, and X-ray workload evaluation and provides a calculation procedure for using these factors to produce a successful X-ray protection barrier at any given distance from the work center.

All relevant data and installation details are included. The first-time user will find it of particular interest to scan through Report

---

*National Council on Radiation Protection and Measurements. 7910 Woodmont Avenue, Bethesda, MD 20814.

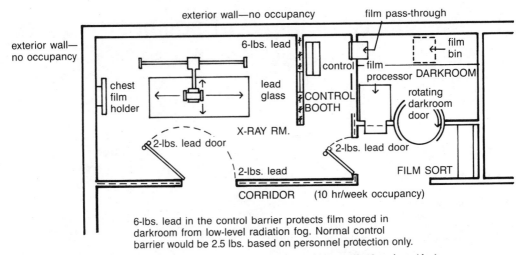

Fig. D.1-1. Typical low-workload private office X-ray room (8–12 patients/day).

49, Appendix C, Tables 5 and 6, which specify shielding requirements as a function of the important variable factors mentioned above. These tables have been reproduced here as Tables D.1-1 and D.1-2.

In order to better understand the concept behind Report 49, let us examine a typical shield specification procedure using a room layout such as that shown in Figure D.1-1 or Figure D.1-2 and Table D.1-1.

Modern X-ray machines are routinely designed to operate at up to 125 or 150 peak kilovolts (KVP). Nevertheless, older 100-KVP machines are frequently relocated to new facilities, so that the tables in Report 49 provide three vertical columns (Table D.1-1, upper left) for selecting low- to high-power machines, i.e, 100, 125 and 150 KVP.

Medium-sized to large hospitals (medical centers) would automatically adopt the maximum workload (WUT), i.e., 1000, 400 or 200 milliamperes per minute (MA min) per week. Private office and clinic X-ray users are likely to encounter fewer patients (i.e., 6 to 12

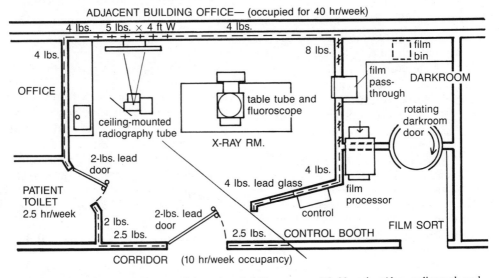

Fig. D.1-2. Typical busy workload, clinic or hospital X-ray room (12–20 patient/day, radiograph and fluoroscopy).

Table D.1-1.* NCRP Report 49 Minimum Shielding Requirements for Radiographic Installations

WUT^a in mA min			Distance in meters from source to occupied area										
100 kV^b	125 kV^b	150 kV^b											
1,000	400	200	1.5	2.1	3.0	4.2	6.1	8.4	12.2				
500	200	100		1.5	2.1	3.0	4.2	6.1	8.4	12.2			
250	100	50			1.5	2.1	3.0	4.2	6.1	8.4	12.2		
125	50	25				1.5	2.1	3.0	4.2	6.1	8.4	12.2	
62.5	25	12.5					1.5	2.1	3.0	4.2	6.1	8.4	12.2
Type of Area	**Material**		**Primary Protective Barrier Thickness^e**										
Controlled	Lead, mm^c		1.95	1.65	1.4	1.15	0.9	0.65	0.45	0.3	0.2	0.1	0.1
Noncontrolled	Lead, mm^c		2.9	2.6	2.3	2.05	1.75	1.5	1.2	0.95	0.75	0.55	0.35
Controlled	Concrete, cm^d		18	15.5	13.5	11.5	9.5	7	5.5	4	2.5	1.5	0.5
Noncontrolled	Concrete, cm^d		25	23	20.5	18.5	16.5	14	12	10	8		
			Secondary Protective Barrier Thickness^e										
Controlled	Lead, mm^c		0.55	0.45	0.35	0.3	0	0	0	0	0	0	0
Noncontrolled	Lead, mm^c		1.3	1.05	0.75	0.55	0.45	0.35	0.3	0.05	0	0	0
Controlled	Concrete, cm^d		5	3.5	2.5	2	0	0	0	0	0	0	0
Noncontrolled	Concrete, cm^d		11.5	9.5	7.5	5.5	4	3	2	0.5	0	0	0

[a]W–weekly workload in mA min, U–use factor, T–occupancy factor.
[b]Peak pulsating x-ray tube potential.
[c]See NCRP Report 49 for conversion of thickness in millimeters to inches or to surface density.
[d]Thickness based on concrete density of 2.35 g cm^{-3} (147 lb ft^{-3}).
[e]Barrier thickness based on 150 kV.
*Tables reproduced in entirety with permission of National Council of Radiation Protection and Measurements, 7910 Woodmont Avenue, Washington D.C. 20014

Table D.1-2.* NCRP Report 49 Shielding Requirements for Radiographic Film [Indicated Thickness Required to Reduce Radiation to 0.2 mR for a Weekly Workload of 1000 mA min at 100 kV, 400 mA min at 125 kV, or 200 mA min at 150 kV.^a]

		Distance from Source to Stored Film							
		2.1 m (7 feet)		3.0 m (10 feet)		4.2 m (14 feet)		6.1 m (20 feet)	
		Lead	Concrete^b	Lead	Concrete^b	Lead	Concrete^b	Lead	Concrete^b
Storage Period	Barrier Type	mm^c	cm	mm^c	cm	mm^c	cm	mm^c	cm
1 day	Primary with	2.3	19.5	2.1	18	1.8	15.5	1.5	13.5
1 week	use factor,	3.0	24	2.7	22	2.4	20.5	2.2	18.5
1 month	U, of ¹⁄₁₆	3.7	29	3.4	27	3.1	24	2.8	23
1 day	Secondary with	1.7	15	1.5	13	1.2	11	1.0	9
1 week	use factor,	2.4	19.5	2.1	17.5	1.8	16	1.5	13.5
1 month	U, of 1	3.0	24	2.8	22	2.5	20	2.2	18.5

Note: In the absence of specific information as to the length of film storage period to be expected, it is suggested that the shielding value for the 1 month's storage period be used.
[a]Peak pulsating x-ray tube potential.
[b]Thickness based on concrete density of 2.35 g cm^{-3} (147 lb ft^{-3}).
[c]See NCRP Report 49 for conversion of thickness in millimeters to inches or to surface density.
*Tables reproduced in entirety with permission of National Council of Radiation Protection and Measurements, 7910 Woodmont Avenue, Washington D.C. 20014

per day) and consequently reduce the design workload to 200 or even 100 MA-min in recognition of their more modest requirements.

Note that in addition to the patient count, the hospital workload rating reflects increased numbers of multiple-film series and higher proportions of body section films, requiring high KVP and high MA's per film compared with routine chest and extremities films which private offices provide.

Turning our attention to individual sections of the X-ray room wall, floor and ceiling, the assigned WUT representing the workload may be reduced when each protected space adjacent to the X-ray room is considered from the point of view of occupancy. For instance, the X-ray control booth is rated as occupancy = 1 (i.e., 10 to 40 hours/week) because a person is always in this position when X-ray films are made. Adjacent offices, examination rooms, and the darkroom film storage area are always regarded as full-occupancy areas. On the other hand, an adjacent corridor or entry passage is not likely to be occupied for more than 10 hours/week by the same individual. In this case, the room WUT can be reduced by a factor of 4 (i.e., in an example based on a clinic, the WUT is reduced from 200 to 50).

Patient dressing booths, toilets and building stairwells are reduced by additional factors of 4 based on an assumed occupancy less than 2.5 hours/week, to a WUT of 12.5 in this example.

The occupancy and resultant workload of each adjacent space are evaluated separately and the overall pattern of shielding is developed wall by wall, partition by partition, including the floor and the ceiling. Reflecting this process of evaluation, the designer is offered a selection of WUT's from which to proceed.

Continuing the shield evaluation process, the designer estimates the metric distance from the X-ray source to each occupied space. This is a case of weighted probabilities, since the designer must allow for transverse and lateral motion of the tube head and recognize that while table-mounted tubes are reasonably restricted, ceiling-hung tubes may frequently be used well beyond the margins of the table top.

Also, during evaluation of secondary protection requirements, the patient and the chest film holder may be regarded as secondary X-ray sources. The upper right quadrant of Table D.1-1 allows selection of an appropriate distance as a function of machine KVP and WUT.

Continuing our examination of the protected spaces beyond each barrier, the shield designer must sort out those spaces where occupants are subject to, if not minute-y-minute supervision by the X-ray operators, then at least hour-to-hour observation and control. These spaces are designated as "controlled areas."

Areas designated as "uncontrolled areas" are not supervised with respect to X-ray use and are the province of employees of other departments, patients, visitors or, outside the building, the general public. Controlled areas are allowed 10 times greater levels of radiation exposure than uncontrolled areas. All other factors being equal, uncontrolled-space barriers will have an extra 0.9 mm of lead protection.

Continuing to the lower left quadrant of Table D.1.1, controlled and uncontrolled area options are provided for, as is the selection of lead or concrete as the shielding material.

The final set of options (lower right quadrant of Table D.1-1) deals with primary and secondary barriers. Any area of the floor or wall which will be in the direct path of the useful beam of X-rays (referred to as the "primary beam") is designated as a "primary barrier." All other walls, which never (or for less than 3% of the workload) are exposed to the primary beam are designated as "secondary barriers." Primary barriers are always designated for the 6 × 10-ft section of floor centered under the X-ray table and the section of wall (4 × 7 ft) centered behind the chest film holder.

In cases where the client cannot be specific about use and occupancy factors, it is accepted practice to design room walls to receive 25% of the primary beam workload. In practice, X-ray rooms should not be laid out in a manner which would require the primary beam to be directed at, either the darkroom wall (or door) or the X-ray operators control booth.

Once the final set of options for each section of wall, floor and ceiling have been selected, Report 49 Tables allow specification of barrier thickness either as fractions of a millimeter of lead or as centimeters of concrete. Where workload factors are small and the distance is great, no lead is required. Also, we keep in mind that routine room wall construction—i.e., ⅝th in. gypsum wallboard on either side of a stud wall—is equivalent to 0.2 mm of lead. A solid-core, particle core door is also equivalent to 0.2 mm of lead and thus can be used to satisfy these marginal shield requirements in some very small office practices.

Not withstanding the precision attainable by shielding calculations, the designer should convert calculated lead requirements to available stock lead sheet.

	Stock Lead Availability			
Lbs/Sq Ft	Lead Equivalent (mm)	Sheet	Doors	Glass
1	0.4 mm		*	
2	0.8 mm	*	*	
2.5	1.0 mm	*	*	
4	1.6 mm	*	*	
5	2.0 mm	*		*
6	2.4 mm	*		*
8	3.2 mm	*		*

*available

D.1.3 Authorities Having Jurisdiction

NCRP reports, even though they are regarded as the final technical authority, are not utilized and interpreted uniformly throughout the United States. Since the early 1970s, state governments have inaugurated state-level radiation protection programs. While these programs utilize Report 49 recommendations, they are selective about priorities and in many cases allow for streamlining of procedures. For instance, in many

states, the designated radiation protection program office requires that all shielding plans be submitted for official review and approval, which is essentially final.

In other states, the radiation protection office requires registration of all X-ray units and will conduct an inspection and test of the shielding after it is installed. In this latter situation, the owner or contractor, while not required to do so, may be inclined to perform his own inspection and test program while the room is still in the construction phase.

Some states do not require shields for dental X-ray machines.

There are also differing practices about X-ray room shield and layout details, such as:

- Size, location and orientation of the control booth with respect to X-ray rooms.
- Size, location and orientation of the control barrier relight (lead glass window).
- Minimum and maximum specified workloads related to various professional specialists who use X-rays, e.g., radiologists, orthopedic surgeons, family practitioners, chiropractors, and single office practice vs. multiple referral clinics.
- Maximum allowable lead equivalent for commonly used building materials, most notably gypsum wallboard, plate glass and solid-core particle-core doors used as a substitute for thin sections of lead.

The prudent designer should contact the local authorities before proceeding.

State radiation control programs are generally reached through the same offices which conduct hospital plan reviews. If not, the *National Directory of Personnel Responsible for Radiological Health Programs* is available from the Conference of Radiation Control Program Directors, Inc., 71 Fountain Place, Frankfort, KY 40601 (502) 227-4543.

Your contact with the state radiation protection official can be best initiated by asking the following questions:

- Are the data in NCRP Report 49, Tables 1 and 6, completely acceptable, or does the state program suggest an additional margin of safety beyond the NCRP exposure limit (i.e., 100 mR/week)?
- Does the state program have a routine procedure for the review of shield plans?
- Does the state program's review procedure apply uniformly to all X-ray machines? Does it include dental and mammography machines?
- Will the state program inspect the installation during or after construction?
- Does the state program identify local contractors who supply and install shielding speciality products such as lead, lead on gypsum wallboard, lead-lined doors, lead glass windows, and adjustable steel frames?
- Has the state program established standardized minimum workloads for various kinds of medical X-ray users, e.g., radiologists, orthopedic surgeons, and pediatricians?
- Does the state program have minimum floor space and clearance requirements for X-ray rooms, control booths and control relights?
- What lead equivalent does the state program allow for routine gypsum wallboard construction? Are multiple layers of gypsum wallboard allowed?

D.1.4 The Need for and Selection of a Consultant

In addition to local regulations and policies, many state radiation control program offices maintain a roster of qualified shield design consultants who do business in their state (NCRP reports refer to consultants as "qualified experts").

The services of a shielding expert are particularly important in addressing two general problems not covered in the present NCRP handbook.

First, in the 1980s, chiropractic and single-office X-ray units (i.e., with low to moderate workloads) outnumbered hospital and professional radiology installations by two to one. NCRP Council contributors are nominated from staffs of large medical and academic institutions, and their technical skills address large, heavily used facilities rather than small office X-ray practices. As a consequence, Report 49 does not deal directly with low-workload situations.

Second, the development of computed tomography (CT) machines has occurred during the last two decades and was not specifically treated in the 1976 edition of Report 49. At this time, many moderate-sized hospitals and private clinics are already using second- and third-generation CT machines. The current market potential for CT X-rays is almost equal to that of all other routine hospital radiography equipment installations.

A final technical note of warning: Up to the 1980s, the use of concrete structures and thick concrete floor slabs in hospitals and professional buildings provided adequate shielding to protect the occupants above and below the X-ray department. Full X-ray protection is achieved only when the floor is 8 in. or more and the ceiling is 2.5 in. or more. Concrete alone does not guarantee protection. As "pan-joist"-type design has allowed progressively thinner floor and overhead slabs, the assumption of adequate X-ray shielding inherent in the floor slab is no longer true. The design of composite concrete and lead floors or concrete with dense aggregate such as barium sulfate as floor shields should be reviewed by qualified experts.

D.2 RADIO FREQUENCY SHIELDED LABORATORIES B. D. Sennewald

D.2.1 Introduction

Still a newcomer to laboratory design, radio frequency (RF) shielding is becoming an important prerequisite for certain types of research. The significance of shielding is directly linked to the proliferation of RF-generating equipment both in the lab and in the outside world. The atomosphere in many urban areas of this country is so cluttered with "radio waves" that it can be described as "electronic smog." According to Federal Communications Commission statistics, there are roughly 10,000 radio stations, 100 million television sets and 20 million cb radios operating in the United States. All of these, along with hundreds of thousands of "microwave" relay towers, satellite dishes, microwave ovens, garage door openers and myriad other electronic gadgets, emit "electromagnetic" radiation.

Yet many experiments in fields as disparate as nuclear physics, molecular biology, superconductivity and radar communications require an RF-quiet environment. In these situations, the laboratory, or at least part of it, must be protected from ambient RF noise. In other instances, research may require the placement of high-energy RF generators inside the lab. Without shielding, a particle smasher, for example, can destroy magnetic disk drives and damage other electronic equipment in the vicinity.

A different need for RF shielding exists in laboratories where the staff must be protected from high-energy microwave experiments. Some RF radiation heats and will cook living tissue—the principle of microwave ovens—if the power levels are high enough. Even at low levels, microwave radiation has been associated with cataracts, blood disorders, cancer and chromosomal damage. The exact threshold of danger for human exposure is unknown, and considerable controversy exists over just how dangerous this form of radiation is. Current American National Standards Institute (ANSI) standards set limits of exposure for the frequency range between 300 KHz and 100 GHz (see Table D.2-1).

In many instances, RF shielding is also used to protect the security of information. Without shielding, it is relatively easy to steal computer and other equipment data from a distance without leaving a trace. Great publicity has been given to "hackers," but there is a much more insidious way to eavesdrop. All computers emanate radio signals which are distinct for each character on the keyboard. These signals can be picked up and analyzed from as far as a quarter mile away, given a sufficiently sensitive receiving antenna.

D.2.2 How Shielding Works

When electrons move from one energy level to another at regular intervals they generate "electromagnetic waves" which can propagate in space or along wires. A wave consists of two parts, an electric field (E-field) and a magnetic field (H-field), located at right angles to each other and to the path of propagation. The waves are characterized by

Table D.2-1. Radiation Exposure Guidelines

Frequency Range (f) MHz	Equivalent Power Density*[†] (MW/cm^2)	(Electric Field)^2 (V/m)	(Magnetic Field)^2 (A^2/m^2)
0.3–3	100	4×10^5	2.5
3.0–30	$900/f^2$	4×10^3	0.025 $(900/f^2)$
30–300	1.0	4×10^3	0.025
300–1500	$f/300$	4×10^3	0.025 $(f/300)$
1500–100,000	5.0	2×10^4	0.125

*Measured 5 cm from any object in the field and averaged for 6 minutes.
[†](Elec. field)^2/1,200π or 12π (magn. field)^2, whichever is greater.
Source: ANSI C95.1-1982.

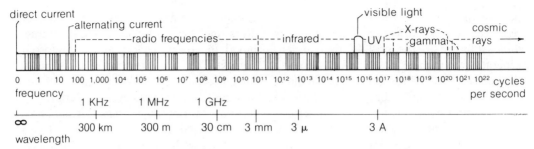

Fig. D.2-1. Electromagnetic spectrum.

their "wavelength" (the distance between two successive crests) and by their "frequency" (the number of crests passing a given point in 1 second). Sunlight, electricity, radio waves and X-rays are all examples of electromagnetic waves. Figure D.2-1 shows the entire spectrum of electromagnetic energy. The RF range which occupies a significant portion of the spectrum—roughly from 80 KHz to 100 GHz—is illustrated in Figure D.2-2.

If the source of an electromagnetic wave generates a large current flow relative to its voltage, the magnetic component of the wave predominates, producing a "magnetic field." When the current flow from a source is relatively small compared to its voltage, the electric component of the wave is dominant, producing an "electric field." The further the wave travels from the source, the more the electric and magnetic fields become balanced. When they reach parity, the wave is called a "plane wave" and has the same impedance (377 ohms) as space.

The premise of a shield is that it constitutes a barrier to passing radio waves: it prevents most of the energy generated outside the shielded enclosure from penetrating inside, and vice versa. This happens both by absorption and by reflection of the signal. The better the absorption and reflection qualities of the shield, the more "attenuation" it can achieve.

Figure D.2-3 illustrates the components of this attenuation in greater detail. When an electromagnetic signal encounters the grounded shield, part of the signal is reflected. Some energy enters the shielding material, is absorbed and is conducted to ground. Another part travels through the shield, strikes the opposite surface and is reflected back and forth between the two surfaces. Some of the energy propagates through the shield. The amount of reduction in energy, or attenuation, between one side of the shield and the other is the sum of the reflection loss (r1), the absorption loss (L1) and the re-reflection factor (r3). If the absorption loss within the shield is small, a good part of the wave hitting the second surface will bounce back to the first surface, then back through the second surface into space (r2). In that case, re-reflection will contribute to the total power that propagates through the shield.

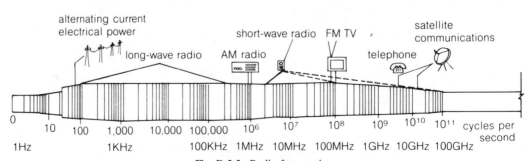

Fig. D.2-2. Radio frequencies.

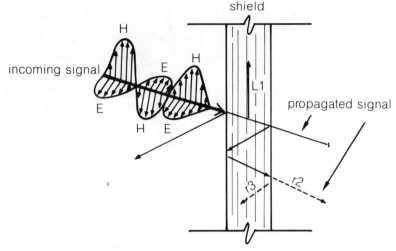

Fig. D.2-3. Diagram of an electromagnetic signal encountering a shield.

Attenuation (A) is measured as the ratio of the field strength on either side of the shield (t) and is expressed in decibels (dB). The mathematical equation for this ratio is

$$A = 20 \log t^1/t^2 \quad \text{(dB)}$$

For example, if the field strength of the incoming signal is 300 volts/meter and that of the propagating signal is 3 volts/meter, the attenuation is

$$A = 20 \log 300/3 = 40 \text{ dB}$$

D.2.3 Shielding Materials

Many materials can be used for shielding purposes: concrete, steel, brick, even earth. The desirable characteristics are conductivity and permeability (the ability to become magnetized). Earth can be a very effective and inexpensive shield in cases where a laboratory can be placed below grade. The reinforced concrete of normal wall and roof construction often suffices to create a shield which can block out interference from local radio and TV stations.

The real winners in shielding efficacy, however, are metals. Many of them are highly conductive, and the ferrous ones are also very permeable. This makes them the most efficient and most commonly used shielding materials. Table D.2-2 shows the conductivity and permeability of a variety of metals relative to copper, which has long been used as the standard against which other materials are measured.

In practice, only a few of these metals are affordable enough to be used in building construction: copper, steel, aluminum, brass and bronze. The shielding performance of

Table D.2-2. Electrical Properties of Shielding Materials Relative to Copper

Metal	Relative Conductivity	Relative Permeability
Silver	1.05	1
Copper	1.00	1
Gold	0.70	1
Aluminum	0.61	1
Magnesium	0.38	1
Zinc	0.29	1
Brass	0.26	1
Cadmium	0.23	1
Nickel	0.20	1
Iron	0.17	1,000
Tin	0.15	1
Steel, black	0.10	1,000
Lead	0.08	1
Monel	0.04	1
Muntz-metal	0.03	80,000
Permalloy	0.03	80,000
Steel, stainless	0.02	1,000

Source: R. B. Shultz et al., *Shielding Theory and Practice.* 1973

Table D.2-3. Calculated Values for 10-mil Shields in Magnetic Fields

Frequency	Material	Reflection Loss	Absorption Loss	Re-Reflection Factor	Total Attenuation
60 Hz	Copper	22.4	0.3	−19.2	3.5
1 KHz	Copper	34.2	1.1	−10.4	24.9
10 KHz	Copper	44.2	3.3	2.6	50.1
150 KHz	Copper	56.0	12.9	0.5	69.4
1 MHz	Copper	64.2	33.4	0.0	97.6
15 MHz	Copper	76.0	129.0	0.0	205.0
100 MHz	Copper	84.0	334.0	0.0	418.0
60 Hz	Steel	−0.9	3.3	.08	3.2
1 KHz	Steel	0.9	13.7	0.1	14.7
10 KHz	Steel	8.0	43.5	0.0	51.5
150 KHz	Steel	19.0	160.0	0.0	179.0
1 MHz	Steel	28.0	363.0	0.0	391.0
15 MHz	Steel	42.0	1060.0	0.0	1102.0
100 MHz	Steel	56.0	1370.0	0.0	1426.0
60 Hz	Steel*	−0.9	83.3	0.0	82.4
1 KHz	Steel*	8.0	1088.0	0.0	1096.0

*Values are for 1/4-in. thick steel.

these metals—the sum of reflection, absorption and re-reflection factors—varies, depending on the type of wave (electric, magnetic or plane) and the frequency. As Tables D.2-3 through D.2-5 show, total attenuation generally increases at higher frequencies. From the tables, it is also evident that reflection loss is important in shielding against electric and plane waves but less significant in magnetic fields. Further, one can see that thin, 10-mil metal shields are not effective at all in low-frequency magnetic fields. Instead, a highly permeable, thick material, such as 0.25-in.-thick steel plate, is usually required.

At high frequencies, on the other hand, thin shields are very efficient.

A shield does not have to be made from solid material. Perforated, expanded metal sheets, wire screens and even grids of welded reinforcing bars make acceptable shield. The key to the performance of nonsolid materials is the number and size of the "holes" in comparison to the wavelength of the radio source. For a long wavelength, the holes may be larger than for a short one. For example, a 4 × 4/W10 welded wire mesh will provide an attenuation of about 40 dB at 1 MHz but only 5 dB at 1 GHz (see Table D.2-6).

Table D.2-4. Calculated Values for 10-mil Shields in Electric Fields

Frequency	Material	Reflection Loss	Absorption Loss	Re-Reflection Factor	Total Attenuation
10 KHz	Copper	212.0	3.3	−2.6	212.7
150 KHz	Copper	176.8	12.9	0.5	190.2
1 MHz	Copper	152.0	33.4	0.0	185.4
15 MHz	Copper	116.0	129.0	0.0	245.0
100 MHz	Copper	92.0	334.0	0.0	426.0
10 KHz	Steel	174.0	43.5	0.0	217.5
150 KHz	Steel	139.0	169.0	0.0	308.0
1 MHz	Steel	116.0	363.0	0.0	479.0
15 MHz	Steel	83.0	1060.0	0.0	1143.0
100 MHz	Steel	64.0	1370.0	0.0	1434.0

Table D.2-5. Calculated Values for 10-mil Shields in Plane Waves

Frequency	Material	Reflection Loss	Absorption Loss	Re-Reflection Factor	Total Attenuation
10 KHz	Copper	128.0	3.3	−2.6	128.7
150 KHz	Copper	117.0	12.9	0.5	130.4
1MHz	Copper	108.0	33.4	0.0	141.4
15 MHz	Copper	96.0	129.0	0.0	225.0
100 MHz	Copper	88.0	334.0	0.0	422.0
10 KHz	Steel	99.5	43.5	0.0	143.0
150 KHz	Steel	79.0	169.0	0.0	248.0
1 MHz	Steel	72.0	363.0	0.0	435.0
15 MHz	Steel	63.0	1060.0	0.0	1123.0
100 MHz	Steel	60.0	1370.0	0.0	1430.0

D.2.4 Shielding Criteria

Before any shielding design can be started, four criteria must be ascertained: (1) the purpose of the shield, (2) the type of wave and the frequency range, (3) the degree of attenuation required and (4) the size of the space to be shielded.

Purpose

If the purpose is freedom from RF interference, the shield would be designed to keep the signals out; if the purpose is signal security, it would be designed to keep the signals in. This distinction is important in deciding where to place the shield in the building construction, as well as in the details of the design.

Type of Wave and Frequency

The type of wave to shield could be magnetic, electric, plane or any combination of these. One example would be to shield an electron beam generator in a microelectronics lab from the emanations of a high-voltage power line. In this case, the type of wave would be electric and the frequency would be 60 Hz (in the United States) or 50 Hz (in European countries). Another example would be an electron microscope which is disturbed by an FM radio station nearby. In this case, the shielding criterion would be for plane waves between 85 and 110 MHz.

In a different application, a research company may want to protect its supercomputer from spying. Large mainframe computers radiate in the upper megahertz and gigahertz

Table D.2-6. Approximate Attenuation Values of Welded Wire Mesh

Wire Spacing (in.)	Wire Diameter (in.)	Wire Denomination	1 MHz	10 MHz	100 MHz	1 GHz
4	0.356	4×4/W10	42	38	21	5
4	0.252	4×4/W5	40	37	19	4
4	0.178	4×4/W2.5	38	36	17	3
4	0.135	4×4/W1.4	37	35	16	2
6	0.356	6×6/W10	37	35	16	3
6	0.252	6×6/W5	36	33	15	1
6	0.178	6×6/W2.5	34	32	14	0
6	0.135	6×6/W1.4	32	31	13	0

ranges of the spectrum, and the wave will almost always be a plane wave because electric and magnetic fields balance within a short distance from the source at these high frequencies.

Degree of Attenuation Required

Attenuation describes the amount of reduction in signal field strength from one side of the shield to the other. Like sound power levels, it is a logarithmic function expressed in decibles. The amount of attenuation required for a given case can be calculated from measurements or known data. In the example above, the manufacturer of the electron microscope may state that the equipment can only tolerate a field strength of 20 millivolts/meter, whereas the ambient level contributed by the radio transmitter is 2 volts/meter. By applying the equation

$$A = 20 \log t^1/t^2$$

the required attenuation would be:

$$A = 20 \log 2/0.020 = 40 \text{ dB}$$

Since it is a logarithmic function, an attenuation of 40 dB is the equivalent of reducing the field strength by a factor of 100 (from 2 volts/meter to 20 millivolts/meter); similarly, 120 dB represents a reduction by a factor of 1 million.

When considering the required performance of the shielded enclosure, the distance of the shield from the radio source is an important factor, because distance itself provides a certain amount of attenuation. A radio wave travels outward from a source in similarly to a wave in a pond into which a stone has been dropped. As the spherical surface at the front of the wave becomes ever larger, the strength of the wave weakens in proportion. This phenomenon, known as "free-field attenuation," can be calculated:

$$A_f = 20 \log (4\pi R/\lambda)$$

where R = distance from source
λ = wavelength in meters
π = pi (value of 3.1415g)

Free-field attenuation is particularly useful at higher frequencies. At 400 MHz, for example, an attenuation of 40 dB can be achieved by moving the offending source 20 ft from a sensitive piece of equipment. This illustrates the important trade-offs that are possible between location of the equipment and performance requirements of the shield. Table D.2-7 shows calculated values for free-field attenuation for plane waves.

Size of the Enclosure

A shielded enclosure can be very small, just large enough to contain a piece of equipment, or it can be the size of a room or even an entire building. In general, the smaller the shield, the less expensive it is to construct. It is also true that smaller shields can be designed to higher performance criteria than larger ones simply because error-free construction is more possible on a smaller scale. Still, as explained above, a larger space surrounding the radio source can drastically reduce the amount of shielding needed and can therefore be more cost effective. In some situations, it may also be cheaper to shield an entire building with especially detailed reinforced concrete walls and roof slabs than to build shielded enclosures inside the building.

D.2.5 Types of Shields

Prior to World War II, there was little need for RF shielding. Engineers and inventors experimenting with new applications for "wireless telegraphy," as it was still called in the 1920s, constructed their own homemade enclosures called "Faraday cages" after the English physicist Michael Faraday. With the spectacular development of radar by the British and Americans during the war, there came a need for an RF-quiet environment for testing antennas and other equipment. By 1951, two reports were published on RF-shielded enclosures, one by Stanford Research Institute and the other by the Naval Research Laboratory.

At about the same time, the first prefabricated shielded enclosures became available. These enclosures, which have been refined

Table D.2-7. Calculated Values for Free-Field Attenuation (dB)

Freq.	Distance								
	2	10	20	30	40	50	100	200	(ft)
	0.6108	3.054	6.108	9.162	12.216	15.27	30.54	61.08	(m)
1 Hz	−152	−138	−132	−128	−126	−124	−118	−112	
10	−132	−118	−112	−108	−106	−104	−98	−92	
60	−116	−102	−96	−93	−90	−88	−82	−76	
100	−112	−98	−92	−88	−86	−84	−78	−72	
1 KHz	−92	−78	−72	−68	−66	−64	−58	−52	
10	−72	−58	−52	−48	−46	−44	−38	−32	
100	−52	−38	−32	−28	−26	−24	−18	−12	
200	−46	−32	−26	−22	−20	−18	−12	−6	
400	−40	−26	−20	−16	−14	−12	−6	0	
600	−36	−22	−16	−13	−10	−8	−2	4	
800	−34	−20	−14	−10	−8	−6	0	6	
1 MHz	−32	−18	−12	−8	−6	−4	2	8	
10	−12	2	8	12	14	16	22	28	
100	8	22	28	32	34	36	42	48	
200	14	28	34	38	40	42	48	54	
300	18	32	38	41	44	46	52	58	
400	20	34	40	44	46	48	54	60	
500	22	36	42	46	48	50	56	62	
600	24	38	44	47	50	52	58	64	
700	25	39	45	49	51	53	59	65	
800	26	40	46	50	52	54	60	66	
900	27	41	47	51	53	55	61	67	
1 GHz	28	42	48	52	54	56	62	68	
2	34	48	54	58	60	62	68	74	
3	38	52	58	61	64	66	72	78	
4	40	54	60	64	66	68	74	80	
5	42	56	62	66	68	70	76	82	
6	44	58	64	67	70	72	78	84	
7	45	59	65	69	71	73	79	85	
8	46	60	66	70	72	74	80	86	
9	47	61	67	71	73	75	81	87	
10	48	62	68	72	74	76	82	88	

Note: Negative values, which occur at a distance of less than 1/4 wavelength, should be taken as equal to 0.

considerably since then, are now offered for many different types of radiation conditions, including low-frequency magnetic fields and high-frequency plane waves. They are also available in several performance grades ranging from 30 to 120 dB. The enclosures are typically marketed as complete systems, assembled at the building site by the manufacturer. The basic material is a prefabricated panel which may be copper or steel, single or double layer and solid or screen type. The advantage of using these types of standardized enclosures is that they have a proven track record and a predictable performance guaranteed by the manufac-

turer. The architect can include them in the project by performance specification without having to detail the entire system.

The main disadvantage of prefabricated systems is their cost. They also often represent an "overdesign," meaning that they achieve an attenuation far in excess of what is actually required. Still, in most cases where there is a need for a room-sized shielded enclosure, they are the solution of choice.

Alongside shielded enclosures, a parts industry has developed that supplies conductive gaskets, caulking compounds, air vents and shielded glass, mostly for use in equipment shielding. Manufacturers of these products are a valuable resource for an architect faced with designing a custom-shielded laboratory. They publish test data on their products and often have an engineering staff knowledgeable about shielding applications theory and practice.

In many scientific applications, a partial shield will be all that is necessdary to isolate a local radio source from another piece of equipment. This can be accomplished by building a metal screen or two and experimenting with their placement until the offending interference has been eliminated. An example of such screens is the panel that separates the technician from the patient in an X-ray room. This solution is a good idea when the location and strength of the radio source are known. It is so much cheaper than shielding an entire room that it is worth the additional time and effort needed to experiment.

Another type of low-grade shield is a system of metal foil or sheets of metal which can be glued to the walls, ceilings and floors of a room. Zinc-rich paint sprayed on a substrate has also been used. The health consequences of zinc in aerosol form, however, have not been studied extensively, and it is questionable whether the paints are safe, both for the applicators and for the people working in the spaces later.

In projects where the space required to be shielded is extensive or where several separate labs have to be shielded, a total building shield should be considered. This could take the form of welded wire mesh in concrete or precast, copper foil or steel sheet metal attached to building sheathing or a metal panel system with specially designed joints. These systems can be an elegant solution because they utilize readily available, low-cost building materials which fulfill another function besides shielding.

If, for example, the shielding requirement is for less than 60 dB higher-frequency plane waves, 26-gauge sheet metal will adequately protect a building's concrete roof and floor slabs. Laps need to be welded, brazed or soldered together for electrical continuity. Since welding is not practical with thin metal

and since solder will not adhere well to steel, stainless steel with a terne coating is a preferred material for this application, despite its higher cost. The sheet metal can also act as a vapor barrier if it is placed at the appropriate location in the floor or roof assembly.

Walls incorporating metal panels can provide economical shielding in some circumstances. Because of all the bare metal-to-metal contact necessary for electrical continuity, the shielding needs to be protected from weather. Therefore the metal liner panels of both insulated and uninsulated systems are better suited for shielding than the exterior metal faces. The joints of these panels usually have a tongue-in-groove or snap-in configuration that permits compressible RF gaskets to be used in lieu of welding or soldering. See Figure D.2-4. The gasket used to provide electrical continuity between the panels is a woven wire wrapped around an elastomeric core. A separate factory-applied seal keeps out the weather.

Copper foil laminated to a kraft paper backing is another material that has been used successfully for RF shielding in exterior and interior wall construction. It can be applied like wallpaper to gypsum board or building sheathing.

Table D.2-8 summarizes the approximate attenuation for various construction systems. It is apparent that the overall performance of these systems is much less than the calculated values shown for the materials in Tables D.2-3 through D.2-5. The reason for this discrepancy lies in the imperfection of construction. The calculated values describe perfect sheets of metal of infinite size. In reality, a room or a building not only has joints but also many building parts, such as doors, ductwork and piping, which are made of different kinds of metal with different electrical properties. The change in conductivity and the unavoidable small gaps at the interfaces limit the total actual attenuation.

D.2.6 Basic Shielding Design

Solid Metal Box

The ideal shield is a grounded seamless metal box. Radio waves hitting the box are either

interior

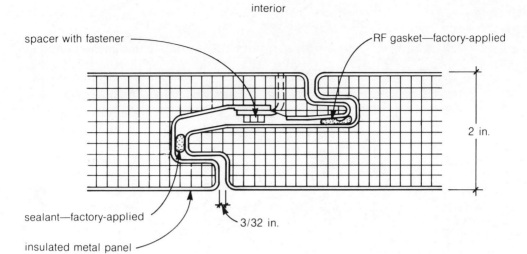

spacer with fastener

RF gasket—factory-applied

2 in.

sealant—factory-applied

3/32 in.

insulated metal panel

exterior

Fig. D.2-4. Detail of a joint gasket between metal panels.

reflected or absorbed and conducted to ground. Only a very small amount of radiation propagates through the shield into or out of the box. The architect's challenge is to design an enclosure that approximates the seamless box as closely as possible. Welding, brazing, soldering and gasketing are the primary means to ensure uninterrupted metal-to-metal contact at seams and at interfaces between different materials.

To function properly, every shield must be grounded. A low-impedance ground—1 ohm or less—is recommended. This ground should be part of the overall building grounding system. A typical gounding detail is shown in Figure D.2-5.

The perimeter of the shield must also be smooth, with no projections which could act as antennae. In cases where the shield serves to keep radiation out, there must be no projections on the inside. If radiation is to be kept in, there must be no projections on the outside. The basics of an RF-shielded building are shown in Figure D.2-6.

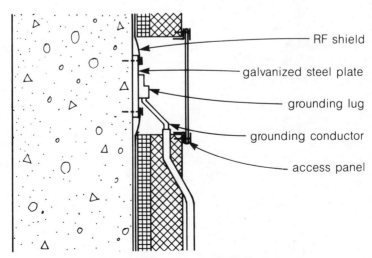

RF shield

galvanized steel plate

grounding lug

grounding conductor

access panel

Fig. D.2-5. Connection detail of a shield to ground.

Table D.2-8. Approximate Attenuation of Various Construction Systems Against Plane Waves

	Walls	Floor	Ceiling or Roof	Doors	Windows	Estimated Attenuation Against Plane Waves
Prefabricated room	Steel, copper or copper screen panels for all surfaces			Special RF doors	No windows	Up to 120 dB
Custom room or suite	Copper foil on gypsum board	Terne metal on isolation board finished floor on sleepers	Copper foil on gypsum board	Hollow metal doors with gaskets	80-OPI or 100-OPI screen or 60-dB coated glass	50–65 dB
Custom building	3-oz copper on kraft paper glued to sheathing with curtainwall over	Terne metal on floor of lowest level, conc. fill over	Terne metal on top of roof slab, roofing system over	Hollow metal with gaskets	80-OPI or 100-OPI screen or 60-dB coated glass	50–65 dB
Custom building	Welded wire mesh in concrete or precast	No protection	Welded wire mesh in roof slab	Hollow metal with gaskets	22-OPI screen or 40-dB coated glass	25–40 dB
Custom building	Metal sandwich panel with gaskets	Terne metal on floor of lowest level, conc. fill over	Terne metal on top of roof slab, roofing system over	Limited number of steel doors with gaskets, entrances protected by waveguide	No windows	60–75 dB

OPI = openings per inch.

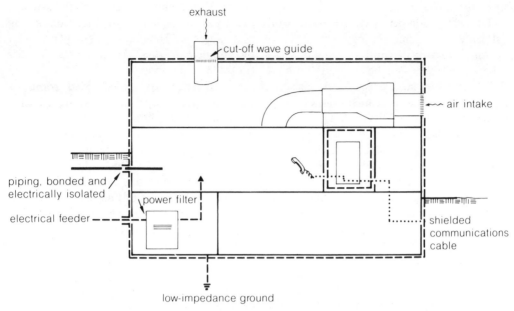

Fig. D.2-6. Diagrammatic section showing elements of a shielded building.

Openings

Unlike a closed box, a room or a building has doors, windows, air supply and exhaust ducts and pipes penetrating the exterior walls and ceiling or roof. These necessary openings are weak points in the shield and will compromise its function unless they are properly treated.

An aid in overcoming this problem is the principle of the "waveguide-below-cutoff." This effect is illustrated by the way radio reception dies in a tunnel. See Figure D.2-7. The wavelength of a typical FM radio signal at, say, 100 MHz is about 10 ft. If the cross section of the tunnel is 15 ft and the tunnel is 50 ft long, only the part of the radio signal that is in perfect alignment with the long axis of the tunnel will pass through. If the tunnel's cross section is any smaller than one-

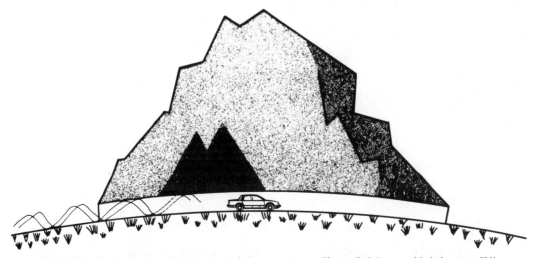

Fig. D.2-7. Radios that go silent in a tunnel demonstrate an effect called "waveguide below cutoff."

half of the wavelength, the signal will break up. The waveguide-below-cutoff effect will work only if the tunnel's length is at least three times that of its width or height.

The same effect can be created for any building opening, large or small. At air supply ducts, for instance, a metal honeycomb designed as a series of little tunnels will let air pass through while each cell attenuates the RF signal. See Figure D.2-8. A pipe penetration through the perimeter of the shield can be designed on the same basis: a steel sleeve, five times as long as its diameter will cut off an RF signal up to about 3 GHz. In both cases, the metal duct or pipe has to be bonded to the shield on the "noisy" side and

an electrical break is required on the "quiet" side to prevent the pipe or duct from acting as an antenna. The break is usually provided by nonmetallic duct sections and "dielectric" pipe couplings.

At entrances to the shielded room or building, a corridor can be designed as a waveguide by shielding the floors, walls and ceiling. The waveguide eliminates the need for RF-shielded doors in high-traffic areas. See Figure D.2-10. Once the waveguide reaches the proportions of a corridor, which may be 8 ft high and 6 ft across, attenuation becomes difficult to achieve at shorter wavelengths. To aid in the absorption performance of the corridor, its walls, floor and ceil-

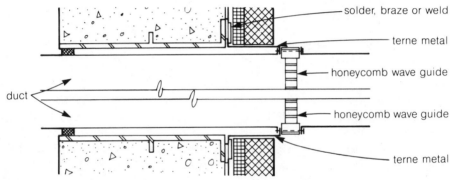

Fig. D.2-8. Standard detail of duct penetration through shielding.

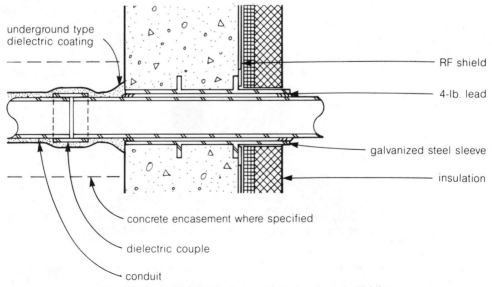

Fig. D.2-9. Standard detail of pipe penetration through shielding.

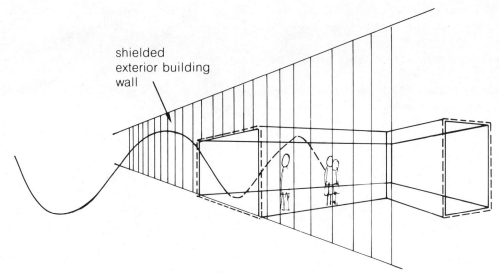

Fig. D.2-10. Waveguide below cutoff principle applied to a building entrance.

ing can be lined with "anechoic material," a carbon-filled foam which drastically reduces the RF reflection of the surfaces.

Where a long, right-angled shielded corridor is impractical, an RF door is the only alternative. Commercially available doors will attenuate up to 120 dB over a wide frequency range, but they are very heavy, difficult to open and close and expensive. If the attenuation requirements are less stringent (60 dB or less), an ordinary hollow metal door can be adapted to RF use by applying special stops and gaskets. Figures D.2-11 and D.2-12 demonstrate how stops and drop seals normally found on lightproof doors can be made RF tight by replacing the elastomeric gaskets with RF gaskets. Other possibilities include the use of spiral springs or copper fingerstock. The problem with all of these options is that the conductive elements are relatively delicate and have to be maintained over time. The shielded waveguide corridor, on the other hand, is relatively maintenance free.

Windows have long been a problem in RF-shielded installations. Several grades of screen are available which can be installed either in a separate layer inside the vision glass or laminated within the glass. A 22 OPI (openings per inch) copper screen provides

about 50 dB attenuation at 1 GHz and an 80 or 100 OPI screen provides about 60 dB attenuation. It is important that any screen be specified to be "blackened," because the orange hue of copper as well as the silver sheen of aluminum are very distracting. Attenuation of 40 to 60 dB on windows can also be achieved by coating the glass with a transparent metal film. The glass has a light transmittance similar to that of solar bronze and is particularly well suited for exterior walls. It is important to note that windows cannot be used in magnetic shields or spaces with attenuation requirements above 60 dB.

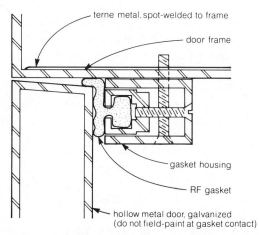

Fig. D.2-11. Jamb detail of an RF-shielded door.

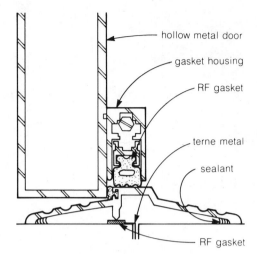

Fig. D.2-12. Sill detail of an RF-shielded door.

D.2.7 Construction Considerations

Whether materials used for shielding are fabricated in factories or on building sites, designing an RF-shielded enclosure and getting it built can be considerably more difficult than conventional lab construction. Water from condensation or wind-driven rain and potential galvanic reactions between dissimilar metals pose difficult detailing problems. To protect the shielding materials from water and from wear and tear, it is desirable to place them away from exposed exterior and interior building surfaces. At the same time, the shield should remain accessible for testing and repairs over the life of the facility.

Given the many conflicting goals in a shielded laboratory, it is important to realize that there is no such thing as perfection. This becomes particularly apparent during the construction stage. Often field conditions develop which could not have been foreseen and which require some on-the-spot detailing changes. Generally, quality control is easier to achieve with prefabricated rooms. When conventional building materials are used, workmanship can become a major problem, due in large measure to the unfamiliarity with shielding on the part of the contractor and workmen. A roofer, for instance, knows from years of experience whether the flashing joint he has just constructed will be watertight. But when he uses the same sheet metal for shielding, he will probably have no idea whether the joint is RF tight.

One way to overcome this problem is to construct a small, expendable test room or building using the same materials and details as the intended overall RF construction. The test structure allows the workers to practice their technique. A small test rig can be used to evaluate the continuity of each seam as it is being built, and gradually the workers can learn how to avoid leaks. Once standards of workmanship are established, construction is more likely to proceed smoothly. The test structure can also serve as a proving ground for new details that the architect may wish to try.

D.2.8 Testing

Shields need to be tested both during and after construction. During assembly, an instrument called a "seam sniffer" will indicate any leaks in the shield. After the enclosure is completed and before the shield is covered by subsequent construction, a series of overall tests need to be performed to demonstrate that the shield can actually meet the design criteria. These tests are usually performed by independent testing agencies employed directly by the project owner. The test setup will vary with the desired attenuation and frequency range but usually includes a transmitter, a receiving antenna and a spectrum analyzer. At present, there are no national standards for these tests except for security-type shields, where military standards have been developed. Any flaws uncovered by the tests should be repaired before finish materials are applied. Once the lab or building is ready for occupancy, detailed measurements are made of the overall performance which become part of the building record.

GLOSSARY

Anechoic Material—Material which readily absorbs sound or radiation with a minimum of reflection.

Attenuation—Reduction in the field strength of a signal achieved by a shielding device. Measured in decibels.

Electric Field—Electromagnetic energy in the near field of an electric source. In the wave, the electric component predominates.

Electromagnetic Waves—One of the four known forces of the universe. Includes electrical power, visible light, radio waves, radar, x-ray, alpha, beta and gamma radiation, and cosmic rays. Described in terms of wavelength and frequency.

Free-Field Attenuation—Reduction in the field strength of a signal due to travel through open space.

Frequency—Number of crests or valleys passing a point in space in 1 second. Expressed in cycles per second or hertz.

Hertz (Kilohertz, Megahertz, Gigahertz)—One hertz equals one cycle per second (*see* Frequency). One kilohertz equals 1,000 hertz, 1 megahertz equals 1,000 kilohertz, 1 gigahertz equals 1,000 megahertz.

Magnetic Field—Electromagnetic energy in the near field of a magnetic source. In the wave, the magnetic component predominates.

Microwaves—Part of the electromagnetic spectrum with wavelengths in the centimeter range. Located between radio waves and the infrared region of the spectrum. Used for cooking and transmission of communications.

Plane Wave—Electromagnetic energy in the far field from any type of source. In the wave, the electric and magnetic components are balanced.

Radio Waves—Portion of the electromagnetic spectrum which is used for the transmission of radio and television signals.

RF Shielding—Placing a barrier in the path of RF radiation. Can be used to prevent radio signals from entering a space or from leaking out of a space.

Seam Sniffer—Testing device used to detect gaps in the seams of conductive material.

Waveguide-Below-Cutoff—A conductive tube with a diameter less than one-half the wavelength it is intended to cut off and with a length at least three times its diameter.

Wavelength—Distance between two successive crests or valleys of an electromagnetic wave. Measured in any metric unit of length (meters, kilometers, centimeters, millimeters).

E. Specialized Facilities: Clean Rooms

W. A. Kohne

E.1 INTRODUCTION

The use of clean rooms in industrial environments has developed from an initial application in aerospace to such diverse fields as manufacturing, bioscience, microelectronics, pharmaceuticals, medicine and food processing. The design and construction of these clean rooms require specialized techniques and materials, which will be briefly described in the following sections.

A clean room generally consists of a specially constructed, enclosed area that is environmentally controlled with respect to airborne particles, temperature, humidity, air motion, electrostatic discharge and lighting. Specialized systems are developed to address each of the parameters of the clean room environment. For example, air contamination control is accomplished through the use of special filtration systems and air recirculation, while temperature and humidity requirements are controlled using special air-handling equipment consisting of fans, humidifiers, preheat coils, cooling coils, reheat coils and associated control systems to coordinate these elements efficiently.

Materials selected for clean room duty must be nonshed construction. The more critical the environment, the better the grade of the materials must be. Standard sealants and fasteners often must be replaced with those developed for clean room environments.

The majority of clean rooms in service today are constructed as vertical downflow rooms. Air enters the space through a high-efficiency filter at the ceiling plane, passes downward through the room, and exits either at the peripheral low wall or through a perforated floor panel.

E.2 CLASSIFICATION OF CLEAN ROOMS

E.2.1 Applicable Standards

Three national standards generally define the requirements for design and certification of clean room environments.

- *Federal Standard 209D (1988):* This standard details the airflow patterns, acceptable particle counts, and clean room definitions that are normally used in the industry. This standard provides good background information for designers, as well as information on field performance testing requirements.
- *American Association for Contamination Control (1970), Standard CS-6T:* This standard is an excellent reference for performance certification of clean rooms. It describes requirements for a room under "unoccupied," "at rest," and "normal" operating conditions. For each of these room occupancies, specific criteria are addressed for performance testing. This standard also contains information on velocity profiles, filter scanning tests, air velocity and distribution, acceptance requirements and particle count allowances.
- *Institute for Environmental Sciences (1984), Standard IES-CC-RP-006:* This standard provides specific tests and testing procedures to be followed in certifying clean rooms. It outlines the specific areas of concern in clean room design.

In addition to the standards listed above, a good reference on the general subject of air contamination control is by Tolliver (1988).

E.2.2 Clean Room Ratings

Federal Standard 209D, referenced above, describes the general clean room classifications used throughout the industry. The ratings limit the number and size of airborne particles allowed in a given volume of air. The rating class of the room is identified by the maximum allowable particle count per cubic foot; therefore, lower classifications imply cleaner rooms. See Figure E-1.

As a standard of reference, most office and laboratory environments have a background count of 200,000 to 500,000 particles per cubic foot. For clean rooms, a room rating of Class 100,000 is the normal, least stringent classification, allowing a maximum of 100,000 particles of 0.5 μM (microns) in size or larger and 700 particles of 5.0 μM or larger per cubic foot of air. The standard also incorporates equivalent metric ratings for special applications.

A Class 10,000 room is one which has a maximum of 10,000 particles of 0.5 μM or larger and 70 particles of 5.0 μM or larger per cubic foot of air.

Following the established pattern, a Class 1,000 room allows a maximum of 1,000 particles, and so forth, through Class 100 to the cleanest standard room at Class 10.

A Class 10 clean room is one in which there is a maximum of 10 particles of 0.5 μM or larger per cubic foot of air and no particles over 5.0 μM. Also, there is a maximum of 350 particles that are 0.1 μM in size or larger.

The most stringent classification currently defined is Class 1. For critical processing environments, the Class 1 definition may be coupled with reduced particle size, with the result being to upgrade the effective cleanliness by several orders of magnitude. For example, a common user design criterion for Class 1 might require a maximum of one particle of 0.2 μM or larger per cubic foot of air. Particles of 0.1 μM or larger might well be limited to five—all values that fall well below the federal standard curves.

Table E-1 lists the requirements for room classifications that are included in Federal Standard 209D. Figure E-1 graphically depicts the particle size limits in the standard.

Relative sizes of some common airborne contaminants are shown in Figure E-2. This figure shows the types of particles that need to be controlled with each classification. As microelectronic technology has advanced, the size of circuitry has progressed to or below 1 μM—roughly 1% of the diameter of a human hair. In this context, a single bacterium on the surface of the silicon is comparable to felling a tree across the road. It becomes evident why the control of airborne contaminants is so important.

E.3 DESIGN CONSIDERATIONS FOR CLEAN ROOMS

E.3.1 Codes

Applicable building codes need to be considered and addressed in the design of clean

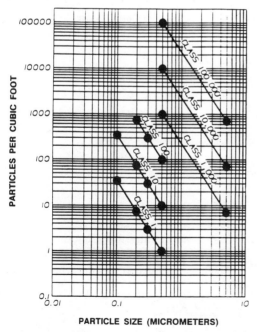

Fig. E-1. Clean room classifications (Federal Standard 209D)

Table E-1. Class Limits in Particles Per Cubic Foot of Size Equal to or Greater Than Particle Sizes Shown (μM)

Class	Measured Particle Size (μm)				
	0.1	0.2	0.3	0.5	5.0
1	35	7.5	3	1	NA
10	350	75	30	10	NA
100	NA	750	300	100	NA
1,000	NA	NA	NA	1,000	7
10,000	NA	NA	NA	10,000	70
100,000	NA	NA	NA	100,000	700

NA = not applicable.
Source: Federal Standard 209D, 1988.

room facilities. Sections of the Uniform Building Code referring to H occupancies are of primary importance in the design process. Microelectronic fabrication facilities are defined as H-6 occupancies with various space and material requirements. Other H occupancies will generally occur within a building housing a lab due to storage of hazardous production materials. Attention must be paid to the maximum quantities of chemicals allowed within given space requirements as part of the design requirements. In addition, sections of the Uniform Fire Code referring to H occupancies must be considered for required area and occupancy separations.

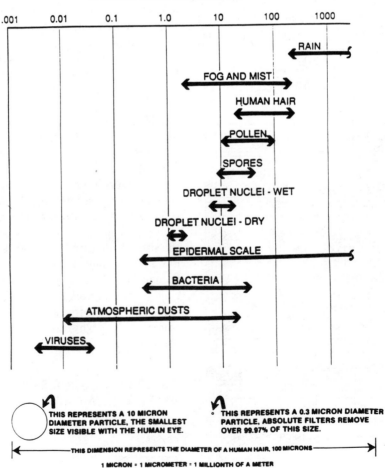

PARTICLE DIAMETER (MICRONS)

THIS REPRESENTS A 10 MICRON DIAMETER PARTICLE, THE SMALLEST SIZE VISIBLE WITH THE HUMAN EYE.

THIS REPRESENTS A 0.3 MICRON DIAMETER PARTICLE, ABSOLUTE FILTERS REMOVE OVER 99.97% OF THIS SIZE.

THIS DIMENSION REPRESENTS THE DIAMETER OF A HUMAN HAIR, 100 MICRONS

1 MICRON = 1 MICROMETER = 1 MILLIONTH OF A METER

Fig. E-2. Relative sizes of common contaminants.

E.3.2 Siting

Facility siting for clean rooms can be critical for many reasons, including vibration, discussed later, and annual energy consumption. Table E-2 lists general figures for building construction costs, airflow requirements and horsepower requirements of various types of facilities. As this table shows, large quantities of air are required for clean rooms. To provide the desired environmental conditions within the clean room, ambient air must be conditioned to the proper temperature and relative humidity. Three significant environmental factors that should then be considered in siting decisions are ambient temperature, specific or absolute humidity and air density. These factors will assist the designer in evaluating different geographical areas from the standpoint of energy uses and annual energy cost.

E.3.3 Airflow

Airflow considerations for clean rooms encompass a combination of the following factors:

- Air change rate
- Airflow patterns
- Return air paths

"Air change rates," defined as the number of times the total volume of air in a given room is changed in an hour, is perhaps the most important factor in providing and maintaining the desired environmental conditions within a clean room. Air change rates can vary from 18 per hour in Class 100,000 clean rooms to 600 per hour in Class 10 clean rooms for a typical design of a clean room with a 10-ft ceiling height. Table E-3 provides a comparison of representative air change rates with resultant room classifications. Most rooms perform better than these charts suggest because all construction personnel and room users focus on the need to maintain cleanliness through a protocol.

Airflow patterns generally are multidirectional or unidirectional. In a multidirectional pattern, air is distributed from the ceiling, usually from a large central area, flows generally downward, and then is removed near the floor level through low-wall return grilles. In a unidirectional system, air is introduced evenly across the full area of one entire surface of the room, such as the ceiling (vertical flow) or a wall (horizontal flow), flows across the room at a constant velocity, and is then removed across the entire area of an opposite surface (a raised floor or wall return). Air velocities across the room are important in maintaining a clean environment and preventing areas of particle buildup. Recommended air velocities for each room classification are presented in Table E-3.

Consideration of an appropriate return air path also enters into the design of a clean room environment. In order to maintain laminar vertical downward airflow, supply air needs to be distributed at the ceiling and directed downward for removal from the room with a minimum number of obstructions. Obstructions in the airflow pattern

Table E-2. Relative Costs, Airflow and Horsepower Requirements for Office, Laboratory, and Clean Room Spaces Per NASF

Space Type	Relative Cost	Required cfm (cfm/NASF)	Required HP (HP/1000 NASF)
Office	1/3	1–2	1–2
Laboratory	1	2–5	2–5
Clean room class 10,000	4	5–15	4–10
Clean room class 10	15	75–90	50–70

Source: CH2M HILL/Industrial Design Corp.

Table E-3. Comparison of Air Change Rates, Air Velocity, and Filter Coverage for Different Clean Room Classifications

Room Classification	Air Change Rate (AC/HR)	Air Velocity (fpm)	Filter Coverage (% Ceiling Area)
Class 100,000	18–30	—	10
Class 10,000	40–60	10	30
Class 1000	150–300	30–50	50
Class 100	400–540	75–90	80–100
Class 10	400–540	75–90	100
Class 1	540–600	90–100	100

Source: CH2M HILL/Industrial Design Corp.

create turbulence and allow the deposit of particles within the work space.

A perforated, raised floor provides the most suitable return path through which air can be extracted and directed back to the fan system. Consideration needs to be given to the processes in these areas in order to provide for spill containment and to allow cleanup where liquid spills could occur through the perforated floor. Operators must be trained to perform routine house-keeping below the floor, as well to maintain strict clean room operating conditions.

Floor grilles are another option that have been employed for return air paths, with mixed success in lower-classification clean rooms. These grilles create limitations because of the quantity required, the difficulty constructing/finishing the floor and the resulting number of structural floor penetrations. Any portion of the frame that is raised also obstructs the movement of people and carts.

If a perforated floor cannot be used due to space limitations of the room, low sidewall return may be a suitable alternative. General design practice dictates that any particle of air in a downward laminar flow pattern should not have to be diverted laterally more than 6 to 7 ft in any one direction. Greater diversion disrupts the proper laminar flow across the full width of the clean room. This then indicates that a given clean area where vertical laminar flow is desired should be limited to 12 to 14 ft in width, with return air paths at the lower part of each of the two side walls. Where large open spaces are required, evenly distributed air returns should be employed, separated by no more than 14 ft in any one direction.

Figure E-3 provides examples of airflow patterns within clean rooms.

E.3.4 Temperature

Strict temperature control is required in a clean room environment to provide stable conditions for materials and instruments. Many of the items used in clean rooms are extremely sensitive to minor temperature variations. In addition, personnel comfort must be considered. Internal heat gains from lighting and equipment need to be accounted for in providing a stable environment. In general, the large quantities of air being supplied to a clean room will diffuse the internal heat gains. However, areas of concentration of heat-producing equipment should be analyzed. It may be necessary to divide large clean rooms into multiple zones to control temperature adequately.

Temperature tolerances vary with clean room function. Many semiconductor fabrication areas are placed in the category of critical applications and require a temperature control range of $\pm 0.5°F$ from the set point. Other applications, such as pharmaceutical and biomedical ones, may be less stringent, with temperature tolerance of $\pm 2.0°F$.

E.3.5 Humidity

Humidity control is necessary in clean rooms to prevent corrosion of surfaces, to reduce

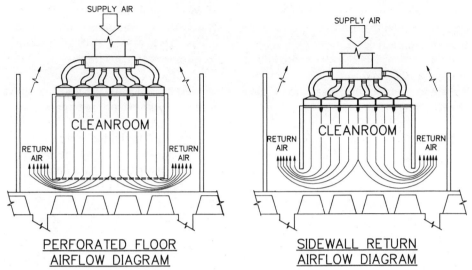

PERFORATED FLOOR
AIRFLOW DIAGRAM

SIDEWALL RETURN
AIRFLOW DIAGRAM

Fig. E-3. Clean room airflow patterns.

the risk of condensation on the product or process equipment, to reduce the buildup of static electricity, to prevent contamination of final products and to provide environmental comfort to personnel. Relative humidity is generally controlled between 40 and 55% in a 70°F environment, with specific applications requiring much tighter control.

Humidification and dehumidification are generally accomplished through proper conditioning of outside makeup air within the central fan system. Humidification is often achieved by injecting steam directly into the airstream. Other methods include evaporative humidification, ultrasonic fog injection, or water bath units which can be effectively used where ambient conditions allow.

Dehumidification poses a more difficult design challenge. Generally, dehumidification is accomplished by cooling the outside makeup airstream, through chilled water, direct expansion or glycol cooling coils if necessary, and then mixing the "overdried" makeup air with the recirculated air from the clean room environment to achieve the required relative humidity. To achieve extremely dry conditions, alternative dehumidification systems must be used, such as chemical-desiccant dehumidifiers.

In many cases, cooled dehumidified air will also need to be reheated before it can be introduced into the clean room. A thorough psychrometric analysis of air conditioning functions is essential to proper selection of air-handling components.

As is the case with temperature control, semiconductor clean rooms generally require tighter control of relative humidity to ±2%. Most applications permit a tolerance of ±5% relative humidity.

E.3.6 Filtration Systems

Filter efficiency, in combination with air change rates, discussed above, are the two most important factors in maintaining the desired environmental cleanliness in a clean room. The filtration system generally consists of several sets of filters within the central fan system, coupled with a final set of filters at the ceiling level of the clean room. Within the fan system, the filters include a 30% efficient prefilter, space for carbon or chemical pollutant filters, a 95% main filter, and an absolute 99.9% final filter.

High-efficiency particulate air (HEPA) filters installed at the ceiling plane of most clean rooms have a minimum efficiency of 99.97 to 99.99% on particles of 0.3 μM or larger. These filters are generally sufficient to provide the appropriate cleanliness levels for Class 100 to Class 100,000 clean rooms.

Ultra-low-penetration air (ULPA) filters are defined as having a minimum efficiency of 99.999% on particles of 0.3 μM or larger. Various grades of ULPA filters are available up to a maximum efficiency of 99.99999999% on 0.05-μM particles. ULPA filters of varying efficiencies are necessary to achieve the cleanliness requirements for Class 1 and Class 10 clean rooms.

Table E-3 includes recommended percentages of ceiling area covered by filters for each cleanliness classification.

Electrophoresis is a relatively new process under development for clean room applications to improve particle removal. This process entails removing contaminants such as bacteria, viruses, spores and vapors as small as 0.001 μM, by electrically charging the particles and then collecting them on special positively charged grid collectors. This process, in combination with a HEPA ceiling filter system, can be extremely effective for particle control.

E.3.7 Material Selection

The selection of materials used in clean room construction is important for the control of particles from sources other than supply air. In general, materials should have smooth surfaces and be cleanable, nonabrasive, and chip resistant, with a minimum number of seams and joints with no crevices or moldings. Off-gassing of vapors from materials, sealants and paints needs to be considered to avoid contamination of the product. Limitations on the amount of volatile condensible materials should be specified in cases where off-gassing is critical.

Specific recommendations for system materials are as follows:

- Floors: Floors that are not being used as return air paths should be coated with plastic, epoxy or polyester, with the coating carried up the wall base. Return-air floors should be perforated, high-pressure phenolic laminant on steel or aluminum panels or a grating that is coated with plastic or epoxy.

- Walls: Walls should be finished with epoxy or baked enamel, unfinished stainless steel, or polyester with a minimum number of projections.
- Ceilings: Clean room ceilings with filtration systems should be inverted heavy-duty tee or U-channel grid assembly of anodized extruded aluminum for mounting individual filters. Grid selection is determined by the room cleanliness classification, air delivery system, and room function.

E.4 SPECIAL CONSIDERATIONS FOR MICROELECTRONICS FACILITIES

E.4.1 Vibration

Vibration control has become a very important consideration in microelectronic facilities. Standard technology used in the semiconductor industry in the late 1970s required resolution in the 2- to 3-μM range. Air-handling equipment was allowed within the clean room and did not require additional vibration consideration. As the technology has advanced into submicron process geometries, fabrication has become critically sensitive to vibration caused by airborne noise and equipment vibration transmitted through the structure and the soil. Therefore, design considerations for microelectronics facilities require extensive coordination between architectural, mechanical, electrical, HVAC, structural and acoustic/vibration specialists.

Vibration control criteria may dictate the actual siting of the building, the arrangement of the fabrication area within the building, the type of structural construction, remote location of all mechanical equipment, specific vibration treatment of all mechanical systems, and noise design criteria. To meet the vibration criteria, all pipes, ducts and conduits within the lab building may need high-deflection isolators. Noise control precautions may be necessary on fan systems serving clean rooms to reduce airborne noise. Adjacency to support buildings, service driveways and neighboring facilities requires scrutiny as well.

E.4.2 Positive Pressurization

In general, microelectronics clean rooms are maintained at a positive pressure with respect to surrounding areas. This precludes contamination from areas outside of the clean room. Air showers, air locks and gowning areas may be used to maintain a separation between the clean room and surrounding areas.

E.4.3 Exhaust Air

Process requirements in microelectronics labs require large quantities of both liquid and gaseous acids and solvents. To maintain a safe environment free of chemical fumes, process tools must be exhausted. This exhaust air is removed in large quantities at high flow rates and treated with acid exhaust scrubbers or solvent treatment systems before being discharged to the atmosphere.

The amount of exhaust air must be considered when determining the makeup air quantity required to maintain appropriate environmental conditions as well as positive pressurization. It is beneficial to focus energy conservation efforts on reducing this exhaust airstream because corresponding reductions in central plant size and operating energy costs can be achieved.

E.4.4 Waste Streams

As noted above, these facilities require a large quantity of process chemicals. Containment of spills must be considered, especially in layouts with perforated floors. In addition, methods of isolating waste streams for treatment and release must be considered.

Table E-4 provides a summary of many of the required conditions for semiconductor clean room facilities.

E.5 SPECIAL CONSIDERATIONS FOR PHARMACEUTICAL/ BIOMEDICAL FACILITIES

E.5.1 Containment

Due to the nature of the processes performed in these facilities, there is often a need to contain contamination within the clean room in order to protect outside and user personnel. These clean rooms should be designed to be negatively pressurized with respect to surrounding areas. Again, this can be accomplished through the use of air locks and/or pressurized corridors and elaborate control systems, but it requires coordinated planning and implementation efforts involving various specialists.

E.5.2 Waste Streams

Waste streams from pharmaceutical/biomedical facilties may contain organisms or

Table E-4. Summary of Requirements for Semiconductor Clean Room Facilities

Clean room (class)	100	10	10	1	1	.5
Filter Type	HEPA	HEPA	HEPA	ULPA	Super-ULPA	Super-ULP
Filter efficiency	99.99	99.999	99.9995	99.99999	99.999999	99.9999999
Particle size (μM)	0.5	0.3	0.2	0.12	0.12	0.05
Temp tolerances (+/− degrees F)	2.0	1.0	0.5	0.3	0.2	0.1
Humidity tolerances (+/− RH)	5	5	3	2	1	1
Air recirculation SW—sidewall return RF—raised-floor return	SW	SW	RF	RF	RF	RF
Noise criteria (PNC)	67	65	60	55	55	50
Vibration criteria	—	250	250	250	125	125

Source: CH2M HILL/Industrial Design Corp.

Table E-5. Clean Room Design Criteria

Item	Microelectronics	Pharmaceutical/Biomedical
Classification	Class 1/10	Class 100
Temperature control	±1/2°F	±2°F
Humidity control	±2% RH	±5% RH
Filtration system	ULPA	HEPA
Pressurization	Positive	Negative
Room layout	Large rooms	Small rooms
	Perforated floor	Sidewall return
	Underfloor services	No underfloor services
Special consider-ations	Vibration control	Containment
	Siting/energy use	Exhaust air control
	Exhaust air requirements	Waste stream control
	Waste stream control	
Controls emphasis	Temperature	Containment
	Humidity	

bacteria that are harmful if released into the environment. Therefore, the design of these facilities must consider methods of containment and disposal to preclude accidental releases. In addition, treatment methods for waste streams as well as exhaust air need to be included in the design to ensure removal of any harmful organisms before release.

Table E-5 provides a comparison of design criteria based on clean room functions.

E.6 CONSTRUCTION CONSIDERATIONS FOR CLEAN ROOMS

E.6.1 Scheduling Concerns

Because a longer construction time results in additional costs, most clean room construction is done fast-track. Due to the nature of the fast-track approach, communication between the owner, engineer and contractor is essential in order to maintain the schedule. In addition, extensive coordination is necessary between electrical, mechanical, architectural and other disciplines in order to integrate all the clean room systems. Design and construction parameters need to be defined and maintained by all disciplines to avoid changes during construction that will impact the schedule. Also, equipment and material items that require a long lead time to procure need to be identified within the design phase

and placed on order. This requires early decisions and attention to the construction schedule in order to allow construction to proceed at a timely rate and in a cost-effective manner. All the trades involved in the construction of the clean room must coordinate in order to schedule construction activities effectively. It should be recognized that if the construction schedule is important, maintaining the schedule and the quality of workmanship may be costly.

E.6.2 Protocol

The final cleanliness of the completed facility requires overall cleanliness in the project area during all phases of construction. Cleaning must be a continual process during construction, as there is no effective way to clean after all the parts are in place. Specialized cleanup crews for clean room facilities exist and are generally a good investment, as the cost of cleanup is much less than the cost of a facility that does not meet its cleanliness certification.

Methods of construction which minimize contaminants are essential to avoid major cleanup efforts. Exposure of large surface areas during construction, such as walls and ceiling, requires a special effort to maintain as clean a surface as possible. Special cleaning methods should be specified to minimize contamination of material surfaces. Daily cleanup and vacuuming of the work area are essential to ongoing control of contaminants as clean room construction progresses. Training and safety classes that focus on clean room construction/cleaning methods, as well as protective clothing for construction personnel, should be included in a construction management program.

E.6.3 Delivery and Storage of Construction Materials

Equipment and materials to be used in the clean room areas should be protected from dust and other contaminants during shipping and delivery and while awaiting installation. All items to be installed in these areas should be kept as clean as possible before, during and after installation to minimize the necessary cleanup effort. Staging areas should be provided in appropriate locations for contractors to perform any necessary cleaning activities after "factory-cleaned" equipment and materials have been inspected. Any items of "dirty" construction should be scheduled early in the project in order to maintain as clean an environment as possible.

E.6.4 Supervision

The attention to detail and coordination necessary among the various trades during installation of clean room equipment requires additional construction supervision. It may be advisable to solicit the services of a full-time quality assurance supervisor empowered with the responsibility and authority to direct installation of those materials and to maintain the cleanliness of the space. On larger projects, a protocol supervisor may be necessary in order to supervise contractors who are unfamiliar with "clean" construction techniques. Having full-time construction inspection specialists on the job is the key to maintaining the cost and schedule of the project.

REFERENCES

General Services Administration, 1988. Federal Standard 209D, Cleanroom and Work Station Requirements, Controlled Environment Wash. D.C.

Institute of Environmental Sciences, 1984. IES-RP-CC-006-84-T, Recommended Practice for Testing Cleanrooms. Illinois.

National Environmental Balancing Bureau, 1988. *Procedural Standards for Certified Testing of Cleanrooms.* Virginia.

Tolliver, Donald L., ed., 1988. *Handbook of Contamination Control in Microelectronics.* NJ: Noyes Publications.

F. Specialized Facilities: Biohazard Containment

E. G. Lunsford and W. E. Barkley

A conventional wisdom has emerged over the last decade for assessing hazards associated with laboratory activities involving pathogenic microorganisms and for selecting safeguards to protect the worker and the environment from these materials. This body of knowledge has been brought together in a document by the Centers for Disease Control and the National Institutes of Health (1984). The designer should have a thorough understanding of this reference document, for it is directly applicable to the design of biomedical research and diagnostic laboratories. A superficial understanding of the principles and guidance provided in this document can result in costly overdesign or failure to incorporate an essential concept, which would make the facility unsuitable for its intended purpose.

Protection of the worker and the environment from biological hazards is achieved by practices and techniques used by the laboratory worker to reduce the possibility of direct or indirect exposure to infectious materials; safety equipment used in the laboratory to contain procedures which may produce infectious aerosols; and certain facility features which are primarily intended to control the potential for persons outside of the laboratory to be exposed to accidentally released infectious aerosols. Specific combinations of practices and techniques, safety equipment and facility features, known as "Biosafety Levels 1, 2, 3, and 4," have been described. Each Biosafety Level provides safeguards that match the assessed degree of hazard with the laboratory use of microorganisms. The selection of the appropriate Biosafety Level depends on the communicability of the pathogen and the severity of disease; on the route of spread of the disease, particularly whether it involves the inhalation of infectious aerosols; the stability of the microorganism in the environment; the nature and function of the laboratory; and the availability of prophylactic and therapeutic measures. BL-1 is intended only for training functions involving microorganisms not known to cause disease in healthy adult humans. BL-2 is appropriate for clinical, diagnostic, teaching and research functions with pathogenic microorganisms that are indigenous and present in the community and cause diseases of varying severity, but for which the route of spread is not normally associated with infectious aerosols. BL-3 is appropriate for work with microorganisms which pose a risk of serious disease from the inhalation of infectious aerosols. BL-4 is a specialized category of safeguards applicable for work with nonindigenous pathogenic microorganisms which present a high individual risk of life-threatening disease.

It is prudent to design new biomedical research facilities and clinical laboratories so that they can accommodate work with pathogenic microorganisms for which BL-2 and BL-3 safeguards are applicable. Limiting the design to BL-2 would make it prohibitively expensive to upgrade the facility to BL-3 in the future. There are only a few laboratories in the world whose functions and purpose require the combination of safeguards described as BL-4. This combination of safeguards, therefore, has limited applicability to most research and clinical functions and should not serve as a basic guideline for facility design. The BL-4 facility and equipment safeguards are expensive and prohibitively restrictive, and should only be applied where the assessed hazards of work with exotic pathogenic microorganisms dictate this level of control.

This appendix provides information on facility safeguards that are generally incorporated in the design of laboratories where work with pathogenic microorganisms may require BL-3 safeguards. Basic criteria for these laboratory facilities as described in "Biosafety in Microbiological and Biomedical Laboratories" (1984) are:

- The laboratory is separated from areas which are open to unrestricted traffic flow within the building. Passage through two sets of doors is the basic requirement for entry into the laboratory from access corridors or other contiguous areas. Physical separation of the high-containment laboratory from access corridors or other laboratories or activities may also be provided by a double-doored clothes change room (showers may be included), airlock or other access facility which requires passage through two sets of doors before entering the laboratory.
- The interior surfaces of walls, floors and ceilings are water resistant so that they can be easily cleaned. Penetrations in these surfaces are sealed or capable of being sealed to facilitate decontamination of the area.
- Bench tops are impervious to water and resistant to acids, alkalis, organic solvents and moderate heat.
- Laboratory furniture is sturdy, and spaces between benches, cabinets and equipment are accessible for cleaning.
- Each laboratory contains a sink for handwashing. The sink is foot, elbow, or automatically operated and is located near the laboratory exit door.
- Windows in the laboratory are closed and sealed.
- Access doors to the laboratory or containment module are self-closing.
- An autoclave for decontaminating laboratory wastes is available, preferably within the laboratory.
- A ducted exhaust air ventilation system is provided. This system creates directional airflow that draws air into the laboratory through the entry areas. The

exhaust air is not recirculated to any other area of the building, is discharged to the outside, and is dispersed away from the occupied areas and air intakes. Personnel must verify that the direction of the airflow (into the laboratory) is proper. The exhaust air from the laboratory can be discharged to the outside without being filtered or otherwise treated.
- The HEPA-filtered exhaust air from Class I and Class II biological safety cabinets is discharged directly to the outside or through the building exhaust system. Exhause air from Class I or II biological safety cabinets may be recirculated within the laboratory if the cabinet is tested and certified at least every 12 months. If the HEPA-filtered exhaust air from Class I or II biological safety cabinets is to be discharged to the outside through the buildings exhaust system, it is connected to this system in a manner (e.g., thimble unit connection) that avoids any interference with the air balance of the cabinets or building exhaust system.

The designer should initiate the planning process for a BL-3 laboratory by developing a basic space layout. The equipment needs of the program should be addressed at this stage, and a preliminary arrangement for the equipment should be included in the space layout. Sequencing of functionally related pieces of equipment is important. For example, incubators should be located adjacent to or near biological safety cabinets to reduce the distance that biological materials are moved within the laboratory. It is good design practice to locate freezers, refrigerators and other equipment basically used for storage in areas not immediately contiguous with the general laboratory areas. This will conserve work space. Similarly, laboratory equipment which produces large amounts of heat such as autoclaves, glasswashers and drying ovens should be located in areas removed from the working laboratory environment to help maintain comfortable conditions in occupied areas. Primary containment equipment such as biological safety cabinets and chemical fumehoods should always be positioned in the rear of the laboratory to ensure proper operation and worker protection. Life safety and other general safety considerations which are fundamental to the design of any modern biomedical research facility must also be established as basic design parameters.

The essential facility design concepts associated with BL-3 involve access control and ventilation. They are particularly important because they provide the means for containing infectious aerosols that may be accidentally generated by work procedures and for lessening the potential of inhalation exposures to those aerosols. Interior surface treatments and provisions for special equipment are also important considerations in the design of BL-3 laboratories.

F.1 ACCESS CONTROL

The requirement for access control is fundamental to the design of the BL laboratory. This requirement is basically met by ensuring that the path of entry from the corridor or other contiguous areas traverses at least two sets of doors. The primary purpose of this feature is to create a visible and positive barrier to help exclude the individuals who have no purpose for being in the laboratory from gaining access to it. A person who does not enter a BL-3 laboratory will not be exposed to an accidentally generated infectious aerosol and is, therefore, protected from acquiring a laboratory-associated disease. The architectural arrangement of the access control feature also serves as a constant reminder of the special operational requirements of this facility on which the objectives of occupational safety and environmental protection are based. The feature also helps to maintain ventilation parameters that are established for the facility.

The size of the access zone is usually a function of the size of the facility. For example, as shown in Figure F-1, the access zone could be as small as a portion of a laboratory

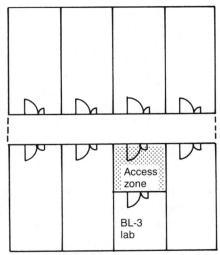

Fig. F-1. Access through part of the BL-3 module.

module which has been so designated for that purpose. Alternatively, in Figure F-2, an existing laboratory module could be used as the access zone for entry into another module or modules. As shown in Figure F-3, a portion of the corridor can be isolated to provide controlled access for those laboratory modules with which it is contiguous. This concept can be expanded, as in Figure F-4, to allow the entire corridor to serve as the access zone for each of the laboratories it serves. This arrangement, however, is not generally recommended because it is difficult

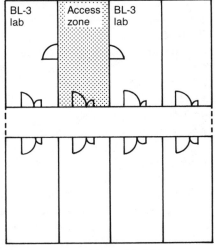

Fig. F-2. Separate module for BL-3 laboratory access.

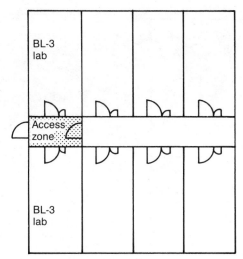

Fig. F-3. Corridor portion serves as access to the BL-3 laboratory.

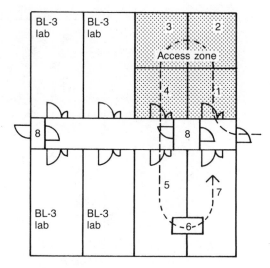

1 Clean clothing change room
2 Drying room
3 Shower room
4 Contaminated-clothing change room
5 Contaminated-waste-handling room
6 Double-door autoclave
7 Waste-marshaling room
8 Air lock

Fig. F-5. Access through change room/shower.

to maintain common access standards where there are many individual laboratory entrances.

Occasionally, a designer is requested to provide an access control arrangement similar to the one required at BL-4. This arrangement (See Figure F-5) incorporates the use of a change room/shower facility to establish the path of controlled entry. This concept is frequently seen in BL-3 pharmaceutical laboratories, where strict standards of cleanliness require workers to change clothes or to

shower on entry. The controlled access may also be a modification or combination of any of the previously described schemes. For example, a shower area could be constructed as a part of the access zone but not be configured to require passage through it. See Figure F-6.

The approach for designing an access control area will depend on all the functions that this area is to provide. In addition to the variations described above, the access control area may be located adjacent to the clean side of the laboratory autoclave or may be designed large enough to accommodate storage or equipment not required for the ongoing procedure in the BL-3 laboratory. An important consideration is to size the access control zone so that it can accommodate the traffic required to travel through it. Usually the access control zone is used for the movement of supplies into and laboratory waste out of the facility. If the use of a cart is involved in this transport, the size of the

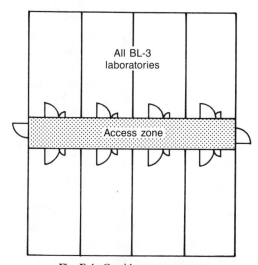

Fig. F-4. Corridors access zone.

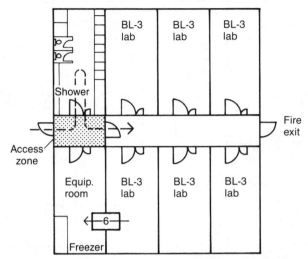

Fig. F-6. Access with shower/change room but not through these areas.

access control zone should be sufficient to accommodate the cart with both doors closed in order to be an effective airlock. Each approach described above, however, is equally effective in achieving the primary purpose of the BL-3 access control criterion, provided that it is properly operated.

F.2 VENTILATION

There are two basic biosafety requirements for ventilation in the BL-3 laboratory. First, there must be directional air flow. Air must flow or migrate toward areas having the greatest potential for an accidental release of microbial aerosols. Thus, air must move from the access control area into the laboratory areas where pathogenic microorganisms are actually handled. The purpose of this requirement is to prevent the dissemination of infectious aerosols to other occupied areas of a building. If pathogenic microorganisms are accidentally released within the BL-3 laboratory, large particles will be captured by the HEPA filter associated with the biological safety cabinet or removed by the building's exhaust air system and discharged to the outdoors. Terminal filtration of exhaust air is not required because dilution within the exhaust air volume and discharge distri-

bution, the impact of ultraviolet rays, and other deleterious effects of the environment on the viability of airborne microorganisms, such as temperature and dehydration, would prevent a situation from occurring whereby a person outside of a building could be exposed to an infectious inhalation. There are special locations, however, where terminal filtration is recommended. These include BL-4 laboratories, special-purpose research laboratories studying dry micronized microbial particles or experimentally created infectious microbial aerosols, and pilot plants growing pathogenic microorganisms in aerated tanks with agitation.

The second biosafety requirement is to support the operation of ventilated primary containment equipment. It is this equipment that protects the laboratory worker from being exposed to aerosols that may be caused by procedures used in handling these materials in the laboratory.

Additional areas that must be addressed by the ventilation engineer include the following:

- The supple air intake for the BL-3 laboratory should be located as far as possible from all building exhausts, loading docks and parking lots. There is no requirement that the air be a separate system dedicated to the BL-3 laboratory; it may be part of the general building supply. The supply air system should be equipped with a prefilter and a moderate-efficiency final filter. There is no requirement that the laboratory air supply pass through a HEPA filter.

- The system exhausting the BL-3 laboratory should discharge directly to the outside of the building. No recirculation of air to any other part of the building is allowed. The exhaust system does not have to be dedicated to the BL-3 laboratory; it may be part of the overall building system as long as it meets all of the requirements specified herein. The general laboratory exhausts, biological safety cabinets and fumehood exhaust may be combined, provided that the exhaust ducting specifications require airtight construction. The exhaust system should discharge upward at high velocity (2,500 fpm or greater) to direct the air outside the building envelope and away from any building air intakes. As previously stated, there is no requirement for HEPA filtration or other terminal exhaust air treatment prior to its discharge directly to the outside.

- An inflow of 50 cfm at each door is considered the minimum which should be provided to maintain directional airflow. The excess air should be provided in the corridor, with the laboratory room air exhaust adjusted accordingly. The laboratory room door should be undercut to provide the air quantity. The door should not be equipped with an air grille.

- Laboratory ventilation should be designed to meet the ASHRAE requirements for air exchange rates. However, laboratory heat loads may require that higher ventilation rates be used. It is acceptable to utilize chilled water-cooling coil units which recirculate the air only within the BL-3 laboratory. All air diffusers should be located in the ceiling,

with exhaust grills located near the floor. This provides the ventilation air with the largest "sweeping" capacity and ensures the greatest potential for heat and odor control.

- The ventilation system should be designed to accommodate the quantity of ventilated Class II, Type A biological safety cabinets; Class II, Type B biological safety cabinets; and chemical fumehoods specified by the research program. Nonventilated Class II, Type A biological safety cabinets may discharge their HEPA-filtered exhaust inside the laboratory if the cabinet is tested and certified at least every 12 months. If the HEPA- filtered exhaust from a Class II, Type A biological safety cabinet is to be discharged through the building's exhaust system, the connection to that system should be designed to be in accordance with National Sanitation Foundation Standard No. 49 (1983).

- The biological safety cabinets and chemical fumehoods are devices which derive their containment capability from a constant, uniform and uninterrupted supply of air. Therefore, the units must be located in areas where air turbulence is at an absolute minimum. This is usually at the rear of the laboratory, as far as possible from the entrance door. The cabinet or hood should be situated so that personnel traffic past its face opening is minimized. The unit should also be positioned so that air movement effects from air diffusers and exhaust grilles have minimal impact.

- Energy recovery systems must be designed to ensure that possible contaminants which might be present in the exhaust air system are not imparted to the supply air. For this reason, systems which feature direct communication between air streams, such as heat wheels, cannot be used. A glycol-water mixture, piped heat exchangers or runaround systems are acceptable. The use of these systems is often encouraged because of the energy demands of the 100% outside air systems utilized in most modern biomedical research facilities.

F.3 INTERIOR SURFACES

Another important architectural feature in the design of the BL-3 laboratory is the selection of the interior surfaces. In general, these should be chosen from materials which are easily cleanable and impervious to liquids. The degree of resistivity will vary with specific laboratory functions. If it is necessary to decontaminate the BL-3 facility with gaseous materials, it may be advisable to seal all surface penetrations before commissioning the laboratory. This is usually accomplished by the use of a silicon caulking material, and requires good workmanship and meticulous application. Individual treatments of the interior surfaces include the following:

- The floors are the surface which will receive the most rigorous cleaning. They should be impervious to liquids, be relatively free of seams and resistant to chemicals, and present a surface which will minimize slipping hazards. Heat-seamed vinyl flooring and poured epoxy flooring provide excellent floor surfaces.
- The walls are generally of drywall or plastic construction. They should be covered with an acrylic latex, enamel, epoxy or other type of paint which will allow frequent cleaning and decontamination. All seams and joints in the walls should be sealed. This allows for control of air movement and provides a deterrent to penetration by insects or other vermin. Mechanical and electrical devices should be sealed to control air leakage from the laboratory.
- The ceilings should receive the same construction, sealing and painting consideration as the walls. Suspended lay-in tile ceilings are not suitable for BL-3 laboratories because of leakage and problems with dirt accumulation and insect control. Light fixtures should be recessed or surface mounted and sealed to minimize dirt accumulation. Ceiling diffusers should be sealed to control air leakage from the laboratory.
- The laboratory bench tops should be impervious to water and easily cleanable. They should also be resistant to acids, alkalis, organic solvents, and moderate heat. Acceptable materials are type 316 stainless steel, acid-grade laminate plastic and resin.
- Shelving and cabinets should satisfy the same cleanability criteria applicable to the bench tops. Units of plastic laminate construction are frequently used and quite acceptable.
- The laboratory windows must be non-operable and sealed in place.

F.4 SPECIALIZED EQUIPMENT

The successful design of a Biosafety Level 3 laboratory should include several pieces of specialized equipment. These are as follows:

- The laboratory facility must contain a sink for handwashing. Ideally, the sink should be located in proximity to the exit door from the laboratory. The sink must be either foot, elbow or automatically operated.
- A safety eyewash facility should be located in every laboratory. It may be located on the laboratory sink and should utilize a "swing-away" design. A unit with dual eyewash streams, as well as a face spray ring, is recommended. Activation should be by a paddle operator and a stay-open valve so that both hands can be free to rinse the eyes once the eyewash facility is activated.
- Every laboratory in the BL-3 facility should be equipped with a safety shower. The designer should specify a model with a deluge-type shower head operated by a stay-open ball valve. The valve should be activated by a rigid metal rod. The shower should be located so as not to interfere with usable laboratory space (preferably near a

doorway), but the rod should also not interfere with egress.

- Access doors to the laboratory must be equipped with self-closing devices. This ensures that the air balance is maintained and that access control is not compromised.
- It is recommended that every BL-3 facility be equipped with an autoclave. The autoclave may pass through into the controlled access area or be located in an equipment room. The units should be installed so that the door swings do not interfere with personnel traffic. A canopy hood or other local exhaust arrangement should be installed near the autoclave door (or doors) so that heat and moisture do not adversely affect the laboratory environment.

This appendix has introduced the concepts of facility safeguards that are necessary for the proper design of laboratories that will support biomedical research and clinical studies involving pathogenic microorganisms. The designer must not only become knowledgeable about these concepts and understand their application but must also become familiar with the practices, techniques and equipment used by biomedical workers to protect themselves from the risk of acquiring a laboratory-associated disease. The competent designer must designer must ultimately become a recognized expert in biological safety.

REFERENCE

Centers for Disease Control and the National Institutes of Health, 1984. Biosafety in Microbiological and Biomedical Laboratories. Atlanta & Bethesda U.S. Dept of Health & Human Services.

National Sanitation Foundation, 1987. Standard No. 49. Class II (Laminar Flow) Biohazard Cabinetry. Ann Arbor.

G. Specialized Facilities: Nuclear Magnetic Resonance

U.M. Lindner

G.1 INTRODUCTION

Safety and liability are of great concern to the laboratory designer. These two concepts make it very difficult to get precise and dependable information for the proper installation and safe operation of a nuclear magnetic resonance (NMR) apparatus.

First is the safety of the researcher and the people around him (and those housed above/below him). Second is the liability by putting in writing (drawing, sketch) any information that might prove inadequate during an experiment or over a period of time, thereby leaving the designer open to litigation.

Manufacturers are, therefore, hesitant to give clear-cut instructions on how to shield a certain instrument and how to make it safe for the operator and the people around him. This is because the final use and application of that instrument are totally in the hands of the operator and are, after all, to a great degree, experimental.

To design a space for such an instrument, one has to make certain commitments and work with the best information available. The following information for the installation of superconducting NMR systems is culled from "Bruker-Spectrospin Site Planning Guide for Superconducting NMR Systems H. Holenweger & E. Ungricht, Oct. 1988. In house manual." and from discussions with researchers including Dr. Regizer Vold, Department of Chemistry, University of California at San Diego.

Professor Vold, an authority on NMR systems, said that to her (and her staff's) knowledge, superconducting, high-resolution NMR machines have been in general use for the last 20 years and there appear to be *no magnetic effects* on people. Trivia, a magnetic resonance imager (MRI), a body scanner used for diagnosis in medicine, has a magnetic field bigger by a factor of 10 than the high-resolution mass spectrometers used in research.

A few things the designer should know are as follows:

- The magnetic field of a superconducting NMR emanates in radial fashion in *all* directions (globular) from the magnet. The field is called a "magnetic stray field."
- The verticle field is always stronger than the horizontal field.
- The magnetic field is always on.
- The magnetic field is easily influenced (disturbed) by external circumstances (elevators, power lines, trams, or subways), thereby affecting its performance.
- Static iron occurrences (ducts, pipes, beams) in the vicinity of the magnet will disturb the field's homogeneity, but as long as they are static and outside the 50-gauss line (see Figure G-1), the operator can compensate for the disturbance.
- The 5-gauss line is approximately 10 times the earth's magnetic field.
- The gauss-line distance from the center of the magnet will vary with the size of the magnet.

It is generally accepted that magnetic stray fields are harmless below 5 gauss. Stronger fields closer to the magnet may disturb heart pacemakers and erase magnetic cards (credit cards), and can adversely affect watches and micro-mechanical devices.

- The 5-gauss line should be marked and warning signs posted.

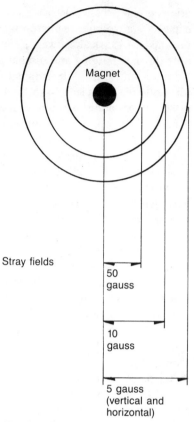

Fig. G-1. Stray fields: gauss-line distance.

member that verticle fields are larger than horizontal fields (affecting rooms above and below the magnet).
- Some local shielding of computer displays, etc., below the 10-gauss line is possible.
- Global shielding of an entire magnet stray field is costly and ineffective.

G.2 ATTRACTIVE FORCES

Strong attraction of ferromagnetic objects will occur close to the magnet, at the 50- to 100-gauss line. The attractive force depends on the mass of the object and its distance from the magnet. It increases rapidly when the distance is reduced (by the seventh power). Hence, it may change from barely noticeable to uncontrollable within a very short distance.

Table G-2. Recommendations for Safety

Feature	Range
Warning signs (safety limit for medical devices)	3–5 gauss
Access limited to NMR staff (safety limit for heavy iron objects)	10–20 gauss
Floor markings (safety limit for attraction of iron)	50–100 gauss
Pressurized gas cylinders	Wall mounted

- Limited access (NMR staff only) should be permitted within the 10-gauss line.
- Be aware, once more, that magnetic stray fields extend in all three dimensions. Walls, floors and ceilings provide no barrier to magnetic fields. Also, re-

Table G-3. Magnetic Field Effects

Effects	Range
Effects on electron microscopes	1 gauss
Disturbance of color computer displays	1–3 gauss*
Disturbance of monochrome computer displays	3–5 gauss*
Erasing of credit cards	10 gauss
Effects on watches and micro-mechanical devices	10 gauss
Lowest known field–effect on pacemakers	17 gauss
Erasing of magnetic tapes	20 gauss
Saturation of transformers and amplifiers	50 gauss
Erasing of floppy disks	350 gauss

Table G-1. Stray Field Examples: Distance from the Magnet's Center

Range	Magnetic Field		
	200 MHz	500 MHz	600 MHz
5-gauss			
Vertical	1.7 m	3.8 m	4.8 m
Horizontal	1.1 m	3.0 m	3.6 m
10 gauss			
Vertical	1.3 m	3.0 m	3.6 m
Horizontal	0.9 m	2.3 m	2.8 m
50 gauss			
Vertical	0.8 m	1.8 m	2.1 m
Horizontal	0.5 m	1.3 m	1.6 m

*Disturbances of computer displays can be effectively reduced by shielding the display as long as the field is below 10 gauss.

It is important to mark and establish a safety zone around the magnet (50-gauss line). Massive iron objects (gas cylinders) are best mounted on walls beyond the 5-gauss line. Steel desks and chairs are not recommended. Tools should be kept safe beyond the 5-gauss line.

G.3 CRYOGENIC LIQUIDS

Superconducting magnets use liquid helium and liquid nitrogen as cooling agents. These liquids expand their volume by a factor of 700 during evaporation and warmup. While these gases are nontoxic, good ventilation is required to prevent suffocation.

During normal operation, 3 to 5 m^3 of nitrogen is evaporated in a day's time. During a "quench," 50 to 100 m^3 of helium is produced in a short period of time (minutes). Proper ventilation for such occurrences is advised (exhaust fan high-low override switch). The room should be laid out so that easy transfer of cryogenic liquids from dewars to magnet is possible. See Section G.5 for clear overhead access requirements, usually in a 4 × 4-ft area.

G.4 UTILITY REQUIREMENTS

- Electric Power: 208 V, 60 Hz, three-phase, 20 amp, well grounded. If fluctuations greater than −10% or +5% are expected, a voltage regulator must be installed. Electrical power is needed only during charging and discharging.
- Compressed Air: Instrument-grade (dry, oil-free and clean) 4 to 8 bar at 3 m^3/hour. An additional 5 to 8 m^3/hour is advised for optional equipment.
- Cooling Water: Not required for the magnet. It may be necessary to access cooling water for future high-performance experiments.
- Nitrogen and Helium Gases: Recommended for refilling the magnet dewar with cryogenic liquid. If gas lines are not available, portable gas cylinders can be used; however, they are a major source of accidents. An effort should be made to pipe helium and nitrogen from a nearby safe cylinder location.
- HVAC: The room temperature should not exceed 77°F (25°C). A constant temperature of 74°F ± 2°F is recommended. Relative humidity should be 50% ± 5%. A minimum of six air changes per hour is recommended. Constant air pressure is advisable. Rapid pressure and temperature fluctuations will reduce NMR performance. The air in the vicinity of the magnet dewar must be free of drafts.

Table G-4. Physical Requirements

Requirements	Magnetic Field		
	200 MHz	500 MHz	600 MHz
Magnet system weight (including cryoliquids and magnet stand)	400 kg	600 kg	1500 kg
Hoist capacity for assembling	250 kg	400 kg	1000 kg
Hoist height for assembling (clear space below hoist hook)	2.6 m	2.8 m	3.7 m
Recommended room dimensions	4 × 5 m^2	5 × 6 m^2	5 × 6 m^2
Door width minimum room height for refilling	0.8 m	0.8 m	1.2 m
Standard dewar*	2.76 m	3.01 m	3.54 m
With hydraulic magnet stand*		2.60 m	3.11 m
Low loss dewar*	2.97 m	3.04 m	
Compact version*	2.63 m		

Note: Exact data for each dewar and magnet type must be verified with manufacturers.
*Clear overhead access requirements.

G.5 LOCATION RECOMMENDATIONS

- The NMR apparatus should be located as far away as possible from large moving objects such as elevators or cars (minimum, 5 m; better, 10 m).
- Lower floors are recommended. Locations in high-rise structures above the fifth floor can cause vibration problems and atmospheric pressure fluctuations.
- Floor support must be rigid to avoid vibrations. Maximum floor vibrations CA. 0.1 mm/sec^2.

- Locate the NMR apparatus 7 to 10 m from other NMR machines (center to center of magnet).
- Locate away from streetcar or subway minimum 100 to 500M.
- Room should be air-conditioned and ventilated, with constant temperature and humidity.
- A hoist will be required for installation and assembly. This can be either a built-in or a portable (A-frame) hoist.

H. Common Equipment Sensible Heat Loads

T. Ruys

Equipment	Sensible Heat Load (BTU/Hr)	Elec. Load	Comments
Lab—heavy equipment use	20–24 BTU/sq ft		Not including large instruments
Instrument room	44–48 BTU/sq ft		
Biological safety cabinet	1,200–2,300		
Glassware washer	5,000–7,000		Cabinet model
Glassware dryer	6,500–8,500		Cabinet model
Autoclave—front	1,600–5,000		Recessed model
Autoclave–recess	3,500–16,500		16 × 16 × 26 to 24 × 36 × 60 chamber models
Refrigerator		12–32 KWH/day	
Freezer		21–29 KWH/day	
Incubator		.9–2.2 KWH/day	
Centrifuge	6,000		
Electron microscope		2500 watts	
Nuclear magnetic resonance machine	350,000		Including 200,000 BTU/hr removed by cooling water
Gaschomatograph/ massspectrometer	19,000		

Note: Sensible heat loads vary by manufacturer and model. A range is given as a guide for the equipment-generated load only, without contents. The time in use for this equipment must be verified with the users. Electrical loads given can be converted to sensible heat loads.

I. Common Equipment Weights

T. Ruys

Equipment	Floor Area	Operating Weight (lb)	Weight per area (lbs/sq ft)	Comments
Lab casework, including top with support frame	Per foot/30-in. deep	140	56	Centerbench is less
Fumehood	48 × 36 in.	1,050	88	Larger hoods weigh less per square foot
Biosafety lab	48 × 34 in.	1,100	92	Larger models weigh less per square foot
Glassware washer, 27 × 21 × 26 in.	40 × 30 in.	1,070–1,500	134–150	
Autoclave,				
20 × 20 × 38 in.	21 × 24 in.	2,240	640	Floor area represents spacing
24 × 36 × 48 in.	21 × 55 in.	5,275	659	of fasteners
24 × 36 × 60 in.	21 × 69 in.	5,700	570	
Electron microscope	Varies	600–3,300	100–280	Power supply about the same
NMR	5 sq. ft.	16,500	3,300	Magnet only
Scintillation counter	47 × 30 in.	800	82	
Refrigerator				
Standard	28 × 30 in.	240	42	
Reach-in	85 × 35 in.	1,275	62	
Freezer				
Chest	96 × 29 in.	965	50	
Reach-in	57 × 35 in.	1,000	72	
Centrifuge standard	39 × 27 in.	1,230	167	Water cooled ultra-centrifuge
Radioisotope storage	Varies	Verify		Lead-lined container or lead bricks
Gaschromatograph/ massspectrometer	48 × 31 in.	1,000	97	
Mass spectrometer	20.9 sq. ft.	6,160	295	

Note: Weights are intended as guides and represent average weights for equipment from several manufacturers where applicable and available. Weights are for equipment in operation in a laboratory facility, i.e., contents have been estimated and added to the actual equipment weight as manufactured. Most equipment is supported on four points within the floor area noted.

J. Common Equipment Utility Services Rough-In Requirements

T. Ruys

Equipment Type	Size W × D × H (In.)	Piped Services (In.)	Exhaust (Cfm/In.)	Electrical Services (Volt/Amps/Phase)	Comments
Lab benches		As needed—rough in to meet plumbing and electrical codes			
Fumehoods	48 × 37 × 86 (96 w/open sash)	CW 1/2; Gas 1/2; Air 1/2; Vacuum 1/2; Cupdrain 1 1/2†	720 to 875/10*	Power; 120 V/20 A/1∅ lights; 120 V/20 A/1∅	See Figure J-1; See Figure J-2
	60 × 37 × 86	Same	960–1,135/10*	Same	
	72 × 37 × 86	Same	1,025–1,345/10*	Same	
	96 × 37 × 86	Two sets	1,485–1,920/10(2)*	Same	
Biological safety cabinets	52 × 33 × 93	Gas 1/2	305/10	120 V/20 A/1∅	See Figure J-3; No exhaust for Type I and Type II, class A
	72 × 33 × 93	Same	444/10		
Water Purity systems	Distillation	CW; Cupdrain	Hood over (100 cfm) for larger models	280V	See Figures J-4 and J-5
	Service exchange deionization	CW 3/4 to 1‡		120 V	See Figure J-6
	Cartridge Deionization	CW 1/2		120 V	See Figure J-7
	Reverse osmosis	CW 1/2–11/2 access to drains	None	110 or 208 V	See Figure J-8
	Ultra-filtration	CW 1/2 to 1-1/2 access to drains	None	110 or 208 V	See Figure J-9
Glassware washers (steam)	Chamber 26 × 28 × 27	Air 1/2 NPT; CW 3/4 NPT; HW 1 NPT; Steam/return 3/4 in.; Drain 4 in.; Deionized 5/8 in. ODT	Equip: 250/6; Recessed exhaust and canopy hood.	208 V/13 A/3∅/4; 208 V/60 A/3∅/4 with booster	Only some manufacturers have CW, exhaust and air; See Figure J-10
	41 × 26 × 21				
Glassware dryer (steam and electric)	Chamber 26 × 26 × 55	Steam 1 in. NPT; return 3/4	Equip: 100/4; Recessed exhaust and canopy hood.	120 V/5 A/1∅; 208 V/7.8 KW/3∅	See Figure J-11
	42 × 26 × 56				

(continued)

Equipment Type	Size W × D × H (In.)	Piped Services (In.)	Exhaust (Cfm/In.)	Electrical Services (Volt/Amps/Phase)	Comments
Autoclave (steam)	Chamber 20 × 20 × 38 24 × 36 × 48	Electrical CW 3/4 in. NPT Steam 1 in. NPT Drain 2 in. ODT	Atm. exhaust; canopy hood and recess.	120 V/20 A/1∅ (with power door)	See Figure J-12
Autoclave (electric)		CW 3/4 in. NPT HW 3/4 in. NPT Drain 2 in. ODT	Atm. exhaust; canopy load and recessed.	120 V/15 A/1∅ (controls) 200/230 V/60 A/ 3∅ or 460/30 A/ 3∅ (heaters)	
Controlled-environment room (water-cooled)	Room Condenser (compressor) fan coil	None Chilled H₂O recirc. Drain 3/4	None	120 V/20 A/1∅ (2) 208 V/1.5 hp/3∅ Same as room	See Figure J-13 See Figure J-13 See Figure J-13
Controlled-environment room (air cooled)	Room Condenser fan coil	None Drain 3/4	None	120 V/20 A/1∅ (2) 208 V/1.5 hp/3∅ Same as room	See Figure J-13 See Figure J-13 See Figure J-13

Note: Rough-in mechanical and electrical services are noted for equipment commonly found in laboratory facilities. This list is intended as a checklist and guide only. Flow rates, pressures, and other requirements must be verified with equipment manufacturers and equipment user. Rough-in piping is generally one size larger than the inlet on the equipment.

*For 100-fpm face velocity, standard hood.

†Larger for washdown hood.

‡3/4 in. up to 1 gpm; 1 in. up to 10 gpm.

LEGEND:
CW - Cold water
HW - Hot water
NPT - National pipe taper
ODT - Outside diameter thread

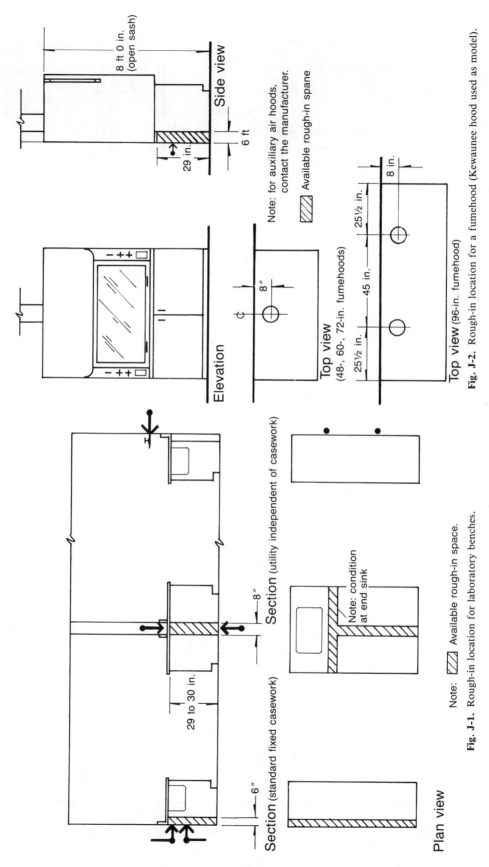

Side view

8 ft 0 in. (open sash)

29 in.

6 ft

Note: for auxiliary air hoods, contact the manufacturer.

▨ Available rough-in spane

Elevation

8″

Top view (48-, 60-, 72-in. fumehoods)

8 in.

25½ in.

45 in.

25½ in.

Top view (96-in. fumehood)

Fig. J-2. Rough-in location for a fumehood (Kewaunee hood used as model).

Section (utility independent of casework)

8″

Section (standard fixed casework)

29 to 30 in.

6″

Note: condition at end sink

Note: ▨ Available rough-in space.

Plan view

Fig. J-1. Rough-in location for laboratory benches.

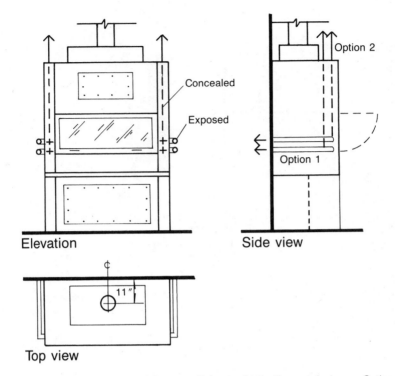

Elevation

Side view

Top view

Note: Option 1, exposed piping to wall, is standard with manufacturers. Option 2, concealed piping to ceiling, must be specified or shown on contract documents.

Fig. J-3. Rough-in location for a biological safety cabinet.

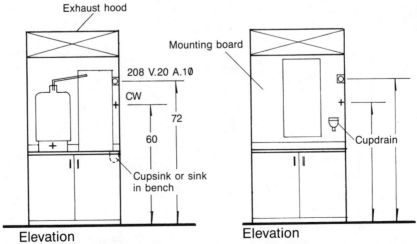

Elevation

Elevation

Fig. J-4. Rough-in location for Corning stills.

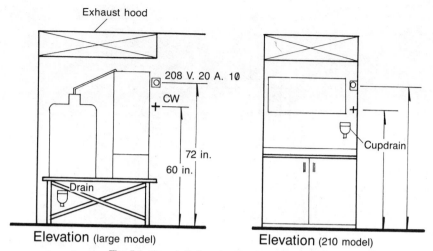

Fig. J-5. Rough-in location for Barnstead stills.

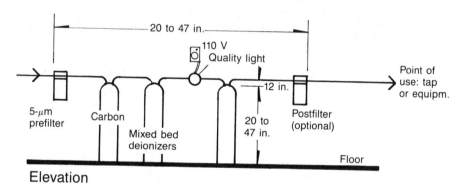

Fig. J-6. Rough-in location for service exchange deionization.

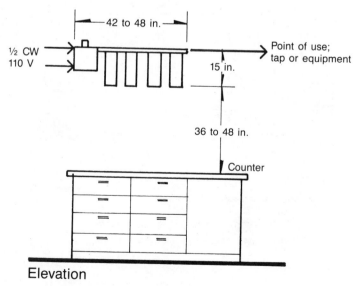

Fig. J-7. Rough-in location for deionized water cartridges.

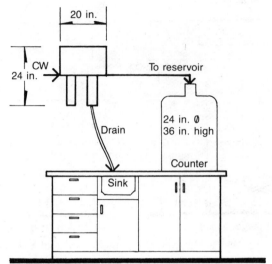

ELEVATION (small unit)
Note: there are many larger sizes; see manufacturers.

Fig. J-8. Rough-in location for a reverse osmosis unit.

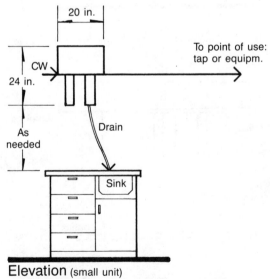

Elevation (small unit)
Note: there are many larger sizes; see manufacturers.

Fig. J-9. Rough-in location for an ultrafiltration unit.

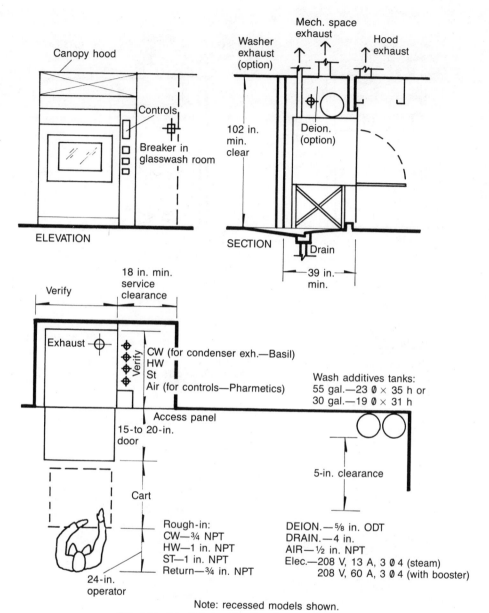

Note: recessed models shown.

Fig. J-10. Rough-in location for glassware washers.

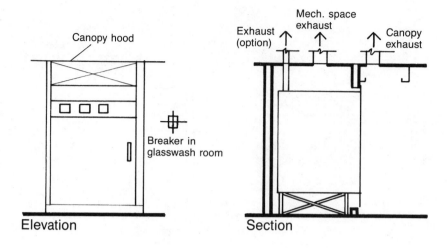

Elevation

Section

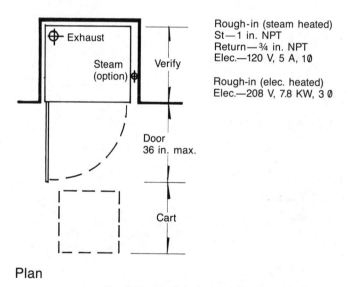

Plan

Rough-in (steam heated)
St—1 in. NPT
Return—¾ in. NPT
Elec.—120 V, 5 A, 1Ø

Rough-in (elec. heated)
Elec.—208 V, 7.8 KW, 3 Ø

Fig. J-11. Rough-in location for glassware dryer.

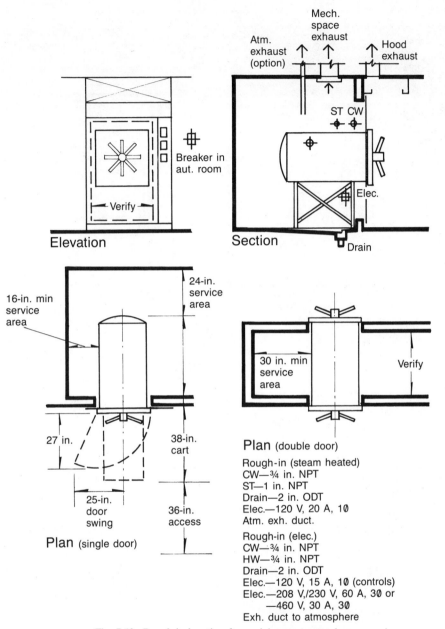

Fig. J-12. Rough-in location for an laboratory autoclave.

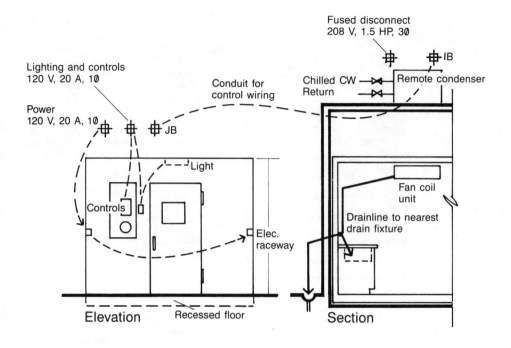

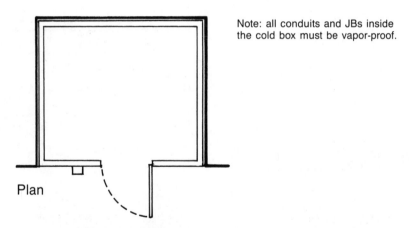

Note: all conduits and JBs inside the cold box must be vapor-proof.

Fig. J-13. Rough-in location for a controlled-environment room (4°C).

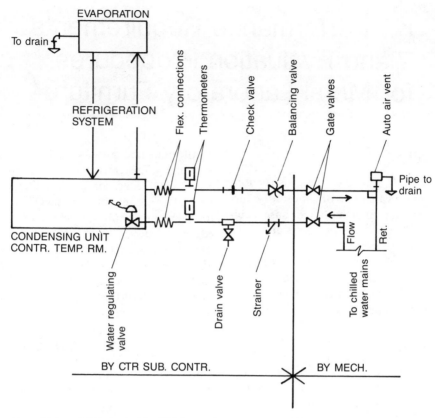

Note: Piping to fixtures inside CTR by mech.

Fig. J-14. Diagram for suggested mechanical connections to a condensing unit.

K. Performance Requirements and Evaluation Procedures for Metal Laboratory Furniture*

K.1 SCOPE

This standard is limited to the construction, function and evaluation of laboratory furniture including floor-mounted base cabinets, full-height storage cabinets, and wall-mounted storage cabinets.

Work surfaces, laboratory fume hoods, service fittings and similar related items of laboratory furniture and equipment are not covered in this standard.

K.2 PURPOSE

This standard sets forth basic criteria of design, function and evaluation for manufacturers, users, and evaluation agencies for metal laboratory furniture. Verification of performance and function can be easily accomplished using the conditions and procedures described in this standard. These tests were developed for typical sizes of laboratory furniture and these configurations are given in each section dealing with a type of cabinet.

K.3 DESIGN REQUIREMENTS

Cabinets shall be of a type specifically designed for installation and use in a laboratory. Cabinet materials, finish, construction details and hardware shall be suitable for use in a mildly corrosive atmosphere and shall be resistant to chemical spills and splashes common to a typical laboratory operation. Structural strength shall be adequate to support heavy laboratory apparatus, high-density shielding, or containers and heavy instruments.

---

*Most of this standard also applies to wood.

All joints and corners shall be well fitting eliminating unsightly openings or seams. All sheet metal edges or corners that may, in normal use, come into contact with laboratory personnel shall be free of burrs or sharp edges. All bends or returns of sheet metal, such as on drawers, shelves or doors, shall be free of fractures or rough edges. Cabinets shall be finished according to manufacturer's standard finishing procedures in manufacturer's standard color(s).

K.4 STATEMENT OF CAUTION

Under actual installed conditions, cabinets are usually attached to, and obtain support from, the building structure. Evaluation procedures set forth in this standard require that the cabinets, in some instances, be free standing. Observers are warned to take safety precautions to prevent injury or damage in case of product failure. Similarly, caution should be exercised in applying these tests to any other sizes or configurations of cabinets than those identified.

Some evaluation procedures involve weights of more than 2000 pounds. Observers are advised to verify floor loading capabilities before conducting test procedures.

K.5 BASE CABINETS

K.5.1 Dimensions

The base cabinet shall have nominal dimensions as follows: four feet wide, three feet high, one foot, ten inches deep.

K.5.2 Configuration

The cabinet shall be a combination of cupboard and drawer. The drawer shall be above the cupboard, full width and approximately one-fourth the height of the cabinet face opening. Cupboard shall be double-door design and contain one adjustable shelf. Cupboard back shall be removable.

K.5.3 Test Conditions

The cabinet shall be free standing, leveled and sitting one inch off the floor on all four leveling screws, a structurally strong top capable of supporting the load over the span of the cabinet shall be installed on cabinet.

5.4 Compliance to Design Requirements

A visual examination shall be conducted to verify compliance with applicable parts of Section K.3. Operate doors and drawers. Discontinue evaluation if unit is not in compliance or if malfunction is noted.

K.5.5 Cabinet Load Test

Performance Requirement

A cabinet leveled and free standing, with its top installed shall support a uniformly distributed load of 2000 pounds. (See Figure K-1 for test configuration.)

Procedure

Preload cabinet to 1000 pounds. Remove load, verify level, and check height from floor to underside of work top at all four corners. Add 2000 pound test load and check that door and drawer operation are not affected. Remove load and remeasure distance from floor to underside of table top.

Test Evaluation

Door and drawer operation shall be normal under condition of test load. The maximum change in distance from underside of top to floor with test load removed shall be 1/16 inch.

K.5.6 Cabinet Door Tests

Load Test

Performance requirement. An open door shall withstand a load of 200 pounds when applied at a point 12 inches from the hinge centerline without permanent distortion that will cause binding of the door or that will adversely affect operation of the door catch.

Procedure. With unit and top set up as described above, add sufficient weight to top

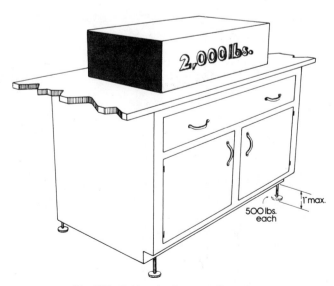

Fig. K-1. Cabinet load test configuration.

to prevent overturning. With cabinet door opened 90 degrees, hang a sling made up of two 100-pound weights (shot bags or solid weights) over top of the door at a point 12 inches out from the hinge centerline (see Figure K-2). Move door through a 160-degree arc recording pounds of force necessary to move door through the arc, when applied at a right angle to the door and at the door edge. Remove weight and swing door through a 180 degree arc and close door.

Test evaluation. Force required to move loaded door through arc shall not exceed 3 pounds. Operation of door after test shall be normal and there shall be no significant permanent distortion that will cause binding of the door or hinges or that will adversely affect operation of the catch.

Impact Test

Performance requirement. A closed door shall be able to withstand a 240 inch-pound impact and operate freely and show no buckling of panels or distortion that will adversely affect function of door.

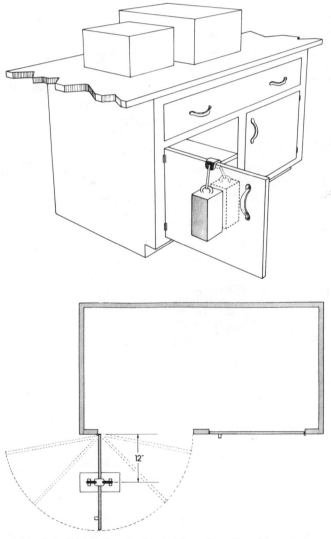

Fig. K-2. Cabinet door load test: (a) configuration; (b) conduct.

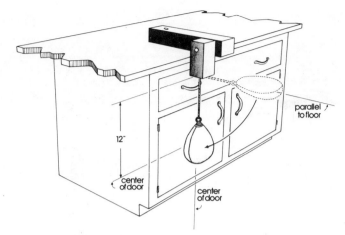

Fig. K-3. Cabinet door impact test configuration.

Test procedure. A 20-pound shot bag shall be suspended and dropped to provide an impact of 240 inch-pounds at the center of the closed door (see Figure K-3).

Test evaluation. After test, door and catch shall operate normally and show no buckling or distortion.

Life Cycle Test

Performance requirement. Door shall operate for 25,000 cycles without deterioration that will significantly affect function.

Test procedure. A cycling mechanism shall swing door 90 degrees and operate catch without adding abnormal loads. Force shall be applied at a right angle to panel surface to handle location when door is in the closed position. Test shall run for 25,000 cycles with speed not greater than 15 cycles per minute.

Test evaluation. After test, the door shall operate freely without binding and catch shall function normally.

K.5.7 Cabinet Drawer Tests

Static Load Test

Performance requirement. An unloaded drawer shall open to 13 inches of travel and

be able to support 150 pounds hung from the drawer head at center line of drawer for 5 minutes.

Test procedure. Open drawer to 13 inches of travel and hang 150 pounds from the drawer head at center line of drawer for 5 minutes (see Figure K-4).

Test evaluation. Close drawer and operate drawer through full cycle. Drawer shall operate normally and there shall be no significant distortion of drawer, drawer run, or cabinet-mounted drawer run channel.

Impact Test

Performance requirement. A drawer open to 13 inches of travel shall withstand an impact of 20 pounds dropped from a height of 12 inches without affecting the operation of the drawer.

Test procedure. Open drawer 13 inches. Drop a 20-pound shot bag weight from a height of 12 inches into the bottom of a drawer at the center of the width of the drawer and 6 inches back from the inside face of the drawer.

Test evaluation. Remove shot bag and operate drawer through full cycle. Drawer shall operate normally. Deformation of metal is

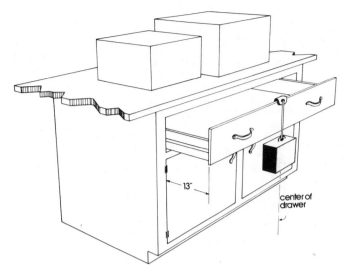

Fig. K-4. Cabinet drawer static load test configuration.

acceptable at impact point, but not to the extent that it will cause binding or otherwise interfere with the operation of the drawer.

Life Cycle Test

Performance requirements. Drawer shall operate with a load of 100 pounds for 10,000 cycles and after test shall operate freely without evidence of dragging or scraping. The force required to open and close loaded drawer shall not be more than a 20 percent increase of that required prior to test as measured at the 50 percent open position.

Test procedure. A load of 100 pounds shall be uniformly distributed in the drawer. Measure force required to open and close drawer. Measurement shall be made at the 50% open position. Operate from a closed position through 13 inches of travel for 10,000 cycles at a rate not to exceed 10 cycles per minute.

Test evaluation. After test, force required to move loaded drawer shall not be more than a 20% increase of that required prior to test as measured at the 50% open position. Drawer shall operate freely without evidence of dragging or scraping.

K.5.8 Cabinet Shelf Test

Performance Requirement

Adjustable shelf shall support a uniformly distributed load of 200 pounds. When load is removed, shelf shall show no significant permanent distortion.

Test Procedure

Shelf shall be installed using four shelf clips and adjusted to be centered vertically in cupboard. The shelf shall be loaded with 200 pounds uniformly distributed on shelf. The load shall be shot bags or weights weighing not more than 20 pounds each and not more than 10 inches in maximum dimension.

Test Evaluation

Remove load from shelf. No significant permanent deflection of the cabinet, the shelf, or its supports shall be noticeable after weights are removed.

K.5.9 Leveling Screw Test

Performance Requirement

Leveling device for floor-mounted cabinets shall be capable of adjustment after positioning of cabinet. Each leveling device shall withstand a load of 500 pounds.

Test Procedure

Cabinet shall be set on a floor of adequate strength and rigidity to support the cabinet on its four adjusting bolts without significant distortion or indentation of the floor surface. A structurally strong top capable of supporting the load over the span of the cabinet shall be installed on cabinet. Level the cabinet, then add 2000 pound test load. (See Figure K-1). Remove load and turn each leveling screw four 360 degree rotations. Re-level cabinet.

Test Evaluation

Each leveling device shall support a weight of 500 pounds without failure and be capable of adjustment after load is removed.

K.5.10 Drawer and Door Pull Test

Performance Requirement

Pulls shall withstand a direct pull of 50 pounds perpendicular to the front surface and withstand a vertically suspended load of 50 pounds with no permanent distortion.

Test Procedure

Verify that pulls are installed in accordance with manufacturer's practice using specified attaching hardware and method. Block door and drawer closed. Using a cable, pulley and weight assembly (see Figure K-5), apply a force of 50 pounds perpendicular to each pull. Revise setup to hang weight from each pull (see Figure K-6). Remove weight.

Test Evaluation

Pulls shall resist force and support weight without breakage. After completion of test and removal of weight no significant permanent distortion shall occur.

K.5.11 Body Surface Finish Tests

Chemical Resistance

Performance requirement. After exposure to selected reagents for one hour, the surface of the test area shall be washed and dried. Failure shall be any visible blistering, bare spots, roughness of surface or more than a slight discoloration.

Test procedure. A door shall be removed from the cabinet and laid flat and level on a horizontal surface. Chemical spot tests shall

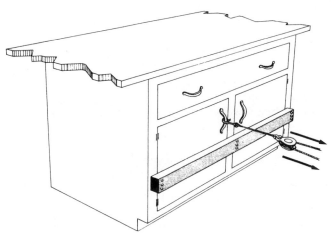

Fig. K-5. Cabinet drawer and door pull horizontal load test configuration.

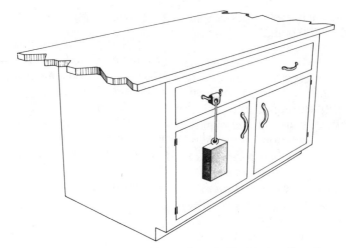

Fig. K-6. Cabinet drawer and door pull vertical load test configuration.

be made by applying 10 drops (approximately 0.5 cm^3) of each reagent listed in Table K-1 to the surface to be tested. Each reagent spot shall be open to the atmosphere. Ambient temperature shall be 68-72°F (20-22°C). After one hour, chemicals shall be flushed away with cold water and the surface washed with detergent and warm water at 150°F (65°C). Surface shall then be examined under 100 foot candles of illumination.

Test evaluation. A maximum of three failure classifications shall be acceptable.

Adhesion

Performance requirement. Ninety or more squares of the test sample shall remain coated after the scratch adhesion test.

Test procedure. Two sets of eleven parallel lines 1/16-inch apart shall be cut with a razor blade to intersect at right angles thus forming a grid of 100 squares. The cuts shall be made just deep enough to go through the coating, but not into the substrate. They shall then be brushed lightly with a soft brush. Examine under 100 foot candles of illumination.
Note: This test is based on ASTM D2197-68, "Standard Method of Test for Adhesion of Organic Coatings."

Test evaluation. Ninety of the squares shall show finish.

Hardness

Performance requirements. The test sample shall have a hardness of 4-H using the pencil hardness test.

Table K.1. Reagents for Surface Finish Chemical Resistance Test

Reagents	Concentrations by Weight
Acetic acid	98%
Formic acid	88%
Hydrochloric acid	37%
Nitric acid	25%
Nitric acid	60%
Phosphoric acid	75%
Sulfuric acid	25%
Sulfuric acid	85%
Ammonium hydroxide	28%
Sodium hydroxide	10%
Sodium hydroxide	26%
Acetone	
Carbon tetrachloride	
Ethyl acetate	
Ethyl alcohol	
Ethyl ether	
Formaldehyde	37%
Hydrogen peroxide	5%
Methylethyl ketone	
Phenol	85%
Xylene	

Test procedure. Pencils, regardless of their brand are valued in this way: 8-H is the hardest, and next in order of diminishing hardness are 7-H, 6-H, 5-H, 4-H, 3-H, 2-H, H, F, HB, B (soft), 2-B, 3-B, 4-B, 5-B (which is the softest).

The pencils shall be sharpened on emery paper to a wide sharp edge. (See Figure K-7) Pencils of increasing hardness shall be pushed across the paint film in a chisel-like manner until one is found that will cut or scratch the film. The pencil used before that one that is, the hardest pencil that will not rupture the film is then used to express or designate the hardness.

Test evaluation. The paint film shall have a hardness of 4-H minimum.

K.6 WALL CABINETS

K.6.1 Dimension

Evaluation shall be conducted on two cases, one with sliding doors and one with swinging doors with nominal dimensions as follows: four feet wide, two feet six inches high, and one foot deep.

K.6.2 Configuration

Cabinet may have either solid panel or framed glass in either type of door. Each cabinet shall contain two adjustable shelves

mounted in accordance with the manufacturer's specifications.

K.6.3 Test Conditions

Cabinets shall be mounted on a wall in the manner recommended by the manufacturer in his installation instruction. Cabinets shall be plumb and level and shelves shall be installed.

K.6.4 Compliance with Design Requirements

A visual examination shall be conducted to verify compliance with applicable parts of Section K.3. Operate doors. Discontinue evaluation if unit is not in compliance or if malfunction is noted.

K.6.5 Load Test

Performance Requirement

Cabinet shall support load and doors shall operate normally on a cabinet with 100 pounds on the cabinet bottom and 100 pounds on each shelf for a total of 300 pounds. When weights are removed, cabinet shall show no significant permanent deflection of cabinet, cabinet bottom, or shelves.

Test Procedure

Load cabinet bottom and each shelf with 100 pounds each uniformly distributed. Load

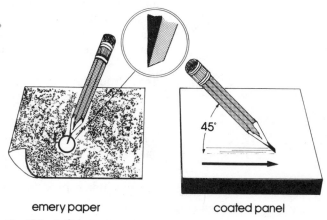

emery paper   coated panel

Fig. K-7. Cabinet body surface hardness test: (a) preparation of test pencil; (b) test conduct.

shall be shot bags or weights weighing not more than 20 pounds each and not more than 10 inches maximum dimension.

Caution: Place structural restraint under and at front corners, but not touching cabinet, to restrain it in case of failure.

Test Evaluation

With weights in place, operate doors through full travel to verify normal operation of doors. Remove weights and operate doors to verify normal operation. Verify that there is no significant permanent deflection of cabinet, cabinet back, cabinet bottom, or shelves.

K.6.6 Shelf Test

Performance Requirement

An adjustable shelf shall support a uniformly distributed load of 200 pounds. When load is removed, shelf shall show no significant permanent distortion.

Test Procedure

A shelf shall be mounted at approximately vertical center position in the cabinet supported by four shelf clips engaged in cabinet adjustment strip to represent a shelf as it would normally be installed in the cabinet. Load shelf to 200 pounds uniformly distributed on shelf. Load shall be shot bags or weights weighing not more than 20 pounds each and not more than 10 inches in maximum dimension.

Test Evaluation

Remove load from shelf. No significant permanent distortion of the cabinet, the shelf or its supports shall be noted.

K.7 TALL STORAGE CABINETS

K.7.1 Dimensions

Evaluation shall be conducted on two cases one with sliding doors and one with swinging doors with nominal dimensions as follows:

four feet wide, seven feet high and one foot ten inches deep.

K.7.2 Configuration

Cabinets may have solid panel or framed glass in either type of door. Each cabinet shall have five adjustable shelves.

K.7.3 Test Conditions

Cabinets shall be free-standing and level. If adjustment bolts are furnished, they shall be used for leveling cabinets. Normal installation of tall storage cabinets requires attachment of cabinet to a supporting structure. For purposes of this test, unit shall be free-standing, plumb and level and shelves shall be installed.

K.7.4 Compliance with Design Requirements

A visual examination shall be conducted to verify compliance with applicable parts of Section K.3. Operate doors. Discontinue evaluation if unit is not in compliance or if malfunction is noted.

K.7.5 Load Test

Performance Requirement

Cabinet shall support load, and cabinet doors shall operate normally on a cabinet with all five adjustable shelves installed and with 100 pounds weight on cabinet bottom and each shelf for a total load of 600 pounds. When weights are removed, cabinet shall have no significant permanent deflection of cabinet, cabinet bottom or shelves.

Test Procedure

Adjustable shelves shall be located with approximately equal spacing between shelves and between shelves and top and bottom of cabinet.

Caution: Locate bracing around cabinet, but not touching cabinet in case cabinet buckles or tilts.

Load cabinet bottom and each shelf with 100

pounds each uniformly distributed. Load shall be shot bags or weights weighing not more than 20 pounds each and not more than 10 inches maximum dimension.

Test Evaluation

Cabinet shall support load. Operate doors through full travel to verify normal operation under conditions of load. Remove weights and operate doors to verify normal operation. Verify that there is no significant permanent distortion of cabinet, cabinet bottom or shelves.

K.7.6 Shelf Test

Performance Requirement

Adjustable shelf shall support an evenly distributed load of 200 pounds. When load is removed, shelf shall show no significant permanent distortion.

Test Procedure

Select a shelf located approximately at the vertical center of the cabinet. Load shelf with 200 pounds, uniformly distributed. Load shall be shot bags or weights weighing not more than 20 pounds each and not more than 10 inches maximum dimension.

Test Evaluation

Remove load from shelf. No significant permanent distortion of the cabinet, the shelf or its supports shall be noted.

L. Common U.S. to Metric Conversions

Measure		Equivalent	Comments
Length			
1 inch	equals	2.54 centimeters	Multiply dimensions (inches) in this handbook by 2.54 to arrive at centimeters.
1 foot	equals	30.48 centimeters	Multiply dimensions (feet) in this handbook by 30.48 to arrive at centimeters, divide by 100 to arrive at meters conversely:
			1 meter equals 100 centimeters or 39.37 inches or 2.38 feet
1 mile	equals	1.609 kilometers	
Area			
1 square foot	equals	144 square inches 929.03 square centimeters 0.0929 square meters	
1 square yard	equals	0.836 square meters	
Volume			
1 cubic foot	equals	0.0283 cubic meters	
1 cubic yard	equals	0.7646 cubic meters	
1 gallon (US)	equals	3.785 liters	
Speed			
100 feet per minute equals 30 meters per minute			See fumehood face relocation
1 mile per hour equals 1.6 kilometers per hour			
Weight			
1 pound	equals	0.454 kilograms	1 kg equals 2.2046 lb
Energy			
1 kilowatt	equals	3042 Btu/hr	
1 kilowatt	equals	1.35 HP	
1 ton (refig)	equals	12,000 Btu/hr	
Pressures			
1 pound/sq. in.	equals	2.036 in of mercury equals .06804 atmospheres	
1 atmosphere	equals	14.696 lbs/sq. in., 29.92 in of mercury	
Temperature			
degree F	equals	1.8 (degree C plus 17.8)	Freezing is 32 degree F, Boiling is 212 degree F
degree C	equals	0.55 (degree F minus 32)	Freezing is 0 degree C, Boiling is 100 degree C

Glossary

Acid-Resistant Plastic Laminates: Special-grade laminates resistant to chemicals, particularly acids. Developed primarily for laboratory bench tops.

Acid Waste: Drainline from laboratory fixtures where acids may be disposed of as opposed to sanitary waste from toilet room fixtures and storm drains for rainwater.

Aerosol Photometer: Used for identifying leaks in HEPA filters in a biological safety cabinet.

Air Intake: The location where the outside air enters the HVAC system to be conditioned before distribution to the various spaces.

Amenities: In this handbook, spaces for gatherings, lunch, relaxation and breaks. Sometimes refered to as "break rooms." See Section 3.4.

Amps: The value in which current flow in a conductor is measured.

Analysis Lab, (Analytical Chemistry Lab): Laboratory designed and equipped for analytical procedures. See Sections 1.1 and 1.2.

Applied Science Lab: Laboratory designed and equipped to transfer basic research findings into useful commercial applications. See Section 1.1.

Architect: A professional trained and licensed to plan and design buildings.

Architectural Finishes: *See* finishes.

Autoclaves: Pressure, vessel that uses saturated steam at elevated pressures to kill microorganisms.

Backflow Preventer: Installed to protect the water source from contamination by laboratory operations.

Balance Room: Activity center designed and equipped for weighing.

Basic Science Lab: Laboratory designed and equipped for basic research. See Section 1.1.

Bench Space: Space typically occupied by benches or other laboratory equipment. *See also* Equivalent linear feet.

Biological Safety Cabinets (BSCs or Biosafety Cabinets): Various hoods or cabinets designed and manufactured (1) to protect personnel from harmful agents inside the cabinet; (2) to protect the work, product,

experiment, or procedure performed inside the cabinet from contaminants in the laboratory environment; (3) to protect the environment from contaminants contained in the cabinet; (4) all of the above.

Building Envelope: The weathertight perimeter or enclosed space of the building.

Building Footprint: The exact size, shape and location of the building's foundation on the site.

Building Owner: The agency, corporation or other legal entity that holds title to the building.

Bus Duct: A metal enclosed system consisting of copper or aluminum bus bars for distribution of large amounts of power between distribution panels or substations.

Cable Tray: A system used for an organized distribution of power or data/voice cables. Generally consisting of an open ladder type, enclosed type and made of steel or aluminum.

Capacitance Detector: Security perimeter protection. Puts an electric charge on a metal object which acts as an antenna. A capacitance coupling is formed between the antenna and an electrical ground. A person who gets too close to the object changes the capacitance, sounding an alarm.

Capital Costs: The owner's site acquisition costs, leasing and occupancy costs, and interim financing costs. Costs relating to or dealing with bankers, lawyers and realtors.

Capture Velocity: The air velocity at any point in front of the hood or at the hood opening necessary to overcome opposing air currents and to capture the contaminated air at that point by causing it to flow into the hood.

Carcinogenic: Cancer causing.

Casework Elevation: Front view of casework in a vertical plane.

Ceiling Grid: The pattern of a suspended ceiling support system.

Ceiling Plenum: The space between a suspended ceiling and the floor or roof above.

Change Orders: Orders to change parts of the construction documents after the owner/contractor agreement is signed, which will result in additional expenses.

Chiller: A device that produces chilled water with a refrigeration system.

Chromatography (Gas and Paper): Techniques to separate mixtures of substances.

Chromatograph: Equipment used in chromatography.

Churn Rate: Rate of facility change.

Clean Power: Power which has been conditioned through an isolation transformer, power conditioner, uninterrupted power supply. Any system that "removes" electronic spikes surges, sags, dips from the normal utility supplied power.

Clean Room: A space designed and equipped to meet the requirements of the various classifications established. See Appendix E.

Clean Room Lab: A laboratory designed and equipped to minimize contaminants from external and internal sources. Examples are tissue culture and media preparation laboratories.

Cogeneration (Cogen): The simultaneous generation of electricity and useful thermal energy from the same fuel input.

Combustible Liquid: A liquid having a flash point at or above 100°F (37.8°C).

Common Path of Travel: The portion of an exit access that must be traversed before two separate and distinct paths of travel to two exits are available.

Conduit: A metal or nonmetallic pipe specifically labelled for use in electrical systems. Can be EMT—electrometallic tubing, IMC—intermediate metallic conduit, RGS—rigid galvanized steel, PVC—poly vinly chloride (for use in outside installations only)

Constant Air Volume (CAV): Temperature control for a constant volume of air and a variable air temperature.

Contact Hour: *See* Weekly student hour.

Containment: A facility or space designed to contain or prevent hazardous substances from getting out.

Contract Document: Document prepared by the design team to enable the contractor to price and build a facility. Contract documents typically include drawings, specifications and a schedule.

Contractor: An individual or organization which contracts to construct a facility based on contract documents.

Convertibility: Accommodation of changing functions or activities by reassembling interchangeable subcomponents into new spatial configurations, new functional assemblies, or both. See Section 3.2.

Cost at Bid: The proposed price for which a general contractor will build the project, based on the construction documents. Includes the general contractor's and subcontractor's direct labor and material costs, plus all applicable markups. See Section 8.2.

Critical Path Method (CPM): A method used to establish which activities come before others in the construction process in order to find the fastest scheduling for the project. See Section 2.5.2.

Cryogenic Container: A container used for cryogenic materials.

Cryogenics: Substances causing low temperatures.

Cupsink: A drain recepticle either on the work surface or mounted on the wall.

Cut Set: A combination of events which can lead to the top event in fault tree analysis. See Section 2.9.

Cytogenetics: A branch of genetics concerned with cells in heredity, i.e., chromosomes.

Data Cable: Any type of cable used to transmit data between two points or systems. Can be either copper or fiberoptic type.

Deionized (Demineralized) Water: Water from which ions or minerals have been removed.

Departmental Gross Square Feet (DGSF): Net assignable square feet plus surrounding and internal walls and partitions, plus internal circulation space but not the public corridors serving the laboratory and other functions. Used primarily for clinical lab space guidelines. See Section 2.6.

Design Development: The phase in the process of planning and designing a facility which documents the final criteria from which the contract documents are prepared.

Dry Bench Work (Dry Lab): Electronics labs, balance rooms, and the like that require power but not other utilities. See Section 2.6.

Egress: A continuous and unobstructed way of exit travel from any point in a building or structure to a public way, consisting of three separate and distinct parts: (1) the exit access, (2) the exit, and (3) the exit discharge. A means of egress comprises vertical and horizontal travel and includes intervening rooms, spaces, doorways, hallways, corridors, passageways, balconies, ramps, stairs, enclosures, lobbies, escalators, horizontal exits, courts, and yards. See Section 7.6.

Electric Raceway: See Conduit.

Electronic Infrastructure: Consists of voice communication systems, data communications systems, monitoring systems, control systems and cable plant(s) required to support the above systems. See Section 5.5.

Environmental Impact Assessment (EIA): An assessment required by many agencies to analyze and document the impact of various elements as the result of a new building or a new occupancy. See Section 2.10.

Equipment Management System: A management system in which each piece of equipment is tracked for ownership, location, age, condition, initial cost, replacement cost, utilization and research program.

Equipment: Standard lab equipment such as lab benches and fumehoods. Research equipment performs a specific task, such as centrifuges, balances, counters, refrigerators, freezers and incubators. Shared equipment, because of its size or cost, is shared and separate from the labs in a central location, such as cyclotrons, electron microscopes and magnetic resonance imagers. Equipment used to scale up research, such as pilot plants, experimental surgeries and decompression chambers. Research equipment that requires a special environment, such as vibration resistance, temperature and humidity control. Special controlled-environment equipment, such as cold rooms, hot rooms, freezers, growth chambers and sound chambers. (These are prefabricated purchased rooms which are considered equipment and require space.) Hazardous or clean standard equipment, such as benches and special hoods in radioisotope and biohazardous containment facilities and clean rooms. Equipment that supports the research effort, such as machine and electronics shops used to produce one-of-a-kind instrumentation, central glasswash and media preparation equipment (includes washers, dryers, sinks, autoclaves, and sterilizers). See Section 2.6.

Equivalent Linear Feet (ELF): Arrived at by measuring the length of benches, sinks, fumehoods, storage, and floor-standing equipment for use in calculating net assignable square feet. See Section 2.6.

Ergometric Dimensions: The dimensions of the human environment based on average human dimensions.

Estimate: A price that anticipates building costs. Four types of estimates are facility, space, systems and detailed estimates. See Section 8.1.

Event Tree Analysis: A graphic representation of the possible sequence of events that might occur following an accident initiation event. See Section 2.9.

Exit: That portion of a means of egress that is separated from all other spaces of the building and provides a protected way of travel to the exit discharge.

Exit Access: That portion of a means of egress that leads to an entrance to an exit.

Exit Discharge: That portion of a means of egress between the termination of an exit and a public way.

Eyewash Fountain: A device to rinse the eyes (and face) in case of a chemical spill. See Section 4.8.

Failure Modes and Effects Analysis (FMEA): Technique used by reliability engineers and product designers to systematically identify and tabulate the ramifications of various component failures in a system, product or process. See Section 2.9.

Failure Modes, Effects, and Criticality Analysis. (FMECA): Extended FMEA with criticality considerations included. See Section 2.9.

Fan Room: Houses the air-handling equipment of the air conditioning system.

Fault Tree Analysis (FTA): A graphic representation of an accident or hazard being caused by combinations of specific equipment failures, human errors and environmental events. See Section 2.9.

FIC: Furnished and installed by the contractor.

Filtration: 5.3.2.2. Process of removing a contaminant.

Finishes: The surface treatment and coatings for floors, walls and ceilings. See Section 3.7.

Fixed Equipment: Equipment fixed to the building structure with piping, conduit or ducts.

Flammable Liquid: A liquid having a flash point below 100°F (37.8°C) and a vapor pressure not exceeding 40 psia. See Section 4.9.

Flexibility: The ability to change in the future. Various types of flexibility are versatility, rearrangeability, convertibility and adaptability. See Section 3.2.

Flow Cytometry: Apparatus to measure the flow of blood cells.

Flow Diagram: A diagram depicting the flow of materials or work used to organize space most efficiently.

Foot-Candles: A measure of illumination.

Footprint (of a building): See Building footprint.

Full-Time Equivalent (FTE): Data measuring a full academic load for a student (typically 15 credit hours per semester) or a full-time worker in staff analysis used to arrive at occupancy ratios and square feet. See Section 2.6.

Fumehood: Safety device used to contain effluents generated by the work performed inside the hood, with or without the operator's presence. Chemical fumehoods include the standard balanced bypass air hood, radioisotope hood, perchloric acid hood, walk-in hood, distillation hood and auxiliary air hood. Nonchemical fumehoods include the canopy hood, conventional hood, california hood, laminar flow cabinet, biological safety cabinet, glove box and local exhaust. See glossary in Section 4.4.

Funnel Drain: Drain which includes a funnel to direct the liquid waste.

Gamma Counter: Analytical instrument to measure gamma radiation.

Ganged Exhaust System: Linkage of several biological safety cabinets to the same exhaust system.

Germicidal Lamp: Ultraviolet light to kill microorganisms.

Gross Square Feet (GSF or Gross Area): The sum of the floor areas included within the outside faces of exterior walls for all stories or areas which have floor surfaces. See Section 8.6 for exceptions.

Grounding: A conductor used to connect equipment to

a common point within a building. All circuits within a facility shall have a common ground potential.

Hard Space: Laboratories and support spaces. *See* Soft space and Section 2.6.

Heat Exchanger: A device which exchanges heat between two different streams.

Heat Pump: A device which transfers heat energy between two different sources.

Heat Wheel: Cylindrical rotating heat transfer device that transfers energy between two air streams.

Hematology: Branch of medicine concerned with the study of blood.

HEPA (High-Efficiency Particulate Air) Filter: Present in all classes of biological safety cabinets. A device which removes particulates, including microorganisms, from the air.

Histology: Branch of anatomy dealing with the functions and structures of minute particles.

Histopathology: Branch of anatomy dealing with diseased tissues.

Hot Lab: A term generally used to describe laboratories designed to handle radioactive materials. See Appendix C.

Humidity, Relative: The ratio of the actual partial pressure of the water vapor in a space to the saturation pressure of pure water at the same temperature.

HVAC System: Heating, ventilation, air conditioning and cooling.

Inch of Water: A unit of pressure equal to the pressure exerted by a column of liquid water 1 in. high at a standard temperature.

Image: In architectural terms, the response one intends to elicit from the user and/or occupant of a building.

Immunohematology: Branch of hematology concerned with immune systems and blood disorders.

Immunology: Branch of biomedical science concerned with the immune system.

In Vitro: Within the glass or observed in a test tube.

In Vivo: Within the living body.

Laboratory: A generic term denoting a building, space or operation.

Laboratory Building: A structure consisting wholly or principally of one or more laboratory units.

Laboratory Casework: Laboratory furniture consisting of fumehoods and benches. Includes cabinets, tops, shelving, sinks and service fixtures. See Section 4.2.

Laboratory Planner: An individual who specializes in planning laboratories. This person may or may not be an architect.

Laboratory Unit: An enclosed space classified as A, B, or C (high, medium, or low hazard) based on the limitations established in NFPA No. 45, Tables 2.2 and 3.1. The space within a laboratory unit may include a number of work areas, offices and support spaces used by the laboratory personnel in a laboratory unit. Laboratory unit separations consist of walls, floors and ceilings, including protected openings such as doors and ducts between and adjacent laboratory units. See Section 7.3.

Laboratory Work Area: A room or space for testing, analysis, research, instruction or similar activities that involve the use of chemicals. This work area may or may not be enclosed.

Laminar Flow Hood or Cabinet: A hood in which the air flow is unidirectional. *See* biological safety cabinets.

Laser Table: A vibration-resistant platform designed to stabilize the laser beam and optical devices.

Life Cycle: Expected life span of a building and its components.

Life Cycle Costs (LCC): Continuing costs associated with a building, including operating (heating, cooling), maintaining (janitorial services, repairing, repainting), security services, repairing and replacing. See Section 8.4.

Lighting Layout: The physical location of a light fixture to produce the most desired effect or least amount of shadows.

Liquid Scintillation Counter: Analytical instrument which provides increased sensitivity to β radiation by emersing the radioactive sample in a liquid scintillation medium.

Live Load Allowance: The load that may be added to the building structure after the building is built, consisting of laboratory casework, equipment and people.

Lot Coverage: The area of a building lot covered by buildings, roads and parking areas.

Magnetic Resonance Imaging (MRI): Using a combination of radio frequency (RF) and a strong magnetic field to develop high-resolution images of the structure and function of a biological organism. See Section 1.4.

Makeup Air: The air necessary to make up the air exhausted from a space.

Manometer (or Microprocessor Controlled Micromanometer): Device for sensing the presence/absence of air. Used in fumehoods and biological safety cabinets.

Markups: Also called "add-ons." The amounts of money added above and beyond direct labor, material and equipment costs or raw costs. There are five basic markup categories: general conditions, taxes and insurance, permits, overhead and profit, escalation and contingencies. See Section 8.2.

Mass Airflow Monitor: Device for sensing the volume of exhaust air in fumehoods and biological safety cabinets.

Mass Spectrophotometry: A method of identifying molecular structures and compounds by transillumination with laser light and detecting the spectrum associated with the mass-charge ratios. The devices are capable of measuring parts per million and in some applications can be operated in real time. See Section 1.4.

Means of Egress: *See* Egress.

Microbial: Caused by or pertaining to microbes.

Micro-Machines: Ultrasmall silicone compound devices that convert electricity, sound or electrostatic charges into physical motion. These devices are on the order of 60–120 μm in size. See Section 1.4.

Microtome: Instrument which slices thin sections of tissue to be viewed under a microscope.

Millwork: Cabinets built locally in a millwork shop to suit a particular need, as opposed to casework which is built in a plant.

Minimal Cut Set: A collection of basic events that must occur simultaneously for the top event to occur in a fault tree analysis. See Section 2.9.

Mobile: Placing movable elements on wheels.

Model (Paper or Block): A two- or three-dimensional representation of a building to scale.

Modular Systems: Systems made up of components that are dimensionally related.

Module: A three-dimensional (repeated) planning unit composed of a specific floor space in a direct proportional relationship with other building system elements. See Section 3.1.

Mycology: Branch of science studying fungi.

Net Assignable Square Feet (NASF or Net Assignable Area): The areas of a building assigned to, or available for assignment to an occupant, including every type of space functionally usable by an occupant. For exceptions, see Section 8.6.

Observation: Systematic viewing coupled with a consideration of the seen phenomena.

Oncogenic: Tumor causing.

Optical Table: A table designed to provide a stable base for optical instruments.

Owner's Representative: An individual legally representing a building owner, which may be a corporation, agency or partnership.

Pan Joist System: A structural floor system in which metal pans are used to form the joists.

Pathogenic: Disease causing.

Petcock: Laboratory service fixture.

Photomicrography: The process of photographing through a light microscope.

Physical Chemistry Lab: A laboratory designed and equipped to perform physical chemistry. See Section 1.2.

Pitot Tube: Device for sensing the velocity or volume of airflow.

Plaster Trap: Device to catch solids to prevent them from going down the drain.

Plenum: That part of an air distribution system which allows the air velocity to be reduced.

Portability: The ability of prefinished assemblies to be grouped and regrouped into functional ensembles. See Section 3.2.

Positron Emission Tomography (PET): An imagining methodology for determining in vivo cross-sectional images of positron-emitting isotopes that demonstrate biological function, physiology or pathology. See Section 1.4.

Power Factor: A function of the amount of reactive power required to offset the lack of efficiency in transmitting the real power required in a motor from the serving utility company.

Preliminary Hazard Analysis (PHA): A simple tabulation of potential hazards, their causes and effects, and possible preventive or corrective measures. See Section 2.9.

Prequalification Samples: Samples submitted before bidding in order to prequalify bidding contractors. See Section 4.1.

Primary Space: Rooms used for primary teaching or research space. In this context, the laboratory as opposed to secondary or service space.

Principal Investigator: Individual who is the primary space generator, such as a faculty member or funded researcher.

Program of Requirements (POR): The document which spells out the goals, facts, concepts and needs of a building project. See Section 2.3.

Project Costs: The costs associated with the project's design, construction and furnishings, excluding capital costs. See Section 8.3.

Rabbetted Joint: A joint made by matching the edge and groove, designed to increase the surface of the glued joint.

Radiation: Energy transmitted by waves through space, such as alpha, beta and gamma waves and X-rays.

Radioisotope Lab: Laboratory designed and equipped for work with radioisotopes. See Appendix C.

Radionuclide: Radioactive types of atoms that exist for a measurable length of time.

Reagent Water: Treated water suitable for use in chemical analysis.

Rearrangeability: The ability to rearrange equipment or furnishings such as tables, benches, hoods, carts, walls or light fixtures within a given room or space because they are modular. See Section 3.2.

Reliability: To secure consistent results by different means.

Risk Assessment: The technique to establish the value of the possible effects and consequences of an event. See Section 2.9.

Risk Logic Tree: A graphic representation of the possible events as the result of a breach of security. See Section 3.10.

Safety: Ways to eliminate or minimize the risk of harm to individuals in the laboratory due to fire or chemical and biological hazards. See Section 3.5.

Sail Switch: Device for sensing the presence/absence of exhaust air in a biological safety cabinet.

Scales: Differentiation scale: $A = B$ or $A \neq B$ in order to distinguish between comparable situations with measuring quantities. Quantitative scale: $A \geq B$ or $A \leq B$. See Section 2.5.

Scanning Ion-Conductance Microscope (SICM): Utilizes a micropipette filled with a conducting electrolytic fluid to scan the surface structure of biological material. The variations in conductance are reconstructed to provide a map or image of the surface. See Section 1.4.

Scanning Tunneling Microscope (STM): Relies on the detection of electrons that have "tunneled" through the sample material. See Section 1.4.

Schematic Design: The phase in the process of planning and designing a facility which establishes the scope of the project: a schematic floor plan, sections and outline specifications.

Security: Planning to prevent the loss of life and/or property due to fire, theft or crime.

Seismic Bracing: Bracing to prevent the collapse of a structure or the moving of building elements due to earthquakes.

Serology: Branch of biomedical science dealing with the measurement of antibodies in serum.

Service Space (see Primary space): The space occupied by equipment or activities supporting the primary activity. Often located adjacent to the primary space. Examples are cold rooms, balance rooms and darkrooms. See Section 2.6.

Setbacks: The distances a building is set back from the property lines as required by local zoning codes.

Shielding: The construction designed to prevent rays or signals from entering or leaving a space.

Site Constraints: The constraints imposed on a building site due to topography, soil conditions, adjacent properties and local zoning and building codes.

Site: The organization's facilities, both external and internal, including laboratories representative of the project.

Soft Space: Includes faculty offices, secretary/receptionist offices, library/conference room, document-copying area, storage, and spaces without extensive utilities. See Hard space and Section 2.6.

Sound Rated Ballast: Ballast is a device used in fluorescent or high intensity discharge (HID) type fixtures. Sound rated being used for quietness or listed in decibels.

Specific Resistance (ohm-centimeter units): Basis for comparing water purity. See Section 5.3.

Spectrometry (Mass and Optical): The determination of the spectrum image produced.

Spectrophotometer: Apparatus which identifies matter based on the color spectrum shown.

Static Pressure (in Exhaust Systems): Differences between total pressure and velocity measure in an air distribution system.

Sterilizer: Device using saturated steam or heated air to kill microorganisms. See Section 4.6.

Structural Bay: The structural system between columns.

Structure: The system that holds up the building, consisting of columns, beams and floor slabs.

Sump: Individual acid neutralizing device which neutralizes acid waste before disposing in the sewage collection system.

Superconductivity: Traditional materials used as electrical conductors pose some resistance to electron flow and thus are inefficient. While superconductivity has been known for some time it was only possible at extremely low temperatures. Recent discoveries have led to superconductivity at ambient temperatures, which is defined as a state in which pairs of electrons moving in opposite directions form "cooper" pairs that condense into a cooperative electronic state. See Section 1.4.

Support Space (see Service space): The space occupied by equipment or activities which indirectly support teaching or research and are usually shared by several faculty members or researchers, such as greenhouses, animal quarters, centralized stockrooms, shops and storage areas.

Switchgear: Electrical equipment used for distribution of electric power. Usually associated with site distribution voltages over 600 volts.

Tensile Strength: The resistance to a pull force.

Terminal Throw Velocity: Velocity at which the air from a diffuser impinges on an object or surface.

Thermoanemometer: Device for sensing the velocity or volume of airflow in biological safety cabinet. Also called a "thermal anemometer." See Section 4.3.

Thermocouple: Device to measure the difference in temperature between two objects.

Thimble Connection: Type of connection in an exhaust system used so that unexpected changes in the system's exhaust air volume will have minimal effects on the exhaust air volume of the biological safety cabinet. See Section 4.3.

Threshold Limit Values (TLV): The values for airborne toxic materials which are to be used as guides in the control of health hazards and represent the time-weighted concentrations to which nearly all workers may be exposed for 8 hours/day over extended periods of time without adverse effects.

Toxic: Poisonous.

Transformer: An electrical device which changes the voltage from one value to another, the later being the end use voltage or secondary voltage.

Transgenic Animals: Animals created with genes from nonparent animals. See Section 1.4.

Unit: Used interchangeable with "research laboratory unit" or "academic teaching unit."

Vacuum Rack: Apparatus used to create a vacuum.

Validity: The degree to which any plan or layout succeeds in doing what it is intended to do. Includes consensual validity and predictive validity. See Section 1.3.

Valves (Ball, Globe or Gate Type): Device to control the flow in a piping system.

Variable Air Volume (VAV) Building: Method of space temperature control that uses a varying air volume with a constant air temperature.

Venipuncture: Puncture of the vein.

Versatility: The ability of the environment to accommodate different functions without physical change. See Section 3.2.

Vibration Isolation Pneumatic Air Table: A table designed to isolate equipment from vibration with air suspension.

Virology: Branch of microbiology concerned with viruses.

Vivarium: Research animal facility.

Voltage Drops, Spikes, Interruptions: Types of electrical interference.

Weekly Room Hours: The number of scheduled hours per week that laboratory sections use a laboratory. Sometimes called "room utilization" or "room contact hours."

Weekly Student Hours (WSH): The enrollment in each laboratory section multiplied by the number of hours per week that section meets (e.g., a lab with 20 students meets for 3 room hours per week. That produces 60 weekly student hours). Utilized as the multiplier for square footage guidelines to determine the amount of space needed for a certain amount of instructional activity. Sometimes called "student contact hours," "weekly student contact hours (WSCH)," or "student-station periods occupied." See Section 2.6.

Wet Laboratory: Chemistry labs and similar facilities that require water and drains.

Working Drawings: One of the components of a set of contract documents. *See* Contract documents.

Wrist Sink Control: A valve on hot and cold water fixtures which can be turned on and off with the wrist.

Zoning Restrictions: Constraints imposed on building sites by local zoning codes.

Bibliography

Note: References are given at the end of sections pertaining to that subject. This bibliography is much more extensive and organized by subject matter as noted. Previous listings may not be repeated here.

General Laboratory Planning

Diberardius L. J. et al, 1987. *Guidelines for Laboratory Design: Health and Safety Considerations.* New York Wiley.

Goldberg, Alfred, and Fluer, Larry, 1986. *H. G. Design Guide to the Uniform Codes for High-Tech Facilities.* Mill Valley, CA: GRDA Publications.

Helpern, David Paul, 1987. *The State of College and University Facilities.* Society for College and University Planning. Ann Arbor, MI.

National Fire Protection Association, 1987. Standard on Fire Protection for Laboratories Using Chemicals No. 45. Quincy, Mass: NFPA.

Ruys, T., 1969. 37 Keys to Laboratory Design. *Research/Development,* Vol. 20 #12 p. 18–25.

Ruys, T., 1970. Flexibility in Laboratory Design. *Lab Manager,* April pp. 22–23, May pp. 24–27, June pp. 28–29, July pp. 20–24, September pp. 20–23.

U.S. Department of Health, Education and Welfare, 1985. *Guide for the Care and Use of Laboratory Animals.* Public Health Service, National Institute of Health. NIH Publication No. 85–23. Government Printing Office, Washington DC.

Ruys, T., 1973. A Multipurpose Multidisciplinary Teaching Laboratory. *American Institute of Architects Journal,* p. 46.

Space Standards

College of American Pathologists, 1985. *Medical Laboratory Planning and Design.* Skokie, IL.

Colorado Commission on Higher Education, 1980. *Policy Manual,* Denver: pp. III-F.7 to III-F.13.

Health and Welfare Canada, 1980. *Evaluation and Space Programming Methodology Series No. 16, Laboratory.* CHI Systems. Ann Arbor, MI.

Time and Territory, 1986. *A Preliminary Exploration of Space and Utilization Guidelines in Engineering and the Natural Sciences.* California Postsecondary Education Commission Report 82-2. Sacramento, Ca.

Laboratory Planning Techniques and Tools

Pena, William, 1987. *Problem Seeking.* Washington, DC: American Institute of Architects Press.

Selltiz, C., Jahoda, M., Deutsch, M. and Cooke, S. W., 1959. *Research Methods in Social Relations.* New York: Dryden Press.

Laboratory Waste

American Chemical Society, 1985. *Less Is Better: Laboratory Chemical Management for Waste Reduction.* Washington, DC: Department of Governmental Relations and Science Policy.

Hopcroft, Francis J.; Vitale, David L.; Anglehart, Donald L. 1989. *Hazardous Materials and Hazardous Waste. A Construction Reference Manual.* R. S. Means Company, Inc.

Laboratory Safety

American Industrial Hygiene Association, 1985. *Biohazards Reference Manual.* Akron, OH: Biohazards Committee.

National Research Council, 1981. *Prudent Practices for Handling Chemicals in Laboratories.* Washington, DC: National Academy Press.

National Research Council, 1983. *Prudent Practices for Disposal of Chemicals from Laboratories.* Washington, DC: National Academy Press.

Pipitone, D. A., 1984. *Safe Storage of Laboratory Chemicals.* New York: Wiley.

U.S. Department of Health and Human Services, 1981. *NIH Guidelines for the Laboratory Use of Chemical Carcinogens.* NIH Publication No. 81-2385. Bethesda, MD: Public Health Service.

U.S. Department of Health and Human Services, 1984. *Biosafety in Microbiological and Biomedical Laboratories.* Bethesda, MD: Public Health Service, Centers for Disease Control.

Fumehoods

American Conference of Governmental Industrial Hygienists, 1984. *Industrial Ventilation,* 18th ed. Cincinnati: Committee on Industrial Ventilation.

ASHRAE, 1985. Method of Testing Performance of Laboratory Fumehoods, Standard No. 110. Atlanta: ASHRAE.

Caplan, K. J., and Knutson, G. W., 1978. Laboratory Fumehood: A Performance Test. *ASHRAE Transactions,* 84, Part I, 511–521.

Fuller, F. H., and Etchells, A. W., 1979. The Rating of Laboratory Hood Performance. *ASHRAE Journal,* 44–53.

Knutson, G. W., 1984. Effect of Slot Position on Laboratory Fumehood Performance. *Heating/Piping/Air Conditioning,* 93–96.

Koeningsberg, J., 1984. The Laboratory Fumehood: Efficiency and Energy Conservation. *American Laboratory,* Vol. 16, No. 10, 59.

Peck, R. C., 1982. Validation of a Method to Determine a Protection Factor for Laboratory Hoods. *American Industrial Hygiene Association Journal,* Vol. 43, No. 8, 596–601.

HVAC

ASHRAE, 1980. Standard 90—Energy Conservation in New and Existing Buildings. Atlanta: ASHRAE.

ASHRAE, 1987. *ASHRAE Handbook 1987—HVAC Systems and Applications.* Atlanta: ASHRAE, Chapter 30.

Carrier Air Conditioning Company, 1965. *Handbook of Air Conditioning System Design.* New York: McGraw-Hill.

Davis, S. J., and Benjamin, R., 1987. VAV with Fumehood Exhaust Systems. *Heating/Piping/Air Conditioning,* 75–78.

Takahashi, A., and Okada, T., 1988. Study of Constant Airflow Rate and Constant Room Pressure Control Systems for Physical Containment Laboratories. *Journal of Environmental Science,* Vol. 31, 56–61.

U.S. Department of Energy, 1980. *Architects and Engineers Guide to Energy Conservation in Existing Buildings.* Washington, DC: U.S. Government Printing Office.

Biological Safety Cabinets

Canadian Standards Association, 1987. *Biological Containment Cabinets: Installation and Field Testing.* CAN/CSA-Z316.3-M87. Rexdale (Toronto), Ontario: CSA.

Fink, R., Liberman, D. F., Murphy, K., Lupo, D., and Israeli, E., 1988. Biological Safety Cabinets, Decontamination or Sterilization with Paraformaldehyde. *American Industrial Hygiene Association Journal,* Vol. 49, No. 6, 277–279.

Harvard University, School of Public Health, Department of Environmental Health Engineering, 1979. *Certification of Biological Safety Cabinets.* Manual for Harvard Workshop. Boston: Harvard University School of Public Health.

Miller, Brinton, ed. 1986. *Laboratory Safety: Principles and Practices.* Washington, DC: American Society for Microbiology.

National Sanitation Foundation, 1987. Standard No. 49: Class II (Laminar Flow) Biohazard Cabinetry. Ann Arbor, MI: National Sanitation Foundation.

Richardson, John, and Barkley, W. Emmett, eds., 1988. *Biosafety in Microbiological and Biomedical Laboratories.* U.S. Department of Health and Human Services Publication No. (NIH) 88-8395. Washington DC: U.S. Government Printing Office.

Stuart, D. G., First, M. W., Jones, R. L., and Eagleson, J. M, Jr., 1983. Comparison of Chemical Vapor Handling by Three Types of Class II Biological Safety Cabinets. *Particulate and Microbial Control,* Vol. 2, 18–24.

U.S. Department of Health, Education and Welfare, latest edition. Design and Construction Standard. Subject: Installation of Canopy Hoods for Class II, Type A, Biological Safety Cabinets. Bethesda, MD: National Institutes of Health, Division of Engineering Services.

U.S. Department of Health, Education and Welfare, 1975. Certification of Class II (Laminar Flow) Biological Safety Cabinets. Bethesda, MD: National Institutes of Health, Office of Biohazards and Environmental Control. (Slide program and pamphlet)

U.S. Department of Health, Education and Welfare, 1976. NCI Specification: General Purpose Clean Air Biological Safety Cabinet (Class II, Type 2 Safety Cabinet). Bethesda, MD: National Cancer Institute.

Equipment

American National Standards Institute, Inc., ANSI Standard Z 358.1-1981 for Emergency Eyewash and Shower Equipment. NY: ANSI.

Factory Mutual Research Corporation, Revised December 12, 1975. Standard Class No. 6050. Norwood, MA.

National Fire Protection Association, 1984, Standard No. 30, Chapter 4-3, Design, Construction, and Capacity of Storage Cabinets. Quincy, MA: NFPA.

Perkins, John J., 1970. *Principles and Methods of Sterilization in Health Sciences,* 2nd ed. Springfield, IL: Charles C. Thomas.

Index